C000185225

Bed & Breakfast

Where to Stay Guide 2003

visitscotland.com

0845 22 55 121

Scotland is split into eight tourist areas.
You will find accommodation listed
alphabetically by location
within each of these areas.
There is an index at the back of this
book which may also help you.

Int...

Wel...	
Usir...	
Disc...	
Signs you need to know	VI-XIV
Travellers' tips	XV
Booking and Information	XVIII
Maps	XIX

Accommodation

A	South of Scotland: *Ayrshire and Arran, Dumfries and Galloway, Scottish Borders*	2
B	Edinburgh and Lothians	43
C	Greater Glasgow and Clyde Valley	91
D	West Highlands & Islands, Loch Lomond, Stirling and Trossachs	107
E	Perthshire, Angus and Dundee and the Kingdom of Fife	151
F	Aberdeen and Grampian Highlands – Scotland's Castle and Whisky Country	209
G	The Highlands and Skye	237
H	Outer Islands: *Western Isles, Orkney, Shetland*	336

Appendix

Visitors with disabilities	348
Index by location	359

Welcome to Scotland
Bed & Breakfast

A bed and breakfast is perfect for a short holiday – an escape to the country, a city break in Edinburgh or Glasgow, or a place to unwind after a day's travel or business. It's also the ideal accommodation for stopping on a touring holiday to take in the history and scenery that make Scotland famous.

There's a wide range of bed and breakfasts to choose from around the country, wherever you may travel – whether it be a farmhouse in a highland glen, a croft on a remote Scottish island, or in the heart of Scotland's buzzing city-life.

Friendly, hospitable and always economical, the bed and breakfast is one of the best ways you can get to know Scotland – and the Scots. The family home atmosphere, where the owner's touch makes all the difference, offers good food, comfortable surroundings, together with local knowledge, advice and information. It's a great combination, offering good value for money.

Welcoming doors – to suit every taste – are awaiting you, so start making your choices now from the hundreds available in this book!

Using this book

Where to stay...?

Over 1000 answers to the age-old question!

Revised annually, this is the most comprehensive guide to bed and breakfast establishments in Scotland.

Every property in the guide has been graded and classified by VisitScotland inspectors. See page *vi* for details

How to find accommodation

This book is split into eight areas of Scotland:

Accommodation

A   South of Scotland: 2
     Ayrshire and Arran,
     Dumfries and Galloway,
     Scottish Borders

B   Edinburgh and Lothians   43

C   Greater Glasgow   91
     and Clyde Valley

D   West Highlands & Islands,   107
     Loch Lomond, Stirling
     and Trossachs

E   Perthshire, Angus   151
     and Dundee and
     the Kingdom of Fife

F   Aberdeen and Grampian   209
     Highlands – Scotland's
     Castle and Whisky Country

G   The Highlands and Skye   237

H   Outer Islands: 336
     Western Isles, Orkney,
     Shetland

The map on page *xix* shows these areas.

Within each area section you will find accommodation listed alphabetically by location.

Alternatively there is an index at the back of this book listing alphabetically the accommodation locations in Scotland.

Using this book

Learn to use the symbols in each entry – they contain a mine of information! There is a key to symbols on the back flap.

Naturally, it is always advisable to confirm with the establishment that a particular facility is still available.

Prices in the guide are quoted per person and represent the minimum and maximum charges expected to apply to most rooms in the establishment. They include VAT at the appropriate rate and service charges where applicable.

The prices of accommodation, services and facilities are supplied to us by the operators and were, to the best of our knowledge, correct at the time of going to press. However, prices can change at any time during the lifetime of the publication, and you should check again when you book.

Bookings can be made direct to the establishment, through local Tourist Information Centres, through a travel agent or through Scotland's National Booking and Information Centre - Tel: 0845 22 55 121. The prices stated are inclusive of a 10% agency commission where applicable.

Remember, when you accept accommodation by telephone or in writing, you are entering a legally binding contract which must be fulfilled on both sides. Should you fail to take up accommodation, you may not only forfeit any deposit already paid, but may also have to compensate the establishment if the accommodation cannot be re-let.

Using this book

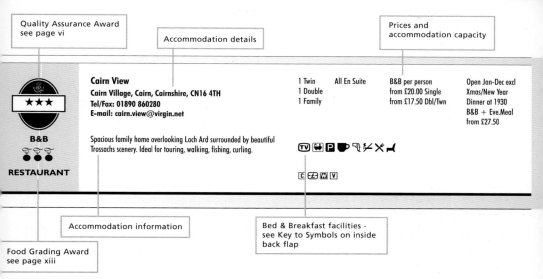

Quality Assurance Award
see page vi

Accommodation details

Prices and
accommodation capacity

Cairn View
Cairn Village, Cairn, Cairnshire, CN16 4TH
Tel/Fax: 01890 860280
E-mail: cairn.view@virgin.net

1 Twin   All En Suite
1 Double
1 Family

B&B per person
from £20.00 Single
from £17.50 Dbl/Twn

Open Jan-Dec excl
Xmas/New Year
Dinner at 1930
B&B + Eve.Meal
from £27.50

B&B

RESTAURANT

Spacious family home overlooking Loch Ard surrounded by beautiful
Trossachs scenery. Ideal for touring, walking, fishing, curling.

Accommodation information

Bed & Breakfast facilities -
see Key to Symbols on inside
back flap

Food Grading Award
see page xiii

Disclaimer

VisitScotland has published this guide in good faith to reflect information submitted to it by the proprietors of the premises listed who have paid for their entries to be included. Although VisitScotland has taken reasonable steps to confirm the information contained in the guide at the time of going to press, it cannot guarantee that the information published is and remains accurate.

Accordingly, VisitScotland recommends that all information is checked with the proprietor of the premises prior to booking to ensure that the accommodation, its price and all other aspects of the premises are satisfactory.

VisitScotland accepts no responsibility for any error or misrepresentation contained in the guide and excludes all liability for loss or damage caused by any reliance placed on the information contained in the guide. VisitScotland also cannot accept any liability for loss caused by the bankruptcy, or liquidation, or insolvency, or cessation of trade of any company, firm or individual contained in this guide.

Signs you need to know
Quality Grading

Follow the stars and you won't be disappointed when you get to the inn.

The VisitScotland Star System is a world-first. Quality is what determines our star awards, not a checklist of facilities. We've made your priorities our priorities.

Quality makes or breaks a visit. This is why the most important aspects of your stay; the warmth of welcome, efficiency and friendliness of service, the quality of the food and the cleanliness and condition of the furnishings, fittings and decor earn VisitScotland Stars, not the size of the accommodation or the range of available facilities.

This easy to understand system tells you at a glance the quality standard of all types and sizes of accommodation from the smallest B&B and self-catering cottage to the largest countryside and city centre hotels.

Quality Assurance awards correct at end September 2002

Look out for this distinctive sign of Quality Assured Accommodation

Please note, although VisitScotland is the new name for what was formerly called the Scottish Tourist Board, we will continue to use 'Scottish Tourist Board' for our Quality Assurance schemes.

Signs you need to know
Quality Grading

The standards you can expect:

★★★★★ Exceptional
★★★★ Excellent
★★★ Very good
★★ Good
★ Fair and Acceptable

A trained VisitScotland Quality Advisor grades each property every year to give you the reassurance that you can choose accommodation of the quality standard you want.

To help you further in your choice the VisitScotland System also tells you the type of accommodation and the range of facilities and services available.

Please turn over for details.

For further information call into any Tourist Information Centre, or contact VisitScotland.

More details available from:

Quality and Standards Department
VisitScotland
Thistle House
Beechwood Park North
INVERNESS
IV2 3ED

Tel: **01463 723040**
Fax: **01463 717244**
Email: **qa@visitscotland.com**

If you have a complaint about your accommodation, make it known to the management as soon as possible so that they can take action to investigate and resolve the problem. You should not feel reluctant to complain if you are dissatisfied with some aspect of your accommodation. Indeed, it is always the best policy to draw attention to the problem on the spot. Proprietors and their staff want you to return and for you to recommend what they provide to your friends. If you let them know what displeases you at the time they have an opportunity to put matters right. However, if you do have a problem with one of our Quality Assured properties which has not been resolved by the proprietor, please contact us at the above address.

Signs you need to know
Quality Grading

Accommodation Types

Self Catering
A house, cottage, apartment, chalet or similar accommodation which is let normally on a weekly basis to individuals where facilities are provided to cater for yourselves.

Serviced Apartments
Serviced apartments are essentially self catering apartments where services such as a cleaning service is available and meals and drinks may be available. Meals and drinks would normally be provided to each apartment or in a restaurant and/or bar which is on site.

Guest House
A guest house is usually a commercial business and will normally have a minimum of 4 letting bedrooms, of which some will have ensuite or private facilities. Breakfast will be available and evening meals may be provided.

B&B
Accommodation offering bed and breakfast, usually in a private house. B&B's will normally accommodate no more than 6 guests, and may or may not serve an evening meal.

Hotel
A hotel will normally have a minimum of twenty letting bedrooms, of which the majority will have ensuite or private bathroom facilities. A hotel will normally have a drinks licence (may be a restricted licence) and will serve breakfast, dinner and normally lunch.

Small Hotel
A small hotel will normally have a maximum of twenty letting bedrooms and a minimum of six. The majority of the bedrooms will have ensuite or private facilities. A small hotel will be licenced (may be a restricted licence) and will serve breakfast, dinner and normally lunch. It will normally be run by owner(s) and reflect their style and personal input.

International Resort Hotel
A hotel achieving a 5 Star quality award which owns and offers a range of leisure and sporting facilities including an 18 hole golf course, swimming and leisure centre and country pursuits.

Lodge
Primarily purpose-built overnight accommodation, often situated close to a major road or in a city centre. Reception hours may be restricted and payment may be required on check in. There may be associated restaurant facilities.

Inn
Bed and breakfast accommodation provided within a traditional inn or pub environment. A restaurant and bar will be open to non-residents and will provide restaurant or bar food at lunchtime and in the evening.

Restaurant with Rooms
In a restaurant with rooms, the restaurant is the most significant part of the business. It is usually open to non-residents. Accommodation is available, and breakfast is usually provided.

Campus Accommodation
Campus accommodation is provided by colleges and universities for their students and is made available-with meals-for individuals, families or groups at certain times of the year. These typically include the main Summer holiday period as well as Easter and Christmas.

Signs you need to know
Quality Grading

Serviced Accommodation: Facility and Service Symbols

TV TV in bedrooms

⚬ Satellite/cable TV

☕ Tea/coffee making facilities in bedrooms

☎ Telephone in bedrooms

✂ Hairdryer in bedrooms

✗ Evening meal available

🔔 Room service

🍴 Restaurant

⚏ Leisure facilities

🏊 Indoor swimming pool

🧺 Laundry service

🛄 Porterage

◀ Lounge

TV TV Lounge

🍷 Full alcohol drinks licence

🍷 Restricted alcohol drinks licence

🚭 Non-smoking establishment

🚬 Smoking restricted

📞 Payphone provided

🚿 Washbasin in bedrooms

🛁 Ensuite bath and/or shower for all bedrooms

🛁 Ensuite bath and/or shower for some bedrooms

🛁 Private bath and/or shower for all bedrooms

🛁 Private bath and/or shower for some bedrooms

P Private parking

P Limited parking

📺 No TV

Signs you need to know

For a Quality Destination

You not only want to be sure of the standard of accommodation you choose to stay in, which ever type it may be, you want to be sure you make the most of your time.

VisitScotland not only grades every type of accommodation every year, but also a wide range of visitor attractions every second year to grade the standard of customer care provided for visitors.

The grading scheme for visitor attractions provides you with the assurance that an attraction has been assessed for the condition and standard of the facilities and services provided – the warmth of welcome, efficiency of service, level of cleanliness, standard of visitor interpretation and of the toilets, restaurant and shop, if provided.

A large world famous castle, or small local museum can attain high grades if their services for the visitor are of a high standard.

The Standards You Can Expect:

★ ★ ★ ★ ★   **Exceptional**
★ ★ ★ ★   **Excellent**
★ ★ ★   **Very good**
★ ★   **Good**
★   **Fair and Acceptable**

In addition to the star grades, every attraction is categorised under one of the following types to help give the visitor an indication of the type of experience on offer:

Visitor Attraction
Castle
Historic Attraction
Museum
Tour
Garden
Activity Centre
Tourist Shop
Leisure Centre
Arts Venue
Historic House

Look for the VisitScotland/Scottish Tourist Board sign of quality:

Signs you need to know
Mobility Needs

Visitors with particular mobility needs must be able to be secure in the knowledge that suitable accommodation is available to match these requirements. Advance knowledge of accessible entrances, bedrooms and facilities is important to enable visitors to enjoy their stay.

Along with the quality awards which apply to all the establishments in this, and every VisitScotland guide, we operate a national accessibility scheme. By inspecting establishments to set criteria, we can identify and promote places that meet the requirements of visitors with mobility needs.

The three categories of accessibility – drawn up in close consultation with specialist organisations are:

 Unassisted wheelchair access for residents

 Assisted wheelchair access for residents

 Access for residents with mobility difficulties

Look out for these symbols in establishments, in advertising and brochures. They assure you that entrances, ramps, passageways, doors, restaurant facilities, bathrooms and toilets, as well as kitchens in self catering properties, have been inspected with reference to the needs of wheelchair users, and those with mobility difficulties. Write or telephone for details of the standards in each category – address on page *vii*.

For more information about travel, specialist organisations who can provide information and a list of all the Scottish accommodation which has had the access inspection, get in touch with our national information and booking line on:
0845 22 55 121
or e-mail: **info@visitscotland.com** (or ask at a Tourist Information Centre) for the VisitScotland booklet "Accessible Scotland".

Holiday Care
7th Floor
Sunley House
4 Bedford Park
Croydon
CR0 2AP

Tel: **0845 124 9974**
Email: **holcare.consult@ virgin.net**
Web: **www.holidaycare.org.uk**

In addition, a referral service to put enquirers in touch with local disability advice centres is:

Update
27 Beaverhall Road
Edinburgh
EH7 4JE

Tel: **0131 558 5200**
Email: **info@update.org.uk**
Web: **www.update.org.uk**

Signs you need to know
Quality Grading

Over 900 quality assured accommodation providers are offering an extra warm welcome for visitors who are cycling or walking for all, or part, of their holiday in Scotland.

As well as having had the quality of the welcome, service, food and comfort assessed by VisitScotland, they will be able to offer the following:-

- ★ hot drink on arrival
- ★ packed lunch/flask filling option
- ★ late evening meal option
- ★ early breakfast option
- ★ drying facilities for wet clothes
- ★ local walking and/or cycling information
- ★ daily weather forecast
- ★ local public transport information
- ★ secure, lockable, covered area for bike storage
- ★ details of local cycle specialists

Walkers Welcome Scheme

Cyclists Welcome Scheme

Look out for the logos in this guide and other accommodation listings.

Green Tourism

In response to the increasing need for businesses throughout the world to operate in an environmentally friendly way, VisitScotland has developed the Green Tourism Business Scheme.

Where tourism businesses are taking steps to reduce waste and pollution, to recycle and to be efficient with resources they are credited in this Scheme with a "Green Award". In our assessment of the degree of environmental good practice the business is demonstrating they are awarded one of the following;

Bronze award   🍃 BRONZE

for achieving a satisfactory level

Silver award   🍃🍃 SILVER

for achieving a good level

Gold award   🍃🍃🍃 GOLD

for achieving a very good level

Signs you need to know
Food Grading

Eating out in Scotland – Look for the Medallions!

Scotland has an ever-growing reputation for quality produce as a source of inspiration for enthusiastic chefs in fine hotels and restaurants. At the same time, straighforward refreshments or meals, such as home baking with coffee or even the humble fish and chip, can also offer both value and merit. For the visitor, finding reliable quality whether in sophisticated dining or simple snacks will add to the enjoyment of a visit to Scotland.

Now it's becoming even easier to be assured of quality food in Scotland, whether you choose a splendid restaurant, a tea room or a takeaway. VisitScotland's own Food Quality Assurance Scheme was launched in 2002 – and a huge variety of catering establishments, from the exclusive to the everyday, have now been assessed.

The Scheme is the first of its kind anywhere in the world. Though other awards exist, for example, operated by private companies and motoring organisations, no other country has a food inspection scheme run by a public organisation. No other scheme is so wide-ranging either, covering so many kinds of food outlets. (The scheme also involves an assessment of the levels of service and the ambience provided, as well as advice on improvements – so that over time, standards will continue to get even better, right across the catering industry.)

That is why, as you are choosing your refreshment stop, you should check the award on display in the establishment. The awards range from one to five medallions – a one medallion establishment has been deemed to reach a good standard, two means very good, three excellent, four outstanding and five world class.

In addition, establishments which meet the new criteria and also make skilful use of fresh locally-produced produce can then be awarded Taste of Scotland accreditation. Look for the 'stockpot' logo. It means a double guarantee – not just of quality alone but quality with a real Scottish flavour.

> **In this guide the award of food medallions appear as:** •
>
> **e.g.** ••
> **RESTAURANT**

Signs you need to know
Taste of Scotland

Taste of Scotland

From Scotland's natural larder comes a wealth of fine flavours. The sea yields crab and lobster, mussels and oysters, haddock and herring to be eaten fresh or smoked. From the lochs and rivers come salmon and trout.

Scotch beef and lamb, venison and game are of prime quality, often adventurously combined with local vegetables or with wild fruits such as redcurrants and brambles. Raspberries and strawberries are cultivated to add their sweetness to trifles and shortcakes, and to the home-made jams that are an essential part of Scottish afternoon tea.

The Scots have a sweet tooth, and love all kinds of baking – rich, crisp shortbread, scones, fruit cakes and gingerbreads. Crumbly oatcakes make the ideal partner for Scottish cheeses, which continue to develop from their ancient farming origins into new – and very successful – styles.

And in over a hundred distilleries, barley, yeast and pure spring water come together miraculously to create malt whisky – the water of life.

Many Scottish hotels and restaurants pride themselves on the use they make of these superb natural ingredients – around 400 are members of the Taste of Scotland Scheme which encourages the highest culinary standards, use of Scottish produce and a warm welcome to visitors. Look for the Stockpot symbol at establishments, or write to Taste of Scotland for a copy of their guide which contains all the places taking part in VisitScotland's Food Grading Scheme and shows these with the Taste of Scotland accreditation.

In Shops		£8.99
By Post:	UK	£9.50
	Europe	£10.50
	US	£12.00

Taste of Scotland Scheme
33 Melville Street
Edinburgh, EH3 7JF
Tel: **0131 220 1900**
Fax: **0131 220 6102**
E-mail: **tastescotland@sol.co.uk**
Web: **www.taste-of-scotland.com**

Traveller's tips

Getting Around

Scotland is a small country and travel is easy. There are direct air links with UK cities, Europe and North America. There is also an internal air network bringing the islands of the North and West within easy reach.

Scotland's rail network not only includes excellent cross-border services but also a good internal network. All major towns are linked by rail and there are also links to the western seaboard at Mallaig (for ferry connections from Skye and the Western Isles) and to Inverness, Thurso and Wick for ferries to Orkney and Shetland.

All the usual discount cards are valid but there are also ScotRail Rovers (multi journey tickets allowing you to save on rail fares) and the Freedom of Scotland Travelpass, a combined rail and ferry pass allowing unlimited travel on Caledonian MacBrayne ferry services to the islands and all of the rail network. In addition Travelpass also offers discounts on bus services.

Cross-border rail services are available from all major centres, for example: Birmingham, Carlisle, Crewe, Manchester, Newcastle, Penzance, Peterborough, Preston, Plymouth, York and many others.

There are frequent rail departures from Kings Cross and Euston stations to Edinburgh and Glasgow. The journey time from Kings Cross to Edinburgh is around 4 hours and from Euston to Glasgow around 5 hours.

Traveller's tips
Getting Around

Coach connections include express services to Scotland from all over the UK; local bus companies in Scotland offer explorer tickets and discount cards. Postbuses (normally minibuses) take passengers on over 130 rural routes throughout Scotland.

Ferries to and around the islands are regular and reliable, most ferries carry vehicles, although some travelling to smaller islands convey only passengers.

Contact **Scotland's National Booking and Information Line – Tel: 0845 22 55 121**, or any Tourist Information Centre, for details of travel and transport.

Many visitors choose to see Scotland by road – distances are short and driving on the quiet roads of the Highlands is a new and different experience. In remoter areas, some roads are still single track, and passing places must be used. When vehicles approach from different directions, the car nearest to a passing place must stop in or opposite it. Please do not use passing places to park in!

Speed limits on Scottish roads: Dual carriageways 70mph/112kph; single carriageways 60mph/96kph; built-up areas 30mph/48kph.

The driver and front-seat passenger in a car must wear seatbelts; rear seatbelts, if fitted, must be used. Small children and babies must at all times be restrained in a child seat or carrier.

Opening Times

Public holidays: Christmas and New Year's Day are holidays in Scotland, taken by almost everyone. Scottish banks, and many offices close in 2003 on 1st January, 18th April, 21st April, 5th May, 26th May, 25th August, 25th and 26th December. Scottish towns also take Spring and Autumn holidays which may vary from place to place, but are usually on a Monday.

Banking hours: In general, banks open Monday to Friday, 0930 to 1700, with some closing later on a Thursday. Banks in cities, particularly in or near the main shopping centres, may be open at weekends. Cash machines in hundreds of branches allow you to withdraw cash outside banking hours, using the appropriate cards.

Pubs and restaurants: Pubs and restaurants are allowed to serve alcoholic drinks between 1100 hours and 2300 hours Monday through to Saturday; Sundays 1230 hours until 1430 hours then again from 1830 hours until 2300 hours.

Residents in hotels may have drinks served at any time, subject to the proprietors discretion.

Extended licensing hours are subject to local council applications.

Traveller's tips
Getting Around

Telephone codes

If you are calling from abroad, first dial your own country's international access code (usually 00, but do please check). Next, dial the UK code, 44, then the area code except for the first 0, then the remainder of the number as normal.

Bring your pet

The Pet Travel Scheme (PETS) means you are able to bring your dog or cat into the United Kingdom from certain countries and territories without it first having to go into Quarantine, provided the rules of the scheme are met. PETS only operates on certain air, rail and sea routes and your own government should be able to provide you with details. Alternatively you may wish to obtain detailed information from:

Department of Environment
Food and Rural Affairs
1a Page Street
London
SW1P 4PQ

Tel:	**0870 241 1710**
Fax:	**0207 904 6834**
E-mail:	**pets.helpline@defra.gsi.gov.uk**
Web:	**www.defra.gov.uk/animalh/ quarantine**

Scotland on the net

Visit our web site at:
visitscotland.com

"VisitScotland is committed to ensuring that our natural environment, upon which our tourism is so dependant, is safeguarded for future generations to enjoy."

How to book your accommodation

0845 2255 121

Planning your visit to Scotland but don't know where to stay and what to do while you are here?

Why not reduce your planning time and contact our **Booking & Information Hot Line.** Simply let our advisors know what type of holiday or accommodation you are looking for, the price you are prepared to pay, where you would like to stay, and when you are planning to visit.

Alternatively, let our advisors know your hobbies and interests and we can suggest places for you to visit in **Scotland**.

How can you contact us?

Telephone or:	**0845 2255 121** (from within the UK) **+44 (0)1506 832 121** (from outside the UK)
Opening Times (GMT)	**8.00 am to 8.00 pm** Monday to Friday **9.00 am to 5.30 pm** Saturday
Fax	**+44 (0)1506 832 222**
Web	**www.visitscotland.com**
Email	**info@visitscotland.com**
Post	**Scottish Booking & Info Centre,** visitscotland.com, PO Box 121, Livingston, EH54 8AF, Scotland.

visitscotland.com

Maps
Scotland's tourist areas

Accommodation

A   **South of Scotland:**   2
Ayrshire and Arran,
Dumfries and Galloway,
Scottish Borders

B   **Edinburgh and Lothians**   43

C   **Greater Glasgow**   91
and Clyde Valley

D   **West Highlands & Islands,**   107
Loch Lomond, Stirling and Trossachs

E   **Perthshire, Angus and**   151
Dundee and the Kingdom of Fife

F   **Aberdeen and Grampian Highlands –**   209
Scotland's Castle and Whisky Country

G   **The Highlands and Skye**   237

H   **Outer Islands:**   336
Western Isles, Orkney,
Shetland

map 5   Lerwick

map 3   H   Kirkwall

map 4

Stornoway

Inverness   G   F

Fort William   Aberdeen

map 1   map 2

D   E

Glasgow   B   Edinburgh

C

A

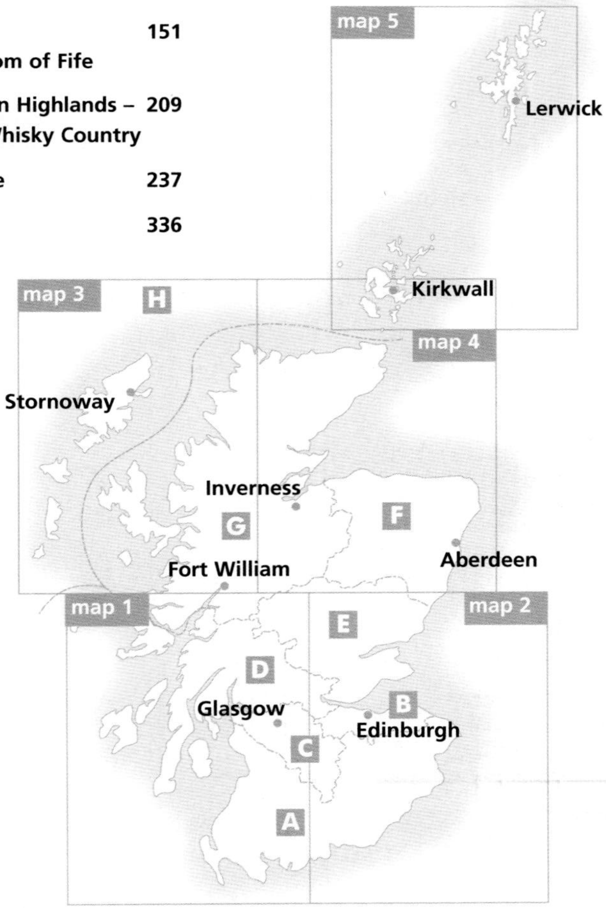

Map 1

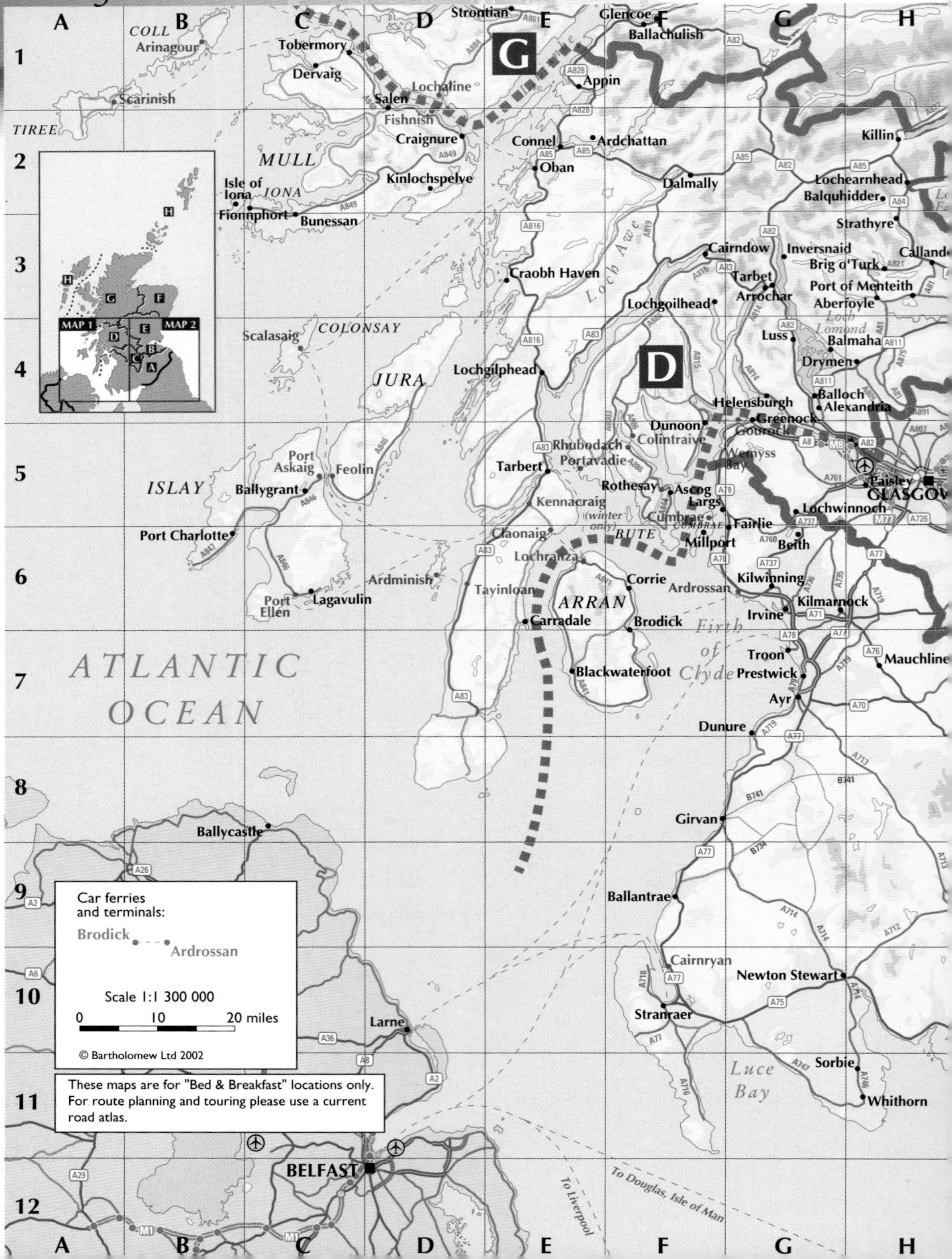

A
B
C
D
E
F
G
H
1
2
3
4
5
6
7
8
9
10
11
12
COLL
Arinagour
Scarinish
TIREE
Tobermory
Dervaig
Strontian
Lochaline
Salen
Fishnish
Craignure
MULL
Kinlochspelve
Isle of Iona
IONA
Fionnphort
Bunessan
Glencoe
Ballachulish
Appin
Connel
Ardchattan
Oban
Dalmally
Killin
Lochearnhead
Balquhidder
Strathyre
Callander
Cairndow
Inversnaid
Brig o'Turk
Tarbet
Arrochar
Port of Menteith
Aberfoyle
Lochgoilhead
Loch Awe
Loch Lomond
Luss
Balmaha
Drymen
Balloch
Alexandria
Craobh Haven
Scalasaig
COLONSAY
JURA
Lochgilphead
Helensburgh
Greenock
Gourock
Dunoon
Colintraive
Rhubodach
Portavadie
Wemyss Bay
Paisley
GLASGOW
Port Askaig
Feolin
ISLAY
Ballygrant
Tarbert
Rothesay
Ascog
Largs
Kennacraig
(winter only)
Cumbrae
Fairlie
Lochwinnoch
Port Charlotte
Claonaig
BUTE
Millport
Beith
Lochranza
Corrie
Ardrossan
Kilwinning
Ardminish
Tayinloan
ARRAN
Kilmarnock
Irvine
Port Ellen
Lagavulin
Carradale
Brodick
Firth of Clyde
Troon
Prestwick
Mauchline
Blackwaterfoot
Ayr
ATLANTIC OCEAN
Dunure
Girvan
Ballycastle
Ballantrae
Cairnryan
Newton Stewart
Stranraer
Larne
Luce Bay
Sorbie
Whithorn
BELFAST
To Liverpool
To Douglas, Isle of Man
MAP 1
MAP 2
Car ferries and terminals:
Brodick
Ardrossan
Scale 1:1 300 000
0
10
20 miles
© Bartholomew Ltd 2002
These maps are for "Bed & Breakfast" locations only. For route planning and touring please use a current road atlas.

Map 2

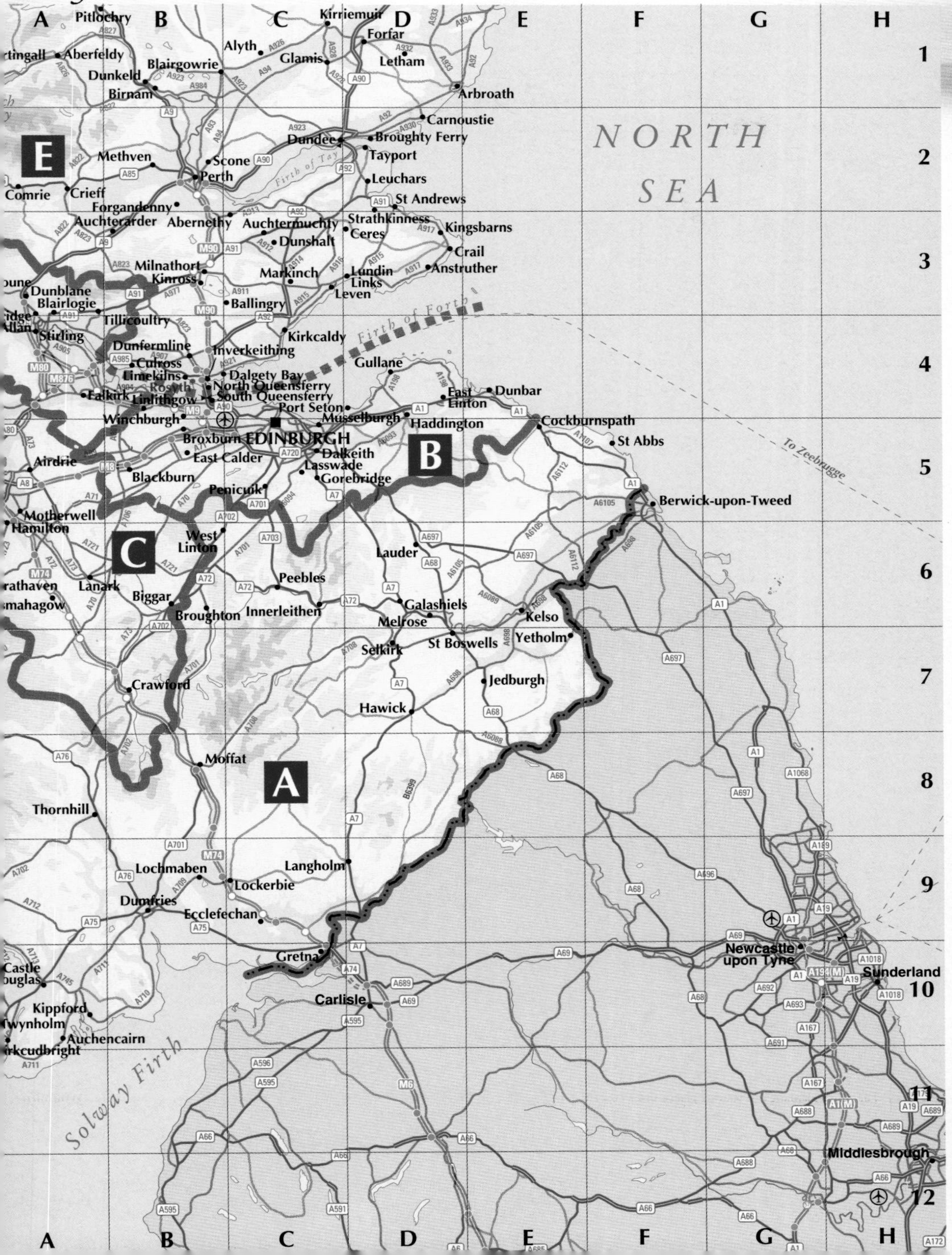

NORTH SEA

To Zeebrugge

Grid columns: A B C D E F G H
Grid rows: 1 2 3 4 5 6 7 8 9 10 11 12

E

B

C

A

Pitlochry
Aberfeldy
rtingall
Dunkeld
Birnam
Blairgowrie
Blairgowrie
Alyth
Glamis
Kirriemuir
Forfar
Letham
Arbroath
Carnoustie
Broughty Ferry
Dundee
Tayport
Leuchars
St Andrews
Strathkinness
Kingsbarns
Ceres
Crail
Anstruther
Methven
Scone
Perth
Comrie
Crieff
Forgandenny
Auchterarder
Abernethy
Auchtermuchty
Dunshalt
Markinch
Lundin Links
Leven
Milnathort
Kinross
Ballingry
Dunblane
Blairlogie
Tillicoultry
Dunfermline
Culross
Limekilns
Inverkeithing
Kirkcaldy
Dalgety Bay
North Queensferry
South Queensferry
Gullane
East Linton
Dunbar
Cockburnspath
St Abbs
Falkirk
Linlithgow
Winchburgh
Broxburn
EDINBURGH
East Calder
Port Seton
Musselburgh
Haddington
Berwick-upon-Tweed
Airdrie
Blackburn
Dalkeith
Lasswade
Gorebridge
Penicuik
Motherwell
Hamilton
West Linton
Peebles
Lauder
Galashiels
Kelso
Yetholm
Melrose
St Boswells
Lanark
Biggar
Broughton
Innerleithen
Selkirk
Jedburgh
Crawford
Hawick
Moffat
Thornhill
Lochmaben
Lockerbie
Langholm
Dumfries
Ecclefechan
Gretna
Carlisle
Castle Douglas
Kippford
Twynholm
Auchencairn
irkcudbright
Newcastle upon Tyne
Sunderland
Middlesbrough

Firth of Tay
Firth of Forth
Solway Firth

Map 3

	A	B	C	D	E	F	G	H

These maps are for "Bed & Breakfast" locations only. For route planning and touring please use a current road atlas.

MAP 3 MAP 4

1

2

3

OUTER HEBRIDES

4
Scourie
Back
Stornoway
Callanish
Aignish
Lochinver ASSYNT

5
LEWIS
Lochs
H

6
HARRIS
Tarbert
Scaristavore
Seilebost
Aultbea
Laide Ullapool
Dundonnell
A835

7
Leverburgh
Berneray
Gairloch
the Minch
Otternish

8
Lochmaddy
Uig
Staffin
Kinlochewe
NORTH
UIST
Glenhimisdale
G

9
BENBECULA
Borve
Dunvegan
Portree
Struan
RAASAY
Lochcarron
SOUTH
UIST
Raasay
Plockton
Sconser
Kyle of
Lochalsh
Dornie
SKYE Broadford
Kyleakin
Breakish
Kylerhea Glenelg

10
Lochboisdale
Elgol
Sleat
Eriskay
CANNA
Kilmore
Armadale
BARRA
Ardvasar
Castlebay
RUM
Mallaig
Morar
Arisaig
EIGG Loch Morar

11
Loch
Lochy
A82

12
MUCK
Corpach
Spean
Bridge
Fort William
ARDNAMURCHAN
Kilchoan
Kinlochleven

Map 4

ORKNEY

Stromness
Orphir
Scapa Flow
St Margaret's Hope
HOY
SOUTH RONALDSAY
Longhope

H

To Kirkwall

To Lerwick
To Faroes & Iceland
(summer only)

Pentland Firth

Strathy Point
Scrabster
Gills Bay
John o' Groats
Thurso
Melvich
Talmine
Tongue
Halkirk
Wick

Lairg
Helmsdale
Brora
Dornoch Firth

Ardgay
Dornoch
Tain

Car ferries and terminals:

Brodick --- Ardrossan

Scale 1:1 300 000

0   10   20 miles

© Bartholomew Ltd 2002

Moray Firth
Lossiemouth
Alness
Invergordon
Cromarty Findhorn
Buckie
Cullen
Portsoy
Macduff
Gardenstown
Banff
Garve
Strathpeffer
Dingwall
Forres
Elgin
Nairn
Cawdor
Keith
Turriff
Peterhead
Contin
North Kessock
Beauly
Dalcross
Culloden Moor
Inverness
Dufftown
Huntly
Fyvie
Methlick
Oldmeldrum
Brackla
Glenlivet
Drumnadrochit
Grantown-on-Spey
Inverurie
Loch Ness
Carrbridge
Nethy Bridge
Invermoriston
Boat of Garten
Aviemore
Tomintoul
Strathdon
Alford
Aberdeen
Glenkindie
Fort Augustus
Kincraig

F

Newtonmore
Kingussie
Aboyne
Ballater
Banchory
Braemar
Stonehaven

E

Blair Atholl
Edzell
Brechin

XXIV

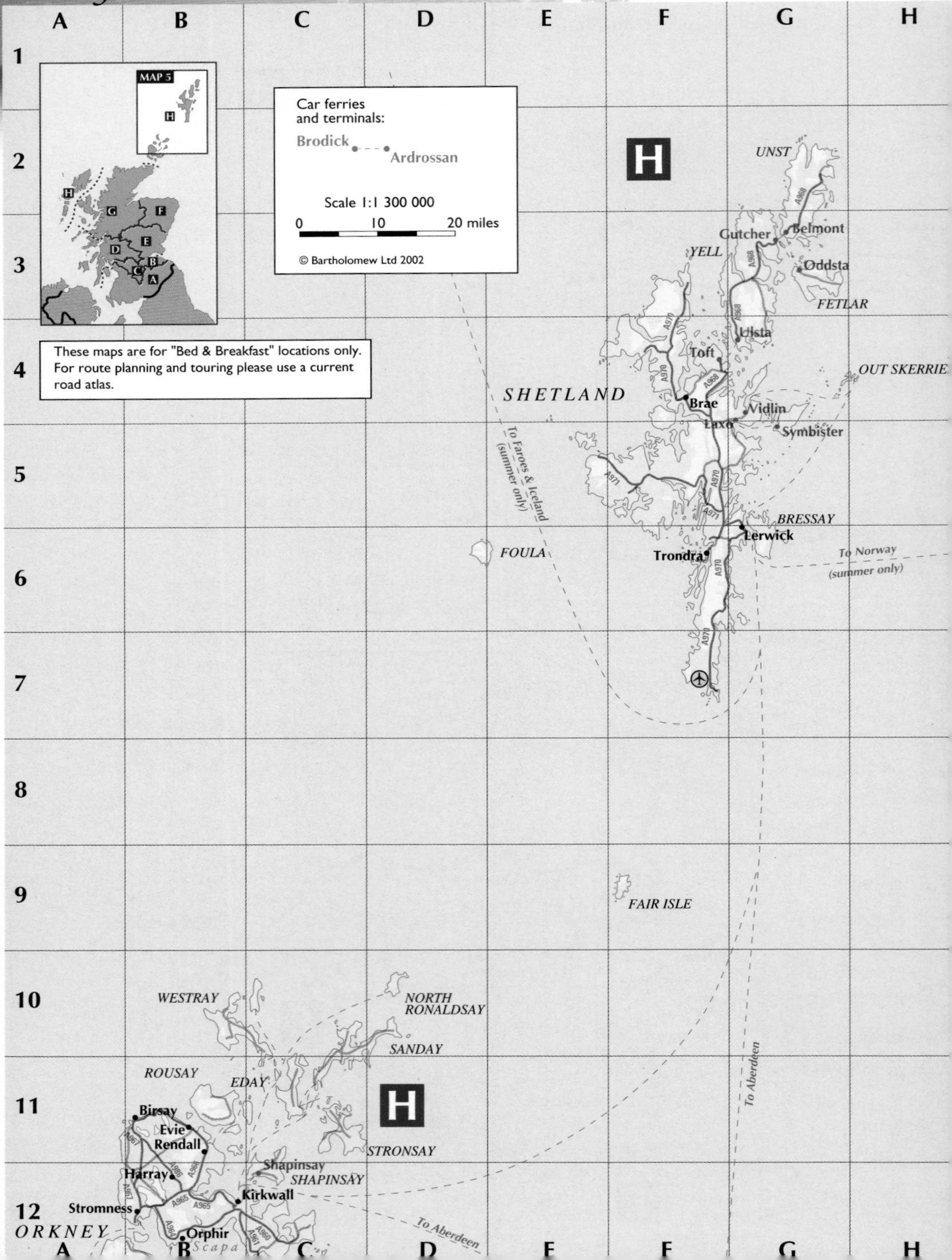

Map 5

| | A | B | C | D | E | F | G | H |

MAP 5

H

Car ferries
and terminals:

Brodick •----• Ardrossan

Scale 1:1 300 000

0   10   20 miles

© Bartholomew Ltd 2002

These maps are for "Bed & Breakfast" locations only.
For route planning and touring please use a current
road atlas.

H

UNST

Gutcher • Belmont
YELL • Oddsta

FETLAR

Ulsta

OUT SKERRIE

SHETLAND

Toft

Brae
Laxo • Vidlin
• Symbister

*To Faroes & Iceland
(summer only)*

BRESSAY

Lerwick
FOULA **Trondra**

*To Norway
(summer only)*

⊕

FAIR ISLE

To Aberdeen

WESTRAY

*NORTH
RONALDSAY*

SANDAY

ROUSAY
EDAY

H

• Birsay
Evie•
Rendall

STRONSAY

Shapinsay
SHAPINSAY

Harray•

Kirkwall

To Aberdeen

Stromness •
ORKNEY
• Orphir

Scapa

SCOTLAND

visitscotland.com

Bed & Breakfast

Where to Stay guide 2003

Welcome to Scotland

*Scotland's south west offers a beautiful and uncrowded
landscape where you can enjoy a real feeling of space.*

Ferry at Brodick, Isle of Arran, with Goat Fell in the background

Here you will find over 400 miles of the
National Cycle network plus superb golf
courses. There is also great walking country to
be found, including the 212 mile coast-to-
coast Southern Upland Way. This long-
distance footpath begins in Portpatrick, goes
through the Galloway Forest Park – the
largest in Britain – then it crosses the Moffat
Hills before it heads into the Scottish Borders.
Back on the south-west coast, the tidal
mudflats and sandy beaches of the Solway
Firth are dotted with attractive villages and
seaside towns including Kirkcudbright, with
its long artistic tradition as well as a thriving
current arts scene. Dumfries is the main town
in the region. Sometimes known as the
Queen of the South, this handsome red
sandstone town has strong associations with
Robert Burns. Some of the many attractions
to visit include Caerlaverock Castle with four
bird reserves nearby, Gretna Green and the
Famous Old Blacksmith's Shop Visitor Centre,

Threave Gardens and its new Countryside
Centre, Wigtown (now a celebrated 'Book
Town') and Sweetheart Abbey.

The Ayrshire coast has some excellent holiday
attractions for all the family, including
Vikingar! in Largs, Culzean Castle and The Big
Idea and the Magnum Leisure Centre both at
Irvine Harbourside. For those interested in
Scotland's national poet, Robert Burns, you
can visit many attractions including his
birthplace in Alloway. And you can relive
some of his dramatic life at the Tam O'
Shanter Experience. Less than an hour's sail
will take you to the Isle of Arran which offers
fine mountains, quiet beaches, the famous
Brodick Castle and the Isle of Arran Distillery.
For those who prefer a sporting holiday, the
region offers horse-racing and football, while
with over forty golf courses, golf is one of the
biggest attractions. There are world famous
courses at Troon, Turnberry and Prestwick.

South of Scotland:

Ayrshire and Arran, Dumfries and Galloway, Scottish Borders

The Grey Mare's Tail, Dumfries and Galloway

South of Scotland:

Ayrshire and Arran, Dumfries and Galloway, Scottish Borders

The Gardens at Manderston House, near Paxton, Scottish Borders

First impressions of the Scottish Borders are of a surprisingly wild area, though river valleys with their woodlands and farms soon give a softer appearance. These borderlands were fought over until the 17th century and as a result there are many magnificent ruined abbeys and towered castles to visit. There are also many grand stately homes such as the magnificent Edwardian mansion of Manderston and the superb Georgian house of Mellerstain. Market towns such as Kelso, Selkirk, Hawick and Melrose offer good shopping and accommodation facilities. In the centre of Melrose you'll find the magnificent ruins of Melrose Abbey and the distinctive triple peaks of the Eildon Hills, a landmark for miles around. Below is the Tweed, one of Scotland's most famous salmon-fishing rivers. Sir Walter Scott's fascinating home of Abbotsford and the secluded Dryburgh Abbey where he is buried are just a few of the fascinating historical sites throughout this region. The colourful past of the border

towns is brought to life each year when the local residents re-enact the Common Ridings by dressing up in period costume and riding around the burgh boundaries. The landscape to the east is a beautiful mosaic of farmland and finally ends at the dramatic cliffs of St Abbs, a favourite place for bird watching.

The South of Scotland offers plenty of scope for those who want an active holiday. Cycling along quiet country lanes, trekking and riding, walking and fishing are just some of the activities widely available.

Events

South of Scotland: Ayrshire and Arran, Dumfries and Galloway, Scottish Borders

11-12 APRIL*
Scottish Grand National, Ayr
The highlight of the Scottish horseracing year.
Tel: 01292 264179
www.ayr-racecourse.co.uk

2-4 MAY
Burns and A' That, Ayrshire
A celebration of Burns' life and contemporary Scottish culture.
Tel: 01292 678100
www.burnsfestival.com

4-7 MAY
**Gathering of the Clans –
Golf Tournament, Ayrshire**
Tel: 01436 821828
www.ttfgolf.com

23 MAY – 1 JUNE
Dumfries and Galloway Arts Festival
Tel: 01387 260447
www.dgartsfestival.org.uk

24-30 MAY
Wake Up To Birds Week
Royal Society for the Protection of Birds. Wide range of events and activities at the 60 RSPB reserves across Scotland. Free entry to all reserves on one day during this week.
Tel: 0131 311 6500
www.rspb.org.uk/scotland

24-31 MAY
Castle Douglas Food Town Week
Gastronomic festival of locally produced food and drink.
www.cd-foodtown.org

2-7 JUNE*
The Amateur Championship, Royal Troon and Irvine Bogside Golf Clubs
Tel: 01292 617420

6-8 JUNE
RSAC Scottish Rally, Dumfries
International motor sports event.
Tel: 0141 204 4999
www.rsacmotorsport.co.uk

2-3 AUGUST
Traquair Fair, Innerleithen
Circus acts, music, puppets and craft stalls.
Tel: 01896 830323
www.traquair.co.uk

15-17 AUGUST
Scottish Championship Horse Trials, Lauder
Tel: 01578 722744
www.thirlestanecastle.co.uk

15 AUGUST – 1 NOVEMBER
Gaelforce 2003, Dumfries and Galloway
Arts festival celebrating Scottish and Celtic culture.
Tel: 01387 260335

26-28 SEPTEMBER
Wigtown Book Festival
Scotland's rural Book Festival includes authors' readings, music, literary and children's events.
www.wigtown-booktown.co.uk

* denotes provisional date. Events can be subject to change, please check before travelling.

For up to date events, log on to:
visitscotland.com

Area Tourist Boards

South of Scotland: Ayrshire and Arran, Dumfries and Galloway, Scottish Borders

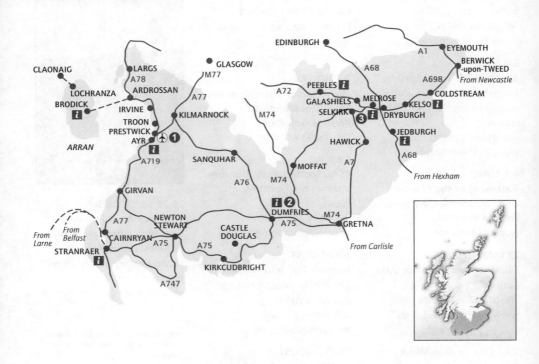

① Ayrshire and Arran
Tourist Board
Customer Information Centre
15 Skye Road
Prestwick
KA9 2TA

Tel: 01292 678100
Fax: 01292 471832
E-mail: info@ayrshire-arran.com
www.ayrshire-arran.com

② Dumfries and Galloway
Tourist Board
64 Whitesands
Dumfries
DG1 2RS

Tel: 01387 253862
Fax: 01387 245555
E-mail: info@dgtb.visitscotland.com
www.dumfriesandgalloway.co.uk

③ Scottish Borders
Tourist Board
Shepherd's Mill
Whinfield Road
Selkirk
TD7 5DT

Tel (Information): 0870 608 0404
Fax: 01750 21886
E-mail: info@scot-borders.co.uk
www.scot-borders.co.uk

Tourist Information Centres
South of Scotland: Ayrshire and Arran, Dumfries and Galloway, Scottish Borders

Ayrshire and Arran Tourist Board

Ayr
22 Sandgate
Tel: (01292) 678100
Jan-Dec

Brodick
The Pier
Isle of Arran
Tel: (01770) 302140
Jan-Dec

Girvan
Bridge Street
Tel: (01292) 678100
Easter-Oct

Irvine
New Street
Tel: (01292) 678100
Easter-Oct

Largs
The Railway Station
Main St
Tel: (01292) 678100
Easter-Oct

Millport
28 Stuart Street
Isle of Cumbrae
Tel: (01292) 678100
Easter-Oct

Dumfries and Galloway Tourist Board

Castle Douglas
Markethill Car Park
Tel: (01556) 502611
Easter-Oct

Dumfries
64 Whitesands
Tel: (01387) 253862
Jan-Dec

Gatehouse of Fleet
Car Park
Tel: (01557) 814212
Easter-Oct

Gretna Green
Headless Cross
Tel: (01461) 337834
Easter-Oct

Kirkcudbright
Harbour Square
Tel: (01557) 330494
Easter-end Oct

Moffat
Unit 1, Ladyknowe
Tel: (01683) 220620
Easter-Oct

Newton Stewart
Dashwood Square
Tel: (01671) 402431
Easter-Oct

Stranraer
28 Harbour Street
Tel: (01776) 702595
Jan-Dec

Scottish Borders Tourist Board

Eyemouth
Auld Kirk, Manse Road
Tel: (0870) 6080404
Easter-Oct

Hawick
Drumlanrig's Tower
Tel: (0870) 6080404
Easter-Oct

Jedburgh
Murray's Green
Tel: (0870) 6080404
Jan-Dec

Kelso
Town House, The Square
Tel: (0870) 6080404
Jan-Dec

Melrose
Abbey House
Tel: (0870) 6080404
Jan-Dec

Peebles
High Street
Tel: (0870) 6080404
Jan-Dec

Selkirk
Halliwell's House
Tel: (0870) 6080404
Easter-Oct

Scotland's National Booking and Information Line
0845 22 55 121

Blackwaterfoot, Isle of Arran | Map Ref: 1E7

★★

SMALL HOTEL

Blackwaterfoot Lodge
Blackwaterfoot, Isle of Arran, KA27 8EU
Tel:01770 860202 Fax:01770 860570
Email:info@blackwaterfoot-lodge.co.uk
Web:www.blackwaterfoot-lodge.co.uk

Situated 50 yards from the picturesque harbour at Blackwaterfoot, this
family run hotel provides a warm & welcoming home during your
holiday. Creature comforts on the windswept west coast. With a small
bistro style restaurant and traditional ale from Arran Breweries in the
fully licensed bar.

1 Single	6 En Suite fac	B&B per person	Open Easter-Oct
3 Twin	1 Priv.NOT ensuite	from £26.00 Single	
2 Double		from £27.00 Double	
2 Family			

★★★

B&B

The Greannan
Blackwaterfoot, Shiskine, Isle of Arran, KA27 8HB
Tel/Fax:01770 860200
Email:susan@thegreannan.co.uk

Comfortable recently refurbished family home set in elevated position
with magnificent views over countryside and sea to Irish Coast. 1 mile
from Blackwaterfoot. En-suite rooms all with colour TV and hospitality
tray. Garden with picnic benches for guest use. A perfect, peaceful place
to stay and enjoy the old world charm of this lovely island. Quality self
catering apartments also available. Credit Cards Accepted.

2 Twin	All En Suite	B&B per person	Open Jan-Dec
1 Double		from £25.00 Single	
2 Family		from £20.00 Double	

★★★

B&B

Laighbent
Blackwaterfoot, Isle of Arran, KA27 8HB
Tel/Fax:01770 860405
Email:s-adamson@corriecnavrhome.fsnet.co.uk

Come and experience traditional Scottish hospitality in this newly built
bungalow in the charming village of Blackwaterfoot. Arran has a lot to
offer for the holidaymaker, including beachcombing, golf (7 courses),
tennis, walking, cycling, swimming or just chilling out.

1 Single	Some En Suite	B&B per person	Open Jan-Dec excl
1 Twin		from £22.00 Single	Xmas/New Year
1 Double		from £22.00 Double	

Brodick, Isle of Arran | Map Ref: 1F7

★★★

GUEST HOUSE

Carrick Lodge
Brodick, Isle of Arran, KA27 8BH
Tel/Fax:01770 302550

Lovely old red sandstone listed building with panoramic views of Brodick
bay. Warm and friendly welcome with comfortable bedrooms. Central to
all areas of Arran and only minutes from ferry terminal.

1 Single	5 En Suite fac	B&B per person	Open Feb-Oct
2 Twin	1 Priv.Bath/Show	from £23.00 Single	
2 Double		from £23.00 Double	
1 Family		from £18.00 Room Only	

Scotland's National Booking and Information Line

Tel: 0845 22 55 121
visitscotland.com

Important: Prices stated are estimates and may be subject to amendments

Brodick, Isle of Arran   Map Ref: 1F7

GLEN CLOY FARMHOUSE

Glen Cloy, Brodick, Isle of Arran KA27 8DA
Tel: 01770 302351
e.mail: mvpglencloy@compuserve.com
Web: www.SmoothHound.co.uk/hotels/glencloy.html

Glen Cloy Farmhouse is situated in a peaceful glen just outside Brodick. Golf, castle and mountains nearby. Our bedrooms are comfortably furnished with tea and coffee making facilities and homemade shortbread. There is a large, cosy drawing room with an extensive library, and a bright dining room with glorious views where you can enjoy a farmhouse tea, and breakfast using home produced preserves, free range eggs from our hens and locally produced bacon and sausages.

Recommended by The Good Bed and Breakfast Guide.

★★★
GUEST
HOUSE

Glen Cloy Farm House
Glen Cloy Road, Brodick, Isle of Arran, KA27 8DA
Tel:01770 302351
Email:mvpglencloy@compuserve.com
Web:www.SmoothHound.co.uk/hotels/glencloy.html

Farmhouse full of character set in peaceful glen with views of hills and sea. Within easy reach of Brodick ferry. Mark and Vicki produce memorable breakfasts with homemade jams and bread, and eggs from their own hens. Embroidery courses held in spring and autumn.

1 Single	2 En Suite fac	B&B per person	Open Jan-Dec excl
2 Twin	2 Pub.Bath/Show	£23.00-29.00 Single	Xmas/New Year
2 Double		£23.00-29.00 Double	

★★
SMALL
HOTEL

Ormidale Hotel
Brodick, Isle of Arran, KA27 8BY
Tel:01770 302293 Fax:01770 302098
Email:reception@ormidale-hotel.co.uk
Web:www.ormidale-hotel.co.uk

Family run, set in mature woodland by the golf course. Home cooked meals for the family served in the conservatory. CAMRA approved. Good pub atmosphere.

1 Single	4 En Suite fac	Bed+Breakfast	Open Apr-Sep
3 Twin	1 Priv.NOT ensuite	from £25.00 Single	BB & Eve.Meal
2 Double		from £50.00 Double	from £35.00
1 Family		Room Only £20.00	

Corrie, Isle of Arran   Map Ref: 1F6

★★
GUEST
HOUSE

Blackrock Guest House
Corrie, Isle of Arran, KA27 8JP
Tel:01770 810282
Web:www.arran.net/corrie/blackrock

Where the mountains meet the sea... that is where we are, on the outskirts of 'the prettiest village in Europe'. Come and enjoy our traditional Scottish guesthouse, established on shore edge in the 1930's. Ensuite accommodation; panoramic views; natural garden; red squirrels; otters and birdlife. Groups welcome - good restaurant nearby.

2 Single	3 En Suite fac	B&B per person	Open Mar-Nov
1 Twin	2 Priv.NOT ensuite	£18.00-21.00 Single	
1 Double		£18.00-26.00 Double	
4 Family			

VAT is shown at 17.5%: changes in this rate may affect prices.   Key to symbols is on back flap.

Auchencairn, by Castle Douglas, Kirkcudbrightshire — Map Ref: 2A10

★★

B&B

The Rossan

Auchencairn, Castle Douglas, DG7 1QR
Tel:01556 640269 Fax:01556 640278
Email:bardsley@rossan.freeserve.co.uk
Web:www.the-rossan.co.uk

Former Victorian manse, with large gardens, on outskirts of the village.
Convenient for touring. Vegetarian, gluten free and special diets
available. Budget accommodation. Keen conservationists since the 1950s.
Packed lunch on request. Clothes dried overnight and dogs welcome at
no extra cost.

3 Family   1 Priv.NOT ensuite

B&B per person
from £20.00 Single
from £15.00 Double

Open Jan-Dec
BB & Eve.Meal
from £25.00

Ayr — Map Ref: 1G7

★★

GUEST
HOUSE

Belmont Guest House

15 Park Circus, Ayr, KA7 2DJ
Tel:01292 265588 Fax:01292 290303
Email:belmontguesthouse@btinternet.com
Web:www.belmontguesthouse.co.uk

Victorian townhouse in a quiet tree lined conservation area, within easy
walking distance of town centre. Ground-floor bedrooms, all with ensuite
facilities. Guest lounge with extensive book collection. On street and
private car parking. Credit/Debit cards are now accepted.

1 Twin   All En Suite
2 Double
2 Family

B&B per person
from £23.00 Single
from £22.00 Double
from £15.00 Room
Only

Open Jan-Dec excl
Xmas/New Year

★★★

GUEST
HOUSE

Coila Guest House

10 Holmston Road, Ayr, KA7 3BB
Tel:01292 262642 Fax:01292 285439
Email:hazel@coila.co.uk
Web:www.coila.co.uk

Traditional sandstone villa ideally situated for road and rail connections.
3 minutes walk from town centre. A warm & friendly atmosphere where
guests return year after year. Families welcome. Totally non-smoking
house.

1 Twin   All En Suite
3 Double

B&B per person
from £25.00 Single
from £20.00 Double

Open Jan-Dec excl
Xmas/New Year

★★★★

B&B

The Crescent

26 Bellevue Crescent, Ayr, Ayrshire, KA7 2DR
Tel:01292 287329 Fax:01292 286779
Email:carrie@26crescent.freeserve.co.uk
Web:www.26crescent.freeserve.co.uk

Built in 1898 this refurbished Victorian terrace house is in a quiet
location with easy access for town centre and beach. Charming rooms
have all been individually styled and decorated in a manner befitting the
opulence of the Victorian era.

2 Twin   All En Suite
2 Double

B&B per person
from £35.00 Single
from £26.00 Double

Open Feb-Dec

★★★★

B&B

Deanbank

44 Ashgrove Street, Ayr, KA7 3BG
Tel:01292 263745
Email:deanbankayr@hotmail.com

Semi-detached late Victorian town house in quiet residential street within
easy walking distance of town centre and seafront. Deanbank offers a
quality breakfast including home baking. Ideal holiday base for golfing,
riverwalks and exploring Burns Country.

1 Twin
1 Double

B&B per person
from £25.00 Single
from £20.00 Double

Open Jan-Dec excl
Xmas/New Year

Important: Prices stated are estimates and may be subject to amendments

Ayr			Map Ref: 1G7	

★★

B&B

The Dunn Thing
13 Park Circus, Ayr, KA7 2DJ
Tel:01292 284531 Fax:01292 262944
Email:SheliaDunn@cs.com
Web:www.smoothhound.co.uk/hotels/dunnthin.html

The Dunn Thing offers a warm welcome and a cup of tea on arrival to all
our guests. This is a Victorian town house close to the town centre and
sea front, situated in quiet area of Ayr. Free pick-up can be arranged
from Prestwick Airport or Ayr Train or Bus Station. Euros now accepted.

2 Twin	All En Suite	B&B per person	Open Jan-Dec
1 Double		from £22.00 Single	
		from £18.00 Double	
		from £15.00 Room	
		Only	

★★

B&B

Failte
9 Prestwick Road, Ayr, KA8 8LD
Tel:01292 265282
Email:jenniferfailte@btinternet.com
Web:www.jenniferfailte.co.uk

Welcome to Failte, a family bed and breakfast situated in residential
area on the Ayr-Glasgow road. Town centre with its variety of eating
establishments 10-15 minutes walk. Prestwick Airport 5 minutes drive.

1 Twin	1 En Suite fac	B&B per person	Open Jan-Dec excl
1 Double	1 Pub.Bath/Show	from £17.00 Single	Xmas/New Year
		from £17.00 Double	
		from £15.00 Room	
		Only	

★★

B&B

Ferguslea
98 New Road, Ayr, KA8 8JG
Tel:01292 268551
Email:wilma.campbell@ntlworld.com

Traditional Scottish hospitality in comfortable family home, within 10
minutes walk of town centre and all amenities. Private parking
available.

1 Single	1 Priv.NOT ensuite	B&B per person	Open Jan-Dec
2 Twin	1 Pub.Bath/Show	from £16.00 Single	
		from £16.00 Double	
		from £14.00 Room	
		Only	

★★

B&B

Garth Madryn
71 Maybole Road, Alloway, Ayr, KA7 4TB
Tel:01292 443346
Email:emackie@garthmadryn.fsnet.co.uk

Warm and friendly B&B. Easy access to town centre and International
golf courses. Near to Rozelle and Belleisle Parks and the Burns National
Heritage Park. Situated close to Burns by Bike cycle route and main cycle
route through Ayr. Close to Brig O'Doon Hotel - ideal for overnight
wedding guests. Cyclists welcome.

2 Twin	All En Suite	B&B per person	Open Jan-Dec
		£18.00-20.00 Single	

★★

B&B

Iona Guest House
27 St Leonards Road, Ayr, KA7 2PS
Tel/Fax:01292 269541
Email:info@iona-guesthouse.co.uk
Web:www.iona-guesthouse.co.uk

Traditional family home in residential area, ideally situated for both the
business and holiday traveller. Some private parking and free on-street
parking.

2 Single	2 En Suite fac	B&B per person	Open Feb-Nov
1 Twin		from £16.00 Single	
1 Double		from £16.00 Double	

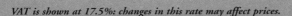

VAT is shown at 17.5%: changes in this rate may affect prices.   *Key to symbols is on back flap.*

Ayr

Map Ref: 1G7

★★★

B&B

Jac-Mar
23 Dalblair Road, Ayr, KA7 1UF
Tel/Fax:01292 264798
Email:email@dgambles.fsnet.co.uk

2 Single	3 En Suite fac	B&B per person	Open Jan-Dec excl
2 Family	1 Pub.Bath/Show	from £22.50 Single	Xmas/New Year
		from £22.50 Double	
		from £18.00 Room	
		Only	

Friendly hosted family run bed and breakfast in terraced house within town centre. 5 minutes from sea front, convenient for railway station and Prestwick airport. Central base for exploring Burns country, Ayrshire and Isle of Arran. Centrally located for easy access to the numerous Golf Courses Ayrshire has to offer. Very near to Ayr Gaiety Theatre.

TV [icons] P [icons]

★★★

B&B

Tramore Guest House
17 Eglinton Terrace, Ayr, KA7 1JJ
Tel/Fax:01292 266019
Email:tramoreguesthouse@amserve.net

2 Twin	B&B per person	Open Jan-Dec
1 Double	from £18.00 Single	BB & Eve.Meal
	from £17.00 Double	from £24.00

Set in a quiet conservation area in a Victorian terraced house - a two minute walk from either town centre or beach. Evening meals available.

TV [icons]

C [icons] V

Ballantrae, Ayrshire

Map Ref: 1F9

★★★

B&B

Mrs Georgina McKinley
Laggan Farm, Ballantrae, Ayrshire, KA26 0JZ
Tel:01465 831402
Email:j&r@lagganfm.freeserve.co.uk

1 Double	1 En Suite fac	B&B per person	Open May-Oct
1 Family	1 Priv.NOT ensuite	from £18.00 Single	
		from £18.00 Double	

Dairy farm with large comfortable farmhouse 0.5 miles south of Ballantrae on the Ayrshire coast. Guests have their own dining room and sitting room with colour tv. Tea/coffee making facilities plus home baking is available in the dining room in the evening. Ideal base for touring, golfing, woodland walks and fishing by arrangement.

[icons] P [icons]

C [icons] W V

Beith, Ayrshire

Map Ref: 1G6

SHOTTS FARM
BEITH, AYRSHIRE KA15 1LB
TELEPHONE: 01505 502273
E.MAIL: Gurlston@hotmail.com
Comfortable friendly accommodation is offered on this 200-acre dairy farm. Situated between the A736 and A737, its location is ideal for golf courses, country parks, shopping centres and the ferries to Arran and Millport. Breakfast has something for all appetites, try our home-baked bread, scones and local farm produce.
STB ★★★   AA ★★★

★★★

B&B

Farmhouse Bed + Breakfast
Shotts Farm, Beith, Ayrshire, KA15 1LB
Tel/Fax:01505 502273
Email:gurlston@hotmail.com

1 Double	1 En Suite fac	B&B per person	Open Jan-Dec
1 Family	1 Priv.NOT ensuite	from £15.00 Single	BB & Eve.Meal
		from £15.00 Double	from £24.00

Family run farmhouse accommodation on a 200 acre dairy farm. Ideal base for Burns country, Arran and cultural Glasgow. Guests can enjoy a welcome cup of tea and homebaking on arrival and try our homemade bread and scones at breakfast time. We only use free range eggs in our varied and generous breakfasts.

TV [icons] P [icons]

C [icons] W V [icons]

Important: Prices stated are estimates and may be subject to amendments

Broughton, by Biggar, Peeblesshire

Map Ref: 2B6

★★★

GUEST HOUSE

The Glenholm Centre
Broughton, by Biggar, Lanarkshire, ML12 6JF
Tel/Fax:01899 830408
Email:glenholm@dircon.co.uk
Web:www.glenholm.dircon.co.uk

A warm welcome awaits you at our family run guest house set on a farm at The Heart of Glenholm in the Scottish Borders. Close to Broughton, 30 miles South of Edinburgh - it is the perfect location to come to unwind and enjoy the hills, glens, nature and history of the valley. Full board available.

2 Twin	All En Suite	B&B per person	Open Feb-Dec excl
1 Double		from £28.00 Single	Xmas/New Year
1 Family		from £25.00 Double	BB & Eve.Meal
			from £37.50

Castle Douglas, Kirkcudbrightshire

Map Ref: 2A10

★★★

GUEST HOUSE

Airds Farm
Crossmichael, Castle Douglas, Kirkcudbrightshire
DG7 3BG   Tel:01556 670418
Email:enquiries@airds.com Web:www.airds.com

Superb views over Loch Ken and the picturesque village and church of Crossmichael will delight visitors to this traditional farmhouse. Lovers of nature will enjoy walking through the wooded glen and pastures nearby or relaxing in the conservatory. Gardens, castles and other attractions are within easy reach, fishing, boating and watersports are available on the loch. A warm welcome, in a comfortable and relaxing home. Booking via establishment only.

1 Twin	2 En Suite fac	B&B per person	Open Jan-Dec
2 Double	1 Priv.NOT ensuite	from £24.00 Single	
1 Family		from £19.00 Double	

CRAIGADAM

Craigadam, Castle Douglas DG7 3HU
Tel/Fax: 01556 650233
e.mail: enquiry@craigadam.com
Web: www.craigadam.com

THE TASTE OF SCOTLAND

Craigadam is an elegant country house within a working farm. Antique furnishings, log fires and friendly atmosphere. Relax in our elegant drawing room and enjoy the views across Galloway. All the bedrooms are ensuite. Dine in our oak panelled dining room where we specialise in venison, duck, salmon and sweets, not for the calorie conscious! Enjoy a game of billiards after dinner, catch a trout on our hill loch and have it for breakfast. All home-cooking using local produce. Booking via establishment only.
AA ◆◆◆◆◆ RAC ◆◆◆◆◆ ⊛

★★★★

B&B

●●●
HOME COOKING

Craigadam
Castle Douglas, Dumfries & Galloway, DG7 3HU
Tel/Fax:01556 650233
Email:enquiry@craigadam.com Web:www.craigadam.com

18th century farmhouse with panoramic views of surrounding countryside. An ideal base for golfing, walking, fishing. All bedrooms are ensuite. There is a billiard room for after dinner entertainment. Come home in the evening to comfort, super food and good Scottish hospitality. We specialise in local produce including venison, pheasant, salmon. There is a trout loch on the estate. Booking via establishment only.

4 Twin	All En Suite	B&B per person	Open Jan-Dec excl
2 Double		from £30.00 Single	Xmas/New Year
		from £30.00 Double	BB & Eve.Meal
			from £45.00

Castle Douglas, Kirkcudbrightshire

Map Ref: 2A10

★★★

B&B

The Craig
44 Abercromby Road, Castle Douglas, DG7 1BA
Tel:01556 504840
Email:mgtgordon@btinternet.com

1 Double	1 En Suite fac	B&B per person	Open Jan-Dec
1 Twin	1 Priv.NOT ensuite	from £18.00 Single	BB & Eve.Meal
1 Single	1 Pub.Bath/Show	from £18.00 Double	from £28.00
		from £21.00 Ensuite	

Large sandstone villa located next to golf course and a short walk to the centre of the market town of Castle Douglas. Well situated for exploring the Solway Coast and Galloway Forrest. Close to the famous Threave Garden and Threave Castle which is surrounded by walks and accessed by boat.

KALMAR
Balmaclellan, Nr New Galloway, Castle Douglas DG7 3QF
Telephone: 01644 420685
e.mail: kalmar@dial.pipex.com Web: www.kalmar.dial.pipex.com

Modern, purpose-built, centrally heated, all rooms ensuite.
Set amidst beautiful Galloway countryside with mountain views –
central for all activities of the area. After dinner, enjoy the ambience of our
large residents' lounge with leather furniture and log-burning stove.
One suite on the ground floor.   Off-road parking.

★★★★

B&B

Kalmar
Balmaclellan, Castle Douglas, DG7 3QF
Tel/Fax:01644 420685
Email:kalmar@dial.pipex.com
Web:www.kalmar.dial.pipex.com

2 Twin	All En Suite	B&B per person	Open all year
		from £22.00 sharing	D,B&B per person
			from £34.00 sharing

Modern warm village home all ensuite with baths, showers and fridges. Golf course 2 miles away £12 per day . This area is world renowned for fishing, walking, sailing and bird watching. The owners cook with enthusiasm and will provide the very best of Scottish food, beautifully presented. Very quiet and peaceful, the whole area is almost traffic free.

★★★★

**SMALL
HOTEL**

●

**HOME
COOKING**

Longacre Manor
Ernespie Road, Castle Douglas, DG7 1LE
Tel:01556 503576 Fax:01556 503886
Email:ball.longacre@btinternet.com
Web:www.longacremanor.co.uk

2 Twin	All En Suite	B&B per person	Open Jan-Dec excl
2 Double		£40.00-50.00 Single	Xmas/New Year
		£35.00-50.00 Double	BB & Eve.Meal
			from £52.50-67.50

A small private country manor hotel surrounded by woodland gardens overlooking green fields on the edge of Castle Douglas. A traditional Scottish country town in one of the most beautiful and undiscovered areas of southern Scotland.

★★

B&B

Old School House
Clarebrand, Castle Douglas, Dumfries-shire
DG7 3AH
Tel:01556 503271

1 Twin	1 Priv.NOT ensuite	B&B per person	Open Jul-Aug
1 Double		from £15.00 Single	BB & Eve.Meal
		from £15.00 Double	from £20.00

Traditional old school house in rural Dumfries & Galloway, tranquil setting yet only 2 miles from Castle Douglas. Ideal base for walking and cycling. Evening meals provided, all vegetarian or vegan organic produce where possible.

Important: Prices stated are estimates and may be subject to amendments

Castle Douglas, Kirkcudbrightshire

Map Ref: 2A10

Smithy House

The Buchan, Castle Douglas, Kirkcudbrightshire DG7 1TH
Tel: 01556 503841
e.mail: enquiries@smithyhouse.co.uk Web: www.smithyhouse.co.uk
Relax in the peaceful tranquillity of our home, enjoying the natural
surroundings of the countryside, within convenient walking distance of the
shops and restaurants in town. Varied breakfast menu concentrating on
local produce. Your comfort is assured. No children under 16. Member of
Scotland's Best B&Bs. **BOOKING VIA ESTABLISHMENT ONLY.**

★★★★

B&B

Smithy House

The Buchan, Castle Douglas, Kirkcudbrightshire
DG7 1TH Tel:01556 503841
Email:enquiries@smithyhouse.co.uk
Web:www.smithyhouse.co.uk

A warm welcome awaits at our home, a traditional old Galloway cottage,
carefully extended and renovated with en-suite facilities and a
comfortable guest sitting room. Beautiful views over Carlingwark loch to
the hills and a gentle stroll into town and Threave Gardens. Centrally
situated for exploring Galloway's coast and countryside; weekly rates
available. Non-smoking.

2 Twin	Some En Suite	B&B per person	Open Jan-Dec excl
2 Double	1 Pub.Bath/Show	from £24.00 Double	Xmas/New Year

Cockburnspath, Berwickshire

Map Ref: 2E5

★★

B&B

B M Russell

Townhead Farm, Cockburnspath, Berwickshire
TD13 5YR
Tel:01368 830465
Email:barbararussell@townhead84.fsnet.co.uk
Web:www.townhead-farm.co.uk

Warm welcome at this family farmhouse set high above the sea. Sandy
beaches nearby. Edinburgh only 38 miles (61kms). Pick-up service from
end of the Southern Upland Way. First B&B on the A1107 just off the A1.

2 Family	1 Priv.NOT ensuite	B&B per person	Open Apr-Oct
		from £18.00 Double	

Millport, Isle of Cumbrae

Map Ref: 1F6

★★

B&B

Cirmhor, Mrs E Roberts

35 West Bay, Millport, Isle of Cumbrae, KA28 0HA
Tel:01475 530723

On the edge of Millport with views to the Wee Cumbrae and Portencross.
Ideal for walking, birdwatching & cycling. Bikes available. Attractive
conservatory and garden available for guests. Packed lunches available.

1 Twin	1 Priv.NOT ensuite	B&B per person	Open Jan-Dec excl
1 Double		from £20.00 Single	Xmas/New Year
		from £18.00 Double	BB & Eve.Meal
			from £25.00

Scotland's National Booking and Information Line

Tel: 0845 22 55 121
visitscotland.com

VAT is shown at 17.5%: changes in this rate may affect prices.   *Key to symbols is on back flap.*

Dumfries   Map Ref: 2B9

★★

B&B

30 Hardthorn Avenue
Dumfries, DG2 9JA
Tel/Fax:01387 253502
Email:anniesbandb@aol.com

Sample old fashioned bed & breakfast hospitality at this welcoming home at No 30, a detached house in residential area, convenient for both town centre and by-pass. The owner is a calligraphy teacher who specialises in writing family trees.

1 Twin	B&B per person
1 Double	from £16.50 Double

Open Easter-Oct

★★

B&B

Glencairn
45 Rae Street, Dumfries, DG1 1JD
Tel/Fax:01387 262467
Email:info@glencairnvilla.co.uk
Web:www.glencairnvilla.co.uk

Comfortable 19c home within easy walking distance of town centre. Close to railway station and library. En-suite rooms available.

1 Single	2 En Suite fac	B&B per person
1 Twin	1 Pub bath/show	from £17.00 Single
1 Double		from £19.00 Double
		from £15.00 Room
		Only

Open Jan-Dec

★★★

SMALL HOTEL

Huntingdon House Hotel & Restaurant
18 St Marys Street, Dumfries, DG1 1LZ
Tel:01387 254893 Fax:01387 262553
Email:ACAME45046@aol.com
Web:www.huntingdonhotel.co.uk

Traditional stone built house personally run by proprietor. Ideal base for touring. All rooms en-suite, ample private parking. 150 metres railway station, 10 mins walk to city centre.

2 Twin	All En-suite	B&B per person
3 Double		from £36.00 Single
3 Family		from £28.00 Double
		from £25.00 Room
		Only

Open Jan-Dec excl Xmas/New Year

★★★

B&B

Low Kirkbride Farmhouse B&B
Low Kirkbride, Auldgirth, Dumfries, DG2 0SP
Tel/Fax:01387 820258
Email:lowkirkbride@btinternet.com
Web:www.lowkirkbridefarm.com

Warm, comfortable farmhouse set in beautiful countryside, lovely views from every room and all rooms en-suite. Family room in new steading conversion. Friendly atmosphere. Superb breakfasts and tasty aga home baking. Evening meals by arrangement. Attractive garden, own walking leaflet. Working dairy and sheep farm. Pedigree herd of Belted Galloways. Walking, golfing, fishing, wildlife. 10 miles north of Dumfries. www.lowkirkbridefarm.com

1 Twin	All En-suite	B&B per person
1 Double		from £18.00 Single
1 Family		from £18.00 Double

Open Jan-Dec
BB & Eve.Meal
from £30.00

Important: Prices stated are estimates and may be subject to amendments

Dumfries   Map Ref: 2B9

Southpark Country House
Quarry Road, Locharbriggs, Dumfries DG1 1QG
Freephone: 0800 970 1588   Tel: 01387 711188 Fax: 01387 711155
e.mail: ewan@southparkhouse.co.uk   Web: www.southparkhouse.co.uk

Southpark's peaceful edge of town location has easy access from all major
routes, ideal base yet only 5 minutes drive from the town centre. This
unspoilt area offers fine shops and excellent restaurants. Relax and enjoy
our panoramic views. AA Landlady of Year Finalists 2000/2001.
AA ♦♦♦♦. Ample secure parking.

★★★

B&B

Southpark Country House

Quarry Road, Locharbriggs, Dumfries, DG1 1QG
Freephone: 0800 9701588 Tel:01387 711188
Email:b&b@southparkhouse.co.uk
Web:www.southparkhouse.co.uk

Situated on the edge of town this substantial country house offers peace,
tranquillity, breathtaking views and the finest hospitality. Safe private
parking and easy access from all major routes, yet only 5 minutes drive
from town centre, making this a very popular establishment.

1 Single	3 En Suite fac	B&B per person	Open Jan-Dec
1 Twin	1 Pub.Bath/Show	from £25.00 Single	Family Room from
1 Double		from £19.50 Dbl/Twn	£49.00 incl.
1 Family		from £18.00 Room	
		Only	

Wallamhill House B&B
Kirkton, Dumfries, DG1 1SL. Tel/Fax: 01387 248249
e.mail: wallamhill@aol.com Web: www.wallamhill.co.uk
Large modern country house with 2 acres of landscaped
garden, nestling in the Nith Valley yet only 5 minutes from
Dumfries. Lovely views from front and rear of house.
Beautifully appointed spacious en-suite bedrooms. All ground
floor. A special experience, come and relax. Small health suite
with sauna and steam room. Safe private parking.

★★★★

B&B

Wallamhill House B&B

Kirkton, Dumfries, DG1 1SL
Tel/Fax:01387 248249
Email:wallamhill@aol.com
Web:www.wallamhill.co.uk

Spacious house in quiet countryside, beautiful views of Nith Valley. 2
miles from Dumfries town centre, safe parking. All rooms ground floor
level, spacious, with ensuite shower rooms. Ideal and luxurious base to
explore Dumfries and Galloway. Small health suite with steam shower
and sauna. Evening meals by arrangement.

1 Twin	All En Suite	B&B per person	Open Jan-Dec excl
1 Double		from £28.00 Single	Xmas/New Year
1 Family		from £22.00 Double	

Dunure, by Ayr, Ayrshire   Map Ref: 1G7

★★★

B&B

Fisherton Farm B&B

Dunure, Ayr, KA7 4LF
Tel/Fax:01292 500223
Email:lesleywilcox@hotmail.com
Web:http://fishertonfarm.homestead.com/webpage.html

Traditional stone-built farmhouse on working mixed farm, with extensive
sea views to Arran. 5 miles from Ayr and convenient for Prestwick
Airport. Ground floor accommodation available. Central base for
exploring Burns Country, places of historical interest, golfing, fishing and
walking.

1 Twin	All En Suite	B&B per person	Open Jan-Dec excl
1 Double		from £20.00 Single	Xmas
		from £20.00 Double	

VAT is shown at 17.5%: changes in this rate may affect prices. | *Key to symbols is on back flap.*

Ecclefechan, Dumfriesshire — Map Ref: 2C9

★

B&B

Mrs M B Martin, Carlyle House
Ecclefechan, Dumfriesshire, DG11 3DG
Tel/Fax:01576 300322

Comfortable family accommodation convenient for M74. Children and
pets welcome. Opposite Carlyle's birthplace.

1 Single	2 Priv.NOT ensuite
1 Twin	
1 Family	

B&B per person
from £14.50 Single
from £14.50 Double
from £10.50 Room
Only

Open Jan-Dec excl
Xmas/New Year

P ☕ ⛄ (▥

Fairlie, Ayrshire — Map Ref: 1G6

★★★

B&B

Mon Abri
12 Main Road, Fairlie, Ayrshire, KA29 0DP
Tel:01475 568241
Email:grace.gardner@btinternet.com

Detached bungalow on main tourist route, overlooking the Firth of Clyde.
45 minutes by road from Glasgow. Personally run. A warm welcome
assures.

1 Twin	1 Priv.NOT ensuite
1 Double	1 Pub.Bath/Show

B&B per person
from £20.00 Single
from £20.00 Double

Open Jan-Dec excl
Xmas/New Year

TV P ☕ ⅍ ⛄ ♣

C ➹ V ♿

Galashiels, Selkirkshire — Map Ref: 2D6

★★

B&B

Ettrickvale
33 Abbotsford Road, Galashiels, TD1 3HW
Tel:01896 755224

Comfortable family run semi-detached bungalow with garden. By A7. On
outskirts of town but only a short walk from local amenities. All
accommodation on ground floor. Evening meals by arrangement.

2 Twin	2 En Suite fac
1 Double	1 Priv.Bath/Show

B&B per person
from £20.00 Single
from £18.00 Double

Open Jan-Dec excl
Xmas/New Year

TV ♦ ♦ P ☕ ⅍ ✕ ♣ (▥ ♣

C ➹ W V ♿   ⚡

Girvan, Ayrshire — Map Ref: 1F8

★★★★

B&B

Glendrissaig Guest House
Newton Stewart Road, by Girvan, Ayrshire, KA26 0HJ
Tel/Fax:01465 714631

Modern detached house with landscaped gardens in elevated position
with excellent outlook westwards over Firth of Clyde towards Mull of
Kintyre. Organic produce when available used in vegetarian meals.
Ground floor bedroom available.

1 Twin	2 En Suite fac
1 Double	1 Pub.Bath/Show
1 Family	

B&B per person
from £25.00 Single
£24.00-28.00 Double

Open Mar-Oct

♦ ♦ P ⅍ ⛄ (▥

C W V ♿

Scotland's National Booking and Information Line

Tel: 0845 22 55 121
visitscotland.com

Important: Prices stated are estimates and may be subject to amendments

Glengennet Farm

Barr, by Girvan, Ayrshire KA26 9TY

Tel/Fax: 01465 861220   e.mail: vsd@glengennet.fsnet.co.uk

Web: www.glengennet.co.uk

Victorian shooting lodge on hill farm, lovely views over Stinchar Valley and neighbouring Galloway Forest Park. Ensuite bedrooms with tea trays. Near conservation village with hotel for evening meals. Good base for Glentrool, Burns Country, Culzean Castle, Ayrshire coast. Price £21-£25 per person per night. *Contact Mrs V. Dunlop for a brochure.*

B&B

Glengennet Farm

Barr, Girvan, Ayrshire, KA26 9TY
Tel/Fax:01465 861220
Email:vsd@glengennet.fsnet.co.uk
Web:www.glengennet.co.uk

1 Twin	All En Suite	B&B per person	Open Apr-Oct
1 Double		£21.00-25.00 Double	

Original shooting lodge in peaceful situation with lovely views over the Stinchar Valley and the neighbouring Galloway Forest Park. Glengennet Farm is 1.5 miles from Barr with hotel for evening meals. A good base for visiting Glentrool, Culzean Castle and Country Park and the Ayrshire coast.

B&B

Hawkhill Farm

Old Dailly, Girvan, Ayrshire, KA26 9RD
Tel:01465 871232
Email:isobel@hawkhillfarm.co.uk
Web:www.hawkhillfarm.co.uk

1 Twin	1 En Suite fac	B&B per person	Open Mar-Oct
2 Double	1 Pub.Bath/Show	from £28.00 Single	
		from £22.00 Double	

Farmhouse B & B with that little bit extra! Former 17th Century Coaching Inn with spacious well-furnished rooms, warm welcome and home baking. Near Culzean Castle, Burns Country, Golf, Walking, Restaurants, Ferries and more. Find out in our brochure, or visit our website. Which Good Bed & Breakfast recommended. Dogs by arrangement.

B&B

St Oswalds

5 Golf Course Road, Girvan, Ayrshire, KA26 9HW
Tel:01465 713786

1 Twin	All En Suite	B&B per person	Open Jan-Dec excl
1 Double		from £25.00 Single	Xmas/New Year
		£18.00-23.00 Double	

Guests are made most welcome at this comfortable semi-detached villa overlooking Ailsa Craig, Arran and Girvan Golf Course. The large double bedroom with private facilities has this wonderful view while the twin ensuite bedroom overlooks the town to the hills beyond. Excellent breakfast. Culzean 7 miles, Turnberry Golf Course 5 miles. Ideal touring area. Unrestricted street parking.

VAT is shown at 17.5%: changes in this rate may affect prices.   Key to symbols is on back flap.

A

Gretna, Dumfriesshire | Map Ref: 2C10

The Beeches
Loanwath Road, off Sarkfoot Road, Gretna
Dumfriesshire, DG16 5EP Tel:01461 337448
Email:info@beeches-gretna.co.uk
Web:www.beeches-gretna.co.uk

B&B

You are assured of a warm welcome at the Beeches, a former 19th
century farmhouse located in a quiet part of Gretna, overlooking the
Solway Firth and Lakeland hills. A non-smoking house with a homely
and peaceful atmosphere. Ensuite facilities available. Self catering
cottage also available.

1 Double   All En Suite
1 Family

B&B per person
£22.00-23.00 Double

Open Jan-Dec excl
Xmas/New Year

Stanfield Farm
Eastriggs, Gretna, DG12 6TF
Tel:01461 40367

B&B

18th C farmhouse within working farm on outskirts of village of
Eastriggs. Ideal base for touring. Families welcome. Gretna/M6 4 miles,
Annan 4 miles, Dumfries 18 miles. Golf courses nearby. Good cycling
country. Birdwatching at Caerlaverock 10 miles.

2 Double   1 En Suite fac
1 Family   1 Priv.NOT ensuite

B&B per person
from £20.00 Double

Open Mar-Oct

Thistlewood B&B
Rigg, nr Gretna, Dumfriesshire, DG16 5JQ
Tel:01461 337810
Email:rodandcelia@thistlewood36.fsnet.co.uk
Web:www.warmanbie.co.uk/thistle.htm

B&B

Rural surroundings. Gretna two miles. Only five minutes from main
tourist routes. Comfortable cosy bedrooms. (One four-poster). Patio
garden for guest use. Off-road parking.

1 Twin   2 Priv.NOT ensuite
2 Double

B&B per person
from £25.00 Single
from £18.00 Double

Open Jan-Dec excl
Xmas/New Year

Hawick, Roxburghshire | Map Ref: 2D7

Craig-lan
6 Weensland Road, Hawick, TD9 9NP
Tel:01450 373506

B&B

Large Victorian terraced house, set above main A698 tourist route and
close to centre of historic Borders town. Long established Bed & Breakfast
with personal attention assured.

1 Twin   2 Priv.NOT ensuite
2 Double

B&B per person
from £18.00 Single
from £16.00 Double

Open Jan-Dec excl
Xmas/New Year

Ellistrin
6 Fenwick Park, Hawick, TD9 9PA
Tel:01450 374216 Fax:01450 373619
Email:eileen@ellistrin.com
Web:www.ellistrin.co.uk

B&B

Comfortable Victorian villa set in extensive, well laid out gardens, in a
commanding elevated position overlooking Hawick. All rooms ensuite.
Private Parking.

1 Twin   All En Suite
2 Double

B&B per person
from £22.00 Single
from £20.00 Double

Open Apr-Oct

Important: Prices stated are estimates and may be subject to amendments

Hawick, Roxburghshire

Map Ref: 2D7

★★

B&B

Kirkton Farmhouse
Kirkton, Hawick, Roxburghshire, TD9 8QJ
Tel/Fax:01450 372421
Email:bell.kirkton@virgin.net

Spacious Border farmhouse with private sitting room, log fire and colour TV. Private loch fishing.Ideal touring base. Evening meal by prior arrangement.

1 Twin	2 Priv.NOT ensuite	B&B per person	Open Jan-Dec
2 Double		from £22.00 Single	BB & Eve.Meal
		from £16.00 Double	from £23.50

★★★

B&B

Wiltonburn Farm
Hawick, Scottish Borders, TD9 7LL
Tel:01450 372414   Mob:07711 321226
Email:shell@wiltonburnfarm.u-net.com
Web:www.wiltonburnfarm.co.uk

You will be warmly welcomed and cared for on our lovely hill farm. Only 5 minutes from Hawick. Our cashmere knitwear shop will make your stay more pleasurable. Farmstay member. Welcome Host.

1 Twin	Pub.Bath	B&B per person	Open Jan-Dec excl
1 Double	Priv.NOT ensuite	from £25.00 Single	Xmas
1 Family	Ensuite fac	from £22.50 Double	

Innerleithen, Peeblesshire

Map Ref: 2C6

★★

B&B

The Schoolhouse
Traquair, Innerleithen, Peeblesshire, EH44 6PL
Tel/Fax:01896 830426   Mobile:07986 682426
Email:schoolhouse@jcaird.force9.co.uk

A former traditional village school house recently modernised to provide all the creature comforts in a traditional setting. A lovely old cottage with comfortable bedrooms and warm guest sitting room. Open views of fields with sheep grazing, cherry trees and forested hills. Two child friendly dogs, log fires and home cooking with evening meals by arrangement. Innerleithen close by and Southern Upland Way 50 mts.

1 Twin	2 Priv.NOT ensuite	B&B per person	Open Jan-Dec excl
1 Double		from £21.00 Single	Xmas/New Year
1 Family		from £20.00 Double	BB & Eve.Meal
			from £30.00

Irvine, Ayrshire

Map Ref: 1G6

★★

B&B

The Conifers
40 Kilwinning Road, Irvine, Ayrshire, KA12 8RY
Tel:01294 278070

Bungalow with large well maintained garden. Ample off-street parking in safe location. All rooms can be let as singles. Central for bus routes, station and town centre with all its amenities including a variety of restaurants.

1 Single	B&B per person	Open Jan-Dec excl
2 Dbl/Twn	from £22.50 Single	Xmas/New Year
	from £17.50 Double	

Jedburgh, Roxburghshire

Map Ref: 2E7

★★

B&B

15 Hartrigge Crescent
Jedburgh, Roxburghshire, TD8 6HT
Tel:01835 862738

Warm hospitality in this friendly family house. In quiet residential area within walking distance of the town. Parking facilities near house.

1 Twin	B&B per person	Open Jan-Dec
1 Double	from £19.00 Single	
	from £16.00 Double	
	from £10.00 Room	
	Only	

VAT is shown at 17.5%: changes in this rate may affect prices.   Key to symbols is on back flap.

Jedburgh, Roxburghshire   Map Ref: 2E7

Crailing Old School B&B
Crailing, by Jedburgh, Roxburghshire, TD8 6TL
Tel/Fax:01835 850382
Email:jean.player@virgin.net
Web:www.crailingoldschool.co.uk

A welcoming family home with cosy bedrooms, peacefully situated just off Jedburgh/Kelso road. Close to the river Teviot, St. Cuthbert's Way, Harestanes Visitor Centre, golf driving range. Excellent base for walking, fishing, golfing (several courses in the area). Tee off times can be arranged. Enjoy our excellent cuisine using local produce. Vegetarians and special diets catered for.

2 Single	1 En-suite	B&B per person
1 Twin	3 Priv.Bath/Show	from £22.00 Single
1 Double		from £22.00 Double

Open Jan-Dec excl Xmas
BB & Eve.Meal from £34.50

B&B ★★★★

FROYLEHURST
The Friars, Jedburgh TD8 6BN
Tel/Fax: 01835 862477

An impressive Grade 'B' listed Victorian town house dated 1894, retaining original fireplaces, stained glass windows, cornices and tiled vestibule. Offering spacious and comfortable guest rooms and residents' lounge. Enjoying an elevated position in a large secluded garden in a quiet residential area with ample private off-street parking, yet only 2 minutes from town centre. All bedrooms have wash basins, shaver points, tea/coffee-making facilities, colour TV and radio. Full Scottish breakfast. This is a family home, and guests are made welcome by the owner, Mrs H Irvine.

Froylehurst
Friars, Jedburgh, Roxburghshire, TD8 6BN
Tel/Fax:01835 862477

Detached Victorian house (retaining many original features) with large garden and private parking. Spacious rooms. Overlooking town, 2 minutes walk from the centre.

1 Twin	2 Priv.NOT ensuite	B&B per person
1 Double		from £20.00 Single
2 Family		from £20.00 Double

Open Mar-Nov

B&B ★★★★

Riverview
Newmill Farm, Jedburgh, TD8 6TH
Tel:01835 864607/862145 (eve)
Email:liz.kinghorn@amserve.net
Web:http://mysite.freeserve.com/riverviewbandb

Modern villa on quiet country road in rolling Scottish Borders Farmland. Overlooking the river Jed. Large residents lounge with balcony. Free trout fishing available for guests. Spacious car park area. Jedburgh 2 miles. Kelso 8 miles. Close to St Cuthberts Way (Grid ref NT659227)

1 Twin	All En Suite	B&B per person
2 Double		from £25.00 Single
		from £18.00 Double

Open Apr-Oct

B&B ★★★

Important: Prices stated are estimates and may be subject to amendments

Jedburgh, Roxburghshire | Map Ref: 2E7

THE SPINNEY

Langlee, Jedburgh, Roxburghshire TD8 6PB
Telephone: 01835 863525 Fax: 01835 864883
e.mail: thespinney@btinternet.com Web: www.thespinney-jedburgh.co.uk

Set in mature gardens, bordering woodland and open countryside The Spinney offers accommodation of the highest standard. The en-suite bedrooms have many extra touches to make your stay more comfortable. There is a varied menu at breakfast which is served in the elegant dining room at separate tables.

B&B

The Spinney

Langlee, Jedburgh, Roxburghshire, TD8 6PB
Tel:01835 863525 Fax:01835 864883
Email:Thespinney@btinternet.com
Web:www.thespinney-jedburgh.co.uk

A warm welcome at this attractive house with large pleasant garden, lying just off the main A68 2 miles south of Jedburgh. Private parking. Quality self-catering lodges available. Two rooms are en-suite and one has a private bathroom.

1 Twin	2 En Suite fac	B&B per person	Open Mar-Nov
2 Double	1 Pub.Bath/Show	from £23.00 Double	

GUEST HOUSE

Willow Court

Friars, Jedburgh, Roxburghshire, TD8 6BN
Tel:01835 863702 Fax:01835 864607
Email:mike@willowcourtjedburgh.co.uk
Web:www.willowcourtjedburgh.co.uk

Set in 2 acres of grounds above the town, with excellent views. Peaceful setting, yet close to all amenities including Abbey, Castle and a good selection of restaurants. All rooms are either ensuite or with private bathroom or shower-room. Most rooms are on the ground floor.

1 Twin	3 En Suite fac	B&B per person	Open Jan-Dec
2 Double	1 Priv.Bath/Show	from £28.00 Single	
1 Family		from £18.00 Double	
		from £18.00 Room Only	

VAT is shown at 17.5%: changes in this rate may affect prices.

Key to symbols is on back flap.

Jedburgh, Roxburghshire — Map Ref: 2E7

Windyridge

39 Dounehill, Jedburgh TD8 6LJ Tel: 01835 864404
e.mail: jlowelowc6r@supanet.com
Web: www.smoothhound.co.uk/hotels/windyridge
Enjoy a warm, friendly welcome in our modern quiet home perched
above historic Jedburgh. Panoramic views of the Abbey, Castle and
surrounding hills. Hungry people catered for with home-made
preserves etc. Off-street parking. Secure garaging for cycles/motor cycles.
Ensuite rooms. No smoking. Pets welcome. Tea/coffee, TVs in rooms.

★★★★
B&B

Windyridge
39 Dounehill, Jedburgh, Roxburghshire, TD8 6LJ
Tel:01835 864404
Email:jlowelowc6r@supanet.com
Web:www.smoothhound.co.uk/hotels/windyridge

Conveniently situated for the Abbey and town centre, this family home in
a quiet, residential location, offers a warm welcome with tea and home
baking and panoramic views over Jedburgh. Garage and parking. Ideal
location for outdoor activities. Families welcome.

1 Single	2 En Suite fac	B&B per person	Open Jan-Dec
1 Twin	1 Priv.NOT ensuite	from £19.00 Single	
1 Family		from £21.00 Double	

Kelso, Roxburghshire — Map Ref: 2E6

★★★
B&B

Abbey Bank B&B
The Knowes, Kelso, Roxburghshire, TD5 7BH
Tel/Fax:01573 226550
Email:diah@abbeybank.freeserve.co.uk
Web:www.aboutscotland.com/kelso/abbeybank.html

Elegant, historic 1820 town house. Full of character, providing a true
Scottish welcome with oriental style comfort. 3 min walk to the Abbey,
town centre and River Tweed. Ideal touring base. Private parking, lock up
garage available on request.

1 Single	All En Suite	B&B per person	Open Jan-Dec
2 Twin		from £30.00 Single	
2 Double		from £22.00 Double	

★★★
B&B

Mrs Jan McDonald
Craignethan House, Jedburgh Road, Kelso
Roxburghshire, TD5 8AZ
Tel:01573 224818

Experience a warm Scottish welcome at this delightful detached house
overlooking the town and the river Tweed, with panoramic views of
Floors Castle and surrounding countryside. Ground floor bedroom. Ample
off street parking adjoining the house.

1 Twin	1 Priv.NOT ensuite	B&B per person	Open Jan-Dec
2 Double	1 Pub.Bath/Show	from £19.00 Single	
		from £19.00 Double	

★★★★
B&B

Whitehill Farm
Nenthorn, Kelso, Roxburghshire, TD5 7RZ
Tel/Fax:01573 470203
Email:besmith@whitehillfarm.freeserve.co.uk
Web:www.whitehillfarm.freeserve.co.uk

18c farmhouse on mixed farm with superb views. Ideally placed for
touring the Borders region and just off the Kelso/Edinburgh road. Real
cooking, fresh food, meal by arrrangement.

2 Single	1 Pub.Bath/Show	B&B per person	Open Jan-Dec excl
2 Twin	1 Ensuite	from £22.00 Single	Xmas/New Year
		from £23.00 Double	BB & Eve.Meal
			from £37.00-38.00

Important: Prices stated are estimates and may be subject to amendments

Kilmarnock, Ayrshire | Map Ref: 1G6

HILLHOUSE FARM
Grassyards Road, Kilmarnock, Ayrshire KA3 6HG
Telephone/Fax: 01563 523370
Web: http://www.SmoothHound.co.uk/hotels/hillhouse.html
Spacious, comfortable and friendly accommodation on working dairy
farm one mile east of Kilmarnock. Lovely views over open countryside.
Well situated to visit Ayrshire coast, Burns country, Arran, Glasgow
and Loch Lomond. Large selection of golf courses nearby. Large
farmhouse breakfasts and supper with homebaking. Further details
and brochure on request from Mrs Mary Howie.

★★★★
B&B

Hillhouse Farm B&B (Mrs Mary Howie)
Grassyards Road, Kilmarnock, Ayrshire, KA3 6HG
Tel/Fax:01563 523370
Web:http://www.SmoothHound.co.uk/hotels/hillhouse.html

1 Twin	All En Suite	B&B per person	Open Jan-Dec
2 Family	1 Priv.NOT ensuite	from £21.00 Single	
	1 Pub.Bath/Show	from £20.00 Double	

The Howie family welcome you to their working farm in peaceful central
location, 1 mile east of Kilmarnock. Large bedrooms, TV lounge and sun
porch have superb views of the garden and open countryside. Farmhouse
breakfasts and home baking for bedtime supper.

"Tamarind"
24 ARRAN AVENUE, KILMARNOCK KA3 1TP
Tel: 01563 571788   Fax: 01563 533515
e.mail: James@tamarind25.freeserve.co.uk

The accommodation at 'Tamarind' was created with the International
visitor in mind. Rooms are equipped with remote control TV and all
are ensuite. A heated swimming pool (in season) is also available for
your enjoyment. *Discerning travellers will feel at home here.*

★★★
B&B

Tamarind
24 Arran Avenue, Kilmarnock, Ayrshire, KA3 1TP
Tel:01563 571788   Fax:01563 533515
Email:James@tamarind25.freeserve.co.uk

1 Single	All En Suite	B&B per person	Open Jan-Dec
2 Twin		£25.00-30.00 Single	
1 Family		£17.50-20.00 Double	

Ranch style bungalow with small heated swimming pool in residential
area. Convenient base for touring, and centrally situated for Ayrshire's
many golf courses.

★★★
B&B

West Tannacrieff Bed + Breakfast
Fenwick, by Kilmarnock, Ayrshire, KA3 6AZ
Tel:01560 600258 Fax:01560 600914
Email:westtannacrieff@btopenworld.com
Web:www.smoothhound.co.uk/hotels/westtannacrieff.html
West Tannacrieff is a working dairy farm with a new high quality purpose
built bed and breakfast unit with all modern amenities. Large spacious
bedrooms all tastefully decorated. All rooms are en-suite with televisions and
tea/coffee making facilities. Large parking area and garden. Enjoy breakfast
made with Scottish and local produce with homemade breads and preserves.
Homebaking also available with tea/coffee making facilities.

2 Twin	All En Suite	B&B per person	Open Jan-Dec
1 Family		from £22.50 Single	
		from £20.00 Double	

VAT is shown at 17.5%: changes in this rate may affect prices. | Key to symbols is on back flap.

Kilwinning, Ayrshire

Map Ref: 1G6

★★

B&B

Blairholme
45 Byres Road, Kilwinning, KA13 6JU
Tel:01294 552023
Email:pcullinane@whsmithnet.co.uk

1 Double	2 Pub.Bath/Show	B&B per person	Open Jan-Dec excl
1 Family		£15.00-20.00 Single	Xmas/New Year
		£15.00-20.00 Double	

Turn of the century, semi detached bungalow with one bedroom on ground floor level, and the other upstairs. Close to town centre and only 2 mins walk to The Railway Station, 15 mins by Train/Car to Prestwick Airport. No smoking house. Close to Arran ferry.

Kippford, by Dalbeattie, Kirkcudbrightshire

Map Ref: 2A10

ROSEMOUNT
ROSEMOUNT, KIPPFORD, DALBEATTIE DG5 4LN
Tel / Fax: 01556 620214 e.mail: sanjes@ukonline.co.uk

Sandy and Jess Muir extend a warm welcome for you to relax in our small friendly guest house. Ideal base for touring, walking, golfing, fishing and bird-watching. Home-cooked meals and preserves available to guests. Kippford is an unspoilt village with breathtaking sunsets and view. 10% reduction per week.

★★★

GUEST
HOUSE

Rosemount
The Front, Kippford, Dalbeattie, DG5 4LN
Tel/Fax:01556 620214
Email:sanjes@ukonline.co.uk

2 Twin	3 En Suite fac	B&B per person	Open Feb-Oct
2 Double	2 Pub.Bath/Show	from £26.00 Single	
1 Family		from £21.00 Double	

Small friendly guest house on the Urr Estuary offering a superb view and spectacular sunsets. Smoking and non-smoking lounges.

Kirkcudbright

Map Ref: 2A10

★★★★

B&B

Eileen at Benutium
2 Rossway Road, Kirkcudbright, Kirkcudbrightshire
DG6 4BS Tel:01557 330788
Email:eileen.malcolm@benutium.freeserve.co.uk
Web:www.benutium.co.uk

1 Double	Ensuite fac	B&B per person	Open Jan-Dec
1 Single	Priv.facilities	from £28.00 Single	
		from £28.00 Double	

One of Scotland's best B&B's. Exceptional standard of cuisine and comfort. Magnificent views; quiet location; off street parking. Perfect retreat for short breaks and longer stays. Double bedroom has sole use of lounge. Single room is a bed-sitting room. Seasonal discounts available.

Largs, Ayrshire				Map Ref: 1F5

★★★

B&B

Broom Lodge

5 Broomfield Place, Largs, Ayrshire, KA30 8DR
Tel:01475 674290
Email:mills@broomlodge.freeserve.co.uk

Set overlooking the bay of Largs towards Cumbrae with commanding views of the ferries and yachts. Close to town with its shops, restaurants and pubs. All rooms ensuite or private facilities. 2 single rooms on first floor.

2 Single	2 En Suite fac	B&B per person	Open Jan-Dec excl
1 Twin	2 Pub.Bath/Show	from £20.00 Single	Xmas/New Year
1 Double		from £20.00 Double	
		from £18.00 Room Only	

C ⊨ V

★★★

GUEST HOUSE

Lea-Mar Guest House

20 Douglas Street, Largs, Ayrshire, KA30 8PS
Tel/Fax:01475 672447
Email:leamar.guesthouse@fsbdial.co.uk
Web:www.smoothhound.co.uk/hotels/leamar.html

Detached bungalow in quiet area, yet close to town. 100 yards from the promenade and beach. Ideal base for touring. Private parking. All rooms ensuite.

2 Twin	All En Suite	B&B per person	Open mid Mar-Jan excl
2 Double		from £25.00 Double	Xmas/New Year

★★★

B&B

The Old Rectory

Aubery Crescent, Largs, Ayrshire, KA30 8PR
Tel:01475 674405
Email:ashrona@aol.com

A warm welcome at this family home situated on the sea front with views over Cumbrae to Arran. A five minute stroll along the promenade into town. Large garden with private parking area. Spacious residents lounge with separate dining room and good sized bedrooms makes for a comfortable and relaxing stay.

1 Twin	1 Priv.NOT ensuite	B&B per person	Open Jan-Nov excl
1 Double		from £20.00 Single	Xmas/New Year
		from £18.00 Double	

C ⊨ V

★★★★

B&B

South Whittlieburn Farm

Brisbane Glen, Largs, Ayrshire, KA30 8SN
Tel:01475 675881   Fax:01475 675080
Email:largsbandb@southwhittlieburnfarm.freeserve.co.uk
Web:www.smoothhound.co.uk/hotels/whittlie.html

Warm friendly hospitality, enormous delicious breakfasts. Ample parking. AA four diamonds, chosen by 'Which Best Bed & Breakfast'. Enjoy a great holiday on our working sheep farm, only five mins drive from the popular tourist resort of Largs. (45 minutes from Glasgow or Prestwick Airport). A warm welcome from Mary Watson.

1 Twin	All En Suite	B&B per person	Open Jan-Dec
1 Double		from £21.50 Single	
1 Family		from £21.50 Double	

C W V

VAT is shown at 17.5%: changes in this rate may affect prices.

Key to symbols is on back flap.

Largs, Ayrshire

Map Ref: 1F5

★★★★

B&B

Stonehaven Guest House
8 Netherpark Crescent, Largs, Ayrshire, KA30 8QB
Tel:01475 673319
Email:stonehaven.martin@virgin.net

Situated in quiet residential area in front of Routenburn Golf Course, overlooking the Largs Bay, Isle of Cumbrae with the Isle of Arran and Ailsa Craig in the distance.

1 Single	2 En Suite fac	B&B per person	Open Jan-Dec
1 Twin	1 Priv.NOT ensuite	from £20.00 Single	
1 Double		from £23.00 Double	

Tigh-na-Ligh Guest House

104 Brisbane Road, Largs, Ayrshire KA30 8NN
Tel: 01475 673975 E.mail: tighnaligh@tinyonline.co.uk
Web: www.s-h-systems.co.uk/a06156
Tigh-na-Ligh offers attractively decorated apartments. Pleasant dining room where we serve a hearty Scottish breakfast, with a small sitting area. All rooms have en-suite/private facilities with CTV, tea/coffee making facilities/radio alarm and hairdryer. Ample off-street parking. Children under five are free. No smoking establishment.

★★★

GUEST
HOUSE

Tigh-na-Ligh Guest House
104 Brisbane Road, Largs, Ayrshire, KA30 8NN
Tel:01475 673975
Email:tighnaligh@tinyonline.co.uk
Web:www.s-h-systems.co.uk/a06156

A warm and friendly welcome awaits you at Tigh-na-Ligh which is situated in a quiet residential area, some upstairs rooms have super views over the town to the hills and surrounding countryside. Good sized ground and first floor bedrooms. Ideal base for a day of cruising on the Clyde or touring Burns country. No smoking.

2 Twin	4 En Suite fac	B&B per person	Open Jan-Dec excl
2 Double	1 Pub.Bath/Show	from £25.00 Single	Xmas/New Year
1 Family		from £23.00 Double	
		from £20.00 Room	
		Only	

★★★★

GUEST
HOUSE

Whin Park Guest House
16 Douglas Street, Largs, Ayrshire, KA30 8PS
Tel:01475 673437 Fax:01475 687291
Email:enquiries@whinpark.co.uk
Web:www.whinpark.co.uk

Close to seafront, within 10 minutes walk from the town centre. Whin Park built in the 1930's offers 4 star accommodation, comfort & service combined with a warm & friendly welcome from Jennifer & Ian Henderson. Visit our web site for more details.

1 Single	All En Suite	B&B per person	Open Mar-Jan
1 Twin		from £27.00 Single	
2 Double		from £27.00 Double	
1 Family		from £22.00 Room	
		Only	

Lauder, Berwickshire

Map Ref: 2D6

★★★

B&B

Tricia & Peter Gilardi
The Grange, 6 Edinburgh Road, Lauder, Berwickshire
TD2 6TW Tel/Fax:01578 722649
Email:trishnpete.lauder@amserve.net
Web:http://www.aboutscotland.co.uk/grange.html

Detached house standing in large garden with lovely views of surrounding countryside. A non-smoking house. Located on the Southern Upland Walk and close to several stately homes and castles. 45 minutes drive to Edinburgh.

2 Twin		B&B per person	Open Jan-Dec excl
1 Double		from £18.00 Single	Xmas
		from £18.00 Double	
		from £13.00 Room	
		Only	

Important: Prices stated are estimates and may be subject to amendments

Lochmaben, Dumfriesshire

Map Ref: 2B9

★★★

B&B

Ardbeg Cottage
19 Castle Street, Lochmaben, Dumfries-shire
DG11 1NY
Tel/Fax:01387 811855

1 Twin	All En Suite	B&B per person	Open Jan-Dec excl
1 Double		from £19.00 Single	Xmas/New Year
		from £19.00 Double	BB & Eve.Meal
			from £27.00

Elma and Bill welcome you to their happy home, Ardbeg Cottage, situated in a residential area near the town centre. Ground floor en-suite bedrooms. No children under 12, no pets, a totally non-smokinjg house. Home cooked evening meals by prior arrangement.

nr Lockerbie, Dumfriesshire

Map Ref: 2C9

CARIK COTTAGE
Waterbeck, Lockerbie, Dumfries & Galloway DG 11 3EU
Tel/Fax: 01461 600652
E.mail: cehislop@aol.com Web: www.b-and-b-scotland.co.uk/carik.htm
Set in the peaceful village of Waterbeck only 3 miles from Junction 20 of the M74. Carik Cottage offers excellent accommodation with many little extras for your enjoyment. We are an ideal stop travelling north or south and a good base for touring beautiful southern Scotland and north Cumbria.

★★★★

B&B

Carik Cottage
Waterbeck, Lockerbie, Dumfriesshire, DG11 3EU
Tel/Fax:01461 600652
Email:cehislop@aol.com
Web:www.b-and-b-scotland.co.uk/carik.htm

1 Single	2 En Suite fac	B&B per person	Open Mar-Nov
1 Twin		from £22.00 Single	
1 Double		from £22.00 Double	

Tastefully converted cottage in peaceful rural setting with beautiful views where in the summertime you can see Molly and Daisy our Belted Galloways. Only 3 miles(5km) from the M74. Ideal for touring south west Scotland or an overnight stop between North and South. Lounge available.

Lockerbie, Dumfriesshire

Map Ref: 2C9

★★★★

B&B

The Elms
Dumfries Road, Lockerbie, Dumfriesshire, DG11 2EF
Tel/Fax:01576 203898
Email:theelms@gofornet.co.uk
Web:www.lockerbie-lodging.com

1 Twin	All En Suite	B&B per person	Open Feb-Nov
1 Double		from £26.00 Single	
		from £22.00 Double	
		from £18.00 Room	
		Only	

A traditional Victorian house with all modern comforts yet retaining many period features. Very comfortable accommodation with separate dining room and guests lounge. In easy walking distance of town centre. Hotel bar and restaurant next door, and enclosed, private parking.

★★★

**GUEST
HOUSE**

Rosehill Guest House
Carlisle Road, Lockerbie, Dumfriesshire, DG11 2DR
Tel/Fax:01576 202378

1 Single	3 En Suite fac	B&B per person	Open Jan-Dec excl
2 Twin	2 Pub.Bath/Show	from £25.00 Single	Xmas/New Year
1 Double		from £22.50 Double	
1 Family			

Attractive Victorian villa with large well stocked garden in residential area, within walking distance of the town centre and with a choice of restaurants. Private parking.

VAT is shown at 17.5%: changes in this rate may affect prices. | *Key to symbols is on back flap.*

Mauchline, Ayrshire | Map Ref: 1H7

★★★

B&B

Ardwell Bed + Breakfast
103 Loundoun Street, Mauchline, Ayrshire, KA5 5BH
Tel:01290 552987
Email:ardwell@zetnet.co.uk Web:www.ardwell.zetnet.co.uk

Ardwell is a detached house situated in the historic village of Mauchline. It is situated near the village centre within easy walking distance of shops and eating establishments. Its rooms are both en-suite and extremely comfortable. Ardwell prides itself on its hospitality and the standard of the breakfasts and home cooking. Mauchline has access to Scotlands' scenic West Coast and is convenient for Glasgow Prestwick Airport, Ayr, Kilmarnock and Cumnock.

2 Family   All En Suite

B&B per person
from £19.00 Single
from £17.00 Double

Open Jan-Dec

TV ☕ P ☕ ☜ ✂

C V

★★

B&B

Treborane
Dykefield Farm, Mauchline, Ayrshire, KA5 6EY
Tel:01290 550328

Bed and breakfast accommodation in cottage on working farm in the heart of Burns Country. Friendly atmosphere, evening meal and ensuite bedroom. 1 mile from the village of Mauchline. 20 mins to the centre of Ayr town.

2 Family   1 En Suite fac
            1 Priv.NOT ensuite

B&B per person
£15.00-17.00 Double
from £13.00 Room
Only

Open Jan-Dec
BB & Eve.Meal
from £20.00-22.00

☕ P ✗ ☕

C 🛏 ♿

Melrose, Roxburghshire | Map Ref: 2D6

★★★

B&B

Braidwood
Buccleuch Street, Melrose, Roxburghshire, TD6 9LD
Tel:01896 822488
Email:braidwood.melrose@virgin.net
Web:http://homepage.virgin.net/braidwood.melrose

Friendly welcome in attractive listed town house only a stones throw from Melrose Abbey and Priorwood Gardens. Home baking.

1 Twin   2 En Suite fac
3 Double 2 Pub.Bath/Show

B&B per person
from £25.00 Single
from £20.00 Double

Open Jan-Dec

TV ☕ ☕ ☕ ✂

C 🛏 W V

 📷 🍃

★★★★

GUEST
HOUSE

Dunfermline House
Buccleuch Street, Melrose, Roxburghshire, TD6 9LB
Tel/Fax:01896 822148
Email:bestaccom@dunmel.freeserve.co.uk
Web:www.dunmel.freeserve.co.uk

Overlooking Melrose Abbey. A highly respected and well established guest house offering very high standards. All rooms (except one) with en-suite facilities, the single room has a private bathroom. Traditional Scottish breakfasts with interesting variations. Non-smoking house.

1 Single   4 En Suite fac
2 Twin   1 Pub.Bath/Show
2 Double

B&B per person
from £25.00 Single
from £25.00 Double

Open Jan-Dec

TV ☕ ☕ ☕ ☜ ✂ ⬅ 🍴

W V

📷 🍃 🔖

★★★

B&B

The Gables
Darnick, Melrose, Roxburghshire, TD6 9AL
Tel/Fax:01896 822479

Georgian villa in centre of quiet village, 3/4 mile (1kms) from Melrose. Ideal base for touring the Borders. Home baking. Non-smoking.

1 Single   1 Priv.NOT ensuite
1 Twin
1 Double

B&B per person
from £23.00 Single
from £19.00 Double

Open Jan-Dec

TV ☕ ☜ ✂ ⬅ ♿

🛏 W V

 📷 🍃

Important: Prices stated are estimates and may be subject to amendments

Melrose, Roxburghshire   Map Ref: 2D6

★★★

INN

Kings Arms Hotel
High Street, Melrose, Roxburghshire, TD6 9PB
Tel:01896 822143 Fax:01896 823812
Email:enquiries@kingsarmsmelrose.co.uk
Web:www.kingsarmsmelrose.co.uk

Former coaching Inn dating back some 300 years, in centre of historic Border town. Cosy lounge bar with open fires.

1 Single	7 En Suite fac
3 Twin	
1 Double	
2 Family	

B&B per person
from £38.00 Single
from £29.75 Double

Open Jan-Dec
BB & Eve.Meal
from £37.50

by Melrose, Roxburghshire   Map Ref: 2D6

★★★★

B&B

Fauhope House
Gattonside, Melrose, Roxburghshire, TD6 9LU
Tel:01896 823184/822245
Email:fauhope@bordernet.co.uk

A charming and secluded Country house built in 1897, set in its own spacious grounds with views to the River Tweed, Melrose Abbey and The Eildon Hills. 7 Minutes scenic walk into Melrose. Non smoking.

2 Twin	All En Suite
1 Double	

B&B per person
from £30.00 Single
from £25.00 Double

Open Jan-Dec excl
Xmas/New Year

Moffat, Dumfriesshire   Map Ref: 2B8

★★

GUEST HOUSE

Barnhill Springs Country Guest House
Moffat, Dumfriesshire, DG10 9QS
Tel:01683 220580

Barnhill Springs is an early Victorian country house standing in its own grounds overlooking upper Annandale. It is a quiet family run guest house situated ¹/₂ a mile from the A74/M at the Moffat junction no.15. Barnhill Springs is ideally situated as a centre for touring Southern Scotland, for walking and cycling on the Southern Upland Way or for a relaxing overnight stop for holiday makers heading North or South.

2 Twin	1 Priv.NOT ensuite
2 Double	2 Pub.Bath/Show
1 Family	

B&B per person
from £23.00 Single
from £23.00 Double

Open Jan-Dec
BB & Eve.Meal
from £39.00

★★

GUEST HOUSE

Buchan Guest House
Beechgrove, Moffat, Dumfriesshire, DG10 9RS
Tel/Fax:01683 220378
Email:buchanhouse220@aol.com
Web:www.buchanguesthouse.co.uk

Victorian house in quiet residential area, close to centre of Moffat. Ideal base for touring. Evening meal by prior arrangement.

1 Twin	Priv.Shower
2 Triple	En Suite Shower
2 Double	En Suite Shower
1 Double	Priv.Bathroom
1 Suite	Priv.Shower

B&B per person
from £22.00 Single
from £20.00 Double

Open Jan-Dec excl
Xmas
BB & Eve.Meal
from £30.00

Scotland's National Booking and Information Line

Tel: 0845 22 55 121
visitscotland.com

VAT is shown at 17.5%: changes in this rate may affect prices. | Key to symbols is on back flap.

Moffat, Dumfriesshire Map Ref: 2B8

B&B

Coxhill
Old Carlisle Road, Moffat, Dumfriesshire, DG10 9QN
Tel:01683 220471

1 Twin	All En Suite	B&B per person	Open Jan-Dec excl
1 Double		from £30.00 Single	Xmas/New Year
		from £25.00 Double	

Stylish country house with en-suite bedrooms. Set in 70 acres of unspoilt, peaceful countryside, with outstanding views, attractive gardens and complete privacy. Coxhill is located just 1 mile from Moffat town centre and 1/2 mile from the Southern Upland Way. A peaceful base for South West Scotland and all sporting activities. Non-smoking.

C V

B&B

Hazel Bank
Academy Road, Moffat, DG10 9HP
Tel:01683 220294 Fax:01683 221675
Email:ruth@hazelbankmoffat.co.uk
Web:www.hazelbankmoffat.co.uk

1 Single	1 En Suite fac	B&B per person	Open Jan-Dec excl
1 Double	1 Pub.Bath/Show	£25.00-30.00 Single	Xmas/New Year
1 Family		£22.50-25.00 Double	

Family home, centrally situated 2 minutes from town centre. Many hotels and restaurants in the immediate vicinity. Good base for touring. Ground floor ensuite available. Many extra touches in the bedrooms.

C 🛏 W V ⚲

GUEST HOUSE

Limetree House
Eastgate, Moffat, Dumfries & Galloway, DG10 9AE
Tel/Fax:01683 220001
Email:limetree-house@btconnect.com
Web:www.limetreehouse.co.uk

2 Twin	All En Suite	B&B per person	Open Mar-Jan
3 Double		from £25.00 Single	
1 Family		from £20.00 Double	

Friendly hosts, beautifully decorated rooms and wonderful breakfasts offer a truly memorable experience at Limetree House. Free locking garage parking available.

🛏 ⚲ W V ⚲

B&B

Morag Bed & Breakfast
19 Old Carlisle Road, Moffat, Dumfriesshire
DG10 9QJ Tel:01683 220690
Email:morag_moffat44@btopenworld.com

1 Single	1 Priv.NOT ensuite	B&B per person	Open Jan-Dec
1 Twin		from £20.00 Single	BB & Eve.Meal
1 Double		from £19.00 Double	from £29.00

A warm welcome is assured at this family run Victorian house located within quiet suburbs 1/2 mile from Moffat town centre. It is an excellent base for exploring the Moffat Water Valley and the Galloway countryside to the west. Golf, fishing, walking and other country pursuits available locally. Southern upland way 1/2 mile. Evening meals by arrangement. Non-smoking.

🛏 V

Queensberry House
12 Beech Grove, Moffat, Dumfriesshire, DG10 9RS
Tel:01683 220538
Email:queensberryhouse@amserve.net

B&B

3 Double	All En Suite	B&B per person	Open Jan-Dec excl
		from £23.00 Single	Xmas/New Year
		from £20.00 Double	

A warm welcome is guaranteed at this well appointed Victorian house in a quiet area opposite the bowling green and within a few minutes walk from town centre.

V ⚲

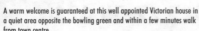 *Important: Prices stated are estimates and may be subject to amendments*

Moffat, Dumfriesshire

Map Ref: 2B8

★★

GUEST HOUSE

Rockhill Guest House

14 Beechgrove, Moffat, Dumfriesshire, DG10 9RS
Tel:01683 220283 Fax:01683 220822
Web:www.moffattown.com/moffat/accommodation

2 Single	5 En Suite fac	B&B per person	Open Jan-Dec excl
1 Twin		from £19.00 Single	Xmas
3 Double		from £19.00 Double	BB & Eve.Meal
4 Family			from £29.00

Victorian house overlooking bowling green and park, in quiet area close to town centre. Open outlook to hills. Own private car park. Ensuite rooms; all rooms with colour television. Pets welcome by arrangement. Evening meals available also by prior arrangement.

★★★

GUEST HOUSE

Seamore Guest House

Academy Road, Moffat, Dumfriesshire, DG10 9HW
Tel:01683 220404 Fax:01683 221313
Email:john@seamorehouse.co.uk
Web:www.seamorehouse.co.uk

1 Twin	4 En Suite fac	B&B per person	Open Jan-Dec
1 Double	1 Priv.fac	from £19.00 Double	
3 Family			

Comfortable family run guest house in centre of Moffat. All rooms with own private bathroom, plus a comfortable guests lounge. Children and pets welcome. Good centre for touring. Walkers welcome. Private off road parking.

WOODHEAD FARM

OLD CARLISLE ROAD, MOFFAT, DUMFRIESSHIRE DG10 9LU
Telephone/Fax: 01683 220225
e.mail: sylvia@woodhead4.freeserve.co.uk

Luxuriously appointed country house set in 100 acres of rolling countryside, two miles from the beautiful spa town of Moffat. All bedrooms are en suite with panoramic views. Breakfast is served in our garden conservatory overlooking mature garden and hills. Murray and Sylvia extend a warm welcome to their peaceful home. Ample safe parking.

★★★★

B&B

Woodhead

Old Carlisle Road, Moffat, Dumfriesshire, DG10 9LU
Tel/Fax:01683 220225
Email:sylvia@woodhead4.freeserve.co.uk

2 Twin	All En Suite	B&B per person	Open Jan-Dec excl
1 Double		from £35.00 Single	Xmas/New Year
		£27.00-30.00 Double	BB & Eve.Meal
			from £42.00-45.00

Luxuriously furnished farmhouse situated on 100 acres. All bedrooms have panoramic views of the surrounding, very peaceful countryside. Breakfast served in conservatory overlooking mature garden. Ample safe parking. Just 2 miles from spa town of Moffat.

Newton Stewart, Wigtownshire

Map Ref: 1G10

★★★

B&B

Benera Bed and Breakfast

Corsbie Road, Newton Stewart, Wigtownshire
DG8 6JD
Tel:01671 403443

1 Double	En Suite	B&B per person	Open Apr-Oct
1 Twin	Priv.Bath/Show	from £24.00 Single	
		from £20.00 Double	

Modern bungalow peacefully situated on the edge of the town with superb views of the Galloway Hills. Ideal location for golfing, fishing, walking, cycling and bird watching as well as exploring this scenic corner of Scotland.

VAT is shown at 17.5%: changes in this rate may affect prices.

Key to symbols is on back flap.

Newton Stewart, Wigtownshire   Map Ref: 1G10

Flowerbank Guest House

Millcroft Road, Minnigaff, Newton Stewart, Wigtownshire DG8 6PJ
Tel: 01671 402629
e.mail: flowerbankgh@btopenworld.com Web: www.flowerbankgh.com

With its quiet, picturesque location and stunning riverside gardens Flowerbank, run by Geoff and Linda for well over a decade, is the ideal setting for a relaxing and memorable holiday. We pride ourselves on our friendly, personal service and excellent home cooked meals. We also offer reductions for weekly stays.

★★★

**GUEST
HOUSE**

Flowerbank Guest House

Millcroft Road, Minnigaff, Newton Stewart, DG8 6PJ
Tel:01671 402629
Email:flowerbankgh@btopenworld.com
Web:www.flowerbankgh.com

Geoff and Linda Inker welcome you to Flowerbank, a charming 18th century house where the River Cree runs alongside our 1 acre landscaped gardens, just half a mile from Newton Stewart. Warm, comfortable, non-smoking accommodation with colour TVs, tea/coffee, lounge with log fire and ample parking. Spacious dining room, separate tables, good home cooking. Quiet and friendly - a warm welcome awaits you.

1 Twin	4 En Suite fac	B&B per person	Open Jan-Dec excl
2 Double	1 Pub.Bath/Show	from £20.00 Double	Xmas/New Year
2 Family			BB & Eve.Meal
			from £32.00

📺 ⛺ 🏠 🅿️ ☕ ⅙ ✕ 🍷 🛎️

© 🐕 📹

★★

B&B

Tarff House

Kirkcowan, Dumfries & Galloway, DG8 0HW
Tel:01671 830312
Email:sandra@tarffhouse.ndo.co.uk

Late Victorian house on edge of the village providing two very spacious bedrooms with superb views of the Galloway Hills. Tv's and tea trays in both. Peacefuly situated in 1 acre of ground. Guests are invited to use the garden . Ideal centre for sightseeing, golfing, fishing and walking.

1 Twin	2 Pub.Bath/Show	B&B per person
1 Double		from £18.00 Single
		from £18.00 Double
		from £12.00 Room
		Only

Open Jan-Dec

📺 🏠 🅿️ ☕ 🗝️

© 🐕 📹 📹

---

by Newton Stewart, Wigtownshire   Map Ref: 1G10

★★

B&B

Clugston Farm

nr Newton Stewart, Wigtownshire, DG8 9BH
Tel:01671 830338

About 5 miles (8kms) off the A75. Near the sea, hill walking and easy access to 3 golf courses. Two ground floor rooms.

1 Twin	1 Priv.NOT ensuite	B&B per person	Open Apr-Oct
1 Double		from £16.00 Single	BB & Eve.Meal
		from £16.00 Double	from £23.00
		from £12.00 Room	
		Only	

🅿️ ☕ ⅙ ✕ 🍽️ 🌷

🐕 📹 ⚿

Important: Prices stated are estimates and may be subject to amendments

DROCHIL CASTLE FARMHOUSE

Contact: Mrs A Black, Drochil Castle Farm, By Peebles
West Linton, Peeblesshire EH46 7DD
Tel/Fax: 01721 752249 e.mail: black.drochil@talk21.com

Spacious and comfortable accommodation awaits you at Drochil Castle Farm. Log fires in the lounge. Afternoon tea and cakes to greet you on arrival. Stunning views and tranquility is yours. Peebles and West Linton a mere 10 minutes drive. Edinburgh 30 minutes. Childrens outside play area. Large garden and private parking.

★★★★

B&B

Drochil Castle Farmhouse

Drochil Castle Farm, West Linton. by Peebles
Peeblesshire, EH46 7DD
Tel/Fax:01721 752249
Email:black.drochil@talk21.com

A warm welcome awaits you at this traditional working beef and sheep farm. Set amongst rolling borders hills with fine views down the Lyne & Tweed Valley. Located beside the ruins of the 16th century Drochil Castle.

1 Twin	Some En Suite	B&B per person	Open Jan-Dec excl
1 Double	1 Priv.NOT ensuite	£20.00-24.00 Double	Xmas
1 Family		£18.00-22.00 Room	
		Only	

★★★

B&B

Eastgate House

1 Innerleithen Road, Peebles, Tweeddale, EH45 8BA
Tel:01721 720396   Fax:01721 724154
Email:info@eastgatehouse.com
Web:www.eastgatehouse.com

Self-contained first floor, with own entrance in traditional stone-built house in centre of Peebles, a short walk from all amenities.

1 Twin	All En Suite	B&B per person	Open Jan-Dec
1 Double		from £22.00 Double	
1 Family			

★★★

SMALL HOTEL

Kingsmuir Hotel

Springhill Road, Peebles, EH45 9EP
Tel:01721 720151   Fax:01721 721795
Email:enquiries@kingsmuir.com
Web:www.kingsmuir.com

A 19c mansion in its own grounds with ample parking, situated in a quiet corner of Peebles near the River Tweed. A warm welcome and friendly service are a feature of this personally run hotel. Restaurant and bar meals available.

2 Single	All En Suite	B&B per person	Open Jan-Dec
1 Twin		from £39.00 Single	BB & Eve.Meal
6 Double		from £33.00 Double	from £47.00
1 Family			

Peebles   Map Ref: 2C6

LYNE FARMHOUSE

Lyne Farm, Peebles, Peeblesshire EH45 8NR
Tel: 01721 740255 Fax: 01721 740255
e.mail: awaddell@farming.co.uk Web: www.lynefarm.co.uk

Beautiful Georgian farmhouse with character. Tastefully decorated rooms overlooking scenic Stobo Valley. Walled garden, picnic area with barbeque, hill-walking. Archaeological site, major Roman Fort all on farm. Ideally placed for Edinburgh – 23 miles, Glasgow – 47 miles and picturesque town of Peebles – 4 miles, plus beautiful Border towns, gardens and historic houses.

★★★

B&B

Lyne Farmhouse

Lyne Farm, Peebles, EH45 8NR
Tel/Fax:01721 740255
Email:awaddell@farming.co.uk
Web:www.lynefarm.co.uk

Victorian farmhouse on mixed farm with magnificent views over Stobo Valley. 4 miles (6kms) west of Peebles on A72. 23 miles (32kms) from Edinburgh.

1 Twin	2 Priv.NOT ensuite	B&B per person	Open Jan-Dec excl
2 Double		£20.00-22.00 Single	Christmas Day
		£18.00-22.00 Double	BB & Eve.Meal
			by prior arrang.

★★★

B&B

Shalem B&B

March Street, Peebles, EH45 8EP
Tel/Fax:01721 721047

Friendly family home deceptively spacious in central location offering comfortable relaxed atmosphere. 5 minutes walk from High Street. Ideal for sightseeing and walking. Only 25 miles from Edinburgh city centre.

1 Double	1 En Suite fac	B&B per person	Open Jan-Dec excl
1 Family	1 Pub.Bath/Show	£22.00-25.00 Single	Xmas/New Year
		£18.00-20.00 Double	

★★★★

B&B

The Steading

Venlaw Castle Road, Peebles, EH45 8QG
Tel:01721 720293

Tastefully converted steading with spacious rooms peacefully situated in an elevated position with panoramic views over Peebles. 10 minutes walk to town centre and River Tweed. 22 miles from Edinburgh. Ample parking.

1 Twin	All En Suite	B&B per person	Open Jan-Dec
2 Double		from £25.00 Single	
		from £20.00 Double	

★★★

B&B

Whitestone House

Innerleithen Road, Peebles, EH45 8BD
Tel/Fax:01721 720337
Web:www.aboutscotland.com/whitestone.html

Spacious Victorian house with fine views to surrounding hills on the A72. A comfortable sitting/breakfast room to relax in. German and French spoken. Ideal base for fishing/walking and central for Edinburgh and the Borders. Private parking. Safe storage available for bicycles.

1 Twin	2 Priv.NOT ensuite	B&B per person	Open Jan-Dec
3 Double		from £21.00 Single	
1 Family		from £18.50 Double	

Important: Prices stated are estimates and may be subject to amendments

Peebles — Map Ref: 2C6

★★★

B&B

Winkston Farmhouse Bed+Breakfast
Edinburgh Road, Peebles, EH45 8PH
Tel:01721 721264 Fax:01721 730365

| 1 Twin | Some En Suite | B&B per person | Open Jan-Dec excl |
| 2 Double | | from £17.50 Double | Xmas/New Year |

Welcoming & pleasant country house 2 miles from Peebles. Very centrally situated for good local amenities and touring lovely Border countryside and Edinburgh.

★★★★

B&B

Woodlands
Venlaw Farm Road, Peebles, EH45 8QG
Tel:01721 729882
Email:woodlands7@btinternet.com

1 Twin	2 En Suite	B&B per person	Open Jan-Dec excl
2 Double	1 Pub.Bath/Show	from £22.00 Single	Xmas/New Year
		from £20.00 Double	

Modern detached house on edge of town in quiet rural location within walled garden. Pleasant homely atmosphere. Ample parking.

---

by Peebles — Map Ref: 2C6

★★★

B&B

Colliedean Bed+Breakfast
4 Elibank Road, Eddleston, Peebles, EH45 8QL
Tel/Fax:01721 730281
Email:mcteir@talk21.com

1 Double	Some En Suite	B&B per person	Open Apr-Oct
1 Family		from £20.00 Single	
		from £17.00 Double	

Quietly situated in small village on main bus route to Edinburgh and Borders towns. Homely and friendly atmosphere. Restaurant within walking distance.

Prestwick, Ayrshire — Map Ref: 1G7

Fernbank Guest House [W]

213 MAIN STREET, PRESTWICK, AYRSHIRE KA9 1LH
TEL: 01292 475027 FAX: 01292 678944
E.MAIL: bandb@fernbank.co.uk WEB: www.fernbank.co.uk

Superb family run guest house offering clean, warm accommodation and off road parking. All rooms either en-suite or private bathroom, with tea/coffee, CTV, heating. Excellent location for golf, sailing, walking and close to all transport links including airport. A friendly Scottish welcome awaits you. Arrive as guests, depart as friends.

★★★

**GUEST
HOUSE**

Fernbank Guest House
213 Main Street, Prestwick, Ayrshire, KA9 1LH
Tel:01292 475027 Fax:01292 678944
Email:bandb@fernbank.co.uk
Web:www.fernbank.co.uk

1 Single	5 En Suite fac	B&B per person	Open Jan-Dec excl
4 Dbl/Twn	1 Priv.Bath/Show	from £21.00 Single	Xmas/New Year
1 Family		from £23.00 Double	
		from £19.00 Room	
		Only	

Modernised Edwardian villa near beach and local sports facilities. 0.5 mile (1km) from Glasgow Prestwick Airport and Prestwick town rail station.

VAT is shown at 17.5%: changes in this rate may affect prices. | **Key to symbols is on back flap.**

St Abbs, Berwickshire — Map Ref: 2F5

★★★

B&B

Murrayfield
7 Murrayfield, St Abbs, Berwickshire, TD14 5PP
Tel:01890 771468 mobile 07719 703796

Former fisherman's cottage in quiet village, close to beach, harbour and
nature reserve. Both rooms comfortably furnished, one ensuite and one
with wash-hand basin. Lounge available for guests' use with TV. On
street parking available.

1 Double	1 En Suite fac	B&B per person	Open Jan-Dec
1 Family	1 Priv.NOT ensuite	from £22.50 Single	
		from £16.50 Double	

St Boswells, Roxburghshire — Map Ref: 2D7

★★★

B&B

Mainhill
St Boswells, Roxburghshire, TD6 0HG
Tel:01835 823788

Traditional Georgian House set well away from the road in its own
spacious grounds. Peaceful and relaxing atmosphere. Good touring base.
1 mile from St Boswells.

2 Twin	2 Priv.Bath/Show	B&B per person	Open Jan-Dec
		from £25.00 Single	
		from £20.00 Double	
		from £20.00 Room Only	

Selkirk — Map Ref: 2D7

THE GARDEN HOUSE
Whitmuir, Selkirk TD7 4PZ
Tel: 01750 721728 Fax: 01750 720379
e.mail: hilarydunlop@hotmail.com Web: www.whitmuirfarm.co.uk
Warm, comfortable, modern farmhouse in delightful walled garden in
central Borders. Good home cooking using locally grown fresh produce.
Spacious bedrooms with private bathrooms, many extra facilities. Private
loch for coarse fishing; excellent walks; grazing for horses; pets welcome.
Dinners and packed lunches available. Collection service. Open all year.

★★

B&B

The Garden House
Whitmuir, Selkirk, TD7 4PZ
Tel:01750 721728 Fax:01750 720379
Email:hilarydunlop@hotmail.com
Web:www.whitmuirfarm.co.uk

A spacious modern farmhouse, set in extensive 2 acre garden. Croquet
lawn, coarse fishing and variety of walks available for guests. Golfing
and riding nearby. Evening meals by prior arrangement, using home
grown produce.

2 Twn/Dbl	2 En Suite fac	B&B per person	Open All Year
1 Double	1 Priv.Bath/Show	from £26.00 Single	BB & Eve.Meal
		from £26.00 Double	from £38.00
		from £18.00 Room Only	

★★★

B&B

Mrs J Lindores
Dinsburn, 1 Shawpark Road, Selkirk, TD7 4DS
Tel:01750 20375 mobile 07790 728001
Email:moama2000@aol.com

Semi-detached, sandstone Victorian house in residential area on east
side of town centre. Next to bowling green. Well appointed ensuites and
furnishings.

1 Twin	2 En Suite fac	B&B per person	Open Jan-Dec
1 Double	1 Pub.Bath/Show	from £20.00 Single	BB & Eve.Meal
1 Family		from £20.00 Double	from £29.00

Important: Prices stated are estimates and may be subject to amendments

Selkirk

Map Ref: 2D7

★★

B&B

Mrs Janet F Mackenzie
Ivy Bank, Hillside Terrace, Selkirk, TD7 2LT
Tel/Fax:01750 21470
Email:ivybankselkirk@freeserve.co.uk

Detached stone built villa situated in own grounds with beautiful views over the Linglie Hills. Central for touring the Borders and Edinburgh. Private parking.

1 Twin	Ensuite
1 Double	Priv.Bathroom

B&B per person
from £20.00 Single
from £20.00 Double
from £15.00 Room
Only

Open Mar-Nov

★★★

B&B

Sunnybrae House
75 Tower Street, Selkirk, TD7 4LS
Tel:01750 21156
Email:bookings@sunnybraehouse.fsnet.co.uk

A warm welcome awaits you at Sunnybrae which has 2 suites, both with sitting room and en-suite bathroom. Bedrooms have views over the town to the hills beyond. Home cooking using local produce. Private parking.

1 Twin	All En Suite
1 Double	

B&B per person
from £21.00 Double

Open Jan-Dec
BB & Eve.Meal
from £35.00

Sorbie, Wigtownshire

Map Ref: 1H11

★★★

B&B

East Culkae Farm House
Sorbie, Newton Stewart, Wigtownshire, DG8 8AS
Tel:01988 850214
Web:www.ewetoyou.co.uk

Set in a lovely peaceful situation this restored farmhouse B&B is offering very comfortable accommodation with modern ensuites and an attractive guests TV lounge. One bedroom is on the ground floor and is ideal for those wanting to avoid the stairs. Well situated for nearby tourist attractions and beaches.

1 Twin	All En Suite
1 Double	
1 Family	

B&B per person
from £25.00 Single
from £21.00 Double

Open Mar-Oct

Stranraer, Wigtownshire

Map Ref: 1F10

★★★★

B&B

Glenotter
Leswalt Road, Stranraer, Wigtownshire, DG9 0EP
Tel:01776 703199
Email:lilian@glenotter.co.uk Web:www.glenotter.co.uk

A warm and friendly welcome awaits you at Glenotter which is situated in a quiet residential area with large private car park, yet only 4-5 minutes drive from the town centre, Stena ferries. Guests are welcome to relax in the spacious TV lounge or in the summer evenings to sit in the large colourful garden. Stranraer is an ideal centre for exploring beautiful Galloway with so much to do and see.

1 Twin	All En Suite
2 Double	
1 Family	

B&B per person
from £27.00 Single
from £21.00 Double
from £19.00 Room
Only

Open Jan-Dec excl
Xmas/New Year

Scotland's National Booking and Information Line

Tel: 0845 22 55 121
visitscotland.com

Stranraer, Wigtownshire — Map Ref: 1F10

★★

B&B

Ivy House, Bed+Breakfast + Ferry Link
Ivy Place, London Road, Stranraer, Wigtownshire
DG9 8ER
Tel:01776 704176
Email:ivyplace3@hotmail.com
Web:www.ivyplace.worldonline.co.uk

A friendly welcome awaits you at this family run B&B situated close to
town centre and Irish Ferry Terminals. Convenient base for visiting Castle
Kennedy, Ardwell and Logan Botanic Gardens. Parking available at all
times.

1 Twin 2 En Suite fac
1 Double 1 Priv.NOT ensuite
1 Family 1 Pub.Bath/Show

B&B per person
from £18.00 Single
from £16.00 Double
from £26.00 Room
Only

Open Jan-Dec

★★★★

B&B

Kildrochet House
Kildrochet, by Stranraer, Wigtownshire, DG9 9BB
Tel/Fax:01776 820216
Email:kildrochet@compuserve.com
Web:www.kildrochet.co.uk

Early 18th century William Adam Dower House set in peaceful 6 acres of gardens,
pasture and woods. The large garden room windows open out onto the terrace
and croquet lawn which is surrounded by herbaceous borders, rhododendrons,
azaleas and a backdrop of mature trees. Non smoking house. Evening meals by
prior arrangement using fresh local produce when available.

1 Twin 1 En Suite fac
1 Double 1 Priv.Bath/Show

B&B per person
from £34.00 Single
from £28.00 Double

Open Jan-Dec

---

nr Stranraer, Wigtownshire — Map Ref: 1F10

★★★★

B&B

Chlenry Farmhouse
Castle Kennedy, Stranraer, Wigtownshire, DG9 8SL
Tel:01776 705316 Fax:01776 899488
Email:wolseleybrinton@aol.com

Peace, Tranquility and Relaxation in gracious and welcoming
surroundings with Golf, Gardens and beautiful walks close by. Explore
glorious Galloway with packed lunches provided. Delicious dinners
cooked on request.

1 Twin 1 Priv.Bathroom
1 Double 1 Shared Bath.

B&B per person
from £34.00 Single
from £28.50 Double

Open 2 Jan-20 Dec

East Challoch Farmhouse
DUNRAGIT, STRANRAER, WIGTOWNSHIRE DG9 8PY
TEL: 01581 400391

A warm welcome awaits at our farmhouse set in open
countryside with beautiful views over Luce Bay. Our bedrooms
are tastefully decorated with C.H., colour TV, tea/coffee
facilities and all en-suite bathrooms. Delicious home cooked
dinners available on request. Ideal for golf, fishing and
exploring gardens in unspoilt S.W. Scotland.

★★★

B&B

East Challoch Farmhouse
Dunragit, Stranraer, Wigtownshire, DG9 8PY
Tel:01581 400391

A warm welcome awaits you at our family run traditional farmhouse with
views over Luce Bay. Spacious double or twin rooms with ensuite
facilities. Both rooms with TVs and tea trays. Comfortable lounge for
guests' use. Evening meal available. Feel free to use our well established
garden. Only 7 miles from Stranraer. Pony trekking, golf course within 1
mile.

1 Twin All En Suite
1 Double

B&B per person
from £25.00 Single
from £20.00 Double

Open Jan-Dec excl
Xmas/New Year
BB & Eve.Meal
from £32.00

Important: Prices stated are estimates and may be subject to amendments

Troon, Ayrshire

Map Ref: 1G7

★★★

B&B

The Cherries
50 Ottoline Drive, Troon, Ayrshire, KA10 7AW
Tel:01292 313312 Fax:01292 319007
Email:thecherries50@hotmail.com
Web:www.smoothhound.co.uk/hotels/cherries

Warm welcome in family home. Quiet residential area backing onto golf course. Beach and a variety of restaurants nearby. En-suite accommodation available on ground floor.

1 Single	1 En Suite fac	B&B per person	Open Jan-Dec
1 Twin	1 Priv.NOT ensuite	from £21.00 Single	
1 Family	1 Pub.Bath/Show	from £21.00 Double	

★★★

B&B

Mrs Morag Mathieson
Fordell, 43 Beach Road, Barassie, Troon, KA10 6SU
Tel:01292 313224 Fax:01292 312141
Email:morag@fordell-troon.co.uk
Web:www.fordell-troon.co.uk

This Victorian sandstone semi-villa offers a comfortable, homely atmosphere directly overlooking the Firth of Clyde and the Island of Arran. It is situated within easy walking distance of Barassie Railway Station and Kilmornock (Barassie) Golf Club. Ideally placed for fast exit to major routes.

2 Twin	2 Priv.NOT ensuite	B&B per person	Open Jan-Dec excl
		from £25.00 Single	Xmas/New Year
		from £22.00 Double	

Twynholm, Kirkcudbrightshire

Map Ref: 2A10

★★

B&B

Miefield Farm
Miefield, Twynholm, Kirkcudbright, DG6 4PS
Tel:01557 860254

Working sheep and beef farm at the head of a quiet glen. See sheep dogs and shepherds at work.

1 Twin	1 Priv.NOT ensuite	B&B per person	Open Apr-Nov
1 Double		£15.50-16.00 Single	BB & Eve.Meal
1 Family		£15.50-16.00 Double	from £23.00

West Linton, Peeblesshire

Map Ref: 2B6

★★

B&B

Jerviswood
Linton Bank Drive, West Linton, Peeblesshire
EH46 7DT
Tel/Fax:01968 660429

Comfortable modern home with attractive garden, located in picturesque historic village with excellent eating places all within easy walking distance. Within easy reach of Edinburgh and Scottish Borders. Ideal centre for walking, touring and golfing.

| 2 Twin | B&B per person | Open Jan-Dec excl |
| 1 Double | from £17.00 Double | Xmas/New Year |

VAT is shown at 17.5%: changes in this rate may affect prices.

Key to symbols is on back flap.

West Linton, Peeblesshire

Map Ref: 2B6

★★★

B&B

The Meadows
4 Robinsland Drive, West Linton, Peeblesshire
EH46 7JD
Tel/Fax:01968 661798
Email:mbthain@ntlworld.com
Web:www.west-linton.org.uk/the.meadows.html

A modern house situated on a small new development. Attractive rooms
(one en-suite) and use of the owners sitting room. A lovely rural area yet
only 14 miles from the centre of Edinburgh. Golf course nearby.

1 Single	B&B per person
1 Twin	from £20.00 Single
1 Double	from £20.00 Double

Open Jan-Dec

Whithorn, Wigtownshire

Map Ref: 1H11

★★★

B&B

Baltier
Whithorn, Wigtownshire, DG8 8HA
Tel:01988 600241

Stone built house on dairy farm 0.3 miles from the main road. Large
garden and sun room gives fine views over surrounding countryside
towards the south and west. 3 miles from local town and village.

1 Single	1 En Suite fac	B&B per person
1 Twin		from £20.00 Single
1 Double		from £20.00 Double
1 Family		from £15.00 Room Only

Open Feb-Nov

★★★

B&B

Old Bishopton
Whithorn, Newton Stewart, Wigtownshire, DG8 8DE
Tel:01988 500754
Email:forsythmidbish@aol.com

Stone built bungalow with open views of the rolling farmland to the
historic town of Whithorn. After a busy days sightseeing, guests can relax
in their own sun lounge or private walled garden. Ideal for couples. Only
10 miles from Wigtown which has created much interest in its selection as
the Scottish Book Town.

1 Double	All En Suite	B&B per person
		from £25.00 Single
		from £22.00 Double

Open May-Oct

Yetholm, by Kelso, Roxburghshire

Map Ref: 2E7

★★

B&B

Bluntys Mill
Yetholm, Roxburghshire, TD5 8PG
Tel:01573 420288
Email:info@galrowan.co.uk

Peaceful accommodation in family home set in 6 acres of pasture. In
picturesque conservation village right at the end of the Pennine Way.
Evening meal by arrangement. Children and pets welcome. Ground floor
room available.

2 Twin	Some En Suite	B&B per person	Open Jan-Dec excl
	1 Pub.Bath/Show	from £25.00 Single	Xmas/New Year
		from £22.00 Double	BB & Eve.Meal
		from £25.00 Room Only	from £36.00

Scotland's National Booking and Information Line

Tel: 0845 22 55 121
visitscotland.com

Important: Prices stated are estimates and may be subject to amendments

Welcome to Scotland
Edinburgh and Lothians

*With a city skyline every bit as spectacular as the postcards suggest,
Scotland's capital is simply outstanding in world terms.*

Museum of Scotland, Edinburgh, with view from restaurant towards the Castle

The Scottish Parliament has brought a buzz to the city. Edinburgh Castle is one of the most famous symbols of Scotland, but it is only one of a whole range of attractions stretching down the Royal Mile in the heart of the Old Town. The city is steeped in history and culture, from the Palace of Holyroodhouse, where the tragic story of Mary Queen of Scots unfolded, to the striking architecture of the Museum of Scotland which tells the nation's story from its geological beginnings to the present day. The Royal Yacht Britannia and Our Dynamic Earth are just two of the city's other visitor attractions.

The most famous events the city host are the spectacular International Festival and the Festival Fringe, but it remains the liveliest of cities all year round with other events such as the Science Festival, Film Festival and the biggest New Year street party in the world – Edinburgh's Hogmanay. As a major cultural centre, Edinburgh has many art galleries, theatres and cinemas. There are many street cafés and restaurants specialising in both international and modern Scottish cuisine, while over 700 bars in the city offer fine locally brewed beers and, of course, a wide range of malt whiskies.

Edinburgh and Lothians

Barges on the Union Canal, Ratho, near Edinburgh

Edinburgh and Lothians

Yellowcraig Beach, East Lothian

This fast-paced and cosmopolitan city offers superb shopping in the many department stores along the famous thoroughfare of Princes Street as well as Princes Mall and the many designer shops along elegantly proportioned George Street in the heart of the 18-century New Town. The village-like suburbs of Stockbridge and Bruntsfield offer small shops where a friendly welcome is guaranteed. A relaxing alternative within the bustling city are the many quiet green spaces including Holyrood Park, Calton Hill, the Dean Village and the Royal Botanic Garden, which features Britain's tallest palm house and the world-famous Rock Garden.

Within a few miles of the city centre are the Lothians. This is soft rolling farmland with splendid hill-walking in the surrounding Pentland, Moorfoot and Lammermuir Hills. There are almost 70 miles of coastline along the Firth of Forth combining nature reserves, sandy beaches and seaside resorts. Dunbar has been officially recorded as Scotland's driest and sunniest town. The award-winning Scottish Seabird Centre in North Berwick uses the latest technology to allow all the family to view the famous gannet colony on the nearby Bass Rock. To the west, South Queensferry is set in a dramatic location immediately below the gigantic structures of the famous Forth Bridges.

Experience and enjoy one of Europe's most exciting regions, by combining city and countryside. With easy access by air, rail and road, Edinburgh and the Lothians is a year-round destination for everyone.

Events
Edinburgh and Lothians

1-31 JANUARY
Turner Exhibition, Edinburgh
Annual show of Turner
watercolours.
Tel: 0131 624 6200
www.natgalscot.ac.uk

20 APRIL
Easter Parade, Edinburgh
4000 performers
participating in a parade
through the main streets of
the city.
Tel: 0131 473 3800
www.edinburgh.org

MAY – SEPTEMBER
Arthur's Secrets, Holyrood
Park, Edinburgh
Every Wednesday. Guided
walks around Holyrood Park,
exploring history and natural
history of the park.
Tel: 0131 668 8600
www.historic-scotland.gov.uk

23-26 MAY
Festival of the Sea, Leith,
Edinburgh
Celebrating Scotland's
maritime traditions.
Tel: 0131 473 2000
www.festivalofthesea.co.uk

24-30 MAY
Wake Up To Birds Week
Royal Society for the
Protection of Birds. Wide
range of events and activities
at the 60 RSPB reserves across
Scotland. Free entry to all
reserves on one day during
this week.
Tel: 0131 311 6500
www.rspb.org.uk/scotland

EARLY SUMMER
State Opening of the
New Scottish Parliament,
Edinburgh
Unveiling of the New Scottish
Parliament building.
Tel: 0131 348 5000
www.scottish.parliament.uk

19-22 JUNE
Royal Highland Show,
Edinburgh
The highlight of Scotland's
country calendar.
Tel: 0131 335 6200
www.rhass.org.uk

30 JUNE – 4 JULY*
East Lothian Golf Classics
Tel: 01292 293040
www.scottishgolfclassics.co.uk

1-23 AUGUST
Edinburgh's Military Tattoo
The Capital's annual military
extravaganza.
Tel: 08707 555 1188
www.edintattoo.co.uk

3-25 AUGUST
Edinburgh Festival Fringe
The largest arts festival in the
world, including theatre,
comedy, music and magic.
Tel: 0131 226 5257
www.edfringe.com

9-25 AUGUST
Edinburgh International
Book Festival
Tel: 0131 228 5444
www.edbookfest.co.uk

10-30 AUGUST
Edinburgh International
Fesitval
One of the world's most
prestigious arts festivals.
Tel: 0131 473 2001
www.eif.co.uk

13-24 AUGUST
Edinburgh International Film
Festival
Tel: 0131 228 4051
www.edifilmfest.org.uk

29 DECEMBER –
1 JANUARY 2004
Edinburgh's Hogmanay
www.edinburghshogmanay
.org

** denotes provisional date. Events can be
subject to change, please check before
travelling.*

For up to date events, log on to:
visitscotland.com

Area Tourist Boards

Edinburgh and Lothians

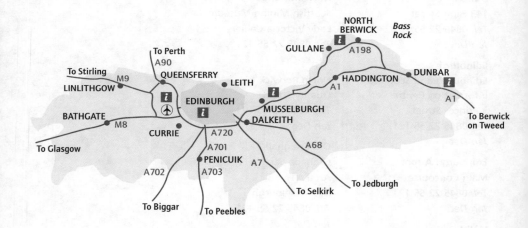

**Edinburgh and Lothians
Tourist Board**
Edinburgh and Scotland
Information Centre
3 Princes Street
Edinburgh
EH2 2QP

Tel: 0845 22 55 121
Fax: 01506 832 222
E-mail: info@visitscotland.com
www.edinburgh.org

Tourist Information Centres
Edinburgh and Lothians

**Edinburgh and Lothians
Tourist Board**

Dunbar
143 High Street
Tel: 0845 22 55 121
Jan-Dec

Edinburgh
Edinburgh and Scotland
Information Centre
3 Princes Street
Tel: 0845 22 55 121
Jan-Dec

Edinburgh Airport
Main Concourse
Tel: 0845 22 55 121
Jan-Dec

Linlithgow
Burgh Halls
The Cross
Tel: 0845 22 55 121
Apr-Oct

Newtongrange
Scottish Mining Museum
Lady Victoria Colliery
Tel: 0845 22 55 121
Easter-Oct

North Berwick
Quality Street
Tel: 0845 22 55 121
Jan-Dec

Old Craighall
Granada Service
Area A1
by Musselburgh
Tel: 0845 22 55 121
Jan-Dec

Penicuik
Edinburgh Crystal
Visitor Centre
Eastfield
Tel: 0845 22 55 121
Easter-Sep

Scotland's National Booking and Information Line
0845 22 55 121

CRUACHAN BED & BREAKFAST
78 EAST MAIN STREET, BLACKBURN, WEST LOTHIAN EH47 7QS
Tel: 01506 655221 Fax: 01506 652395
e.mail: cruachan.bb@virgin.net Web: www.cruachan.co.uk

A relaxed and friendly base is provided at Cruachan from which to explore central Scotland. Hosts Kenneth and Jacqueline ensure you receive the utmost in quality of service, meticulously presented accommodation and of course a full Scottish breakfast. They look forward to having the pleasure of your company.

★★★

B&B

Cruachan Bed & Breakfast

78 East Main Street, Blackburn, West Lothian
EH47 7QS
Tel:01506 655221 Fax:01506 652395
Email:cruachan.bb@virgin.net
Web:www.cruachan.co.uk

Located on A705 in Blackburn. Cruachan is 1.5 miles from junction 4 of M8 allowing easy access to road links for Edinburgh and Glasgow, or enjoy the benefit of a 30 minute rail journey to Edinburgh from nearby Bathgate. An ideal central location for your visit to Scotland.

3 Double	3 En Suite fac
1 Family	1 Pub.Bath/Show

B&B per person
from £30.00 Single
from £22.00 Double
from £20.00 Room
Only

Open Jan-Dec excl
Xmas/New Year

BANKHEAD FARMHOUSE B&B
Bankhead Farm, Dechmont, Broxburn, West Lothian EH52 6NB
Tel: 01506 811209 Fax: 01506 811815
e.mail: Bankheadbb@aol.com Web: www.bankheadfarm.com

Perfectly placed for exploring Edinburgh and Scotland. Bankhead has 7 modern ensuite bedrooms in traditional farmhouse building. Panoramic views of local hills and over the Forth to Fife, yet close to 3 historic towns and less than 20 minutes from Edinburgh Airport. Easy access to main Scottish routes. Car essential.

★★★

B&B

Bankhead Farm B&B

Dechmont, Broxburn, West Lothian, EH52 6NB
Tel:01506 811209 Fax:01506 811815
Email:bankheadbb@aol.com
Web:www.bankheadfarm.com

Perfectly placed for Edinburgh and airport. Stay in a traditional farmhouse with modern en-suite bedrooms. Panoramic views of Scottish countryside.

3 Single	All En Suite
2 Double	
2 Family	

B&B per person
from £30.00 Single
from £22.00 Double

Open Jan-Dec excl
Xmas

Scotland's National Booking and Information Line

Tel: 0845 22 55 121
visitscotland.com

VAT is shown at 17.5%: changes in this rate may affect prices. | *Key to symbols is on back flap.*

Dunbar, East Lothian   Map Ref: 2E4

★★

SMALL
HOTEL

Goldenstones Hotel
Queens Road, Dunbar, East Lothian, EH42 1LG
Tel:01368 862356 Fax:01368 865644
Email:info@goldenstones.co.uk
Web:www.goldenstones.co.uk

Family run hotel centrally situated in Dunbar. Near town centre and beaches. Golfing packages available.

15 Twin	All En Suite	B&B per person	Open Jan-Dec
4 Family		from £40.00 Single	BB & Eve.Meal
		from £32.50 Double	from £42.50

★

SMALL
HOTEL

Hillside Hotel
3 Queens Road, Dunbar, East Lothian, EH42 1LA
Tel/Fax:01368 862071

Personally run hotel with a reputation for good food using fresh local produce. Ideal for golf and touring East Lothian.

4 Single	12 En Suite fac	B&B per person	Open Jan-Dec
5 Twin	2 Priv.NOT ensuite	from £24.00 Single	BB & Eve.Meal
4 Double		from £31.50 Double	from £34.00
3 Family			

★★

GUEST
HOUSE
●
HOME
COOKING

Springfield Guest House
Belhaven Road, Dunbar, East Lothian, EH42 1NH
Tel/Fax:01368 862502
Email:smeed@tesco.net

An elegant 19c villa with attractive garden. Family run with home-cooking. Ideal base for families, golf and touring.

1 Single	2 Priv.NOT ensuite	B&B per person	Open Jan-Nov excl
1 Twin	1 Pub.Bath/Show	from £22.00 Single	Xmas/New Year
1 Double		from £20.00 Double	BB & Eve.Meal
2 Family			from £32.00

East Calder, West Lothian   Map Ref: 2B5

Near EDINBURGH
OVERSHIEL FARM, EAST CALDER EH53 0HT
Telephone: 01506 880469 Fax: 01506 883006
e.mail: Jandic5@aol.com
PEACEFUL COUNTRY SETTING, 6 MILES WEST OF EDINBURGH. EASY ACCESS INTO CITY CENTRE BY CAR, BUS OR TRAIN (STATION 1.5 MILES). ALL ROOMS HAVE COLOUR TV PLUS TEA/COFFEE-MAKING FACILITIES. SAFE PARKING.

★★★

B&B

Overshiel Farm Bed + Breakfast
East Calder, West Lothian, EH53 0HT
Tel:01506 880469 Fax:01506 883006
Email:Jandic5@aol.com

Stone built farmhouse set in large garden and surrounded by arable farmland. 5 miles (8kms) from Edinburgh Airport. Easy access to M8 and M9. Non-smoking establishment. Wide range of eating places within short drive.

2 Twin	2 En-suite fac	B&B per person	Open Jan-Dec
1 Double	1 Pub.Bath/Show	from £25.00 Single	
		from £18.00 Double	

Important: Prices stated are estimates and may be subject to amendments

East Calder, West Lothian

Map Ref: 2B5

ASHCROFT FARMHOUSE

EAST CALDER, NR EDINBURGH EH53 0ET

Tel: 01506 881810 Fax: 01506 884327

e.mail: ashcroft30538@aol.com Web: www.ashcroftfarmhouse.com

New ranch-style farmhouse set in beautifully landscaped gardens, enjoying lovely views over surrounding farmland. 10m city centre, 5m airport, Ingliston, A720 City Bypass, M8/M9. Ideal base for touring, golfing, walking. Regular bus and train service nearby takes guests to the city centre within 20 minutes therefore no parking problems. All rooms are on ground floor. Bedrooms, including romantic four-poster are attractively furnished in antique pine with bright co-ordinating fabrics. Varied choice of breakfasts including home-made sausage, smoked salmon, kippers etc, even whisky marmalade. *Derek and Elizabeth extend a warm Scottish welcome to all guests. Sorry, no pets.*

AA ◆◆◆◆◆ NO SMOKING

★★★★

GUEST HOUSE

Ashcroft Farmhouse

East Calder, Nr Edinburgh, EH53 0ET
Tel:01506 881810 Fax:01506 884327
Email:ashcroft30538@aol.com
Web:www.ashcroftfarmhouse.com

A warm Scottish welcome awaits you at this modern bungalow with interesting landscaped garden and quality choice of breakfast. Half an hour by bus to Edinburgh city centre, 5 miles from the airport and within easy access to all major routes. Ample parking. Totally non-smoking.

3 Twin	All En Suite	B&B per person	Open Jan-Dec
1 Double		from £42.50 Single	
2 Family		from £30.00 Double	

📺 🛏️ P ☕ 🍴✈️🚗 📶

C 📠 W V ♿

WHITECROFT

7 RAW HOLDINGS, EAST CALDER, WEST LOTHIAN EH53 0ET

Telephone: 01506 882494 Fax: 01506 882598

e.mail: Lornascot@aol.com Web: www.whitecroftbandb.co.uk

Douglas and Lorna extend a warm Scottish welcome with all rooms on ground level. Whitecroft is surrounded by farmland yet only 10 miles from city centre. Airport 5 miles. Safe private parking. A full hearty Scottish breakfast is served using local produce. There are restaurants in the area providing evening meals.

★★★

B&B

Whitecroft B&B

East Calder, West Lothian, EH53 0ET
Tel:01506 882494 Fax:01506 882598
Email:lornascot@aol.com
Web:www.whitecroftbandb.co.uk

Family bungalow on 5 acre small holding adjacent to Almondell Country Park. On main bus route to Edinburgh (20 mins) and 5 minutes drive to Livingston. Private parking. Ground floor accommodation. No Smoking.

1 Twin	All En Suite	B&B per person	Open Jan-Dec excl
2 Double		£30.00-35.00 Single	New Year
		from £25.00 Double	

📺 🛏️ P ☕ 🍴✈️ 📶

📠 W V ♿

VAT is shown at 17.5%: changes in this rate may affect prices.

Key to symbols is on back flap.

East Linton, East Lothian Map Ref: 2D4

Kiloran House

East Linton, East Lothian EH40 3AY
Tel: 01620 860410 e.mail: kiloran@btinternet.com

Victorian house close to A1. Enjoy the benefits of countryside, coast and Edinburgh city. Half-hour drive or train journey to Princes Street and Castle. Short drive to coast and all golf courses.
NO SMOKING THROUGHOUT

★★★★

B&B

Kiloran House
East Linton, East Lothian, EH40 3AY
Tel:01620 860410
Email:kiloran@btinternet.com

1 Twin	All En Suite	B&B per person	Open Jan-Dec excl
2 Double		from £30.00 Single	Xmas/New Year
		from £25.00 Double	

A Victorian house of great character, furnished to a high standard. Relaxed and friendly atmosphere. Non-smoking house. Short drive to all Lothians Golf Courses and beaches. Within half hour of Edinburgh.

Kippielaw Farmhouse

**East Linton, East Lothian EH41 4PY Tel/Fax: 01620 860368
e.mail: info@kippielawfarmhouse.co.uk
Web: www.kippielawfarmhouse.co.uk**
Comfortable, welcoming, tastefully restored 18th-century farmhouse 30 miles from Edinburgh. Stunning views over East Lothian countryside. Pleasant local walks to Traprain Law, Hailes Castle, East Linton village. Enjoy candlelit dinners in our elegant dining room overlooking attractive courtyard. Relax in our log-fired lounge.

★★★★

B&B

Kippielaw Farmhouse B&B
East Linton, East Lothian, EH41 4PY
Tel/Fax:01620 860368
Email:info@kippielawfarmhouse.co.uk
Web:www.kippielawfarmhouse.co.uk

1 Twin	1 En Suite fac	B&B per person	Open Jan-Dec excl
1 Double	1 Pub.Bath/Show	from £37.00 Single	Xmas
		from £27.00 Double	BB & Eve.Meal
			from £49.00

18c farmhouse overlooking open farmland to the coast. 25 miles from Edinburgh. Interesting garden. Imaginative candlelit dinners. An ideal place to come and unwind and enjoy the peace and beauty of East Lothian.

Edinburgh Map Ref: 2C5

★

B&B

17 Hope Park Terrace
Edinburgh, EH8 9LZ
Tel:0131 667 7963

1 Single	1 Priv.NOT ensuite	B&B per person	Open Apr-Oct
1 Double		from £28.00 Single	
		from £26.00 Double	

Ground floor flat 15 minutes walk to Princes Street (1 mile) 10 mins. Royal mile, 7 mins University and Royal College of Surgeons. Central to all attractions.

Important: Prices stated are estimates and may be subject to amendments

Edinburgh

Map Ref: 2C5

Abacus Bed+Breakfast
7 Crawford Road, Newington, Edinburgh, EH16 5PQ
Tel/Fax:0131 667 2283
Email:abacus1@blueyonder.co.uk

★★★

B&B

2 Twin	1 Priv.NOT ensuite	B&B per person	Open Mar-Oct
1 Double	1 Pub.Bath/Show	from £22.00 Double	

Semi-detached traditional, stone villa in quiet residential area with well maintained garden. Approx. 2 miles (3 kms) to city centre: close to main bus route. Free on street parking. Near Cameron Toll Shopping Centre, University Buildings and Commonwealth pool.

Abcorn Guest House
4 Mayfield Gardens, Edinburgh EH9 2BU
Tel: 0131 667 6548 Fax: 0131 667 9969
e.mail: abcorn@btinternet.com Web: www.abcorn.co.uk
The Abcorn is a family run guest house in a detached Victorian villa, near to the city centre, with a private car park. All our rooms are ensuite and also have colour TV and tea/coffee-making facilities.

Abcorn Guest House
4 Mayfield Gardens, Edinburgh, EH9 2BU
Tel:0131 667 6548   Fax:0131 667 9969
Email:abcorn@btinternet.com
Web:www.abcorn.co.uk

★★★

GUEST HOUSE

1 Single	All En Suite	B&B per person	Open Jan-Dec
2 Twin		from £26.00 Single	
2 Double		from £26.00 Double	
2 Family			

Personally managed by the owners Jimmy and Marjorie Kellacher this detached guest house is centrally located on the bus route 5 mins from the city centre. Ample private parking.

Adria Hotel
11-12 Royal Terrace, Edinburgh, EH7 5AB
Tel:0131 556 7875   Fax:0131 558 7782
Email:manager@adriahotel.co.uk
Web:www.adriahotel.co.uk

★★★

GUEST HOUSE

2 Single	9 En Suite fac	B&B per person	Open Feb-Nov
6 Twin	1 Priv.NOT ensuite	£29.00-45.00 Single	
9 Double	6 Pub.Bath/Show	£21.00-35.00 Double	
6 Family			

Friendly family run private hotel in quiet Georgian terrace. Spacious bedrooms. Ten minutes walk from centre.

Afton Guest House
1 Hartington Gardens, Edinburgh, EH10 4LD
Tel/Fax:0131 229 1019
Email:sales@afton-g-house.co.uk
Web:www.afton-g-house.co.uk

★★

GUEST HOUSE

2 Single	2 En Suite fac	B&B per person	Open Jan-Dec
1 Twin	5 Priv.NOT ensuite	from £18.00 Single	
1 Double		from £18.00 Double	
3 Family			

End terraced Victorian house in residential area but near main bus route to city centre. Variety of restaurants nearby. Ensuite bedrooms available.

VAT is shown at 17.5%: changes in this rate may affect prices.

Key to symbols is on back flap.

Edinburgh				Map Ref: 2C5		

SMALL HOTEL
★★

Ailsa Craig Hotel
24 Royal Terrace, Edinburgh, EH7 5AH
Tel:0131 556 6055/1022 Fax:0131 556 6055
Email:ailsacraighotel@ednet.co.uk
Web:www.townhousehotels.co.uk

3 Single 16 En Suite fac
5 Twin   2 Pub.Bath/Show
4 Double
6 Family

B&B per person
from £22.50 Single
from £22.50 Double
from £22.50 Room
Only

Open Jan-Dec

BB & Eve.Meal
from £37.50

Elegant Georgian town house in city centre with tastefully decorated bedrooms, situated in quiet residential area overlooking landscaped public gardens. Front facing top floor bedrooms have views across Edinburgh to the Firth of Forth and the Fife Coast. Evening meals by arrangement.

GUEST HOUSE
★★★

Airdenair Guest House
29 Kilmaurs Road, Edinburgh, EH16 5DB
Tel:0131 668 2336
Email:jill@airdenair.com
Web:www.airdenair.com

1 Single All En Suite
2 Twin
2 Double

B&B per person
from £30.00 Single
from £25.00 Double

Open Jan-Dec

Double upper flatted Victorian stonebuilt house situated in quiet residential area on south side of city. Near Royal Commonwealth Pool and Holyrood Park. Views to local hills of Arthurs Seat and Blackford Hill. Unrestricted street parking. Home made scones.

B&B
★★

Mrs Linda J Allan
10 Baberton Mains Rise, Edinburgh, EH14 3HG
Tel:0131 442 3619
Email:LJA_bandb_edin@hotmail.com
Web:www.edinburghbandb.fsnet.co.uk

1 Double

B&B per person
from £16.00 Double

Open May-Oct

Family home in quiet residential area. Unrestricted parking. Frequent bus service to Princes Street. Convenient for Golf courses and Heriot Watt University.

B&B
★★★

Ms Allan, The Meadows B&B
17 Spottiswoode Street, Edinburgh, EH9 1EP
Tel:0131 228 1845
Email:meadowsbb@hotmail.com

2 Double 1 En Suite fac
        1 Pub.Bath/Show

B&B per person
£24.00-28.00 Double

Open May-Sep
plus New Year

Small, friendly, newly refurbished Victorian main door flat with attractive garden in the Meadows area. Ideally situated for cinemas, theatres, conference centre, teaching hospital, university, galleries, city centre and varied selection of restaurants. Free on street parking available. On bus route.

B&B
★★★★

Allt-nan-Craobh
28 Cammo Road, Edinburgh, EH4 8AP
Tel:0131 339 3613

2 Double

B&B per person
from £27.00 Single
from £22.00 Double

Open Apr-Oct

A warm welcome awaits you at this family home in quiet residential area with easy access to Queensferry Rd and Airport. Ideal base for touring Edinburgh and surrounding countryside. Ample parking.

Important: Prices stated are estimates and may be subject to amendments

B

Edinburgh

Map Ref: 2C5

★★

**GUEST
HOUSE**

Alness Guest House
27 Pilrig Street, Edinburgh, EH6 5AN
Tel:0131 554 1187

Friendly family run guest house. On main bus route, 1 mile (2kms) from Princes Street and Castle. Close to Port of Leith and Britannia.

2 Single	1 En Suite fac	B&B per person	Open Jan-Dec excl
1 Twin	2 Priv.NOT ensuite	£20.00-30.00 Single	Xmas
1 Double	1 Pub.Bath/Show	£20.00-30.00 Double	
3 Family		£15.00-18.00 Room Only	

★★★

**GUEST
HOUSE**

Arden Guest House
126 Old Dalkeith Road, Edinburgh, EH16 4SD
Tel:0131 664 3985   Fax:0131 621 0866
Email:dot@baigan.freeserve.co.uk
Web:www.ardenedinburgh.co.uk

Newly built, privately owned guest house, all rooms ensuite with ground floor level accommodation. On main A7 road, situated on south side of city 10 minutes from city centre. Ideal base for business guests. Off-street parking. Easy access to all amenities. Walking distance from the New Royal Infirmary.

1 Single	All En Suite	B&B per person	Open Jan-Dec excl
4 Twin		from £20.00 Single	Xmas/New Year
4 Double		from £20.00 Double	
3 Family		from £18.00 Room Only	

★★★

**GUEST
HOUSE**

Ardgarth Guest House
1 St Mary's Place, Portobello, Edinburgh, EH15 2QF
Tel:0131 669 3021   Fax:0131 468 1221
Email:rooms@ardgarth.demon.co.uk
Web:www.ardgarth.demon.co.uk

Comfortable accommodation in friendly guest house. Close to sea. Special diets catered for, full ensuite disabled facilities. French spoken. On street parking available.

3 Single	4 En Suite fac	B&B per person	Open Jan-Dec excl
3 Twin	2 Priv.NOT ensuite	from £17.00 Single	Xmas
1 Double		from £17.00 Double	
2 Family			

VAT is shown at 17.5%: changes in this rate may affect prices.

Key to symbols is on back flap.

Mrs Helen Baird

'Arisaig', 64 Glasgow Road, Edinburgh EH12 8LN
Tel: 0131 334 2610 Fax: 0131 334 1800
e.mail: helen_baird@hotmail.com

Warm Scottish welcome awaits you here at this highly commended private home with lovely gardens. The bedrooms (all ensuite) are kept to a very high standard with tea/coffee-making facilities and delicious breakfast. Good local restaurants. Three miles from city centre. Parking spaces. Good bus service. All private facilities. Lounge with TV.

★★★★

B&B

Arisaig
64 Glasgow Road, Edinburgh, EH12 8LN
Tel:0131 334 2610   Fax:0131 334 1800
Email:helen_baird@hotmail.com

Personally run comfortable and friendly accommodation in detached dormer bungalow. Good bus service to town centre, approx 3 miles (5 kms). Ideal base for exploring this historic city and enjoying the many events and attractions on offer. Ground floor accommodation available.

1 Twin	All En Suite	B&B per person	Open Apr-Oct
1 Double		£24.00-28.00 Double	

★★★

B&B

Aros House
1 Salisbury House, Edinburgh, EH9 1SL
Tel:0131 667 1585
Email:aros.house@virgin.net
Web:http://freespace.virgin.net/aros.house

Georgian House on first floor, family home 1 mile S of city centre with excellent bus service. Qualified tour guide.

1 Single	2 En Suite fac	B&B per person	Open Feb-Nov
1 Twin	1 Priv.Bath/Show	from £22.00 Single	
1 Double		from £20.00 Double	

★★★

B&B

Ascot Garden
154 Glasgow Road, Edinburgh, EH12 8LS
Tel/Fax:0131 339 2092

A warm Scottish welcome awaits you in this family home situated on the main Edinburgh to Glasgow A8 road. Close to the city by-pass and all major routes north and south. Short drive from Edinburgh Airport. Directly opposite Marriot Hotel.

1 Double	All En Suite	B&B per person	Open Jan-Dec
1 Family		from £20.00 Single	
		from £20.00 Double	

★★

GUEST HOUSE

Ballarat Guest House
14 Gilmore Place, Edinburgh, EH3 9NQ
Tel:0131 229 7024 Fax:0131 228 8811
Email:ballarat.house@virgin.net
Web:www.thomweb.co.uk

Comfortable friendly family home, on south west side of city, ideally situated for Princes Street, Castle, restaurants and theatres, and majority of city's main attractions. Non-smoking policy.

1 Single	1 En Suite fac	B&B per person	Open Jan-Dec
1 Twin		£22.00-35.00 Single	
1 Double		£22.00-35.00 Double	
2 Family			

Important: Prices stated are estimates and may be subject to amendments

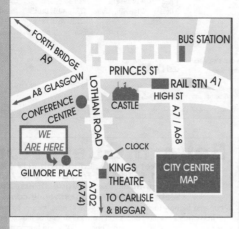

CENTRAL EDINBURGH
AVERON GUEST HOUSE

Built in 1770 as a farmhouse, charming, centrally situated Georgian period house offers a high standard of accommodation at favourable terms.

• Full cooked breakfast •
• All credit cards accepted •
• 10 minutes' walk to Princes Street and Castle •
• STB ★ • AA Listed • RAC Listed •
• LES ROUTIERS Recommended •
• PRIVATE CAR PARK •

44 Gilmore Place, Edinburgh EH3 9NQ
Tel: 0131 229 9932

e.mail: info@averon.co.uk Web: www.averon.co.uk

★

GUEST HOUSE

Averon Guest House

44 Gilmore Place, Edinburgh, EH3 9NQ
Tel:0131 229 9932
Email:info@averon.co.uk
Web:www.averon.co.uk

Central location with private car park to rear. 10 minute walk to Princes Street and Castle. Near Kings Theatre and Conference Centre. Many rooms on ground floor.

1 Single	6 En Suite fac	B&B per person	Open Jan-Dec
2 Twin	2 Priv.NOT ensuite	from £24.00 Single	
4 Double		from £22.00 Double	
3 Family			

📺 🖥️ 🅿️ ☕ ⚥ 📞

💷 ♿

BALQUHIDDER GUEST HOUSE

94 Pilrig Street, Edinburgh EH6 5AY
Telephone: 0131 554 3377
e.mail: enquiries@balquhidderguesthouse.co.uk
Web: www.balquhidderguesthouse.co.uk
Built in 1857 as a church manse, this charming centrally situated Victorian detached house offers a high standard of accommodation at very favourable terms. Personally supervised by same family for 20 years. Own keys with access to rooms at all times. B&B from £25 per person per night.
For details contact Proprietor: Mrs N. Ferguson.

★★★

GUEST HOUSE

Balquhidder Guest House

94 Pilrig Street, Edinburgh, EH6 5AY
Tel:0131 554 3377
Email:enquiries@balquhidderguesthouse.co.uk
Web:www.balquhidderguesthouse.co.uk

Detached house built in 1857, and a former church manse, in its own grounds overlooking public park and on bus routes to the city centre.

1 Single	5 En Suite fac	B&B per person	Open Jan-Dec
2 Twin	1 Priv.NOT ensuite	from £25.00 Single	
2 Double	1 Pub.Bath/Show	from £25.00 Double	
1 Family			

📺 🖥️ 🍵 🛏️ 📞

Ⓥ ♿

VAT is shown at 17.5%: changes in this rate may affect prices.

Key to symbols is on back flap.

Edinburgh

Map Ref: 2C5

★★

GUEST HOUSE

Barrosa
21 Pilrig Street, Edinburgh, EH6 5AN
Tel:0131 554 3700

1 Twin	4 En Suite fac	B&B per person	Open Jan-Dec excl
2 Double	3 Priv.NOT ensuite	£23.00-40.00 Double	Xmas/New Year
3 Family		£20.00-30.00 Room Only	

Family run Georgian house only a short walk from city centre on main bus routes. Ensuite rooms available. Unrestricted street parking.

[TV icons]

[additional icons]

Belford Guest House
13 Blacket Avenue, Edinburgh EH9 1RR
Tel: 0131 667 2422 Fax: 0131 667 7508
e.mail: mailbox@belfordguesthouse.com
Web: www.belfordguesthouse.com
Small and friendly family run guest house in quiet tree-lined avenue 1 mile from the city centre. Buses run from either end of the avenue to all attractions in the city. Three rooms ensuite. TV's and hairdryers in all rooms.
Private parking. No smoking.

★★

GUEST HOUSE

Belford Guest House
13 Blacket Avenue, Edinburgh, EH9 1RR
Tel:0131 667 2422   Fax:0131 667 7508
Email:mailbox@belfordguesthouse.com
Web:www.belfordguesthouse.com

4 Twin	3 En Suite fac	B&B per person	Open Jan-Dec
3 Family	2 Priv.NOT ensuite	from £25.00 Single	
		from £20.00 Double	

Family run guest house in quiet road just off main A7/A701. Conveniently situated for main tourist attraction and city centre, buses run to the city centre from either end of the avenue. Variety of eating establishments locally.

[icons]

Ben-Craig House
3 Craigmillar Park, Edinburgh EH16 5PG
Tel: 0131 667 2593   e.mail: bencraighouse@dial.pipex.com
Fax: 0131 667 1109   Web: www.bencraighouse.co.uk
Attractive detached Victorian villa tastefully restored and decorated with your comfort in mind. Large appointed bedrooms all with en-suite facilities. Warm and friendly atmosphere. Private secure parking on excellent bus route to the city. Completely non-smoking house.
Bed and breakfast £25-£45 per person per night.

★★★★

GUEST HOUSE

Ben Craig House
3 Craigmillar Park, Newington, Edinburgh, EH16 5PG
Tel:0131 667 2593   Fax:0131 667 1109
Email:bencraighouse@dial.pipex.com
Web:www.bencraighouse.co.uk

1 Twin	All En Suite	B&B per person	Open Jan-Dec excl
3 Double		£29.00-45.00 Single	Xmas
1 Family		£25.00-45.00 Double	

Traditional detached sandstone Victorian villa with quiet gardens. Family run, chef proprietor also runs a well known Edinburgh restaurant. On main route for city centre. (1.5 miles south of Princes Street.) Tastefully restored and decorated to high standard. All bedrooms en-suite. Secure private parking. Special diets catered for.

[icons]

Important: Prices stated are estimates and may be subject to amendments

Edinburgh		Map Ref: 2C5		

GUEST HOUSE ★★★★

Ben Doran Guest House
11 Mayfield Gardens, Edinburgh, Lothian, EH9 2AX
Tel:0131 667 8488   Fax:0131 667 0076
Email:info@ben-doran.com
Web:www.ben-doran.com

Charming and historically listed Georgian townhouse, elegantly refurbished. Central, on bus routes, close to City Centre and Edinburgh attractions. Lovely city and hillside views from the windows. The Ben Doran is run with pride.

2 Single	6 En Suite fac	B&B per person	Open Jan-Dec
8 Double	3 Priv.NOT ensuite	from £35.00 Single	
		from £30.00 Double	

📺 📞 🛗 🅿 ⚡ 📠

♨ V

GUEST HOUSE ★★

Blossom House
8 Minto Street, Edinburgh, EH9 1RG
Tel:0131 667 5353   Fax:0131 667 2813
Email:blossom_house@hotmail.com
Web:www.blossomguesthouse.co.uk

Comfortable, family run guest house. City centre within walking distance. Excellent bus service. Private car park. Close to Commonwealth pool.

2 Twin	4 En Suite fac	B&B per person	Open Jan-Dec
3 Double	2 Priv.NOT ensuite	from £20.00 Single	
2 Family		from £17.50 Double	
		from £15.00 Room Only	

📺 🛗 🅿 ☕ 🍴 📠

C ♨ V

BONNINGTON GUEST HOUSE
202 Ferry Road, Edinburgh EH6 4NW
Telephone/Fax: 0131 554 7610
e.mail: bonningtongh@btinternet.com

A comfortable early Victorian house (built 1840), personally run, where a friendly and warm welcome awaits guests. Situated in residential area of town on main bus routes. Private car parking.
For further details contact Eileen and David Watt, Proprietors.

GUEST HOUSE ★★★★

Bonnington Guest House
202 Ferry Road, Edinburgh, EH6 4NW
Tel/Fax:0131 554 7610
Email:bonningtongh@btinternet.com

Early Victorian Listed building with private parking. On the north side of the city. Convenient bus routes to centre. Well appointed rooms with many of the period features retained. Very comfortable accommodation of a high standard.

1 Twin	3 En Suite fac	B&B per person	Open Jan-Dec excl
2 Double	2 Priv.NOT ensuite	from £28.00 Double	Xmas/New Year
3 Family	1 Pub.Bath/Show		

📺 🛗 🖥 🅿 ☕ 🍴 📠

C 🐕 ♨ V

Scotland's National Booking and Information Line

Tel: 0845 22 55 121
visitscotland.com

VAT is shown at 17.5%: changes in this rate may affect prices. | *Key to symbols is on back flap.*

BRODIES GUEST HOUSE
22 East Claremont Street, Edinburgh EH7 4JP
Telephone: 0131 556 4032   Fax: 0131 556 9739
e.mail: info@brodiesguesthouse.co.uk Web: *www.brodiesguesthouse.co.uk*

A warm Scottish welcome awaits you at our Victorian town house set in a landscaped cobbled street only 5-10 minutes walk from the city centre. Princes Street, bus/rail stations, Botanic Gardens, Castle, Dynamic Earth, Britannia and Playhouse are close by. Many extras provided. Full Scottish breakfasts a speciality.

★★★

GUEST HOUSE

Brodies Guest House
22 East Claremont Street, Edinburgh, EH7 4JP
Tel:0131 556 4032 Fax:0131 556 9739
Email:info@brodiesguesthouse.co.uk
Web:www.brodiesguesthouse.co.uk

Small, friendly, family run Victorian town house in a cobbled street within ½ mile of Princes Street. Convenient for bus/railway station, Playhouse theatre, pubs and restaurants nearby. Scottish breakfasts a speciality.

1 Single	3 En Suite fac	B&B per person	Open Jan-Dec
1 Twin	1 Priv.NOT ensuite	from £25.00 Single	
1 Double		from £25.00 Double	
2 Family			

BURNS B&B
Tel: 0131 229 1669
Fax: 0131 229 9225

67 Gilmore Place, Edinburgh EH3 9NU
e.mail: burnsbandb@talk21.com

Popular homely B&B in city centre close to Princes Street, Castle, E.I.C.C., tourist attractions, theatres and restaurants. Comfortable rooms all ensuite. Good breakfasts. Parking. Non-smoking. No pets. Access with your own keys. B&B from £23 - £30 pppn. Single rooms available November - February £26 pppn. Credit cards accepted. Open all year. *Contact Mrs Burns as above.*

★★★

B&B

Burns Bed and Breakfast
67 Gilmore Place, Edinburgh, EH3 9NU
Tel:0131 229 1669 Fax:0131 229 9225
Email:burnsbandb@talk21.com

Charming pre-Victorian terraced house, personally run by Mrs Burns. Close to city centre, tourist attractions, Kings Theatre, E.I.C.C and local restaurants. All ensuite. Non-smoking.

1 Twin	All En Suite	B&B per person	Open Jan-Dec excl
2 Double		from £23.00 Double	Xmas/New Year

★★

B&B

Clarence St B&B
3a Clarence Street, Edinburgh, EH3 5AE
Tel:0131 557 9368

Garden flat in Georgian terrace in New Town. Central location yet in quiet area. Close to Botanic Gardens, sports grounds (Highland Games every weekend in Summer). Theatre workshop and numerous restaurants nearby. Private garden.

1 Twin	1 Priv.NOT ensuite	B&B per person	Open Apr-Oct
1 Family	1 Pub.Bath/Show	from £20.00 Single	
		from £19.00 Double	

Important: Prices stated are estimates and may be subject to amendments

B

Edinburgh

Map Ref: 2C5

Castle Park Guest House
75 Gilmore Place, Edinburgh EH3 9NU
Telephone: 0131 229 1215 Fax: 0131 229 1223
Family run close to Kings Theatre and city centre
conference centre. Always a warm welcome awaits you.
All bedrooms have colour TV, Sky, tea and coffee.
Central heating. Full Scottish breakfast. Children welcome.
Special prices. Private lane parking. £17.50–£27 pppn.

★

GUEST HOUSE

Castle Park Guest House
75 Gilmore Place, Edinburgh, EH3 9NU
Tel:0131 229 1215 Fax:0131 229 1223

Family run guest house close to city centre. Convenient for Kings Theatre and Conference Hall. A variety of local restaurants and bistros. Children welcome.

2 Single	Some En Suite	B&B per person	Open Jan-Dec excl
2 Twin	1 Priv.NOT ensuite	from £17.50 Single	New Year
2 Double		from £20.00 Double	
2 Family		from £15.00 Room Only	

★★★

B&B

Cockle Mill
School Brae, Cramond, Edinburgh, EH4 6JN
Tel:0131 312 7657
Email:bnbmill98@aol.com
Web:www.edinburgh.org

Unique riverside residence 4.5 miles from city centre, on main bus route. Easy access to airport, bridges and ring road. A little French & German spoken. Pub food nearby. Attractive riverside walk to fine views over the Firth of Forth.

1 Single	All En Suite	B&B per person	Open Mar-Nov
1 Twin		from £25.00 Double	
1 Double			

★★★

B&B

The Conifers
56 Pilrig Street, Edinburgh, EH6 5AS
Tel:0131 554 5162
Email:liz@conifersguesthouse.com
Web:www.conifersguesthouse.com

Friendly family home close to city centre. Recently refurbished, three rooms ensuite. Spacious superior quality ground floor bedroom retaining original features. Within walking distance of Playhouse Theatre. Non-smoking house.

1 Twin	All En Suite	B&B per person	Open Jan-Dec
1 Double		£25.00-35.00 Single	
1 Family		£25.00-35.00 Double	
		£22.00-30.00 Room Only	

★★★

B&B

The Corner House
1 Greenbank Place, Morningside, Edinburgh, EH10 6EW
Tel:0131 447 1077

Comforatble accommodation in this family home situated on the south side of Edinburgh. Convenient for Napier University and Braid Hills Hotel. Spacious rooms and free street parking.

1 Twin	2 Priv.NOT ensuite	B&B per person	Open Jan-Dec
2 Double		from £21.00 Single	
		from £18.00 Double	

VAT is shown at 17.5%: changes in this rate may affect prices.

Key to symbols is on back flap.

Edinburgh   Map Ref: 2C5

★★★

B&B

Craigievar B&B
112 Glasgow Road, Edinburgh, EH12 8LP
Tel/Fax:0131 539 2485
Email:craigievar@mail.com

A warm Scottish welcome awaits you at Craigievar, ideally located on a
main bus route into the city centre. We have easy access to the city
bypass, Edinburgh Airport, Ingliston Exhibition Centre, Murrayfield
Stadium, the Zoo, the David Lloyd Tennis Centre, & the Gyle shopping
centre. Spacious ensuite rooms are located at ground level to the rear of
the house & one is wheelchair friendly. Non-smoking.

3 Twin	All En Suite	B&B per person	Open Jan-Dec
3 Double		from £25.00 Double	
3 Family			

★★★

**GUEST
HOUSE**

Crioch Guest House
23 East Hermitage Place, Edinburgh, EH6 8AD
Tel/Fax:0131 554 5494
Email:welcome@crioch.com Web:www.crioch.com

Only 10 minutes from the city centre, Crioch overlooks the leafy park of
Leith Links. Our recent major refurbishment means that all rooms now
have ensuite shower or private bathroom, and you still receive the same
warm welcome. Free parking and a frequent bus service leaves you to
enjoy Edinburgh's sights on foot, and later a short stroll takes you to
Leith's fine cafes, bars and restaurants.

2 Single	5 En Suite fac	B&B per person	Open Jan-Dec
1 Twin	1 Pub.Bath/Show	from £25.00 Single	
1 Double		from £22.50 Double	
2 Family		from £20.00 Room Only	

Mrs Moira Conway

Crannoch But & Ben

**467 QUEENSFERRY RD
EDINBURGH EH4 7ND**
TEL/FAX: 0131 336 5688

STB Grade of 4 Stars and Classification of Bed
& Breakfast has been awarded to this
outstanding family home. This bungalow has
private facilities for all rooms. Near Airport on
A90 and 3 miles from city centre with excellent
bus service and car parking. *All guests receive
a warm welcome.*

e.mail:moiraconway@crannoch467.freeserve.co.uk

★★★★

B&B

Crannoch But & Ben
467 Queensferry Road, Edinburgh, EH4 7ND
Tel/Fax:0131 336 5688
Email:moiraconway@crannoch467.freeserve.co.uk

Detached bungalow with warm and friendly atmosphere, on Forth Road
Bridge route, 3 miles (5kms) from city centre. Non-smoking house.
Ensuite bathrooms, parking.

1 Twin	All En Suite	B&B per person	Open Jan-Dec
1 Double		from £30.00 Single	
1 Family		from £25.00 Double	
		from £50.00 Room Only	

★★★

B&B

Doris Crook
2 Seton Place, Edinburgh, EH9 2JT
Tel:0131 667 6430 Fax:0131 667 6652
Email:mail@dcrook.co.uk
Web:www.dcrook.co.uk

Upper flatted Victorian house in quiet residential area. Private parking.
Easy access to town centre on good bus route.

2 Twin	2 En Suite fac	B&B per person	Open Jan-Dec
1 Double	1 Pub.Bath/Show	from £25.00 Single	
		from £20.00 Double	

Important: Prices stated are estimates and may be subject to amendments

Edinburgh

Map Ref: 2C5

GUEST HOUSE

Dene Guest House
7 Eyre Place, off Dundas Street, Edinburgh
EH3 5ES
Tel:0131 556 2700 Fax:0131 557 9876
Email:deneguesthouse@yahoo.co.uk
Web:www.deneguesthouse.com

Charming Georgian townhouse offering friendly service and a relaxed
atmosphere. Perfectly located in city centre to experience Edinburgh's
culture, history, restaurants and bars.

3 Single	5 En Suite fac	B&B per person	Open Jan-Dec
2 Twin		from £19.50 Single	
3 Double		from £19.50 Double	
2 Family			

B&B

Mr & Mrs T Divine
116 Greenbank Crescent, Edinburgh, EH10 5SZ
Tel:0131 447 9454
Email:mary@greenbnk.fsnet.co.uk

Family home in quiet residential area with easy access to city centre and
bypass. Parking. On main bus routes.

1 Single	2 Priv.NOT ensuite	B&B per person	Open Mar-Oct
1 Twin		from £18.00 Single	
		from £18.00 Double	
		from £15.00 Room Only	

B&B

Doocote House
15 Moat Street, Edinburgh, EH14 1PE
Tel:0131 443 5455

Terraced house in quiet street just off main bus route. Approx. 2 miles
(3kms) from city centre. Unrestricted street parking. Kitchen available for
guests use.

1 Twin	2 Priv.NOT ensuite	B&B per person	Open Mar-Oct
1 Double		from £18.00 Double	
1 Family			

SMALL HOTEL

●●
RESTAURANT

Dunstane House Hotel
4 West Coates, Haymarket, Edinburgh, EH12 5JQ
Tel:0131 337 6169 Fax:0131 337 6060
Email:reservations@dunstanehousehotel.co.uk
Web:www.dunstanehousehotel.co.uk

Impressive Listed Victorian mansion retaining many original features
enjoying imposing position within large grounds on the A8 airport road
(major bus route). 10 mins walk from city centre. Close to Edinburgh
Conference Centre, Murrayfield and Edinburgh Zoo. Private secluded car
park. Unique lounge bar and restaurant themed on the Scottish Islands.

4 Single	All En Suite	B&B per person	Open Jan-Dec
2 Twin		from £40.00 Single	
6 Double		from £39.00 Double	
4 Family			

B&B

Jean Durbin B&B
4 Inverleith Row, Edinburgh, EH3 5LP
Tel/Fax:0131 556 5398

Late Georgian town house with period furnishings. Boundary on Royal
Botanic Gardens. The house has its own landscaped garden with
sheltered seating areas. 5 minutes by bus to Princes Street, the heart of
the city, or to the port of Leith, with its many restaurants and pubs and
popular dockland developments.

1 Double	1 Priv.NOT ensuite	B&B per person	Open Jun-Sep
		from £45.00 Single	
		from £30.00 Double	

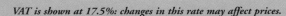

VAT is shown at 17.5%: changes in this rate may affect prices.

Key to symbols is on back flap.

121 CAPTAINS ROAD

Edinburgh EH17 8DT Tel/Fax: 0131 658 1578
e.mail: dorothy_mckay@lineone.net
Web: www.visitscotland.com; www.edinburgh.org

Bungalow situated in residential area served by excellent bus service. *'£1.50 unlimited travel for the day'*. Convenient city centre shopping, exploring Castle, Royal Mile, Holyrood Palace and Park, Dynamic Earth, art galleries, museums, observatory, Britannia, zoo. Venues, theatres, concert halls, rugby stadium. Activities easy access, swimming, golf, ski-centre, hill-walking. City-bypass 1/2 mile.

★★

B&B

Edinburgh, Dorothy M G McKay	1 Double	Ensuite fac	B&B per person	Open Jan-Dec
The Haven, 121 Captains Road, Liberton, Edinburgh	1 Twin	Shared fac	£20.00-22.00	

Edinburgh, Dorothy M G McKay
The Haven, 121 Captains Road, Liberton, Edinburgh
EH17 8DT
Tel/Fax:0131 658 1578
Email:dorothy_mckay@lineone.net
Web:www.edinburgh.org

1 Double   Ensuite fac
1 Twin   Shared fac

B&B per person
£20.00-22.00
Double En-suite
£16.00-18.00
Twin shared facilities
£22-25 Single

Open Jan-Dec

Mrs McKay has been offering B&B in Edinburgh for many years now and recently moved to this modern semi detached bungalow, set back from the road and 1 mile from the city bypass. On main bus routes to the city centre.

Edinburgh First, University of Edinburgh

18 Holyrood Park Road, Edinburgh EH16 5AY
Tel: 0800 028 7118   Overseas Tel: +44 (0)131 651 2007
Fax: 0131 667 7271
e.mail: Edinburgh.First@ed.ac.uk   Web: www.EdinburghFirst.com

In the heart of Edinburgh great value rooms in our properties minutes from the old town and overlooking Holyrood Park. Excellent catering at nearby John McIntyre centre. Ensuite as well as good quality standard rooms. Send for our free colour brochure today.

★★

CAMPUS ACCOMMODATION

Edinburgh First
18 Holyrood Park Road, Edinburgh, EH16 5AY
Tel:0800 028 7118 Fax:0131 667 7271
Email:edinburgh.first@ed.ac.uk
Web:www.EdinburghFirst.com

1366   591 En Suite fac
Single   898 Pub.Bath/Show
17 Twin
123
Double

B&B per person
from £20.00 Single
from £28.00 Double

Open Jun-Sep,Mar,Apr
BB & Eve.Meal
from £28.50-50.50

On campus in Holyrood Park beside Arthur's Seat. Close to Royal Commonwealth Pool, 3 km from city centre. In beautiful surroundings, we offer comfortable accommodation with en-suite facilities. Particularly suitable for groups. Alternative annexe accommodation available. Conference and meeting facilities.

★★★★

GUEST HOUSE

Ellesmere Guest House
11 Glengyle Terrace, Edinburgh, EH3 9LN
Tel:0131 229 4823 Fax:0131 229 5285
Email:celia@edinburghbandb.co.uk
Web:www.edinburghbandb.co.uk

1 Single   All En Suite
2 Twin
2 Double
1 Family

B&B per person
from £28.00 Single
from £28.00 Double

Open Jan-Dec

City centre Victorian terraced house in quiet location overlooking Bruntsfield Links. Kings Theatre, Conference Centre and all amenities within walking distance. All rooms en suite. Full Scottish Breakfast is served and a warm welcome is extended to all guests.

Important: Prices stated are estimates and may be subject to amendments

B

Ellesmere House

11 Glengyle Terrace,
EDINBURGH
Tel: 0131 229 4823   EH3 9LN   Fax: 0131 229 5285
e.mail: celia@edinburghbandb.co.uk Web: www.edinburghbandb.co.uk

"Your home away from home"

Ellesmere House is situated in an enviable location overlooking "Bruntsfield Links" in the **CENTRE** of Edinburgh, within easy walking distance of most places of interest. The International Conference Centre, theatres and various good restaurants are very close by. Rooms are all ensuite and are tastefully furnished and decorated to a very high standard and many extras added with your comfort in mind. For honeymooners or that special anniversary there is a four-poster bed available. Start the day with our delicious full Scottish breakfast.
Prices from £28, all rooms ensuite. Excellent value and competitive prices.

Personally run by Cecilia & Tommy Leishman who extend a very warm welcome to all of their guests.

STB ★★★★   AA ◆◆◆◆ Selected

VAT is shown at 17.5%: changes in this rate may affect prices.   Key to symbols is on back flap.

Edinburgh   Map Ref: 2C5

★★

B&B

Elliston B&B
5 Viewforth Terrace, Edinburgh, EH10 4LH
Tel:0131 229 6698
Email:elliston@lineone.net
Web:http://website.lineone.net/~elliston/

Victorian villa approx 2 miles (3kms) from Princes Street. In quiet
residential location, and within walking distance of restaurants and
theatres. Close to bus route. Non smoking house. Television in twin
bedroom.

2 Single	1 Priv.NOT ensuite	B&B per person	Open Apr-Sep
1 Twin		from £24.00 Single	
		from £22.00 Double	

EMERALD GUEST HOUSE
3 Drum Street, Gilmerton, Edinburgh EH17 8QQ
Tel: 0131 664 5918 or 664 1920
Fax: 0131 664 1920 Mobile: 07930 889598

Family run Victorian villa situated on main bus route into city centre.
15 mins from city airport, 5 mins from city bypass which leads to all national
routes. Good quality rooms. Good food. Private parking. Long stays or short
breaks welcome. Small groups, good rates. A warm welcome assured.

★★

B&B

Emerald Guest House
3 Drum Street, Gilmerton, Edinburgh, EH17 8QQ
Tel:0131 664 5918/1920 Fax:0131 664 1920

Family run bed and breakfast located on convenient bus route to city
centre. Private parking available.

1 Single	Some En Suite	B&B per person	Open Jan-Dec
2 Twin	1 Priv.NOT ensuite	from £25.00 Single	BB & Eve.Meal
2 Double		from £20.00 Double	from £30.00
1 Family			

Falcon Crest
70 South Trinity Road
Edinburgh EH5 3NX
Tel/Fax: 0131 552 5294

A friendly welcome awaits at our family run guest house in a
quiet residential Victorian terrace. Located between the Royal
Botanic Gardens, Newhaven Harbour and Granton Marina.
Ten minutes by frequent bus service from the city centre.
Good road links. Private parking. Special diets by prior request.

★

GUEST
HOUSE

Falcon Crest Guest House
70 South Trinity Road, Edinburgh, EH5 3NX
Tel/Fax:0131 552 5294

Victorian terraced family home in attractive residential area, near main
bus route to city centre. Free on street parking.

1 Single	Some En Suite	B&B per person	Open Jan-Dec
2 Twin	2 Priv.NOT ensuite	from £18.00 Single	
2 Double		from £17.00 Double	
1 Family		from £17.00 Room	
		Only	

Important: Prices stated are estimates and may be subject to amendments

Edinburgh	Map Ref: 2C5

★★★

B&B

Finlaystone

19 Meadowplace Road, Corstorphine, Edinburgh
EH12 7UJ
Tel/Fax:0131 334 8483
Email:nancymitchell@beeb.net

On the West side of the city, detached bungalow offering ground floor accommodation and off street parking. Excellent bus service to city centre and airport. Various type of eating establishments within walking distance.

2 Twin

B&B per person
from £18.00 Double

Open Jan-Dec excl Xmas/New Year

★★★

LODGE

Frederick House Hotel

42 Frederick Street, Edinburgh, EH2 1EX
Tel:0131 226 1999   Fax:0131 624 7064
Email:frederickhouse@ednet.co.uk
Web:www.townhousehotels.co.uk

Situated in the heart of Edinburgh close to all city centre amenities and with a wide variety of restaurants and bars in the immediate vicinity. Georgian building with all rooms recently refurbished to a high standard with en-suite facilities, fridges and modem points. Princes Street just 50 yards away. Breakfast available across the road at the award winning Rick's Bar/Restaurant. Street parking.

5 Single   All En Suite
9 Twin
15 Double
16 Family

B&B per person
from £25.00 Single
from £25.00 Double
from £25.00 Room
Only

Open Jan-Dec

★★★

GUEST HOUSE

Galloway

22 Dean Park Crescent, Edinburgh, EH4 1PH
Tel/Fax:0131 332 3672

Friendly, family run guest house, beautifully restored and situated in a residential area, 10 minutes walk from Princes Street and convenient for Edinburgh International Conference Centre. Free street parking.

1 Single   6 En Suite fac
3 Twin   1 Priv.NOT ensuite
3 Double   2 Pub.Bath/Show
3 Family

B&B per person
from £30.00 Single
from £20.00 Double

Open Jan-Dec

★★★★

GUEST HOUSE

Gifford House

103 Dalkeith Road, Edinburgh, EH16 5AJ
Tel/Fax:0131 667 4688
Email:giffordhotel@btinternet.com
Web:www.giffordhousehotel.co.uk

A well appointed Victorian stone built house situated on one of the main routes into Edinburgh. Close to Holyrood Park and Arthur's Seat and only 300 metres from Royal Commonwealth Swimming Pool. Regular bus services to all city amenities. Well positioned for conference centre.

1 Single   All En Suite
2 Twin
2 Double
2 Family

B&B per person
from £25.00 Single
from £22.00 Double
from £20.00 Room
Only

Open Jan-Dec

★★★

GUEST HOUSE

Gildun Guest House

9 Spence Street, Edinburgh, EH16 5AG
Tel:0131 667 1368   Fax:0131 668 4989
Email:gildun.edin@btinternet.com
Web:www.gildun.co.uk

A warm and friendly run guest house situated in cul de sac with private parking. Close to Commonwealth Pool and bus route to city centre. Cameron Toll Shopping Centre nearby and situated near University Halls of Residence. A variety of eating establishments within walking distance.

1 Single   6 En Suite fac
1 Twin   1 Priv.NOT ensuite
2 Double   1 Pub.Bath/Show
4 Family

B&B per person
from £20.00 Single
from £20.00 Double

Open Jan-Dec

VAT is shown at 17.5%: changes in this rate may affect prices. | *Key to symbols is on back flap.*

B

Map Ref: 2C5

GLENDEVON
50 GLASGOW ROAD, EDINBURGH EH12 8HN
Telephone/Fax: 0131 539 0491

A warm welcome awaits visitors at 'Glendevon'. A detached bungalow with attractive garden, open outlook and private parking. On good bus route to city centre and 3 miles from airport. All rooms centrally heated and tastefully furnished with W.H.B., tea/coffee making facilities and colour TV. Residents lounge available. Non-smoking.

★★★

B&B

Glendevon
50 Glasgow Road, Edinburgh, EH12 8HN
Tel/Fax:0131 539 0491

1 Single	2 Pub.Bath/Show	B&B per person	Open Apr-Oct
1 Twin		£20.00-24.00 Single	
1 Double		£20.00-24.00 Double	
		from £18.00 Room Only	

1930's family bungalow on major bus route to city centre and 3 miles from the Airport. Private parking. Some ground floor accommodation. Non-smoking.

★★★

SMALL HOTEL

Glenora Hotel
14 Rosebery Crescent, Edinburgh, EH12 5JY
Tel:0131 337 1186   Fax:0131 337 1119
Email:reservations@glenorahotel.co.uk
Web:www.glenorahotel.co.uk

2 Single	All En Suite	B&B per person	Open Jan-Dec excl
2 Twin		from £25.00 Single	Xmas
2 Double		from £23.50 Double	
2 Family		from £23.50 Room Only	

Victorian terraced town house a short walk to city centre and within easy reach of city's tourist attractions. Airport bus stops next to hotel.

★★★

SMALL HOTEL

Greenside Hotel
9 Royal Terrace, Edinburgh, EH7 5AB
Tel:0131 557 0121/0022 Fax:0131 557 0022
Email:greensidehotel@ednet.co.uk
Web:www.townhousehotels.co.uk

3 Single	All En Suite	B&B per person	Open Jan-Dec
2 Twin		from £22.50 Single	BB & Eve.Meal
3 Double		from £22.50 Double	from £37.50
8 Family		from £22.50 Room Only	

Personally run hotel in traditional Georgian terraced house. Quiet location, close to Princes Street and all amenities. 10 minutes walk from Waverley Station and Princes Street. Excellent selection of restaurants in immediate vicinity. Building of architectural interest. Evening meals on request.

★★★

GUEST HOUSE

Hanover House Hotel
26 Windsor Street, Edinburgh, EH7 5JR
Tel:0131 556 1325
Email:enquiries@hanoverhousehotel.co.uk
Web:www.hanoverhousehotel.co.uk

1 Twin	All En Suite	B&B per person	Open Jan-Dec excl
3 Double		from £35.00 Single	Xmas
1 Family		from £25.00 Double	

A recently refurbished family run Guest House offering comfortable accommodation in quiet area near to free on street parking.

Important: Prices stated are estimates and may be subject to amendments

Edinburgh

Map Ref: 2C5

GUEST HOUSE

★

Harvest Guest House

33 Straiton Place, Portobello, Edinburgh EH15 2BA
Tel:0131 657 3160   Fax:0131 468 7028
Email:sadol@blueyonder.co.uk
Web:www.edinburgh-bb.com

Terraced house in quiet residential area with garden giving direct access to beach and promenade. Front bedrooms have super views of the Firth of Forth. Some private and street parking. Variety of eating establishments locally. Frequent bus service provides easy access to city centre.

1 Single	Some En Suite	B&B per ppn	Open Jan-Dec
1 Twin		from £30.00 Single	
3 Double		from £25.00 Double	
2 Family		from £25.00 Room Only	

HERIOT-WATT UNIVERSITY

Riccarton, Edinburgh EH14 4AS
Tel: 0131 451 3669 Fax: 0131 451 3199
e.mail: info@eccscotland.com Web: www.eccscotland.com

Set in parkland, just six miles from the city centre, Heriot-Watt University offers comfortable and cost competitive year round accommodation. There are 165 rooms available throughout the year in addition to the student accommodation available during vacation. Rooms are serviced daily and all year round rooms have en-suite shower and toilet, television, telephone and tea/coffee facilities. On site amenities include restaurants, bar, shop, hairdressers and sport centre. Situated a short distance from the airport, with excellent access to major road networks and ample onsite free car parking, the University offers an ideal base for Edinburgh and the surrounding area.

CAMPUS ACCOMMODATION

★★

Heriot-Watt University

Riccarton, Edinburgh, EH14 4AS
Tel:0131 451 3669 Fax:0131 451 3199
Email:info@eccscotland.com
Web:www.eccscotland.com

Situated in 370 acre picturesque campus of Heriot Watt University. 6 miles (10kms) west of city centre, 3 miles (5kms) from Edinburgh airport.

1487	1106 En Suite fac	B&B per person	Open Jan-Dec excl
Single	381 Priv.NOT ensuite	from £27.50 Single	Xmas/New Year
98 Twin		from £22.50 Double	

B&B

★★★

Hopetoun

15 Mayfield Road, Edinburgh, EH9 2NG
Tel:0131 667 7691 Fax:0131 466 1691
Email:hopetoun@aol.com
Web:www.hopetoun.com

Completely non-smoking, small, friendly bed and breakfast on the south side of the city, 1.5 miles (2.5kms) from Princes Street. Choice of traditional, healthy or vegetarian breakfast. Guests are encouraged to make use of the owners wide knowledge of what the city has to offer.

1 Double	En suite	B&B per person	Open Jan-Dec excl
1 Family	Private bathroom	from £25.00 Single	Xmas/New Year
	NOT En-suite	from £22.00 Double	

VAT is shown at 17.5%: changes in this rate may affect prices.

Key to symbols is on back flap.

Hotel Ceilidh-Donia
14/16 Marchhall Crescent, Edinburgh, EH16 5HL
Tel: 0131 667 2743 Fax: 0131 668 2181
e.mail: reservations@hotelceilidh-donia.co.uk
Web: www.hotelceilidh-donia.co.uk

Friendly family run hotel 1½ miles from city centre. Excellent bus service.
Close to university, Commonwealth Pool, Holyrood. Extensive breakfast menu,
special diets catered for. Evening dinners Mon-Fri. Off-season offers B&B+D.
Unrestricted parking. Quiet residential area. Group bookings welcome.
Theatre and tours can be arranged.

★★★

**SMALL
HOTEL**

Hotel Ceilidh-Donia

14-16 Marchhall Crescent, Edinburgh, EH16 5HL
Tel:0131 667 2743 Fax:0131 668 2181
Email:reservations@hotelceilidh-donia.co.uk
Web:www.hotelceilidh-donia.co.uk

Fully refurbished small family run hotel in a quiet residential area, near
main bus routes. New restaurant leading onto landscaped area, for
guests use. Close to City Centre and all major tourist attractions. Good
base for the business traveller, or for leisure breaks to the city. Computer
points in all bedrooms, internet friendly.

3 Single	12 En Suite fac	B&B per person	Open Jan-Dec
6 Twin	1 Shared Shower	from £22.00 Single	BB & Eve.Meal
4 Double		from £20.00 Double	from £35.00
1 Family			

📺 📞 🛁 ☕ 🍴 ✂ 🍷

Ⓒ 📠 Ⓥ 🛗   🚶

INGLENEUK
31 DRUM BRAE NORTH, EDINBURGH EH4 8AT
Tel/Fax: 0131 317 1743
e.mail: ingleneukbnb@btinternet.com
Web: www.accomodata.co.uk/110999.htm

For an enjoyable stay, visit our comfortable home
situated in a quiet residential area. As well as a
double ensuite, we have a self contained annex
with private entrance, comprising large twin
bedded room with lounge/breakfasting area
having two rooms off, a double bedroom and a
shower room – ideal for two couples travelling
together – family/double or twin. Breakfast is
served in your room giving a totally relaxed
breakfast setting looking out onto a lovely
landscaped garden. Ample private parking.
Four miles from city, 3 miles from airport.
Good bus service. Close to Forth Bridge.

★★

B&B

Ingleneuk

31 Drumbrae North, Edinburgh, EH4 8AT
Tel/Fax:0131 317 1743
Email:ingleneukbnb@btinternet.com
Web:www.accomodata.co.uk/110999.htm

On the west side of town, convenient for the Forth Bridge and the
airport, this cottage styled B&B backs onto a private woodland garden
alive with birds and squirrels in amongst the ornamental Japanese
bridge. Both rooms have their own private entrance, one is a family suite
suitable for four persons. Enjoy a relaxed breakfast, served in the
comfort of your own room.

1 Double	All En Suite	B&B per person
1 Family		from £25.00 Single
		from £23.00 Double

Open Jan-Dec

📺 🚿 🅿 💷 🍴 ℃ ✕

Ⓒ Ⓥ 🛗

Important: Prices stated are estimates and may be subject to amendments

Edinburgh

Map Ref: 2C5

International Guest House

GUEST HOUSE

★★★★

37 Mayfield Gardens, Edinburgh, EH9 2BX
Tel:0131 667 2511   Fax:0131 667 1112
Email:intergh@easynet.co.uk
Web:www.accommodation-edinburgh.com

4 Single	All En Suite	B&B per person	Open Jan-Dec
1 Twin		from £30.00 Single	
1 Double		from £25.00 Double	
3 Family			

Stone built Victorian house in residential area with regular bus service to city centre. All rooms have ensuite facilities. Some private parking and on-street parking. Ground floor room available for persons with limited mobility.

INVERMARK ★★ B&B

60 Polwarth Terrace, Edinburgh EH11 1NJ
Telephone: 0131 337 1066

Invermark is situated in quiet suburbs on main bus route into city, 5 minutes by car. Private parking. Accommodation: single, twin, family with wash-hand basins and tea/coffee-making facilities. TV lounge/dining room, toilet, bathroom/shower. Friendly atmosphere, children and pets welcome.

Invermark

★★

B&B

60 Polwarth Terrace, Edinburgh, EH11 1NJ
Tel:0131 337 1066

1 Single	1 Priv.NOT ensuite	B&B per person	Open Apr-Oct
2 Twin		from £20.00 Single	
1 Family		from £20.00 Double	

Georgian house situated in quiet residential area, 15 minutes by bus from city centre. Next to main bus route. Local hotels offer a range of evening meals. Convenient for Craiglockhart Sports Centre.

Scotland's National Booking and Information Line

Tel: 0845 22 55 121
visitscotland.com

VAT is shown at 17.5%: changes in this rate may affect prices. *Key to symbols is on back flap.*

Important: Prices stated are estimates and may be subject to amendments

Edinburgh

Map Ref: 2C5

GUEST HOUSE
★★★

Kenvie Guest House

16 Kilmaurs Road, Edinburgh, EH16 5DA
Tel:0131 668 1964 Fax:0131 668 1926
Email:dorothy@kenvie.co.uk Web:www.kenvie.co.uk

A charming, comfortable, warm, friendly family run Victorian town house in a quiet residential street. Very close to bus routes and the city by-pass. We offer for your comfort, lots of caring touches including complimentary tea / coffee, colour TV and no-smoking rooms. En-suite available and vegetarians catered for. You are guranteed a warm welcome from Richard and Dorothy.

2 Twin	Some En Suite	B&B per person	Open Jan-Dec
1 Double	2 Priv.NOT ensuite	from £25.00 Single	
2 Family		from £20.00 Double	
		from £20.00 Room Only	

Kingswood

30 Arboretum Place, Inverleith, Edinburgh EH3 5NZ
Telephone: 0131 332 7315

Luxury modern home situated in a quiet residential area next to the Royal Botanic Gardens overlooking Inverleith Park. Within easy walking distance of city centre and tourist attractions. Private car parking available and near main bus routes.

B&B
★★★

Kingswood

30 Arboretum Place, Inverleith, Edinburgh, EH3 5NZ
Tel:0131 332 7315

Comfortable family house of modern architectural design located in a quiet residential area adjacent to the Royal Botanic Garden and overlooking Inverleith Park. Ample private parking and un-restricted street parking. Easy access to the city centre and main attractions.

1 Twin	1 En Suite fac	B&B per person	Open Apr-Oct
2 Double	1 Priv.NOT ensuite	from £20.00 Double	

Kirkland Bed and Breakfast

6 Dean Park Crescent, Edinburgh EH4 1PN
Telephone: 0131 332 5017 e.mail: m.kirkland@blueyonder.co.uk
Web: www.kirkland.pwp.blueyonder.co.uk
Warm friendly Victorian home only 10 minutes' walk from city centre. The Botanical Gardens and many interesting local shops and restaurants are also nearby. Breakfast is ample and varied, and we are happy to meet any special needs you may have.

B&B
★★★

Kirkland Bed & Breakfast

6 Dean Park Crescent, Edinburgh, EH4 1PN
Tel:0131 332 5017
Email:m.kirkland@blueyonder.co.uk
Web:www.kirkland.pwp.blueyonder.co.uk

Warm, friendly, Victorian home 10 minutes walk from city centre. Interesting local shops, restaurants and pubs.

1 Twin	1 En Suite fac	B&B per person	Open Apr-Oct
1 Double	1 Priv.NOT ensuite	from £45.00 Single	
1 Family	1 Pub.Bath/Show	from £22.00 Double	

VAT is shown at 17.5%: changes in this rate may affect prices. | *Key to symbols is on back flap.*

Edinburgh

Map Ref: 2C5

GUEST HOUSE
★★★★

Lauderville House
52 Mayfield Road, Edinburgh, EH9 2NH
Tel:0131 667 7788   Fax:0131 667 2636
Email:res@laudervilleguesthouse.co.uk
Web:www.LaudervilleGuestHouse.co.uk

Brian and Yvonne Marriott welcome visitors to their restored Victorian Town House, centrally situated with easy access to city centre. Comfortable rooms, excellent breakfast, including vegetarian. Some secure private parking available. Totally non smoking house.

1 Single	All En Suite	B&B per person	Open Jan-Dec
2 Twin		£30.00-50.00 Single	
6 Double		£25.00-45.00 Double	
1 Family			

I LAURIE
59 CRAIGCROOK AVENUE, EDINBURGH, MIDLOTHIAN EH4 3PU
TEL: 0131 467 4284 FAX: 0131 312 6775
E.MAIL: ELLALAURIE@AOL.COM
Private house set in quiet location. Convenient city centre, airport, Murrayfield Rugby Stadium. Breakfast served in conservatory overlooking Corstorphine Hill. Private parking. Non-Smoking house. Rates £22-£25 p.p.p night single with breakfast. £22 p.p.p night sharing.

B&B
★★★

Laurie
59 Craigcrook Avenue, Edinburgh, EH4 3PU
Tel:0131 467 4284   Fax:0131 312 6775
Email:ellalaurie@aol.com

Family home, conveniently located for city centre and airport. Breakfast served in the conservatory overlooking Corstorphine Hills. Private parking. Non smoking house.

1 Single	1 En Suite fac	B&B per person	Open Mar-Oct
1 Twin	1 Pub.Bath/Show	from £22.00 Single	
1 Double		from £22.00 Double	

B&B
★★★

Lindenlea
6 St Marks Place, Portobello, Edinburgh, EH15 2PY
Tel:0131 669 6490
Email:betty@lindenlea6@freeserve.co.uk

Traditional stone-built Victorian villa set in quiet residential area within Portobello. All local amenities nearby with only a short distance to the beach, promenade and historic Victorian baths. Free on-street parking with frequent bus services on the doorstep. Ideal base for enjoying the city's attractions and exploring the coastline of East Lothian.

1 Twin	2 En Suite fac	B&B per person	Open Jan-Dec
2 Double	1 Priv.NOT ensuite	from £22.00 Single	
		from £22.00 Double	
		from £20.00 Room Only	

GUEST HOUSE
★★★

The McDonald Guest House
5 McDonald Road, Edinburgh, EH7 4LX
Tel/Fax:0131 557 5935
Email:white@5mcdonaldroad.co.uk
Web:www.5mcdonaldroad.co.uk

Comfortable accommodation a short walk from Princes Street. Adjacent to main bus routes. Many good restaurants locally. Playhouse Theatre nearby. Free on street parking. French and German spoken.

1 Twin	4 En Suite fac	B&B per person	Open Mar-Dec
1 Double	1 Pub.Bath/Show	from £25.00 Single	
2 Family		from £23.00 Double	
		from £21.00 Room Only	

Important: Prices stated are estimates and may be subject to amendments

Edinburgh

Map Ref: 2C5

★★★

B&B

McCrae's Bed + Bfst

44 East Claremont Street, Edinburgh, Midlothian
EH7 4JR
Tel/Fax:0131 556 2610
Email:mccraes.bandb@lineone.net
Web:http://website.lineone.net/~mccraes.bandb

Comfortable accommodation in the Victorian part of the New Town, conveniently located, 15 mins walk to city centre. Unrestricted on-street parking.

3 Twin	All En Suite	B&B per person from £28.50 Single from £24.50 Double	Open Jan-Dec

★★★

B&B

Meadows Festival Rooms

7 Hope Park Terrace, Edinburgh, Midlothian
EH8 9LZ
Tel:07900 348977
Email:sylv.robertson@virgin.net

Recently renovated and totally re-furbished Victorian, main door house with original features retained. Offering spacious accommodation with ensuite or private facilities. On ground floor. Ideally situated near the city's meadows. Two four-poster rooms.

3 Single	2 En Suite fac	B&B per person	Open Jan-Dec
1 Twin	1 Pub.Bath/Show	£35.00-45.00 Single	
2 Double		£29.00-39.00 Double	
1 Family			

★★★★

HOTEL

Menzies Belford Hotel

69 Belford Road, Edinburgh, EH4 3DG
Tel:0131 332 2545 Fax:0131 332 3805
Email:belford@menzies-hotels.co.uk
Web:www.menzies-hotels.co.uk

Modern purpose built hotel in a quiet area of the city overlooking the Water of Leith. An old granary has been incorporated in the new building. Conference and wedding facilities.

19 Single	All En Suite	B&B per person	Open Jan-Dec
39 Twin		from £65.00 Single	BB & Eve.Meal
88 Double		from £42.50 Double	from £80.00 Sgl
1 Suite			

Menzies Guest House

33 Leamington Terrace, Edinburgh EH10 4JS
Telephone and Fax: 0131 229 4629
e.mail: menzies33@blueyonder.co.uk Web: www.menzies-guesthouse.co.uk

Small family run guest house situated in the heart of Edinburgh, 10 minutes' walk to Princes Street, Edinburgh Castle, King's Theatre and all main attractions. Central heating, colour TV, tea/coffee-making facilities. Some rooms ensuite. Friendly service and a warm welcome assured. Private parking.
Prices from £13.50 per person.

★

GUEST HOUSE

Menzies Guest House

33 Leamington Terrace, Edinburgh, EH10 4JS
Tel/Fax:0131 229 4629
Email:menzies33@blueyonder.co.uk
Web:www.menzies-guesthouse.co.uk

Situated in residential area near Bruntsfield Links and close to main bus route to city centre. Private parking. Princes Street and West End with theatres and restaurants approx. 0.75 mile.

1 Twin	4 En Suite fac	B&B per person	Open Jan-Dec
3 Double	3 Priv.NOT ensuite	from £15.00 Single	
3 Family		from £15.00 Double	

VAT is shown at 17.5%: changes in this rate may affect prices.

Key to symbols is on back flap.

MINGALAR

2 EAST CLAREMONT STREET, EDINBURGH EH7 4JP

Telephone: 0131 556 7000

e.mail: mingalar@criper.com   Web: www.criper.com/mingalar

Townhouse 10 minutes walk from city centre, combining late-Georgian elegance with modern conveniences: all rooms with en-suite bathroom, TV, tea/coffee, fridge. Guest kitchenette. Simple restful decor to match. Emphasis on free relaxed atmosphere for guests. Suit longer stays with 5/7 day discounts off-season/peak. Internet/web access available. Non smoking.

GUEST HOUSE

Mingalar

2 East Claremont Street, Edinburgh, EH7 4DU
Tel:0131 556 7000
Email:mingalar@criper.com
Web:www.criper.com/mingalar

Refurbished late Georgian terraced house, within walking distance of the city centre. All bedrooms ensuite; with guest kitchenette and comfortable facilities, suitable for longer stays. Free and metered parking on surrounding streets.

| 4 Family | All En Suite | From £45 per room – | Open Feb-Dec |
| 4 Double | 1 Pub.Bath/Show | Double | |

B&B

Moores

44B Stevenson Drive, Edinburgh, EH11 3DJ
Tel:0131 443 9370

Comfortable, well furnished personally run bed and breakfast with both bedrooms ensuite. Unrestricted street parking. Door to door bus service to city centre.

1 Single	All En Suite	B&B per person	Open Jan-Dec excl
2 Twin		from £22.00 Single	Xmas/New Year
		from £20.00 Double	

Scotland's National Booking and Information Line

Tel: 0845 22 55 121
visitscotland.com

Important: Prices stated are estimates and may be subject to amendments

No 45 Bed & Breakfast
45 Gilmour Road, Newington, Edinburgh EH16 5NS
Tel: 0131 667 3536 Fax: 0131 662 1946
e.mail: w.cheape@gilmourhouse.freeserve.co.uk
Web: www.edinburghbedbreakfast.com
Centrally situated in quiet residential area but
close to most tourist attractions i.e. Castle,
Palace, Princes Street and Royal Mile. Also near
the University and Commonwealth Pool.
No 45 Gilmour Road is a beautiful Victorian villa
overlooking bowling green but just around the
corner from the main bus route. Our lovely home
is very tastefully decorated with a lovely
sitting-room and also a conservatory overlooking
our garden at the rear of our house. Parking
unrestricted. Colour TV in all rooms.
Tea and coffee facilities.

No 45 Bed + Breakfast

45 Gilmour Road, Edinburgh, Midlothian, EH16 5NS
Tel:0131 667 3536   Fax:0131 662 1946
Email:w.cheape@gilmourhouse.freeserve.co.uk
Web:www.edinburghbedbreakfast.com

Semi-detatched Victorian house in quiet residential street furnished to a very high standard with free parking yet close to main bus route. City centre 2 miles. University Kings buildings and Cameron Toll shopping centre nearby. Quality compact en-suite shower rooms.

1 Single	2 En Suite fac	B&B per person	Open Jan-Dec
1 Twin	1 Priv.NOT ensuite	from £30.00 Single	
1 Family		from £25.00 Double	

Number Five

5 Dean Park Crescent, Edinburgh, EH4 1DN
Tel:0131 332 4620   Fax:0131 315 4122
Email:mdmiller@sol.co.uk
Web:www.aboutedinburgh.com/deanpark/5.html

Lovely Victorian home with comfortable atmosphere situated close to city centre in delightful residential area with interesting shops and restaurants nearby. Enjoy breakfast in the comfort of your bedroom.

3 Double	2 En Suite fac	B&B per person	Open Apr-Oct
	1 Priv.NOT ensuite	from £55.00 Single	
		from £30.00 Double	

Pringles Ingle

26 Morningside Park, Edinburgh, EH10 5HB
Tel:0131 447 5847
Email:mipringle@aol.com
Web:www.pringlesingle.com

Traditional terraced villa, unrestricted on-street parking with shops, restaurants, cinema and a theatre locally. By the Royal Edinburgh Hospital and Napier University. On main bus route to city centre. Continental style breakfast, home made bread and preserves a speciality.

3 Double	1 En Suite fac	B&B per person	Open Jan-Dec
	2 Priv.NOT ensuite	from £30.00 Single	
		from £25.00 Double	

VAT is shown at 17.5%: changes in this rate may affect prices.   **Key to symbols is on back flap.**

Edinburgh

Map Ref: 2C5

★★★

GUEST
HOUSE

The St Valery
36 Coates Gardens, Edinburgh, EH12 5LE
Tel:0131 337 1893 Fax:0131 346 8529
Email:thestvalery@aol.com
Web:www.stvalery.com

Traditional guest house, centrally situated in West End of Edinburgh.
½ mile from Princes Street. 3 minutes walk from Haymarket Station.
Evening meal on request.

1 Single	All En Suite
3 Twin	
4 Double	
3 Family	

B&B per person
from £25.00 Single
from £25.00 Double
from £25.00 Room
Only

Open Jan-Dec
BB & Eve.Meal
from £33.00

★

GUEST
HOUSE

Sakura House
18 West Preston Street, Edinburgh, EH8 9PU
Tel/Fax:0131 668 1204
Email:margaret@sakurahouse.freeserve.co.uk

Victorian house in central location, close to castle and shopping centre.
Continental breakfast only. Numerous good restaurants and pubs in
immediate vicinity. On main bus route. Video recorders in bedroom and
a selection of videos for guests use. Single guests welcome.

2 Twin	Some En Suite
1 Double	1 Priv.NOT ensuite
3 Family	1 Pub.Bath/Show

B&B per person
£18.00-25.00 Single
£18.00-25.00 Double
£15.00-22.00 Room
Only

Open Jan-Dec

★★★

GUEST
HOUSE

Salisbury Guest House
45 Salisbury Road, Edinburgh, EH16 5AA
Tel/Fax:0131 667 1264
Email:brenda.wright@btinternet.com
Web:www.salisbury-guest-house.co.uk

Georgian Listed building in quiet conservation area, 1 mile (2kms) from
city centre. Ensuite and private facilities. Private car park. Non-smoking
house.

2 Single	Some En Suite
3 Twin	1 Pub.Bath
2 Double	
1 Family	

B&B per person
from £28.00 Single
from £25.00 Double
from £22.00 Room
Only

Open Feb-Dec excl
Xmas/New Year

Important: Prices stated are estimates and may be subject to amendments

St. Margaret's

13 Corstorphine High Street, Edinburgh EH12 7SU
Tel: 0131 334 7317 Fax: 0131 334 7317
e.mail: CHRISBRYAN2@activemail.co.uk
A warm welcome awaits you at this small friendly newly
refurbished main door flat. 10 minutes from city centre and 10
minutes from Edinburgh Airport. Excellent bus service. Many
restaurants nearby. Parking. Non smoking house. Price £25 per
person sharing double room. £30 for single.

★★★★

B&B

St Margaret's

13 Corstorphine High Street, Edinburgh, Midlothian
EH12 7SU
Tel/Fax: 0131 334 7317
Email:chrisbryan2@activemail.co.uk

Newly refurbished ground floor accommodation with ensuite facilities.
Well appointed bedroom. Experience the atmosphere of the old 17th
century village of Corstorphine. Situated Equal distance from Edinburgh
Airport and City Centre, (both 3 miles away). Non - smoking.

| 1 Double | All En Suite | B&B per person from £30.00 Single from £25.00 Double | Open Jan-Dec |

📺 ♿ P ☕ ⚲ ✗

Ⓦ Ⓥ ♿

SANDEMAN HOUSE

33 COLINTON ROAD, EDINBURGH EH10 5DR
Tel/Fax: 0131 447 8080   e.mail: joycesandeman@freezone.co.uk
Web: www.freezone.co.uk/sandemanhouse
A charming non-smoking Victorian Home. (circa 1860) Centrally located. Beautifully
restored. All bedrooms with private/en-suite bathrooms, T.V/Radio, tea/coffee making
facilities. Wonderful breakfasts. Unrestricted parking. On major bus routes, theatres,
restaurants and specialist shops minutes walk away. Most credit cards accepted.
Open all year.

★★★★

B&B

Sandeman House

33 Colinton Road, Edinburgh, EH10 5DR
Tel/Fax:0131 447 8080
Email:joycesandeman@freezone.co.uk
Web:www.freezone.co.uk/sandemanhouse

Victorian end terraced family house. Non-smoking. Centrally situated.
Unrestricted parking. Warm welcome and wonderful breakfasts.

1 Single	2 En Suite fac	B&B per person from £35.00 Single from £30.00 Double	Open Jan-Dec
1 Twin			
1 Double			

📺 ♿ 📠 ☕ ⚲ ✗ 🛏 🍴 ♿

💷 Ⓦ Ⓥ

★★★

GUEST HOUSE

Sherwood Guest House

42 Minto Street, Edinburgh, EH9 2BR
Tel:0131 667 1200 Fax:0131 667 2344
Email:enquiries@sherwood-edinburgh.com
Web:www.sherwood-edinburgh.com

A friendly and hospitable welcome is assured from Mrs Greig. The guest
house has been fully refurbished throughout to a high standard. On
main bus route to city centre 1.5 miles distance (2.5 kms). Limited
parking.

2 Twin	5 En Suite fac	B&B per person from £35.00 Single from £25.00 Double	Open Jan-Dec excl Xmas/New Year
2 Double	1 Pub.Bath/Show		
2 Family			

📺 ♿ 📠 P ☕ ⚲ ✗ 🍴

Ⓒ 💷 Ⓥ ♿

VAT is shown at 17.5%: changes in this rate may affect prices.

Key to symbols is on back flap.

Edinburgh

Map Ref: 2C5

★★

**GUEST
HOUSE**

Smiths' Guest House
77 Mayfield Road, Edinburgh, EH9 3AA
Tel:0131 667 2524 Fax:0131 668 4455
Email:mail@smithsgh.com
Web:www.smithsgh.com

Victorian town house, recently refurbished. Near to city centre.

1 Single	All En Suite	B&B per person	Open Jan-Dec
3 Twin	1 Priv.Bath/Show	from £20.00 Single	
2 Double		from £20.00 Double	
1 Family			

STEWARTS BED & BREAKFAST
21 Hillview, Queensferry Road, Edinburgh EH4 2AF
Tel: 0131 539 7033 Fax: 0131 332 3116
e.mail: ann@amayo.fslife.co.uk Web: www.stewartsbandb.co.uk

Attractive Edwardian terraced villa just 10
minutes from Edinburgh city centre. Bus services pass
the door. Friendly welcome in a relaxed
family home with comfortable rooms.

★★★

B&B

Stewarts Bed & Breakfast
21 Hillview, Queensferry Road, Edinburgh, EH4 2AF
Tel:0131 539 7033 Fax:0131 332 3116
Email:ann@amayo.fslife.co.uk
Web:www.stewartsbandb.co.uk

Attractive Edwardian terrace villa just 10 minutes from Edinburgh city
centre. Near airport and bypass. Bus services pass door. Friendly welcome
in a relaxed family home with comfortable rooms.

1 Twin	All En Suite	B&B per person	Open Jan-Dec
1 Double		from £25.00 Single	
1 Family		from £20.00 Double	

Sure and Stedfast
76 MILTON ROAD WEST, DUDDINGSTON, EDINBURGH EH15 1QY
Telephone: 0131-657 1189 e.mail: a_t_taylor@ednet.co.uk
Web: www.ednet.co.uk/~a_t_taylor

1 twin, 2 double rooms. B&B per person from £18.00. Open April-
October. Family run establishment situated 3km from city centre on
main bus route. All bedrooms have wash basins, shaver points, TV,
tea/coffee-making facilities. Parking and pay phone facilities available.

★★★

B&B

Sure + Stedfast B+B
76 Milton Road West, Duddingston, Edinburgh
EH15 1QY
Tel:0131 657 1189
Email:a_t_taylor@ednet.co.uk
Web:www.ednet.co.uk/~a_t_taylor

Comfortable family home in Duddingston area of Edinburgh. Easy access
from city by-pass and main A1 road. All rooms on ground floor.

1 Twin	1 Priv.NOT ensuite	B&B per person	Open Apr-Oct
2 Double		from £25.00 Single	
		from £18.00 Double	

Important: Prices stated are estimates and may be subject to amendments

Edinburgh

Map Ref: 2C5

The Thistle Bed & Breakfast

111 Drum Street, Gilmerton, Edinburgh EH17 8RJ

Tel/Fax: +44 (0)131 258 2511

e.mail: ethel.taylor@tesco.net Web:www.thethistlebandb.co.uk

A warm Scottish welcome awaits you at The Thistle B&B. A small family run home. All home cooking. Special diets catered for. Just off city by-pass. On bus route to city centre. Non smoking. Price including breakfast: Twin Bedded from £28-£35pp/ Three Bedded from £25-£30pp. Single Room £28-£35pn. Evening meal £8pp-£10pp. Credit cards accepted.

★★

B&B

The Thistle B&B

111 Drum Street, Gilmerton, Edinburgh, EH17 8RJ
Tel/Fax:+44(0) 131 258 2511
Email:ethel.taylor@tesco.net
Web:www.thethistlebandb.co.uk

The Thistle B&B is situated close to Edinburgh city centre and market town of Dalkeith and within easy reach of the border towns of Jedburgh and Galashiels home of the Tweed and Tartan Mills. Very convenient for the site of the new Royal Infirmary of Edinburgh. Specialist diets catered for when prior notice is given.

1 Single	1 NOT ensuite
1 Twin	

B&B per person
from £28.00-35.00
Single
from £28.00-35.00
Twin

Open Jan-Dec
BB & Eve.Meal
from £38.00 pp

★★★★

GUEST HOUSE

Turret Guest House

8 Kilmaurs Terrace, Edinburgh, EH16 5DR
Tel:0131 667 6704   Fax:0131 668 1368
Email:contact@turretguesthouse.co.uk
Web:www.turretguesthouse.co.uk

Listed Victorian house in quiet residential area, furnished to a high standard. Quick, frequent bus service to city centre. Commonwealth Pool nearby.

2 Single	4 En Suite fac
2 Twin	1 Priv.NOT ensuite
3 Double	1 Pub.Bath/Show
1 Family	

B&B per person
from £24.00 Single
from £23.00 Double

Open Jan-Dec excl
Xmas

★

GUEST HOUSE

Valentine Guest House

19 Gilmore Place, Edinburgh, EH3 9NE
Tel/Fax:0131 229 5622

Centrally situated family run guest house, situated on second floor level, 50 metres from King's Theatre. Approx. ½ mile (1 km) to Princes Street and West End. Variety of restaurants in the vicinity.

1 Twin	
2 Double	
2 Family	

B&B per person
£14.00-25.00 Single
£14.00-25.00 Double
£12.00-20.00 Room
Only

Open Jan-Dec

Scotland's National Booking and Information Line

Tel: 0845 22 55 121
visitscotland.com

VAT is shown at 17.5%: changes in this rate may affect prices.

Key to symbols is on back flap.

Edinburgh   Map Ref: 2C5

Villa Nina House

39 LEAMINGTON TERRACE, EDINBURGH EH10 4JS
Tel/Fax: 0131 229 2644
E.mail: villanina@amserve.net

Comfortable accommodation in central Edinburgh, within walking
distance of Princes Street. Fully cooked breakfast. Part en-suite.
Member of STB, GHA.
Bed and Breakfast from £17.50 per person.

**GUEST
HOUSE**

Villa Nina

39 Leamington Terrace, Edinburgh, EH10 4JS
Tel/Fax:0131 229 2644
Email:VillaNina@amserve.net

Terraced house. Convenient for the city centre. Near Kings Theatre, the
Castle, conference centre and shops. Showers in bedrooms.

1 Twin	2 Priv.NOT ensuite	B&B per person	Open Feb-Nov
2 Double		from £17.50 Double	
1 Family			

📺 ☕ ⅍ 🍴

🅦 🅥

---

nr Edinburgh   Map Ref: 2C5

★★★

B&B

Anne Marie Ross Bed + Breakfast

5 Linn Mill, South Queensferry, West Lothian
EH30 9ST
Tel:0131 331 2087
Email:b&b@drossco.com
Web:www.drossco.com

Scandinavian style chalet. Garden with magnificent view over Firth of
Forth to the famous bridges and Ochil hills. Short drive to variety of
restaurants. Local walks nearby. Ideal touring base from edge of city and
Hopetoun House 1 mile (2km) away. Plenty of private parking.

1 Twin	1 Priv.NOT ensuite	B&B per person	Open Apr-Sep
1 Double		£20.00-25.00 Single	
		£20.00-25.00 Double	
		from £16.00 Room	
		Only	

📺 🅿 ☕ 🍴 ⅍ 🍴

🐕 🅥

CARLETHAN HOUSE

WADINGBURN LANE, LASSWADE, MIDLOTHIAN EH18 1HG
Tel: 0131 663 7047 Fax: 0131 654 2657
e.mail: carlethan@aol.com Web: www.carlethan-house.co.uk

Margaret and Quin Dunlop offer superb, friendly, helpful hospitality in their
beautiful Georgian home. The lovely one acre garden has a large patio and
water feature. Great local restaurants and pubs. Ideal base for sightseeing, golf
and touring. 6 miles to city centre. Ample private parking. A Gem of
Midlothian. Please see our 'Gems of Midlothian' Display advert on page 84

★★★★

B&B

Carlethan House

Wadingburn Lane, Lasswade, Midlothian, EH18 1HG
Tel:0131 663 7047 Fax:0131 654 2657
Email:carlethan@aol.com
Web:www.carlethan-house.co.uk

Carlethan house is a listed Georgian home, lovingly restored and set in
tranquil rural surroundings only 5 miles from Edinburgh city centre.
Ideally situated for approximately 40 golf courses within 30 minutes
drive and many interesting historic sites including Roslyn chapel.

1 Twin	2 En Suite fac	B&B per person	Open Dec-Oct
1 Double	1 Priv.Bath/Show	from £39.00 Single	
1 Family		from £29.00 Double	

📺 🔳 🔳 🅿 ☕ 🍴 ⅍ 🍴

🅲 🐕 🔳 🅥

Important: Prices stated are estimates and may be subject to amendments

Eskbank, Dalkeith

Map Ref: 2C5

ESKBANK GUEST HOUSE
45 Eskbank Road, Eskbank, Dalkeith, By Edinburgh EH22 3BH
Tel/Fax: 0131 663 3291
e.mail: Guesthouse@eskbank.scot.cc Web: www.eskbank-guest.scot.cc
An award winning Midlothian Gem. De-Stress at this upmarket guesthouse set in
the leafy, peaceful and enchanting Eskbank conservation area.
Play croquet in the beautiful walled garden and then dine at the fabulous
Dalhousie Castle nearby. After a low fat healthy breakfast next morning
your bus ride to the Royal Mile will take 20 minutes.
Please see our 'Gems of Midlothian' display advert on page 84.

★★★

GUEST
HOUSE

Eskbank Guest House

Rathan, 45 Eskbank Road, Eskbank, Dalkeith
EH22 3BH
Tel/Fax:0131 663 3291
Email:GuestHouse@eskbank.scot.cc
Web:www.eskbank-guest.scot.cc

Award winning Victorian house with own grounds set in leafy
conservation area. Croquet lawn and private parking. Excellent
Edinburgh park and ride base. Low fat breakfast.

1 Single	5 En Suite fac	B&B per person	Open Feb-Dec excl
1 Twin	1 Pub.Bath/Show	from £35.00 Single	Xmas
2 Double		from £31.00 Double	
1 Family		from £29.00 Room	
		Only	

Gorebridge, Midlothian

Map Ref: 2C5

IVORY-HOUSE
14 Vogrie Road, Gorebridge, Midlothian, Scotland EH23 4HH
Tel: 01875 820755 Fax: 01875 823345
e.mail: barbara@ivory-house.co.uk Web: www.ivory-house.co.uk

Peaceful Victorian House. Lovely large secluded garden. Private parking.
Wonderful local restaurant. Perfect wedding guest accommodation, close
to Borthwick, Dalhousie and Oxenford castles. 10 miles to Edinburgh
city centre. Excellent public transport. Ideal base for touring and golf.
Please see our 'Gems of Midlothian' display advert on page 84.

★★★★

GUEST
HOUSE

Ivory-House

14 Vogrie Road, Gorebridge, Midlothian, EH23 4HH
Tel:01875 820755 Fax:01875 823345
Email:barbara@ivory-house.co.uk
Web:www.ivory-house.co.uk

Peaceful Victorian house, warm welcome. Ideal base. 10 miles to
Edinburgh and easy access to Border country. Private parking. En suite
and private facilities now available. Coach-house and Old Surgery
available on bed and breakfast or as self catering unit. Excellent access to
Borthwick, Dalhousie and Oxenford Castles.

2 Twin	4 En Suite fac	B&B per person	Open Jan-Dec
3 Double	1 Pub.Bath/Show	from £39.00 Single	
1 Family		from £29.00 Double	

Scotland's National Booking and Information Line

Tel: 0845 22 55 121
visitscotland.com

VAT is shown at 17.5%: changes in this rate may affect prices. | Key to symbols is on back flap.

Gems of Midlothian
on the doorstep of Edinburgh

Relax in the comfort of charming Georgian and Victorian stone built houses set in large, tranquil gardens. Your hosts will extend the warmest of welcomes and be happy to advise you on how to make the most of the beautiful surrounding countryside.

Unwind with gentle walks or trekking through the Pentland Hills on sturdy Icelandic horses. Try your hand at blowing glass at Edinburgh Crystal; Marvel at the magic and mystery of unique Rosslyn Chapel. Visit Arniston House, designed by William Adam, with it's beautiful grounds. Vogrie Country Park has woodland walks and an adventure playground. Enjoy a game of golf at stunning Kings Acre Golf Course.

Children of all ages love the Butterfly World and Bird of Prey Centre at Dobbies Garden World. The Scottish Mining Museum at the old Lady Victoria coal mine must be seen and enjoyed.

All this and you have barely started!

Dining out is a pleasure. Choose between friendly restaurants and traditional country pubs serving excellent, good value meals, or the splendour of historic castles where dining is, truly, a gastronomic treat.

Carlethan House

Relax to the sound of water and birdsong

Carlethan House is a lovingly restored Georgian home with a Victorian extension set in 1 acre of landscaped gardens in a tranquil, rural setting. Only one mile from the city bypass and six miles from the centre of Edinburgh.
(1D, 1T/D, 1T, ES)

Margaret & Quin Dunlop
Wadingburn Lane,
Lasswade,
Midlothian
EH18 1HG

Tel: +44 (0)131 663 7047
Fax: +44 (0)131 654 2657
e.mail: carlethan@aol.com
web: www.carlethan-house.co.uk

Eskbank Guest House

Quality De-Stress

Excellent Edinburgh Park & Ride base (7m). You can wholly de-stress at this award winning guest house. This Gem is set within a leafy conservation area. Perhaps croquet in the beautiful walled garden – then a fabulous dinner at nearby Dalhousie Castle.
(1Q, 1D, 1T, ES)

Ewan MacRae
45 Eskbank Road, Eskbank
Dalkeith EH22 3BH

Tel/Fax: +44 (0)131 663 3291
e.mail: GuestHouse@eskbank.scot.cc
web: www.eskbank-guest.scot.cc

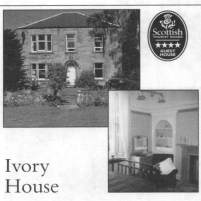

Ivory House

Seclusion without Isolation

Peaceful Victorian house with beautiful gardens and private parking. Ideal base. Ten miles from city centre. Nearby Dalhousie, Borthwick and Oxenfoord Castles.
(3D, 1T/D, 1T, ES)

The Coach House
Adjacent to main house. Complete with attractive walled garden. Well appointed self catering or B&B accommodation suitable for assisted wheelchair access.
(2-4 people)

Barbara Maton
14 Vogrie Road
Gorebridge
EH23 4HH
Tel: +44 (0)1875 820755
Fax: +44 (0)1875 823345
e.mail: barbara@ivory-house.co.uk
web: www.ivory-house.co.uk

**WINNER SCOTTISH THISTLE AWARD
FOR EXCELLENCE 2002
- SMALL BUSINESS MARKETING**
WWW.GEMS.SCOT.INFO

Important: Prices stated are estimates and may be subject to amendments

Gullane, East Lothian | Map Ref: 2D4

JADINI GARDEN
Goose Green, Gullane, East Lothian EH31 2BA
Tel: 01620 843343 Fax: 01620 843453
e.mail: marychase@jadini.com Web: www.jadini.com

Located in the quiet coastal village of Gullane 30 minutes drive from Edinburgh. Jadini Garden is 2 minutes walk from the 3 famous golf courses and beautiful sandy beaches. Quiet secluded walled garden for the use of guests. Private parking. French, German and Spanish spoken.

★★★
B&B

Jadini Garden
Goose Green, Gullane, East Lothian, EH31 2BA
Tel:01620 843343 Fax:01620 843453
Email:marychase@jadini.com
Web:www.jadini.com

Family home located in a secluded walled garden, on the road to the beach. Only a few minutes walk from Gullane's three famous public golf courses and a half hour drive from Edinburgh city centre. Comfortable rooms, garden facilities for the use of guests and private parking. French, Spanish and German spoken.

2 Twin	2 En Suite fac	B&B per person	Open Jan-Dec
1 Double	1 Pub.Bath/Show	£25.00-35.00 Single	
		£20.00-30.00 Double	

Faussetthill House
20 Main Street, Gullane EH31 2DR
Tel: 01620 842396 Fax: 01620 842396
e.mail: faussetthill@talk21.com

A delightful Edwardian house in well tended gardens. Immaculately maintained, the house is both comfortable and inviting. The well proportioned bedrooms are tastefully decorated and a first floor lounge with TV and well stocked bookshelves. Full Scottish breakfast is served in the attractive dining room.

★★★★
B&B

Mr & Mrs G Nisbet
Faussetthill House, 20 Main Street, Gullane
East Lothian, EH31 2DR
Tel/Fax:01620 842396
Email:faussetthill@talk21.com

Detached Edwardian house lovingly restored and redecorated throughout. Retaining many of its period features, well tended garden and private parking. Edinburgh 30 minutes by car. Sandy beaches and several golf courses nearby. Non-smoking.

2 Twin	All En Suite	B&B per person	Open Apr-Nov
1 Double		from £40.00 Single	
		from £28.00 Double	

Haddington, East Lothian | Map Ref: 2D4

★★★★
B&B

Carfrae Farmhouse
Garvald, Haddington, East Lothian, EH41 4LP
Tel:01620 830242 Fax:01620 830320
Email:DgCarfrae@aol.com
Web:www.carfraefarmhouse.com

19c listed farmhouse on a working farm with open aspect overlooking the walled garden. Furnished to a high standard. Edinburgh, the Borders and many golf courses within easy reach. Extremely peaceful location. All rooms have private or en suite facilities.

1 Twin	2 En Suite fac	B&B per person	Open Apr-Oct
2 Double	1 Pub.Bath/Show	£20.00-45.00 Single	
		£25.00-27.00 Double	

VAT is shown at 17.5%: changes in this rate may affect prices. | Key to symbols is on back flap.

Haddington, East Lothian — Map Ref: 2D4

★★★★

B&B

Eaglescairnie Mains
by Gifford, Haddington, East Lothian, EH41 4HN
Tel/Fax:01620 810491
Email:williams.eagles@btinternet.com

Beautiful house in quiet rural situation, on working mixed farm. Winner of National Conservation Awards. Farm walks with wonderful views. 4 miles (6kms) from Haddington, 30 mins drive from Edinburgh.

2 Single	3 En Suite fac	B&B per person
1 Twin	1 Pub.Bath/Show	from £25.00 Single
1 Double		from £25.00 Double

Open Jan-Dec excl Xmas

★★

B&B

Fieldfare B&B
Upper Bolton Farm, Haddington, East Lothian
EH41 4HW
Tel/Fax:01620 810346

Victorian farm cottage in peaceful rural situation convenient for many sites of historic interest, only half an hour's drive from Edinburgh and 20 minutes drive to the coast. Pets welcome.

2 Twin	Some En Suite	B&B per person
2 Double		from £20.00 Single
1 Family		from £18.00 Double

Open Jan-Dec excl Xmas/New Year

★★★

B&B

Schiehallion
19 Church Street, Haddington, East Lothian
EH41 3EX
Tel:01620 825663   Fax:01620 829663
Email:Catherine@schiehallion.fsbusiness.co.uk

Large Victorian house in the country town of East Lothian. Sandy beaches, golf courses nearby. Small towns and villages with excellent restaurants. Large lounge with a view of historic St. Mary's Cathedral. Library with TV. All rooms have wash basins, tea/coffee and TV facilities. Large walled garden available. Two old english sheepdogs in residence. Edinburgh 17 miles.

1 Twin	1 En Suite fac	B&B per person
1 Double		from £25.00 Single
		from £20.00 Double
		from £18.00 Room
		Only

Open Jan-Dec

Lasswade, Midlothian — Map Ref: 2C5

★★

B&B

Droman House
Lasswade, Midlothian, EH18 1HA
Tel/Fax:0131 663 9239

Former Georgian manse in secluded setting. Informal and warm welcome assured. Ample private parking. Only 6 miles from Edinburgh city centre.

1 Single	2 Priv.NOT ensuite	B&B per person
2 Twin		from £20.00 Single
1 Family		from £20.00 Double

Open Apr-Oct

Scotland's National Booking and Information Line

Tel: 0845 22 55 121
visitscotland.com

Important: Prices stated are estimates and may be subject to amendments

Linlithgow, West Lothian

Map Ref: 2B4

ARAN GUEST HOUSE

Woodcockdale, Lanark Road, Linlithgow, West Lothian EH49 6QE
Tel: 01506 842088 Fax: 01506 843079
e.mail: sheona@arnhouse.co.uk Web: www.aranhouse.co.uk
Don't delay call today. Enjoy the delights of staying on a working farm.
Be among the many guests who return regularly to Aran House where
it is the perfect way to enjoy the attractions of Central Scotland. Easy
access to M8, M9, M90 and Edinburgh airport. Parking.
Phone now – 01506 842088.

★

B&B

Aran House

Woodcockdale Farm, Lanark Road, Linlithgow
West Lothian, EH49 6QE
Tel:01506 842088 Fax:01506 843079
Email:sheona@arnhouse.co.uk
Web:www.aranhouse.co.uk

Look no further for a modern farmhouse on a working farm in rural
area yet with easy access to Edinburgh, Glasgow and the Lothians.
Edinburgh and Glasgow airports within easy reach. Full fire certificate
held. Ground floor rooms. Phone now.

1 Single	3 En Suite fac	B&B per person	Open Jan-Dec
1 Twin	1 Pub.Bath/Show	£20.00 basic	
1 Double		£25.00 ensuite	
1 Family		from £20.00 Room	
		Only	

★★★

B&B

Belsyde House/Farm

Lanark Road, Linlithgow, West Lothian, EH49 6QE
Tel/Fax:01506 842098
Email:belsyde.guesthouse@virgin.net
Web:www.belsydehouse.co.uk

Late 18c house with interesting garden,set on a 100 acre sheep farm
beside Union Canal. Views over Forth Estuary and Ochil Hills. Easy access
to M8, M9, M90 and Edinburgh Airport.

2 Single	1 En Suite fac	B&B per person	Open Jan-Dec excl
1 Double	1 Bath/Show	from £20.00 Single	Xmas/New Year
1 Family	1 Show/toilet	from £20.00 Double	

★★★★

B&B

Bomains Farm

by Bo'ness, Linlithgow, West Lothian, EH49 7RQ
Tel:01506 822188 Fax:01506 824433

A warm welcome to this family home. Rural but central location.
Excellent views over the River Forth. Ideally located for motorways,
Glasgow and Edinburgh. Gateway to the Highlands.

1 Twin	All En Suite	B&B per person	Open Jan-Dec
2 Double		from £30.00 Single	BB & Eve.Meal
		from £25.00 Double	from £37.00
		£27.00-44.00 Room	
		Only	

★★★

B&B

Strawberry Bank House B&B

13 Avon Place, Strawberry Bank, Linlithgow
West Lothian, EH49 6BL
Tel/Fax:01506 848372
Email:gillian@strawberrybank-scotland.co.uk
Web:www.strawberrybank-scotland.co.uk

A fully modernised and comfortable B&B with all rooms ensuite.
Decorated and furnished to a high standard. A non-smoking
establishment. Historic Linlithgow Palace is in the view of the house and
the canal behind. Edinburgh is within easy driving distance.

2 Twin	All En Suite	B&B per person	Open Jan-Dec excl
1 Double		from £25.00 Single	Xmas/New Year
		from £25.00 Double	

VAT is shown at 17.5%: changes in this rate may affect prices.

Key to symbols is on back flap.

Linlithgow, West Lothian   Map Ref: 2B4

Thornton

Edinburgh Road, Linlithgow, West Lothian EH49 6AA
Tel: 01506 844693 Fax: 01506 844876
e.mail: inglisthornton@aol.com Web: www.thornton-scotland.co.uk

Relaxed, friendly family home with ground floor accommodation. Located only
5 minutes walk along canal towpath from town centre and Linlithgow Palace
(birthplace of Mary Queen of Scots). Excellent choice of pubs and restaurants.
Visit historic houses and the unique Falkirk boatlifting wheel.
Frequent trains to Edinburgh, Glasgow, Stirling.

★★★★

B&B

Thornton

Edinburgh Road, Linlithgow, West Lothian, EH49 6AA
Tel:01506 844693 Fax:01506 844876
Email:inglisthornton@aol.com
Web:www.thornton-scotland.co.uk

Comfortable, non-smoking family run Victorian house with original
features retained. Large garden, private parking. 1km from railway
station and town centre and 20 mins by train to Edinburgh. Airport and
Rosyth Ferry Terminal easily accessible. Personal attention assured - a
real home from home!

1 Twin	All En Suite	B&B per person	Open Feb-Nov
1 Double		from £30.00 Single	
		from £25.00 Double	

Musselburgh, East Lothian   Map Ref: 2C5

Mrs Elizabeth Aitken   ★★ B&B

18 WOODSIDE GARDENS, MUSSELBURGH, EAST LOTHIAN EH21 7LJ
Telephone: 0131 665 3170/3344

Well-appointed bungalow within 6 miles of Edinburgh in quiet
suburb with private parking. Excellent bus/train service to city. Two
minutes from oldest golf course in world and race course. Easy
access to beaches and beautiful countryside.

All rooms hot and cold water, colour TV and tea/coffee. Private parking.

★★

B&B

Mrs Elizabeth Aitken

18 Woodside Gardens, Musselburgh, East Lothian
EH21 7LJ
Tel:0131 665 3170/3344

Detached bungalow in quiet residential area, close to Musselburgh
Racecourse and golf course. Private parking. 7 - 8 miles from Princes
Street, Edinburgh. Close to sandy beaches and river walks.

1 Twin	B&B per person	Open Jan-Dec
1 Double	from £18.00 Single	
1 Family	from £17.00 Double	

★★★

GUEST
HOUSE

Arden House

26 Linkfield Road, Musselburgh, EH21 7LL
Tel/Fax:0131 665 0663
Email:accommodation@ardenhouse-guesthouse.co.uk
Web:www.ardenhouse-guesthouse.co.uk

A warm and friendly welcome awaits you at this Victorian stone turretted
house. Situated 15 mins by car or bus from the hustle and bustle of
Edinburgh city centre. Views overlooking the race course and golf course.

3 Twin	Some En Suite	B&B per person	Open Jan-Dec
2 Double	1 Priv.NOT ensuite	£20.00-40.00 Single	
2 Family	1 Pub.Bath/Show	£20.00-30.00 Double	

Important: Prices stated are estimates and may be subject to amendments

Penicuik, Midlothian — Map Ref: 2C5

Braidwood Farm
Penicuik, Midlothian EH26 9LP
Tel: 01968 679959 Fax: 01968 679805
e.mail: braidwoodfarm@aol.com
Braidwood is an attractive modern farmhouse set in 240 acres.
On the edge of the Pentland Hills only 10 miles from
Edinburgh. Ideal base for visitors to both Edinburgh and
the Borders. No children please.

★★★
B&B

Braidwood Farm
Penicuik, Midlothian, EH26 9LP
Tel:01968 679959 Fax:01968 679805
Email:braidwoodfarm@aol.com

Braidwood is an attractive modern farmhouse set in 240 acres on the edge of the Pentland hills only 10 miles from Edinburgh. Ideal base for visitors to both Edinburgh and the Borders. No children please.

1 Twin   All En Suite
3 Double

B&B per person
£25.00-35.00 Single
£25.00-30.00 Double
from £22.00 Room
Only

Open Apr-Nov

---

by Penicuik, Midlothian — Map Ref: 2C5

Walltower Bed & Breakfast
Howgate, Midlothian EH26 8PY Tel: 01968 674686
e.mail: thewalltower@yahoo.com
Web: www.geocities.com/thewalltower
Stay with us in our charming Georgian country house in Midlothian.
Only twenty minutes drive from Edinburgh, Scotland's beautiful capital
city. Set in two acres of mature garden. Real log fires. Cosy atmosphere.
Good restaurant two minutes walk away. Bed and breakfast from £20.

★★
B&B

Walltower Bed & Breakfast
Howgate, Midlothian, EH26 8PY
Tel:01968 674686
Email:thewalltower@yahoo.com
Web:www.geocities.com/thewalltower

Traditional farmhouse with conservatory on working farm, set in mature garden. 10 miles (16 kms) from Edinburgh, the airport and Scottish Borders. Non-smoking bedrooms.

1 Twin   All En Suite
1 Family

B&B per person
from £23.00 Single
from £20.00 Double

Open Jan-Dec excl
Xmas/New Year

Port Seton, East Lothian — Map Ref: 2D5

★★★
B&B

Anchorage
1 Elcho Place, Port Seton
Prestonpans, East Lothian, EH32 0DL
Tel/Fax:01875 813947

Traditional stonebuilt family home on harbour front with a lot of fishing activity. 20 minutes drive from Edinburgh (10 mins by train). Convenient location for access to various golf courses in East Lothian. Non-smoking house.

2 Family   1 En Suite fac
1 Pub.Bath/Show

B&B per person
£19.00-27.00 Double

Open Jan-Dec

VAT is shown at 17.5%: changes in this rate may affect prices. | **Key to symbols is on back flap.**

| South Queensferry, West Lothian | | | | Map Ref: 2B4 |

DI & HK Maclean
98 Provost Milne Grove, South Queensferry
West Lothian, EH30 9PL
Tel/Fax:0131 331 1893

★★★

B&B

In residential estate, semi-detached modern house close to local shops and amenities. Two minutes drive to Forth Road Bridge and access to Scotlands motorway system. Suitable base for touring Kingdom of Fife, historic Dunfermline and Edinburgh. Interesting sea-front with many restaurants and a view of the famous bridges. Street parking.

1 Twin   1 Priv.NOT ensuite
1 Double

B&B per person
from £18.00 Single
from £22.00 Double

Open Jan-Dec

PRIORY LODGE
8 The Loan, South Queensferry EH30 9NS
Tel/Fax: 0131 331 4345
e.mail: calmyn@aol.com
Web: www.queensferry.com

A warm welcome is extended for guests old and new to this delightful purpose built guest house. Conveniently situated just off the cobbled high street in the picturesque village of South Queensferry which sits between the two famous bridges on the south side of the River Forth.

The attractive bedrooms are maintained to a high standard and are comfortably furnished in antique pine. There is also a cosy guest room where free internet access is available. Visitors are welcome to use the modern kitchen facilities. A hearty Scottish breakfast is served at individual tables. The guest house is totally non-smoking.

Priory Lodge
8 The Loan, South Queensferry, West Lothian
EH30 9NS Tel:0131 331 4345   Fax:0131 331 4345
Email:calmyn@aol.com
Web:www.queensferry.com

★★★★

GUEST HOUSE

Traditional Scottish hospitality in this friendly family run guest house located in the picturesque village of South Queensferry. Edinburgh city centre 7 miles: Airport / Royal Highland Exhibition grounds 3 miles. Priory Lodge is within walking distance of the village shops, variety of eating establishments, Forth Bridges and Dalmeny train station. Internet access available. Non-smoking establishment.

1 Twin   All En Suite
1 Double
3 Family

B&B per person
from £45.00 Single
from £27.00 Double

Open Jan-Dec

| Winchburgh, West Lothian | | | | Map Ref: 2B5 |

Turnlea B&B
123 Main Street, Winchburgh, Broxburn
West Lothian, EH52 6QP
Tel:01506 890124   Fax:01506 891573
Email:royturnlea@hotmail.com

★★★

B&B

Modern family villa on outskirts of a village 6 miles from Edinburgh Airport and the Royal Burgh of Linlithgow. 12 miles from the city centre. Easy access to all routes. Non-smoking house.

2 Twin   All En Suite
1 Double

B&B per person
from £25.00 Single
from £22.00 Double

Open Jan-Dec excl
Xmas/New Year

Important: Prices stated are estimates and may be subject to amendments

Welcome to Scotland

Greater Glasgow and Clyde Valley

For sheer excitement, Glasgow is one of the top UK destinations. This forward-thinking and stylish city offers a choice of shopping, entertainment and culture that should not be missed. The legendary Glasgow friendliness is a bonus, while first-time visitors will be struck by the city's panache.

Looking across the River Clyde to the city of Glasgow

Glasgow's architecture ranges from the magnificent Gothic style of Glasgow Cathedral to the imposing Italian Renaissance of the Victorian City Chambers. As Britain's finest Victorian city, Glasgow offers 19th-century grandeur in its streets, squares and gardens while the fashionable and elegant terraces of the West End have been restored. In the 18th-century Merchant City, you will find cafés and boutiques and the chic Italian Centre with its exclusive designer shops. You can explore the St Enoch's Shopping Centre which is the largest glass-covered building in Europe as well as the Buchanan Galleries and stylish Princes Square. If you have any money left, head for a bargain in the famous Barras Market.

Glasgow has an unrivalled selection of more than 20 art galleries and museums to discover from the innovative Gallery of Modern Art to the internationally acclaimed Burrell Collection. Throughout the city, the unmistakable influence of two of the city's greatest sons – the architects Charles Rennie Mackintosh and Alexander 'Greek' Thomson can been seen. Visit Mackintosh's outstanding Glasgow School of Art and Thomson's recently restored Holmwood House.

Greater Glasgow and Clyde Valley

Gourock on the Firth of Clyde

Greater Glasgow and Clyde Valley

The Falls of Clyde, near Lanark

Another exciting development is the Glasgow Science Centre – an IMAX theatre, Science Mall and the Glasgow Tower with its 100m high viewing cabin.

A year-round programme of events including Celtic Connections, the Glasgow Folk Festival and the International Jazz Festival complements the arts scene in the city which is also home to Scottish Opera, Scottish Ballet and the Royal Scottish National Orchestra. Glasgow's cafés, bars and nightclubs offer plenty of opportunities to enjoy the friendliness and colourful character of the locals.

From Glasgow, there is easy access to the rolling hills of Renfrewshire, the Inverclyde coastline and the fertile Clyde valley. At Paisley, you can visit the restored 12th-century abbey and learn about the famous Paisley textile pattern at the Paisley Museum and art galleries with their world-famous collection of Paisley shawls. Further upriver the River Clyde changes its character tumbling over waterfalls into a rocky gorge at New Lanark Industrial Heritage Village, which is now a World Heritage site.

Events
Greater Glasgow and Clyde Valley

15 JANUARY – 2 FEBRUARY
Celtic Connections, Glasgow
Celebration of Celtic music.
Tel: 0141 353 8000
www.grch.com

24-30 MAY
Wake Up To Birds Week
Royal Society for the
Protection of Birds. Wide
range of events and activities
at the 60 RSPB reserves across
Scotland. Free entry to all
reserves on one day during
this week.
Tel: 0131 311 6500
www.rspb.org.uk/scotland

7 JUNE
Shotts Highland Games
Tel: 01501 821542
www.shottshighlandgames
.co.uk

12 JUNE
Lanimer Celebrations, Lanark
100 year old traditional
procession and events.
Tel: 01555 663251

29 JUNE – 8 JULY
**Glasgow International Jazz
Festival**
Tel: 0141 552 3552
www.jazzfest.co.uk

9 AUGUST*
**World Pipe Band
Championships**
Tel: 0141 221 5414
www.rspba.co.uk

7 SEPTEMBER
**Victorian Fair, New Lanark
World Heritage Village**
Annual Victorian themed
street fair.
Tel: 01555 661345
www.newlanark.org

* denotes provisional date. Events can be subject to change, please check before travelling.

For up to date events, log on to:
visitscotland.com

Area Tourist Boards

Greater Glasgow and Clyde Valley

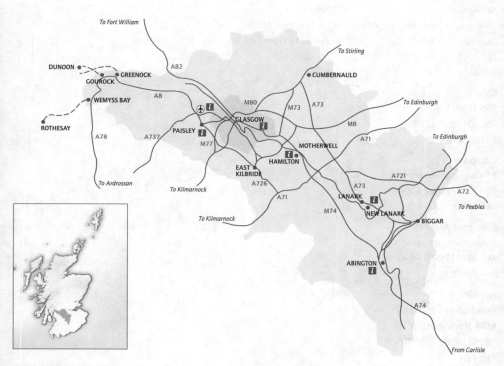

**Greater Glasgow and
Clyde Valley Tourist Board**
11 George Square
Glasgow
G2 1DY

Tel: 0141 204 4400 (information)
Tel: 0141 221 0049
(accommodation)
Fax: 0141 221 3524
E-mail: enquiries@seeglasgow.com
www.seeglasgow.com

Tourist Information Centres
Greater Glasgow and Clyde Valley

**Greater Glasgow
and Clyde Valley
Tourist Board**

Abington
Welcome Break Service Area
Junction 13, M74
Tel: (01864) 502436
Jan-Dec

Biggar
155 High Street
Tel: (01899) 221066
Easter-Sep

Glasgow
11 George Square
Tel: (0141) 204 4400
Jan-Dec

Glasgow Airport
Tourist Information Desk
Tel: (0141) 848 4440
Jan-Dec

Hamilton
Road Chef Services
M74 Northbound
Tel: (01698) 285590
Jan-Dec

Lanark
Horsemarket
Ladyacre Road
Tel: (01555) 661661
Jan-Dec

Paisley
9a Gilmour Street
Tel: (0141) 889 0711
Jan-Dec

Scotland's National Booking and Information Line
0845 22 55 121

by Airdrie, Lanarkshire
Map Ref: 2A5

★★★★

B&B

Easter Glentore Farm B&B
Slamannan Road, Greengairs, by Airdrie
North Lanarkshire, ML6 7TJ Tel/Fax:01236 830243
Email:info@easterglentore.co.uk
Web:www.easterglentore.co.uk

A warm friendly, homely atmosphere can be experienced with Scottish hosts at this 240 acre farm set in open countryside with panoramic views. Relax and enjoy comfortable rooms, home made scones, cakes, preserves and good Scottish hospitality, we have time to spend with our guests. Our ground floor Non-Smoking family farmhouse since 1931 dates back to 1705. Easy motorway connections to Glasgow, Stirling, Falkirk and Edinburgh.

1 Twin	2 En Suite fac	B&B per person	Open Jan-Dec excl
2 Double	1 Pub.Bath/Show	from £30.00 Single	Xmas/New Year
		from £22.00 Double	

Biggar, Lanarkshire
Map Ref: 2B6

LINDSAYLANDS HOUSE
BIGGAR, LANARKSHIRE ML12 6NR
TELEPHONE: 01899 220033/221221 FAX: 01899 221009
E.MAIL: ELSPETH@LINDSAYLANDS.CO.UK WEB: WWW.LINDSAYLANDS.CO.UK
THIS LOVELY LISTED COUNTRY HOUSE IS SET IN ITS OWN GROUNDS SURROUNDED BY 94 ACRES OF ITS OWN FARMLAND. SITUATED OFF MAIN ROAD 1 MILE WEST OF BIGGAR. 3 LARGE BEDROOMS WITH PRIVATE FACILITIES, GUEST LOUNGE AND DINING ROOM. IDEAL BASE FOR TOURING GLASGOW, EDINBURGH, BORDERS OR JUST RELAXING.
PRICES FROM £27 PER PERSON, PER NIGHT.

★★★★

B&B

Lindsaylands House
Biggar, Lanarkshire, ML12 6NR
Tel:01899 220033/221221 Fax:01899 221009
Email:elspeth@lindsaylands.co.uk
Web:www.lindsaylands.co.uk

Attractive country house William Leiper architecture. Set in 6 acres of garden, amidst lovely countryside with views to Border Hills. Hard tennis court and croquet lawn. Ideal base for touring Edinburgh, Glasgow and Scottish borders.

1 Twin	2 En Suite fac	B&B per person	Open Mar-Nov
2 Double	1 Pub.Bath/Show	from £30.00 Single	BB & Eve.Meal
		from £27.00 Double	from £42.00

---

by Biggar, Lanarkshire
Map Ref: 2B6

★★★

B&B

Walston Mansion Farmhouse
Walston, Carnwath, Lanarkshire, ML11 8NF
Tel/Fax:01899 810338
Email:kirkbywalstonmansion@talk21.com

19c stone built farmhouse on a working farm situated on the edge of a small village in the shadow of the Pentland Hills. 5 miles from Biggar, 24 miles from Edinburgh, 30 miles from Glasgow and 16 miles from Peebles, an ideal holiday centre. Home cooking using home produced meat and organic vegetables. Evening meal provided by prior arrangement.

1 Twin	1 En Suite fac	B&B per person	Open Jan-Dec
1 Double	1 Priv.NOT ensuite	from £18.00 Single	BB & Eve.Meal
1 Family		from £17.00 Double	from £26.00

Scotland's National Booking and Information Line

Tel: 0845 22 55 121
visitscotland.com

VAT is shown at 17.5%: changes in this rate may affect prices. | Key to symbols is on back flap.

Crawford, Lanarkshire   Map Ref: 2B7

HOLMLANDS COUNTRY HOUSE
22 CARLISLE RD, CRAWFORD, BY ABINGTON, LANARKSHIRE ML12 6TW
Tel: 01864 502753 Fax: 01864 502313
e.mail: dan.davidson@holmlandscotland.co.uk
Web: www.holmlandscotland.co.uk

If you enjoy good food, peaceful comfortable surroundings with an
outstanding view, Holmlands is the place for you. We are situated within
easy reach of Edinburgh and Glasgow and in the ideal spot for breaking
the cross border journey and for touring the Borders and central areas.

★★★

B&B

Holmlands Country House
22 Carlisle Road, Crawford, by Abington
Lanarkshire, ML12 6TW Tel:01864 502753
Email:dan.davidson@holmlandscotland.co.uk
Web:www.holmlandscotland.co.uk

If you enjoy good food, peaceful comfortable surroundings with a lovely
view Holmlands is the place for you. We are situated within easy reach of
Edinburgh and Glasgow and in the ideal spot for breaking the cross
border journey and touring the borders and central areas. Private
parking.

1 Twin	2 En Suite fac	B&B per person	Open Jan-Dec
1 Double	1 Pub.Bath/Show	from £25.00 Single	BB & Eve.Meal
1 Family		from £22.00 Double	from £32.00
		from £17.00 Room	
		Only	

Eaglesham, by Glasgow, Renfrewshire   Map Ref: 2A5

NEW BORLAND
"New Borland", Glasgow Road, Eaglesham, Glasgow G76 0DN
Tel/Fax: 01355 302051 e.mail: newborland@dial.pipex.com
Quietly situated in landscaped gardens outside the conservation village of
Eaglesham and within easy commuting distance of East Kilbride, Glasgow,
Trossachs, Burns Country. New Borland is a cleverly converted barn extended
to create a comfortable family home. Upgraded bedrooms, relaxing cosy
lounge and dining room with views over open farmland.

★★★

B&B

New Borland
Glasgow Road, Eaglesham, Glasgow, G76 0DN
Tel/Fax:01355 302051
Email:newborland@dial.pipex.com

Quietly situated in landscaped gardens outside the village of Eaglesham
and within easy commuting distance of East Kilbride, Paisley and
Glasgow Airport. New Borland is a cleverly converted barn, extended to
create a comfortable family home with bedrooms upgraded to a smart
contemporary style. Relaxing public rooms include a cosy lounge with
wood burning stove, games room and comfortable dining room with
charming views.

2 Twin	Ensuite fac	B&B per person	Open Jan-Dec
2 Single	Shared fac	from £22.50 Single	
		from £24.00 Double	
		from £20.00 Room	
		Only	

Glasgow   Map Ref: 1H5

★★

GUEST
HOUSE

Alison Guest House
26 Circus Drive, Glasgow, G31 2JH
Tel:0141 556 1431

Victorian semi-villa in quiet residential area of East End yet only 15
minutes walk from city centre, 10 minutes walk from Cathedral, Royal
Infirmary, Strathclyde University Campus. One ground floor room.
Limited access to kitchen available for takeaway's for evening dining.
Ideally situated for Celtic Park.

1 Single	1 En Suite fac	B&B per person	Open Jan-Dec
1 Twin	2 Priv.NOT ensuite	from £20.00 Single	
1 Double		from £17.00 Double	
1 Family		from £17.00 Room	
		Only	

Important: Prices stated are estimates and may be subject to amendments

Glasgow   Map Ref: 1H5

ADELAIDES
209 Bath Street, Glasgow G2 4HZ
Tel: 0141 248 4970 Fax: 0141 226 4247
e.mail: info@adelaides.freeserve.co.uk Web: www.adelaides.co.uk

Part of stunning Baptist Church restoration. City centre guest house, centrally heated modern rooms, most ensuite, non-smoking, families welcome. Colour TV, complimentary tea and coffee in all rooms. Most of Glasgow's main attractions e.g. shops, theatres, museums of this revitalised city are within 10 minutes walk.

★★

GUEST HOUSE

Adelaides
209 Bath Street, Glasgow, G2 4HZ
Tel:0141 248 4970 Fax:0141 226 4247
Email:info@adelaides.freeserve.co.uk
Web:www.adelaides.co.uk

Adelaide's is an unusual conversion of an 1877 church. The Guest House formed from some of the ancilliary accommodation comprises 8 individual rooms. Breakfast available. Centrally located near the Kings Theatre, 10 min walk from the main shopping and entertainment areas, on bus routes to most of Glasgow's tourist attractions and has a wide variety of restaurants in the vicinity. Parking nearby.

2 Single	6 En Suite fac	B&B per person	Open Jan-Dec excl
2 Twin	2 Pub.Bath/Show	from £25.00 Single	Xmas/New Year
2 Double		from £17.50 Double	
2 Family		from £20.00 Room	
		Only	

★★★

GUEST HOUSE

Angus Hotel
970 Sauchiehall Street, Glasgow, G3 7TH
Tel:0141 357 5155 Fax:0141 339 9469
Email:info@angushotelglasgow.co.uk
Web:www.angushotelglasgow.co.uk

Ideally located ¹/₂ mile west of city centre by Kelvingrove Park, the Angus is within walking distance of the Scottish Exhibition and Conference Centre, Glasgow University, Kelvingrove Art Galleries/Museum and the Kelvin Hall International Sports Arena. Recently refurbished and privately owned the Angus offers warm Scottish hospitality and above all, value for money. Guests are welcome to use the bar and restaurant facilities at our sister hotel the Argyll, located directly across the road.

2 Single	All En Suite	B&B per person	Open Jan-Dec
2 Twin		from £44.00 Single	
7 Double		from £58.00 Double	
7 Family			

★★★

B&B

Avenue End B&B
21 West Avenue, Stepps, Glasgow, G33 6ES
Tel:0141 779 1990 Fax:0141 779 1990/1951
Email:AvenueEnd@aol.com

Self built family home in quiet tree lined lane with easy access to motorway network and city centre. Near main route to Stirling, Loch Lomond and the Trossachs. Easy commuting by public or own transport. M8 exit 12.

1 Single	2 En Suite fac	B&B per person	Open Jan-Dec excl
1 Double	1 Pub.Bath/Show	from £25.00 Single	Xmas/New Year
1 Family		from £20.00 Double	

★★★

HOTEL

Bothwell Bridge Hotel
89 Main Street, Bothwell, Glasgow, G71 8EU
Tel:01698 852246 Fax:01698 854686
Email:bothwell_bridge@hotmail.com
Web:www.bothwellbridge-hotel.com

Family run hotel, 9 miles (14kms) from Glasgow city centre and convenient for motorway. Business meeting rooms. Ample parking.

1 Single	All En Suite	Room rate	Open Jan-Dec
28 Twin		from £60.00 Single	
52 Double		from £70.00 Double	
10 Family			

VAT is shown at 17.5%: changes in this rate may affect prices. | *Key to symbols is on back flap.*

THE BELGRAVE GUEST HOUSE
2 BELGRAVE TERRACE, HILLHEAD, GLASGOW G12 8JD
Tel: 0141 337 1850 Fax: 0141 337 1741
e.mail: belgraveguesthse@hotmail.com
Web: www.belgraveguesthouse.co.uk

Situated in the heart of the West End, about 5 minutes' walk from galleries, it is fitted and furnished to a very high standard. Ensuite available. Television, tea/coffee facilities in every room. Private car park also available. Two minutes from underground station and minutes from the city centre.

★★ GUEST HOUSE

Belgrave Guest House
2 Belgrave Terrace, Hillhead, Glasgow, G12 8JD
Tel:0141 337 1850   Fax:0141 337 1741
Email:belgraveguesthse@hotmail.com
Web:www.belgraveguesthouse.co.uk

4 Single	3 En Suite fac	B&B per person	Open Jan-Dec
3 Twin	3 Priv.NOT ensuite	from £18.00 Single	
1 Double		from £20.00 Double	
3 Family			

Refurbished guest house, in the West End. Convenient for Botanic Gardens, other local attractions and amenities. 5 minute walk from two tube stations. Many restaurants, cafes and bus a few minutes walk away. Small private car-park to rear. Ensuite rooms available.

★★★★ B&B

Margaret Bruce
24 Greenock Avenue, Cathcart, Glasgow, G44 5TS
Tel:0141 637 0608

1 Single	2 En Suite fac	B&B per person	Open Apr-Oct
2 Twin	1 Priv.NOT ensuite	from £25.00 Single	
1 Double		from £22.50 Double	

A modern architecturally designed villa with outstanding gardens and levels of comfort, situated within the conservation areas of Old Cathcart Village and Linn Park. But just 12 minutes by public transport to the city centre. Glasgow 20 mins. 10 mins from J22 - M8, Burrell collection 6 mins by car.

★★★ HOTEL

Devoncove Hotel
931 Sauchiehall Street, Glasgow, G3 7TQ
Tel:0141 334 4000 Fax:0141 339 9000
Email:info@devoncovehotel.co.uk
Web:www.devoncovehotel.com

20 Twin	All En Suite	B&B per person	Open Jan-Dec
16 Double		from £40.00 Single	
9 Family		from £25.00 Double	
		from £35.00 Room Only	

Just 5 Mins from the heart of the city, The Devoncove is a fine example of Victorian architectural heritage and is located close to the Museum and Art Gallery with its internationally acclaimed collection. Well appointed bedrooms offering modern comfort in traditional surroundings.

★★ B&B

East Rogerton Lodge
Markethill Road, East Kilbride, G74 4NZ
Tel/Fax:01355 263176
Email:christine.mcleary@ntlworld.com

3 Twin	1 Priv.NOT ensuite	B&B per person	Open Jan-Dec excl
		£18.00-20.00 Twin	Xmas/New Year
		£25.00-27.00 Single	

Farmyard conversion approximately 1 mile from East Kilbride village and 6 miles south of Glasgow. Easy access to all major routes. All accommodation on ground floor level. Also two self-contained 3 star self-catering units adjacent to B & B available. All bedrooms with TV's. Tea making facilities and microwave available in guests seating area. Ample private parking.

Important: Prices stated are estimates and may be subject to amendments

Glasgow

Map Ref: 1H5

GUEST HOUSE

Hillhead Hotel

32 Cecil Street, Hillhead, Glasgow, G12 8RJ
Tel:0141 339 7733 Fax:0141 339 1770
Email:hillhotel@aol.com

Based in fashionable West End, privately owned hotel. Convenient for Glasgow University, Hillhead Underground Station and SECC. Within a five minute walk of many restaurants and shops. Small private car park to rear.

2 Single	All En Suite	B&B per person	Open Jan-Dec
4 Twin		from £39.00 Single	
2 Double		from £25.00 Double	
3 Family		from £23.00 Room Only	

Lochgilvie House

117 Randolph Road, Glasgow G11 7DS
Tel: 0141 357 1593 Fax: 0141 357 1593
e.mail: reservations@lochgilviehouse.co.uk Web: www.lochgilviehouse.co.uk

Prestigious Victorian townhouse nestling quietly in the heart of the West End. Small friendly family establishment provides quality bed and breakfast at attractive prices. Popular with guests wishing to visit university, galleries, museums and SECC. Five minutes drive from Glasgow Airport, walking distance from local train station.

B&B

Lochgilvie House

117 Randolph Road, Glasgow, G11 7DS
Tel/Fax:0141 357 1593
Email:reservations@lochgilviehouse.co.uk

Lochgilvie House is ideally situated in the popular West End of the city 100 yds from the local train station and bus services, convenient to the Scottish Exhibition Centre and Conference Centre, Art Galleries, Transport Museum, Glasgow Strathclyde and Caledonian Universities and most major attractions. Only 10 min by car from Glasgow International Airport and 8 min to City Centre by train. Continental breakfast served in the comfort of your bedroom.

1 Twin	En Suite	B&B per person	Open Jan-Dec excl
1 Family	En Suite	from £25.00 Single	Xmas/New Year
1 Double	Priv.fac	from £25.00 Double	

Lomond Hotel

6 Buckingham Terrace, Great Western Road, Glasgow G12 8EB
Telephone: 0141 339 2339 Fax: 0141 339 5215
e.mail: norman@kelvin-lomond.freeserve.co.uk
Web: www.scotland2000.com/lomondkelvin
Located in a Victorian terrace in the West End. Close to Botanic Gardens, Glasgow University, museum and art galleries. Restaurants and shops 100 metres. This family owned hotel offers comfortable rooms some with ensuite. All have TV, tea/coffee service. A comfortable stay is assured. 5 minutes drive to city centre. Ten minutes Glasgow Airport. Excellent for public transport.

GUEST HOUSE

Lomond Hotel

6 Buckingham Terrace, Great Western Road, Glasgow G12 8EB
Tel:0141 339 2339 Fax:0141 339 5215
Email:norman@kelvin-lomond.freeserve.co.uk
Web:www.scotland2000.com/lomondkelvin

Victorian terraced house in the West End. Close to the BBC, Botanical Gardens and Glasgow University. On main bus routes to city centre and five minutes walk from underground, restaurants and shops.

7 Single	6 En Suite fac	B&B per person	Open Jan-Dec excl
1 Twin	4 Priv.NOT ensuite	from £23.00 Single	Xmas/New Year
4 Double	1 Pub.Bath/Show	from £22.00 Double	
4 Family		from £20.00 Room Only	

VAT is shown at 17.5%: changes in this rate may affect prices. | *Key to symbols is on back flap.*

Glasgow

Map Ref: 1H5

★

GUEST
HOUSE

McLays Guest House
254-275 Renfrew Street, Glasgow, G3 6TT
Tel:0141 332 4796 Fax:0141 353 0422
Email:info@mclaysgh.co.uk Web:www.mclaysgh.co.uk

McLays Guest House situated in the heart of the city was originally 3 townhouses, now interlinked to provide 62 rooms. Of these, 39 have private bathrooms, however all floors have communal bathrooms for guests to use. All our rooms have colour television, satellite channels, tea/coffee making facilities and telephones. You will find our staff members at McLays helpful, warm and friendly. Our staff have a great depth of local knowledge.

18 Single	39 En Suite fac	B&B per person	Open Jan-Dec
20 Twin	9 Priv.NOT ensuite	from £24.00 Single	
12 Double		from £20.00 Double	
12 Family			

★★★★

B&B

Park House
13 Victoria Park Gardens South, Broomhill, Glasgow
G11 7BX
Tel:0141 339 1559 Fax:0141 576 0915
Email:mail@Parkhouseglasgow.co.uk
Web:www.parkhouseglasgow.co.uk

Large Victorian town house in quiet residential area. Convenient for Clydeside Expressway to city centre. Ideal base for touring. Off road parking.

1 Twin	2 En Suite fac	B&B per person	Open Apr-Oct
2 Double		from £35.00 Single	BB & Eve.Meal
		from £30.00 Double	from £50.00

★★★

LODGE

The Sandyford Hotel
904 Sauchiehall Street, Glasgow, G3 7TF
Tel:0141 334 0000 Fax:0141 337 1812

Recently refurbished hotel, enjoying a convenient location in the West End, close to museums, Kelvingrove Park and SECC. On main bus route to city centre, and within walking distance of a host of Glasgow's major attractions.

12 Single	All En Suite	B&B per person	Open Jan-Dec excl
9 Twin		from £32.00 Single	Xmas
28 Double		from £26.00 Double	
6 Family			

★★

GUEST
HOUSE

Seton Guest House
6 Seton Terrace, Dennistoun, Glasgow, G31 2HY
Tel:0141 556 7654 Fax:0141 554 3014
Email:pasway@prestel.seton.co.uk

Stone built townhouse c.1850 in conservation area of East End. Close to city centre and all amenities. Public transport of rail & bus a 2 minute walk away.

1 Single	3 Priv.NOT ensuite	B&B per person	Open Jan-Dec
2 Twin		from £17.00 Single	BB & Eve.Meal
1 Double		from £17.00 Double	from £25.00
3 Family			

Scotland's National Booking and Information Line

Tel: 0845 22 55 121
visitscotland.com

Important: Prices stated are estimates and may be subject to amendments

Glasgow			Map Ref: 1H5	

★★★

GUEST HOUSE

The Town House
4 Hughenden Terrace, Glasgow, G12 9XR
Tel:0141 357 0862   Fax:0141 339 9605
Email:hospitality@thetownhouseglasgow.com
Web:www.thetownhouseglasgow.com

Glasgow's original and long established town house, located in the desirable West End, provides all the comforts one would expect for a relaxing holiday or a hectic business trip. Relax in front of the coal fire with a refreshment, enjoy the quality accommodation and legendary, seafood breakfast in the morning. Parking is free and ample.

4 Twin
4 Double
2 Family

All En Suite

B&B per person
from £60.00 Single
from £36.00 Double

Open Jan-Dec

★★

CAMPUS ACCOMMODATION

Univ. of Glasgow - Kelvinhaugh Gate
Conference + Visitor Services, No 3 The Square
Glasgow, G12 8QQ Tel:0800 027 2030 Fax:0141 334 5465
Email:vacation@gla.ac.uk
Web:www.gla.ac.uk/vacationaccommodation

Modern halls of residence located in the West End of Glasgow in a quiet area, yet providing easy access to the city centre. Light continental breakfast served in your accommodation. Regular bus service nearby. A short walk from Kelvingrove, art galleries and museums and S.E.C.C. Byres Road offers a selection of cafes, bars and restaurants. A comfortable base for exploring Glasgow, or touring west/central Scotland. Ample parking.

150
Single

All En Suite

B&B per person
from £25.50 Single

Open Jul-Sep

★

CAMPUS ACCOMMODATION

Univ. of Glasgow - Wolfson Hall
Conference and Visitor Services, No 3 The Square
Glasgow, G12 8QQ
Tel:0800 027 2030 Fax:0141 334 5465
Email:vacation@gla.ac.uk
Web:www.gla.ac.uk/vacationaccommodation

Modern property in quiet parkland, offering full Scottish breakfast. Located within easy commuting distance for Glasgow City Centre. Sports facilities nearby.

200
Single
80 Twin

All En Suite

B&B per person
from £31.50 Single
from £26.50 Double

Open Mar,Apr,Jun-Sep

University of Strathclyde

Residence and Catering Services
50 Richmond St., Glasgow G1 1XP
Tel: 0141-553 4148   Fax: 0141-553 4149
e.mail: rescat@mis.strath.ac.uk Web: www.rescat.strath.ac.uk

Strathclyde University offers a range of attractive accommodation in Glasgow city centre at affordable prices. En-suite and standard single rooms are located in the modern campus village adjacent to the Lord Todd bar/restaurant and singles are also available at the Jordanhill Campus in the west end of the city.

★★

CAMPUS ACCOMMODATION

University of Strathcylde
Residence and Catering Services
50 Richmond Street, Glasgow, G1 1XP
Tel:0141 553 4148 Fax:0141 553 4149
Email:rescat@mis.strath.ac.uk
Web:www.rescat.strath.ac.uk

Purpose built hall of residence on student campus centrally situated for all amenities in the city.

700
Single
6 Twin
15 Double
2 Family

285 En Suite fac

B&B per person
from £25.00 Single
from £21.50 Double

Open Jun-Sep

VAT is shown at 17.5%: changes in this rate may affect prices.

Key to symbols is on back flap.

by Glasgow

Map Ref: 1H5

★★★

HOTEL

The Westerwood
St Andrews Drive, Cumbernauld, by Glasgow, G68 0EW
Tel:01667 458800 Fax:01667 455267
Email:rooms@morton-hotels.com
Web:www.morton-hotels.com

Modern hotel, with recently completed extension, as well as leisure complex, and own championship golf course. The hotel provides a choice of eating and drinking options, including the Old Masters Restaurant and The Clubhouse bar. Conference and function facilities are available.

55 Double	All En Suite	B&B per person from £57.50 per night Dbl/Twn from £87.50 Suite per night
42 Twin		
3 Suites		

Open Jan-Dec
D,B&B per person from £53.50 per night

Greenock, Renfrewshire

Map Ref: 1G5

★★

B&B

Denholm Bed + Breakfast
22 Denholm Street, Greenock, PA16 8RJ
Tel:01475 781319
Email:dannychundoo@hotmail.com

Semi detached house in quiet suburb yet close to restaurants, shops and waterfront area. Down the hill from Greenock golf club. 5 minute walk from station with its fast train service to Glasgow City Centre. Ideal base for Dunoon and Rothesay ferries. Loch Lomond under an hour's drive. Unmetered street parking available.

2 Twin	All En Suite	B&B pppn from £27.50 Single from £27.50 Double

Open Jan-Dec

Hamilton, Lanarkshire

Map Ref: 2A5

★★

B&B

5A Auchingramont Road
Hamilton, South Lanarkshire, ML3 6JP
Tel:01698 285230

Scandinavian split level villa, with private parking. In quiet residential area only few minutes walk from Town Centre. Ensuite accommodation available. Satellite/Cable TV in lounge. 5 minutes from bus and train station. Friendly welcome and hearty Scottish breakfast.

1 Single	1 En Suite fac	B&B per person from £22.50 Single from £22.50 Double
1 Twin	1 Priv.NOT ensuite	
2 Double		

Open Jan-Dec

Lanark

Map Ref: 2A6

★★★

B&B

Corehouse Farm
Lanark, ML11 9TQ Tel:01555 661377 Fax:01555 660733
Email:corehouse@thegallop.com
Web:www.thegallop.com/corehouse

A warm family welcome awaits you on our traditional working farm. The farm is in a beautiful, sheltered, quiet valley, but also has easy access to Glasgow and Edinburgh. Take a short walk to the dramatic Cora Linn and Bonnington Linn waterfalls and nature reserve. All our rooms are on ground level, have en-suite facilities and central heating. Laundry and e-mail facilities available.

1 Double	All En Suite	B&B per person from £25.00 Single from £20.00 Double
2 Family		

Open Jan-Dec

Scotland's National Booking and Information Line

Tel: 0845 22 55 121
visitscotland.com

Important: Prices stated are estimates and may be subject to amendments

Lanark

Map Ref: 2A6

Jerviswood Mains Farm

LANARK ML11 7RL   Telephone: 01555 663987

e.mail: jerviswoodmains@aol.com

★★★★ B&B

Good hospitality is offered in this early 19th-century traditional farmhouse, 1 mile from Lanark on the A706, heading northwards. We are near a trout and deer farm and provide good food in a relaxed atmosphere. We combine old world charm with modern amenities. The unique 1758 industrial village of New Lanark, now a World Heritage Site, and many places of historical interest are nearby, equidistant between Glasgow and Edinburgh. This is an excellent touring base.

★★★★

B&B

Jerviswood Mains Farm

Cleghorn, Lanark, Lanarkshire, ML11 7RL
Tel:01555 663987
Email:jerviswoodmains@aol.com

A warm welcome awaits you at this 19c stone built farmhouse of considerable character, 1 mile (2 kms) north of the historic market town of Lanark. Less than one hour's drive from both Glasgow and Edinburgh, is an exellent base for touring Scotland. Ample private parking.

1 Twin	2 Priv.NOT ensuite	B&B per person	Open Jan-Dec
2 Double		from £28.00 Single	
		from £22.00 Double	

Lesmahagow, Lanarkshire

Map Ref: 2A6

★★

B&B

Dykecroft

Dykecroft Farm, Kirkmuirhill, Lesmahagow, ML11 0JQ
Tel:01555 892226
Email:dykecroft.bandb@talk21.com

Modern farmhouse bungalow in rural situation 20 miles (32kms) South of Glasgow and airport. An hour's drive from Edinburgh, Stirling, Ayr and Loch Lomond, only 2 miles from the M74. Pub/Restaurant 1 mile. Ample private parking. Fishing and sports nearby.

1 Twin	1 Priv.NOT ensuite	B&B per person	Open Jan-Dec
2 Double		from £23.00 Single	
		from £20.00 Double	

Lochwinnoch, Renfrewshire

Map Ref: 1G5

EAST LOCHHEAD COUNTRY HOUSE & COTTAGES

LARGS ROAD, LOCHWINNOCH PA12 4DX TEL/FAX: 01505 842610

E.MAIL: eastlochhead@aol.com WEB: www.eastlochhead.co.uk

Janet Anderson guarantees you a warm welcome at award winning East Lochhead where you will find every home comfort. 2 acres of beautiful gardens overlooking Barr Loch and Renfrewshire hills.
Cycle track passes the house. Good base for sightseeing.
Glasgow airport 15 mins, Prestwick 30 mins.
Taste of Scotland home cooking awaits you.

★★★★

B&B

●●●●
HOME COOKING

East Lochhead Country House & Cottages

Largs Road, Lochwinnoch, PA12 4DX
Tel/Fax:01505 842610
Email:eastlochhead@aol.com
Web:www.eastlochhead.co.uk

Spacious Victorian country house overlooking Barr Loch. Easy access to Glasgow Airport and motorway network. Convenient for Ayrshire Coast, Burns Country, Loch Lomond and Glasgow. Taste of Scotland member, evening meals available and breakfasts a speciality. All rooms en-suite.

1 Twin	All En Suite	B&B per person	Open Jan-Dec excl
1 Double		from £35.00 Single	Xmas/New Year
1 Family		from £32.50 Double	BB & Eve.Meal
		from £55.00 Room	from £55.00
		Only	

VAT is shown at 17.5%: changes in this rate may affect prices.

Key to symbols is on back flap.

Lochwinnoch, Renfrewshire — Map Ref: 1G5

Garnock Lodge Bed & Breakfast

Boydstone Road, Lochwinnoch, Renfrewshire PA12 4JT
Tel/Fax: 01505 503680
e.mail: enquiries@garnocklodge.co.uk Web: www.garnocklodge.co.uk
A direct route, approx 12 mins from Glasgow Airport will give you the best
start to your holiday.
A warm welcome, ensuite facilities, off road parking, log fires.
Ayrshire coast, Loch Lomond, Edinburgh, Glasgow all within 1 hours travel.
Local facilities include golf, watersports, RSPB centre, Muirshiel Country
Park.

★★★★

B&B

Garnock Lodge Guest House

Boydstone Road, Lochwinnoch, Renfrewshire
PA12 4JT Tel/Fax:01505 503680

Enjoy a hassle-free start and finish to your holiday at a beautiful
detached house in rural situation. Ample private parking. Breakfast
menus allow a wonderful choice or continental tray for early starts. Fresh
fruit, bottled water and towelling robes provided in bedrooms. 10 miles
from Glasgow Airport (10-15 mins) on a direct route. Central for touring
Loch Lomond, Stirling, Edinburgh, Culzean Castle and ferries to Arran,
Bute and Ireland.

1 Single	2 En Suite fac	B&B per person	Open Jan-Dec
2 Twin	1 Pub.Bath/Show	from £16.00 Single	
1 Double		from £21.00 Double	
		from £15.00 Room	
		Only	

Motherwell, Lanarkshire — Map Ref: 2A5

★

**CAMPUS
ACCOMMODATION**

Motherwell College Stewart Hall

Dalzell Drive, Motherwell, Lanarkshire, ML1 2DD
Tel:01698 261890   Fax:01698 232527
Email:mcol@motherwell.co.uk
Web:www.motherwell.co.uk

On college campus and all on one level. Close to Strathclyde Park and
M8/M74 motorway link for Glasgow and Edinburgh.

47 Single	Some En Suite	B&B per person	Open Jan-Dec excl
		from £20.00 Single	Xmas/New Year
		from £17.00 Room	BB & Eve.Meal
		Only	from £24.00

Paisley, Renfrewshire — Map Ref: 1H5

★

**GUEST
HOUSE**

Dryesdale Guest House

37 Inchinnan Road, Paisley, Renfrewshire, PA3 2PR
Tel:0141 889 7178
Email:dd@paisley2001.freeserve.co.uk

Personally run guest house 0.5 mile (1km) from Glasgow Airport and M8
access. Close to Paisley with its station for the 15 minute journey to
Glasgow city centre. Ideal for touring Loch Lomond, Oban and
Edinburgh. Some ground floor rooms.

3 Single	B&B per person	Open Jan-Dec
2 Twin	from £21.50 Single	
3 Double	from £20.00 Double	
2 Family		

Strathaven, Lanarkshire — Map Ref: 2A6

★★★

B&B

Avonlea

46 Millar Street, Glassford, Strathaven, ML10 6TD
Tel:01357 521748

Terraced house in quiet peaceful conservation village one and a half
miles from Strathaven. Traditional furnished bedrooms on 1st floor/ 18
miles South of Glasgow. 4 miles from M74 JN8. Ideal base for visiting
Glasgow, Edinburgh, Clyde Valley and Ayrshire coast-all within easy
driving distance.

2 Twin	1 Priv/Shared	B&B per person	Open Feb-Nov
		£22.00-25.00 Single	
		£18.00-20.00 Twin	
		£14.00-16.00 Room	
		only	

Important: Prices stated are estimates and may be subject to amendments

Welcome to Scotland

West Highlands and Islands, Loch Lomond, Stirling and Trossachs

From the green slopes of the Ochil Hills in the east to the far-flung Hebridean Islands on the western seaboard, you will discover a remarkably diverse region where history is set within a glorious natural environment.

Loch Katrine, Trossachs, Stirlingshire

It is here that the geological Highland boundary fault divides the lowland south from the mountainous north. Scenically, this area has everything, from the bonny banks of Loch Lomond, a playground for generations of visitors, to the bustling town of Stirling and western coastal resort of Oban.

A good place to begin is the Royal Burgh of Stirling. As a gateway to the Highlands and an important centre, Stirling has played a leading role in Scotland's story. Today, the castle with its recently restored Great Hall and the historic Old Town are just one of its many attractions. Nearby is the National Wallace Monument, telling the real story of Scotland's first freedom-fighter, William Wallace.

In the early days of tourism, the location of Loch Lomond and the Trossachs, a highly scenic area just beyond the Highland line, made them easy to reach. Often described as "The Highlands in Miniature", the Trossachs is still easy to reach with its gateway being the bustling and friendly town of Callander.

At the Rob Roy and Trossachs Visitor Centre, you can uncover the legend of this celebrated folk hero. An excellent way to enjoy the captivating beauty of this area is on board the SS Sir Walter Scott which makes regular cruises across the placid waters of Loch Katrine. There are also plenty of cruising options on Loch Lomond, Scotland's largest loch (by surface area), which is part of Scotland's first national park. The story of the loch is interpreted at the new Lomond Shores Centre at Balloch.

Loch Etive from Taynuilt, Argyll

West Highlands and Islands, Loch Lomond, Stirling and Trossachs

"Old Brig", Stirling, with the Wallace monument in the distance

Further west is the delightful Cowal Peninsula with the fine Victorian resort of Dunoon and the lovely Isle of Bute with its magnificent Victorian gothic mansion, Mount Stuart and pleasant seaside resort of Rothesay. Across the sheltered waters of Loch Fyne sits the Georgian planned village of Inveraray and to the south the beautiful peninsula of Kintyre offering miles of shoreline and beaches with unsurpassed views of the islands. Regular ferry services cross to the lively island of Islay, world-famous for its peaty malt whiskies and then to Jura, which in contrast, has one road, one distillery, one hotel and lots of space.

The road west will take you through a panorama of dramatic mountains which sweep down to the coastal resort of Oban. Romantic names and places such as Tobermory with its picture postcard harbour await the visitor to Mull and the island of Iona and Staffa are close by. You could venture further west for a real experience of island life and visit Colonsay, Tiree or Coll, but wherever you choose, you can be sure you will find a warm welcome in the heartland of Scotland.

Events

West Highlands and Islands, Loch Lomond, Stirling and Trossachs

1-5 MAY
Isle of Bute Jazz Festival
Tel: 01700 502151
www.isle-of-bute.com

24-25 MAY*
May Market, Loch Fyne
A feast of west coast seafood
and local produce.
Tel: 01499 600264
www.loch-fyne.co.uk

24-30 MAY
Wake Up To Birds Week
Royal Society for the
Protection of Birds. Wide
range of events and activities
at the 60 RSPB reserves across
Scotland. Free entry to all
reserves on one day during
this week.
Tel: 0131 311 6500
www.rspb.org.uk/scotland

26-27 JULY
**World Championship
Highland Games, Callander**
Traditional Highland games
and Highland dancing
Tel: 01877 330919

29-30 AUGUST
**Cowal Highland Games,
Dunoon**
Largest Highland games in
the world.
Tel: 01369 703206
www.cowalgathering.com

10-12 OCTOBER
Philips Tour of Mull Rally
Exciting car rally using the
demanding roads on Mull.
Tel: 01254 826564
www.2300club.org

10-18 OCTOBER
Royal National Mod, Oban
The premier festival of Gaelic
arts and culture.
Tel: 01631 562850
www.the-mod.co.uk

** denotes provisional date. Events can be
subject to change, please check before
travelling.*

For up to date events, log on to:
visitscotland.com

Area Tourist Boards

West Highlands and Islands, Loch Lomond, Stirling and Trossachs

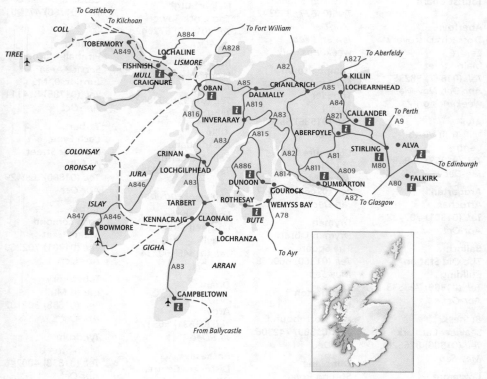

**Argyll, the Isles,
Loch Lomond, Stirling
and Trossachs Tourist Board**
Dept. SOS
7 Alexandra Parade
Dunoon
PA23 8AB

Tel: 01369 701000
Fax: 01369 706085
E-mail: info@scottishheartlands.org
www.scottishheartlands.org

Tourist Information Centres
West Highlands and Islands, Loch Lomond, Stirling and Trossachs

**West Highlands,
Loch Lomond,
Stirling and
Trossachs
Tourist Board**

Aberfoyle
Trossachs Discovery
Centre
Main Street
Tel: (01877) 382352
*Apr-Oct, Nov-Mar
weekends only*

Alva
Mill Trail Visitor
Centre
Tel: (01259) 769696
Jan-Dec

Ardgartan
Arrochar
Tel: (01301) 702432
Apr-Oct

Balloch
The Old Station
Building
Tel: (01389) 753533
Apr-Oct

Bo'ness
Seaview Car Park
Tel: (01506) 826626
May-Sep

Bowmore
Isle of Islay
Tel: (01496) 810254
Jan-Dec

Callander
Rob Roy and
Trossachs
Visitor Centre
Ancaster Square
Tel: (01877) 330342
*Mar-Dec
Jan and Feb
weekends only*

Campbeltown
Mackinnon House
The Pier
Argyll
Tel: (01586) 552056
Jan-Dec

Craignure
The Pier
Isle of Mull
Tel: (01680) 812377
Jan-Dec

Drymen
Drymen Library
The Square
Tel: (01360) 660068
May-Sep

Dumbarton
Milton
A82 Northbound
Tel: (01389) 742306
Jan-Dec

Dunblane
Stirling Road
Tel: (01786) 824428
May-Sep

Dunoon
7 Alexandra Parade
Argyll
Tel: (01369) 703785
Jan-Dec

Falkirk
2-4 Glebe Street
Tel: (01324) 620244
Jan-Dec

Helensburgh
The Clock Tower
Tel: (01436) 672642
Apr-Oct

Inveraray
Front Street
Argyll
Tel: (01499) 302063
Jan-Dec

Killin
Breadalbane
Folklore Centre
Tel: (01567) 820254
*Mar-Oct
Feb weekends only*

Lochgilphead
Lochnell Street
Argyll
Tel: (01546) 602344
Apr-Oct

Oban
Argyll Square
Argyll
Tel: (01631) 563122
Jan-Dec

Rothesay
Discovery Centre,
Winter Gardens
Isle of Bute
Tel: (01700) 502151
Jan-Dec

Stirling
44 Dumbarton Road
Tel: (01786) 475019
Jan-Dec

Stirling
Royal Burgh of
Stirling Visitor
Centre
Castle Esplanade
Tel: (01786) 479901
Jan-Dec

Stirling
Pirnhall Motorway
Service Area
Juntion 9, M9
Tel: (01786) 814111
Apr-Oct

**Tarbert,
Loch Fyne**
Harbour Street
Argyll
Tel: (01880) 820429
Apr-Oct

**Tarbet-
Loch Lomond**
Main Street
Tel: (01301) 702260
Apr-Oct

Tobermory
Isle of Mull
Tel: (01688) 302182
Apr-Oct

Tyndrum
Main Street
Tel: (01838) 400246
Apr-Oct

Scotland's National Booking and Information Line
0845 22 55 121

Aberfoyle, Perthshire

Map Ref: 1H3

CREAG-ARD HOUSE

ABERFOYLE, STIRLING FK8 3TQ Tel/Fax: 01877 382297

e.mail: cara@creag-ardhouse.co.uk Web: www.creag-ardhouse.co.uk

Nestling in three acres of beautiful gardens, this lovely Victorian house enjoys some of the most magnificent scenery in Scotland; overlooking Loch Ard, stunning views of Ben Lomond. Own trout fishing, boat hire available. Perfect for touring the Trossachs, walking, cycling or relaxing in a lovely country house.

★★★★

GUEST HOUSE

Creag-Ard House

Aberfoyle, Stirling, FK8 3TQ
Tel/Fax:01877 382297
Email:cara@creag-ardhouse.co.uk
Web:www.creag-ardhouse.co.uk

Welcoming Guest House with superb views over Loch Ard 3kms from the centre of Aberfoyle Village in the heart of Trossachs. A haven of peace and tranquility. Delicious breakfast with homebaking.

2 Twin	All En Suite
4 Double	

B&B per person
from £45.00 Single
from £29.00 Double

Open Mar-Oct

Alexandria, Dunbartonshire

Map Ref: 1G4

★★★★

B&B

●●●●
HOME COOKING

Sheildaig Farm

Upper Stoney Mollen Road, Alexandria, G83 8QY
Tel:01389 752459   Fax:01389 753695
Email:sheildaigfarm@talk21.com
Web:www.sheildaigfarm.co.uk

Totally refurbished farm courtyard buildings in secluded setting. Conveniently situated for touring Loch Lomond and the Trossachs. Easy access to A82 and Glasgow Airport. Candlelit dinners,Taste of Scotland member with table license. 5 minutes from Balloch station with its service into Glasgow city centre.

3 Double	All En Suite

B&B per person
from £40.00 Single
from £25.00 Double
from £25.00 Room
Only

Open Jan-Dec
BB & Eve.Meal
from £41.00

Appin, Argyll

Map Ref: 1E1

LOCHSIDE COTTAGE - APPIN

Fasnacloich, Appin, Argyll PA38 4BJ Tel/Fax: 01631 730216
e.mail: broadbent@lochsidecottage.fsnet.co.uk
Web: www.lochsidecottage.fsnet.co.uk

Total peace on the shore of Loch Baile mhic Chailen, in an idyllic glen of outstanding beauty. There are many walks from the cottage garden, or alternatively visit Fort William, Glencoe and Oban, from where you can board a steamer to explore the Western Isles – a pleasant way of ensuring a happy, relaxing holiday, away from the hurly-burly of modern life.

★★★★

B&B

●●●●
HOME COOKING

Lochside Cottage – Appin

Fasnacloich, by Appin, Argyll, PA38 4BJ
Tel/Fax:01631 730216
Email:broadbent@lochsidecottage.fsnet.co.uk
Web:www.lochsidecottage.fsnet.co.uk

The friendly atmosphere of the Broadbents' home welcomes you at the end of the day. Delicious home cooked dinner, a log fire and the certainty of a perfect night's sleep in an attractive and comfortable ensuite bedroom, all contribute to an unforgettable holiday at Lochside Cottage.

2 Twin	2 En Suite fac
1 Double	1 Priv.Bath/Show

B&B per person
from £28.00 Single
from £28.00 Double

Open Jan-Dec excl
Xmas/New Year
BB & Eve.Meal
from £50.00

VAT is shown at 17.5%: changes in this rate may affect prices.

Key to symbols is on back flap.

Ardchattan, Argyll | Map Ref: 1E2

Blarcreen Farmhouse
Ardchattan, by Oban, Argyll PA37 1RG
Tel/Fax: 01631 750272 e.mail: j.lace@blarcreenfarm.com
Web: *www.blarcreenfarm.com*
Substantial Victorian farmhouse on the shores of Loch Etive. Best quality,
comfort, service, in tranquil surroundings. Taste of Scotland award for
excellence in food and accommodation. Farmhouse cooking. Enjoy the
superior Loch Etive Room with stunning views, king four poster, dressing
room, en-suite bathroom. Member of Scotland's Best B&B's.

★★★★

B&B

● ●
HOME
COOKING

Blarcreen Farm Guest House

Ardchattan, North Connel, nr Oban, Argyll
PA37 1RG
Tel/Fax:01631 750272
Email:j.lace@blarcreenfarm.com
Web:www.blarcreenfarm.com

Victorian farmhouse overlooking Loch Etive and the hills beyond. Ideal
location for a quiet break. Quality, comfort. Stunning views. Excellence in
accommodation and food. King four poster beds.

1 Twin   All En Suite
2 Double

B&B per person
from £33.50 Double

Open Mar-Dec excl
Xmas/New Year
BB & Eve.Meal
from £49.50

Arrochar, Argyll | Map Ref: 1G3

FERRY COTTAGE
Ardmay, Arrochar, Argyll & Bute G83 7AH
Tel: 01301 702428 Fax: 01301 702729
e.mail: ferrycottagebb@aol.com
Web: www.ferrycottage.com

Quietly situated at the gateway to the Highlands, the freshness
of our non-smoking establishment is appreciated by smokers
and non-smokers alike. In our centrally heated en-suite
bedrooms (one features a waterbed) facilities include tea,
coffee, toiletries and hairdryers – attention to detail alongside a
warm welcome ensure a perfect stay. With panoramic views
across Loch Long towards the Cobbler and the Arrochar Alps
this is the idyllic location for touring and hill-walking.
Loch Lomond is close by. For peace of mind we have a fire
certificate and off-road parking. Payment by credit card is
welcome (small fee applicable).
NON SMOKING ESTABLISHMENT.

★★

B&B

Ferry Cottage

Ardmay, Arrochar, Argyll & Bute, G83 7AH
Tel:01301 702428 Fax:01301 702729
Email:ferrycottagebb@aol.com
Web:www.ferrycottage.com

Refurbished 200 year old house with attractive bedrooms and ensuite
shower-rooms. Scenic views across Loch Long. Major credit cards
accepted. Private parking. Evening meals available & packed lunches. 5
minutes drive from Loch Lomond.

1 Twin   All En Suite
1 Double
1 Family

B&B per person
£20.00-25.00 Double

Open Jan-Dec excl
Xmas/New Year
BB & Eve.Meal
from £32.00-37.00

Important: Prices stated are estimates and may be subject to amendments

Arrochar, Argyll

Map Ref: 1G3

GUEST
HOUSE

Greenbank Guest House
Arrochar, Argyll, G83 7AA
Tel:01301 702305

By road and lochside in village of Arrochar with superb loch and
mountain views. Family run with licensed restaurant. Open all day for
meals & snacks. Rock garden. Private parking.

1 Single	Some En Suite	B&B per person	Open Jan-Dec excl
2 Double	1 Priv.NOT ensuite	from £20.00 Single	Xmas/New Year
1 Family		from £19.00 Double	

Balloch, Dunbartonshire

Map Ref: 1G4

B&B

Aird House
1 Ben Lomond Walk, Balloch, Dunbartonshire
G83 8RJ
Tel:01389 754464 mobile 07814 730176 Fax:01389 732903

Enjoy excellent Scottish hospitality at this newly built modern villa set on
the main A811 Stirling Road in Balloch. Small colourful garden at front.
Ideal base for exploring Loch Lomond and Scotland's National Park.
Non-smoking.

1 Twin	1 En Suite fac	B&B per person	Open Jan-Dec excl
1 Double	1 Pub.Bath/Show	£25.00-30.00 Single	Xmas/New Year
		£20.00-22.00 Double	

GUEST
HOUSE

Anchorage
31 Balloch Road, Balloch, Loch Lomond, G83 8SS
Tel:01389 753336
Email:anchorage_gh@hotmail.com

Extended cottage in centre of village, near river. Railway station and all
other amenities nearby. Ideal touring base. All rooms ground floor.

2 Twin	All En Suite	B&B per person	Open Jan-Dec
2 Double		from £25.00 Single	
1 Family		from £25.00 Double	
		from £20.00 Room Only	

B&B

Glyndale
6 Mackenzie Drive, Balloch, Dunbartonshire
G83 8HL
Tel/Fax:01389 758238 or Tel:0870 225 7024
Email:rossglyndalebb@talk21.com

Modern family home in residential area, 10 minutes walk from Loch
Lomond and Balloch Village with its shops, restaurants and loch cruises.
30 minute drive from Glasgow Airport. Close to Balloch railway station
for trips to Glasgow City centre with its shops, restaurants and museums.
Stirling and the Wallace Monument one hour's drive away.

1 Twin	1 Pub.Bath/Show	B&B per person	Open Jan-Dec excl
1 Double		from £20.00 Single	Xmas/New Year
		from £16.50 Double	

Scotland's National Booking
and Information Line

Tel: 0845 22 55 121
visitscotland.com

VAT is shown at 17.5%: changes in this rate may affect prices.

| Key to symbols is on back flap. |

Balloch, Dunbartonshire

Map Ref: 1G4

HEATHPETE

24 Balloch Road, Balloch G83 8LE
Tel: 01389 752195 e.mail: sheathpete@aol.com

Family run B&B. Four recently upgraded ground floor ensuite
rooms one minute from Loch. Train and bus stations nearby.
Private parking.

★★★

**GUEST
HOUSE**

Heathpete Guest House
24 Balloch Road, Balloch, Alexandria, G83 8LE
Tel/Fax:01389 752195
Email:sheathpete@aol.com

2 Double	All En Suite	B&B per person	Open Jan-Dec
2 Family		from £18.00 Single	
		from £18.00 Double	

Extended family bungalow in heart of village with all amenities close by.
A few minutes walk to bus/rail stations, boat cruises and Country Park.

OAKVALE B&B

OAKVALE, DRYMEN ROAD, BALLOCH G83 8JY
Tel: 01389 751615 or 01389 604240
e.mail: dfelt19459@aol.com

Family run bed and breakfast offers quaint fresh comfortable accommodation in a cosy
relaxed atmosphere. Hospitality and privacy guaranteed. Situated five minutes' walk from
village and Loch Lomond shore. Visitors are well catered for with cruises, restaurants, pubs
and beautiful unspoiled forest, mountain, river and loch scenery never far away.

★★★

B&B

Oakvale B&B
Drymen Road, Balloch, Dunbartonshire, G83 8JY
Tel:01389 751615/604240
Email:dfelt19459@aol.com

1 Twin	All En Suite	B&B per person	Open Jan-Dec
2 Double		from £35.00 Single	
		from £19.00 Double	
		from £16.00 Room	
		Only	

Extended 1940's bungalow near country park. 5 mins walk to Loch
Lomond, cruises, restaurants and pubs.

★★

B&B

Westville
Riverside Lane, Balloch, Dunbartonshire, G83 8LF
Tel:01389 752307

1 Double	1 Priv.NOT ensuite	B&B per person	Open Jan-Dec excl
1 Family		from £19.00 Single	Xmas/New Year
		from £18.00 Double	

Mature bungalow, situated in quiet area of Balloch. Private parking.
Overlooking the marina at River Leven at the southern end of Loch
Lomond. A short flat stroll to shops, cruise boats and restaurants. Ideal
location for touring to Inveraray, Oban, The Trossachs and Stirling with
its Castle. Edinburgh approximately an hour by road.

Important: Prices stated are estimates and may be subject to amendments

by Balloch, Dunbartonshire

Map Ref: 1G4

★★★

B&B

Braeburn Cottage

West Auchencarroch Farm, by Balloch, G83 9LU
Tel:01389 710998 Mobile:07803 682715
Email:braeburn@bigfoot.com
Web:www.braeburncottage.co.uk

New bungalow on family run working dairy farm. 4 miles above Balloch overlooking hills and glens around Loch Lomond. Across its large landscape gardens. Ideally placed for touring Stirling, Loch Lomond or taking the train to Glasgow for shopping, restaurants & galleries. Glasgow Airport 30 minutes.

1 Double	All En Suite	B&B per person	Open Jan-Dec
1 Family	1 Priv.NOT ensuite	from £20.00 Single	
		from £17.00 Double	
		from £15.00 Room	
		Only	

Balmaha, Stirlingshire

Map Ref: 1G4

★★★★

B&B

Dunleen

Milton of Buchanan, Stirlingshire, G63 OJE
Tel:01360 870274

Comfortable modern ranch style home situated in secluded, lovely garden with a trout burn on its border that is overlooked by the guest lounge. On east side of Loch Lomond close to the West Highland Way. Rowardennan and Ben Lomond, the closest Munro are within 8 miles.

1 Twin	1 Priv.NOT ensuite	B&B per person
1 Double		from £20.00 Double
		Open May-Oct

Balquhidder, Perthshire

Map Ref: 1H2

★★★★

B&B

Calea Sona

Balquhidder, Perthshire, FK19 8NY
Tel/Fax:01877 384260
Email:stayatcaleasona@aol.com

Cottage, an interesting blend of old and new, peacefully situated with superb views. Only a short walk to Rob Roy's Grave and with many ties to the Clan Gregor and Clan MacLaren. Balquhidder offers a peaceful village from which to tour the Trossachs and Loch Lomond, many local walks and cycle track. Good walking area.

1 Twin	Ensuite fac	B&B per person	Open Jan-Dec excl
1 Double	Priv.Bath/Show	from £30.00 Single	Xmas
		from £23.00 Double	

Blairlogie, by Stirling

Map Ref: 2A3

★★

B&B

Blairmains Farm B+B

Manor Loan, Blairlogie, Stirling, FK9 5QA
Tel:01259 761338

Traditional stone farmhouse on working dairy farm with both a farm shop and coffee shop. Situated near a small conservation village close to Wallace Monument and University. Only four miles from Stirling. Ideal base for walkers touring central Scotland.

2 Twin	1 Priv.NOT ensuite	B&B per person	Open Jan-Dec excl
1 Double		from £23.00 Single	Xmas/New Year
		from £20.00 Double	
		from £16.00 Room	
		Only	

Bridge of Allan, Stirlingshire

Map Ref: 2A3

★★★

B&B

Sunnylaw House

1 Upper Glen Road, Bridge of Allan, Stirlingshire FK9 4PX
Tel:01786 833429
Email:sunnylawhouse@sol.co.uk
Web:www.sunnylawhouse.co.uk

A warm welcome awaits you all year at this 19th Century villa, now a cosy modernised upper apartment with open views to Ben Vorlich in the north, and the Gargunnock Hills in the West. We have a garden sitting area and off street parking to ensure privacy.

1 Twin	All En Suite	B&B per person	Open Jan-Dec
2 Double		from £25.00 Single	BB & Eve.Meal
		from £20.00 Double	from £35.00-40.00
		from £18.00 Room	
		Only	

VAT is shown at 17.5%: changes in this rate may affect prices.

Key to symbols is on back flap.

Brig O'Turk, Perthshire

Map Ref: 1H3

★★★

B&B

Burnt Inn House

Brig O'Turk, Callander, Perthshire, FK17 8HT
Tel:01877 376212 Fax:01877 339209
Email:burntinnhouse@aol.com
Web:www.burntinnhouse.co.uk

Former Coach House dating back to the 1850's now recently refurbished family home offering comfortable en-suite accommodation. Set in the midst of the Trossachs with views to Ben Venue & Queen Elizabeth Forest Park. Enjoy breakfast in our traditional farmhouse kitchen, complete with welcoming aga.

2 Twin   All En Suite
1 Double

B&B per person
from £22.50 Single
from £22.50 Double
from £20.00 Room
Only

Open Jan-Dec excl
Xmas/New Year

Ascog, Isle of Bute

Map Ref: 1F5

★★★★

B&B

Ascog Farm B&B

Ascog, Rothesay, Isle of Bute, PA20 9LL
Tel:01700 503372

A well appointed sympathetically restored 200-year-old farmhouse in a peaceful setting. Log fires and friendly welcome, come and be spoilt. The farmhouse is decorated with the traditional principles of Feng Shei harmonising with nature.

3 Single   2 Priv.NOT ensuite
1 Double

B&B per person
from £20.00 Single
from £20.00 Double

Open Jan-Nov excl
New Year

Rothesay, Isle of Bute

Map Ref: 1F5

★★

B&B

Cranford

Creek Drive, Port Bannatyne, Rothesay, PA20 0NU
Tel:01700 504688

A warm welcome and traditional Scottish hospitality awaits you at this comfortable home 1 mile from the town centre and a short walk from the shore and the bowling green. The compact bedroom, on the ground floor, has an ensuite shower room.

1 Double   All En Suite

B&B per person
from £19.00 Double

Open Apr-Oct

Cairndow, Argyll

Map Ref: 1F3

★★

INN

Cairndow Stagecoach Inn

Cairndow, Argyll, PA26 8BN
Tel:01499 600286 Fax:01499 600220
Email:cairndowinn@aol.com

Old Coaching Inn on Loch Fyne. Ideal centre for touring Western Highlands. 9 bedrooms with loch view - all en-suite - all fully appointed. 2 rooms with 2 person spa baths. Stables restaurant and lounge meals all day. Half-price golf at Inveraray. Beer garden. Sauna, solarium and multi-gym.

5 Twin   All En Suite
6 Double
2 Family

B&B per person
from £25.00 Single
from £25.00 Double

Open Jan-Dec
BB & Eve.Meal
from £40.00

Callander, Perthshire

Map Ref: 1H3

★★★

B&B

Almardon

Leny Road, Callander, Perthshire, FK17 8AJ
Tel:01877 331597
Email:almardon@lenyroad.freeserve.co.uk

Enjoy a relaxing stay in our spacious bungalow at the west end of town. Adjacent to Meadows Park and River Teith yet only minutes from shopping area and other amenities. Comfortable en-suite bedrooms with tea/coffee facilities, colour T.V, radio/alarm, hairdryer and iron. Ample parking within own grounds. Callander is so centrally situated, it makes an ideal base for touring the Central Highlands,walking,climbing and cycling.

1 Twin   All En Suite
2 Double

B&B per person
from £20.00 Double

Open Feb-Dec

Important: Prices stated are estimates and may be subject to amendments

Callander, Perthshire	Map Ref: 1H3

GUEST HOUSE

★★★

Annfield Guest House
North Church Street, Callander, Perthshire
FK17 8EG
Tel:01877 330204 Fax:01877 330674
Email:janet-greenfield@amserve.com

Centrally situated in a quiet area of the town in close proximity to shops and restaurants. Stepping stone to the Highlands. Ideal for an overnight stop.

2 Twin	7 En Suite fac	B&B per person	Open 5 Jan-23 Dec
4 Double	2 Priv.NOT ensuite	from £25.00 Single	
1 Family	1 Pub.Bath/Show	from £21.00 Double	

GUEST HOUSE

★★★★

Arden House
Bracklinn Road, Callander, Perthshire, FK17 8EQ
Tel/Fax:01877 330235
Email:ardenhouse@onetel.net.uk
Web:www.ardenhouse.org.uk

Elegant Victorian country house, peacefully set in attractive gardens with marvellous views of hills and countryside. Home of BBC TV's 'Dr Finlay's Casebook'. Ideal base for touring the Trossachs and Western Highlands.

1 Single	All En Suite	B&B per person	Open Easter-end Oct
2 Twin		from £30.00 Single	
3 Double		from £27.50 Double	

GUEST HOUSE

★★★★

Brook Linn Country House
Leny Feus, Callander, Perthshire, FK17 8AU
Tel/Fax:01877 330103
Email:derek@blinn.freeserve.co.uk
Web:www.brooklinn-scotland.co.uk

Comfortable, quiet family run Victorian house set in two acres of gardens with magnificent views. Short distance from town centre and all facilities. Non-smoking.

2 Single	All En Suite	B&B per person	Open Easter-Nov
2 Twin		from £25.00 Single	
2 Double		from £25.00 Double	

SMALL HOTEL

★★

Coppice Hotel
Leny Road, Callander, Perthshire, FK17 8AL
Tel:01877 330188

Personally run hotel with emphasis on cuisine using fresh local produce when available. Ideal base for touring the Trossachs or day trips to Stirling with its Castle and the Wallace Monument.

1 Twin	All En Suite	B&B per person	Open Jan-Dec
3 Double		from £23.00 Double	
1 Family			

GUEST HOUSE

★★★

East Mains House
Manse Lane, Bridgend, Callander, FK17 8AG
Tel/Fax:01877 330535
Email:east.mains@tesco.net
Web:www.eastmainshouse.net

Comfortable Georgian house set in large garden with private parking. Close to all amenities. Impressive guest lounge and well appointed bedrooms. Located in Bridgend, the oldest part of Callander. Relaxed atmosphere and warm welcome.

1 Twin	4 En Suite fac	B&B per person	Open Jan-Dec
3 Double	1 Pub.Bath/Show	from £26.00 Single	
2 Family		from £22.00 Double	

VAT is shown at 17.5%: changes in this rate may affect prices. | *Key to symbols is on back flap.*

Callander, Perthshire | Map Ref: 1H3

DUNMOR HOUSE
Leny Road, Callander FK17 8AL
Tel: 01877 330756 Fax: 01877 339558
e.mail: reservations@dunmorhouse.co.uk
Web: www.dunmorhouse.co.uk

Discover Dunmor House nestling underneath Callander Crags in the Trossachs benefiting from a central location in Scotland's first national park. Enjoy quality en-suite accommodation at affordable prices with exceptional service and attention throughout. Be tempted to stay longer and take advantage of our special 2 night and long stay rates. Book yours now!!

★★★★

**GUEST
HOUSE**

Dunmor House
Leny Road, Callander, FK17 8AL
Tel:01877 330756 Fax:01877 339558
Email:reservations@dunmorhouse.co.uk
Web:www.dunmorhouse.co.uk

Indulge yourself and enjoy some special touches with an assured and warm welcome at Dunmor where once is just not enough. For quality ensuite accommodation at affordable prices with first class care and attention throughout - Discover Dunmor!!

1 Twin	All En Suite	B&B per person	Open Feb-Nov
3 Double		from £27.50 Single	
		from £27.50 Double	

INVERTROSSACHS COUNTRY HOUSE
Invertrossachs, by Callander, Perthshire FK17 8HG
Telephone/Fax: 01877 331126
e.mail: reservations@invertrossachs.co.uk   Web: www.invertrossachs.co.uk

Relax in the comfort of our elegant private country house. Stunning setting by Loch Venachar in the beautiful Trossachs. Perfect base for touring, offering walking, cycling and fishing in woodland estate with golf and sailing nearby. Also available self-catering apartments and cottage. Advanced booking recommended.
★★★★ B&B

★★★★

B&B

Invertrossachs Country House
Callander, Perthshire, FK17 8HG
Tel/Fax:01877 331126
Email:reservations@invertrossachs.co.uk
Web:www.invertrossachs.co.uk

Comfortable large rooms and suites within an Edwardian mansion offering country house bed & breakfast and enjoying privacy and seclusion by the shores of Loch Venachar. Spacious accommodation with outstanding loch or mountain views.

1 Twin	All En Suite	B&B per person	Open Jan-Dec
2 Double		from £45.00 Single	BB & Eve.Meal
		from £45.00 Double	from £67.50

★★

B&B

Inver-Enys
Ancaster Road, Callander, Perthshire, FK17 8EL
Tel:01877 330908
Email:inverenys@btinternet.com

Comfortable ground floor accommodation in modern chalet bungalow situated in quiet residential area close to town centre. Callander is an ideal base for touring The Trossachs and Loch Lomond.

1 Single	2 Priv.NOT ensuite	B&B per person	Open Jan-Dec excl
1 Twin		from £20.00 Single	Xmas/New Year
1 Double		from £18.00 Double	

Important: Prices stated are estimates and may be subject to amendments

Callander, Perthshire

Map Ref: 1H3

LENY HOUSE ★★★★★ B&B

Callander, Perthshire FK17 8HA
Tel: 01877 331078 Fax: 01877 331078
e.mail: res@lenyestate.com Web: www.lenyestate.com

Historic Leny House, a family country mansion in Parkland.
Paddocks with goats, sheep. Built 1513, fortified 1691, extended
1845, restored 1999. First used for B&B by the Jacobites
marching to the rebellion in 1745!! Magnificent views to
mountains and glens. Private glen with abundant wildlife for
intrepid visitors. Spacious, Victorian four poster bedrooms, with
luxury ensuites. Antiques, tapestries, grand piano, baronial
surroundings, open fires, warm welcomes. Own estate pub,
restaurant and ceilidh music. Luxury self-catering also.
Recommended by numerous books and guides including Which
magazine. **Winner of the Automobile Association Guest**
Accommodation of the year for Scotland and N Ireland.
Central for both coasts. Tranquil retreat to unwind. Enjoy our
home with us. Price from £50 pp.

B&B

Leny House

Leny Estate, Callander, Perthshire, FK17 8HA
Tel/Fax:01877 331078
Email:res@lenyestate.com Web:www.lenyestate.com

A Jacobite Country House in the midst of idyllic rural scenery in the new
National Park. Fascinating history and of architectural importance.
Recently restored in close consultation with Historic Scotland to recreate
rooms of Authentic Victorian Luxury. Ideal quiet location for walking and
outdoor pursuits or just to relax. 'Winner of AA, Best Accommodation in
Scotland & N.Ireland Award'.

| 1 Twin | All En Suite | B&B per room | Open Apr-Oct |
| 2 Double | | £100.00-110.00 | |

GUEST
HOUSE

Lubnaig House

Leny Feus, Callander, Perthshire, FK17 8AS
Tel/Fax:01877 330376
Email:info@lubnaighouse.co.uk
Web:www.lubnaighouse.co.uk

Enhanced by its secluded location, large garden, private parking and
within easy walking distance of the town centre. A genuine Scottish
welcome awaits all guests. Why not stay longer, see Scotland and pay
less.

4 Twin	All En Suite	B&B per person	Open May-Sep
6 Double		from £25.00 Single	
		from £29.00 Double	

B&B

Trean Farm

Leny Feus, Callander, Perthshire, FK17 8AS
Tel/Fax:01877 331160
Email:contact@treanfarm.co.uk
Web:www.treanfarm.co.uk

Farmhouse situated on a 235 acre working farm on the outskirts of
Callander. Magnificent views of Ben Ledi. Within an easy 15 minutes
walk to the town centre. An ideal base for walking, cycling and touring
the Trossachs and Loch Lomond.

1 Twin	2 En Suite fac	B&B per person	Open May-Oct
2 Double	1 Pub.Bath/Show	from £21.00 Single	
		from £21.00 Double	

VAT is shown at 17.5%: changes in this rate may affect prices.

Key to symbols is on back flap.

Callander, Perthshire — Map Ref: 1H3

RIVERVIEW GUEST HOUSE

Leny Road, Callander FK17 8AL
TEL: 01877 330635 FAX: 01877 339386
E.MAIL: **auldtoll@aol.com**
WEB: **www.nationalparkscotland.co.uk**
Detached stone-built Victorian house in own grounds with private parking.
Convenient for town centre, leisure complex and local restaurants. An ideal
location for walking, cycling and motoring holidays. Cycle storage available.
All rooms en-suite with TV and tea making. Good home cooking.
Dinner by arrangement from £13. B&B from £21 pppn.

★★★

**GUEST
HOUSE**

Riverview House

Leny Road, Callander, Perthshire, FK17 8AL
Tel:01877 330635 Fax:01877 339386
Email:auldtoll@aol.com
Web:www.nationalparkscotland.co.uk

Detached stone built Victorian house set in its own garden with private
parking. Close to town centre, leisure complex and local amenities.
Within easy walking distance of pleasant riverside park and cycle track.
Ideal base for exploring the beautiful Trossachs.

1 Single	All En Suite	B&B per person	Open Mar-Nov
2 Twin		from £21.00 Single	BB & Eve.Meal
2 Double		from £20.00 Double	from £32.00

Carradale, Argyll — Map Ref: 1E6

★★

**SMALL
HOTEL**

Ashbank Hotel

Carradale, by Campbeltown, Argyll, PA28 6RY
Tel/Fax:01583 431650
Email:ancurie@btopenworld.com

Comfortable family hotel with compact rooms in small village with views
from the rear across the Kilbrannan Sound to Arran and Ailsa Craig.
Overlooking Carradale Golf Course and close to safe and sandy beach
(10 minutes walk). 25 minutes drive to Campbeltown and Ireland ferry
terminal. Good base for Island hopping, walking, relaxing, touring and
visitor attractions.

1 Single	3 En Suite fac	B&B per person	Open Jan-Dec excl
3 Twin	2 Priv.NOT ensuite	from £24.50 Single	Xmas/New Year
1 Double		from £21.50 Double	BB & Eve.Meal
		from £19.00 Room	from £33.50
		Only	

★★

B&B

Mains Farm

Carradale, Campbeltown, Argyll, PA28 6QG
Tel/Fax:01583 431216
Email:maccormick@mainsfarm.freeserve.co.uk

Traditional farmhouse on working farm, on the outskirts of the village
and a short walk from the beach. Panoramic views across to the Isle of
Arran, near golf, fishing and forest walks. Restaurants available within
walking distance.

1 Single	1 Pub.Bath/Show	B&B per person
1 Twin		from £17.50 Single
1 Double		from £17.50 Double
1 Family		Open Apr-Oct

Connel, Argyll — Map Ref: 1E2

★★★

B&B

Ach-Na-Craig

Grosvenor Crescent, Connel, Argyll, PA37 1PQ
Tel:01631 710588
Email:achnacraig@talk21.com

Ach-Na-Craig is a modern family run house within a peaceful wooded
glade in the quiet village of Connel, located 5 miles (8kms) from Oban.
All rooms, including bedrooms are at ground floor level. There is ample
secure parking. No smoking.

2 Twin	All En Suite	B&B per person	Open Easter-Oct
1 Double		from £19.00 Double	
		from £19.00 Twin	

Important: Prices stated are estimates and may be subject to amendments

Connel, Argyll   Map Ref: 1E2

KILCHURN

Kilchurn, Connel, Argyll PA37 1PG
Telephone: 01631 710581   e.mail: kilchurn@msn.com

Kilchurn is a detached villa situated on the A85 over-looking Loch
Etive and Ben Lora in the picturesque village of Connel which is 5
miles from Oban. The comfortable accommodation is decorated to
a high standard and there is ample private parking.

★★★★

B&B

Kilchurn
Connel, by Oban, Argyll, PA37 1PG
Tel:01631 710581
Email:kilchurn@msn.com

1 Twin	All En Suite	B&B per person	Open Apr-Oct
2 Double		from £20.00 Double	

Expect to receive a warm welcome into this family run Victorian villa,
located on the edge of Connel village with pleasant views across Loch
Etive, toward Ben Lora, and the Connel Bridge. Several hotels nearby for
evening meals. House is well placed for exploring Oban, Kintyre, the
islands and north towards Fort William.

★★★★

**GUEST
HOUSE**

Ronebhal Guest House
Connel, by Oban, Argyll, PA37 1PJ
Tel/Fax:01631 710310
Email:ronebhal@btinternet.com
Web:www.ronebhal.co.uk

1 Twin	4 En Suite fac	B&B per person	Open Feb-Nov
3 Double	1 Pub.Bath/Show	£20.00-30.00 Single	
1 Family		£20.00-30.00 Double	

Victorian Villa set in beautiful gardens with magnificent views of Loch
Etive and the mountains beyond. Superior standard of hospitality and
comfort with a hearty breakfast served at individual tables. Within
walking distance of two restaurants. Ideal touring base. Private parking.
Oban 5 miles (8kms).

★

B&B

Rosebank
Connel, by Oban, Argyll, PA37 1PA
Tel:01631 710316

1 Single	1 Priv.NOT ensuite	B&B per person	Open May-Oct
1 Twin		from £16.00 Single	
1 Double		from £15.00 Double	

A warm welcome is to be expected into this family home in the heart of
Connel village, close to hotels, post office and local shops. Railway station
100 metres walk. Oban 6 miles (9 km). Pets welcome.

Scotland's National Booking
and Information Line

Tel: 0845 22 55 121
visitscotland.com

VAT is shown at 17.5%: changes in this rate may affect prices. | *Key to symbols is on back flap.* |

Carron Bridge, Stirlingshire | Map Ref: 2A4

Drum Farm

Carronbridge, Stirling, Stirlingshire FK6 5JL
Telephone and Fax: 01324 825518
e.mail: drumfarm@ndirect.co.uk Web: www.ndirect.co.uk/~drumfarm

Beautiful 200 year-old farmhouse situated in unspoilt countryside with views overlooking Carron Dam, just 15 minutes from Stirling and the M9 and M80, where you can start your tours around this beautiful part of Scotland.

★★

B&B

B&B Drum Farm

Carronbridge, Stirlingshire, FK6 5JL
Tel/Fax:01324 825518
Email:drumfarm@ndirect.co.uk
Web:www.ndirect.co.uk/~drumfarm

Beautiful farmhouse situated in unspoilt countryside with views overlooking Carron Dam. Just 15 minutes from Stirling and the M9 & M80 where you can start your tours around this beautiful part of Scotland.

1 Twin	1 En Suite fac	B&B per person	Open Jan-Dec
1 Double	1 Pub.Bath/Show	from £25.00 Single	BB & Eve.Meal
1 Family		from £20.00 Double	from £29.50

Craobh Haven, by Lochgilphead, Argyll | Map Ref: 1E3

BUIDHE LODGE

Craobh Haven, by Lochgilphead, Argyll PA31 8UA
Tel: 01852 500291 e.mail: simone@buidhelodge.com
Web: www.buidhelodge.com

Beautiful Swiss-style lodge on perfect sealoch-side setting. Excellent home cooking, carefully selected wines. All six rooms ground level and ensuite. National Trust gardens, historic sites and boat trips nearby. Lodge featured in Which? Good Bed and Breakfast Guide. Phone Nick or Simone for colour brochure. Let us spoil you!

★★★

**GUEST
HOUSE**

●●

**HOME
COOKING**

Buidhe Lodge

Craobh Haven, By Lochgilphead, Argyll, PA31 8UA
Tel:01852 500291
Email:simone@buidhelodge.com
Web:www.buidhelodge.com

Architect designed, timber lodge with panoramic views. Personally run Guest House, on unique peaceful island setting. Connected by causeway to attractive marina village of Craobh Haven. Evening meal by prior arrangement. Ideal for touring West Coast of Scotland.

4 Twin	All En Suite	B&B per person	Open Jan-Dec excl
2 Double		from £35.00 Single	Xmas
		from £25.00 Double	BB & Eve.Meal
		from £25.00 Room	from £42.00
		Only	

Scotland's National Booking and Information Line

Tel: 0845 22 55 121
visitscotland.com

Important: Prices stated are estimates and may be subject to amendments

Craobh Haven, by Lochgilphead, Argyll　　　　　　　　Map Ref: 1E3

Lunga Estate

Craobh Haven, Argyll PA31 8QR
Telephone: 01852 500237 Fax 01852 500639
e.mail: colin@lunga.demon.co.uk Web: www.lunga.com
Lunga, a 17th-century mansion overlooking Firth of Lorne and
Sound of Jura, home to the MacDougalls for over 300 years, who
offer comfortable rooms for Bed and Breakfast and self-catering flats
or cottages. Join us for our famous candle-lit dinners and share the
facilities of this beautiful 3,000-acre coastal estate.

★

B&B

●●
**HOME
COOKING**

Lunga

Craobh Haven, Argyll, PA31 8QR
Tel:01852 500237   Fax:01852 500639
Email:colin@lunga.demon.co.uk
Web:www.lunga.com

18c mansion house on 3000 acre estate. Riding, fishing, sailing and hill-
walking available. Annexe accommodation. Evening meal by
arrangement.

1 Single	All En Suite	B&B per person	Open Jan-Dec
1 Twin		from £18.00 Single	BB & Eve.Meal
2 Double		from £18.00 Double	from £34.00
1 Family			

Dalmally, Argyll　　　　　　　　Map Ref: 1F2

★★★

B&B

Craigroyston

Dalmally, Argyll, PA33 1AA
Tel:01838 200234
Email:b&b@craigroyston.com Web:www.craigroyston.com

A stone built Edwardian villa on the edge of the quiet village of
Dalmally. Three comfortable first-floor rooms and ample parking. Guests
are welcome to use the conservatory and good sized gardens. There is
grand walking, cycling and fishing in the area or you can just relax.
Dalmally is an ideal base for touring in the Oban - Inveraray - Glencoe
area. Fine home-cooked meals are offered and a friendly welcome is
assured.

1 Single	1 En Suite fac	B&B per person	Open Jan-Dec excl
1 Twin	1 Priv.NOT ensuite	from £17.00 Single	Xmas/New Year
1 Double		from £18.00 Double	BB & Eve.Meal
		from £15.00 Room	from £28.00
		Only	

★★★

**GUEST
HOUSE**

Craig Villa Guest House

Dalmally, Argyll, PA33 1AX
Tel/Fax:01838 200255
Email:tonycressey@craigvilla.fsnet.co.uk
Web:www.craigvilla.co.uk

Personally run guest house in own grounds amidst breathtaking scenery.
Good touring base. Home cooking. Evening meal by arrangement.
Ground floor en-suite and 4 Poster bedroom.

2 Twin	5 En Suite fac	B&B per person	Open Jan-Dec excl
2 Double	1 Pub.Bath/Show	from £25.00 Single	Xmas/New Year
2 Family		from £21.00 Double	BB & Eve.Meal
			from £33.50

★★★

B&B

Cruachan Guest House

Monument Hill, Dalmally, Argyll, PA33 1AA
Tel:01838 200496   Fax:01838 200650
Email:mborrett@ontel.net.uk
Web:www.cruachan-dalmally.co.uk

Comfortable Victorian family home in peaceful village offers warm
welcome and excellent home cooking. Wonderful mountain views and
walks. 2 ground floor en-suite rooms.

1 Twin	2 En Suite fac	B&B per person	Open Jan-Dec excl
2 Double	1 Pub.Bath/Show	from £23.00 Single	Xmas/New Year
		from £18.00 Double	BB & Eve.Meal
			from £33.00

VAT is shown at 17.5%: changes in this rate may affect prices.　　　　**Key to symbols is on back flap.**

Dalmally, Argyll

Map Ref: 1F2

★★

GUEST
HOUSE

Orchy Bank Guest House

Dalmally, Argyll, PA33 1AS
Tel:01838 200370
Email:aj.burke@talk21.com
Web:www.loch-awe.com/orchybank

Victorian house situated on the banks of the River Orchy and surrounded
on 3 sides by mountains over 3000 feet. Fishing, golf, walking and bird
watching. Within 2 hours of Stirling, Glasgow, Fort William, Perth and
Campbeltown and half an hour of Oban and Inveraray. Pets welcome.

2 Single	2 Priv.NOT ensuite	B&B per person	Open Jan-Dec excl
2 Twin	2 Pub.Bath/Show	from £20.00 Single	Xmas/New Year
1 Double		from £20.00 Double	
2 Family			

★★★

B&B

Strathorchy

Dalmally, Argyll, PA33 1AE
Tel/Fax:01838 200373

Recently built traditional style house in countryside setting beside No 1
tee on golf course. Good base for touring Argyll, the glens and islands.
Close to the beautiful Kilchurn Castle at the head of Loch Awe. Walkers
and cyclists welcome. Ideal base for Munro Baggers with 5 in the
surrounding area. Loch fishing nearby.

1 Twin	2 En Suite fac	B&B per person	Open Jan-Dec excl
2 Double	1 Priv.NOT ensuite	from £17.00 Single	Xmas/New Year
		from £17.00 Double	
		from £14.00 Room	
		Only	

Doune, Perthshire

Map Ref: 2A3

Inverardoch Farm House

INVERARDOCH MAINS FARM, DOUNE (B824), DUNBLANE FK15 9NZ
Telephone: 01786 841268 Fax: 01786 841268

Working farm over looking Doune Castle with beautiful views
from the bedrooms. Close to Doune Antique Centre and
Safari Park. 4 miles from Dunblane and Bridge of Allan.
8 miles from Stirling and the Trossachs.

★★

B&B

Farmhouse Bed + Breakfast

Inverardoch Mains Farm, Doune, by Dunblane
Perthshire, FK15 9NZ
Tel:01786 841268   Fax:01786 841268
Email:macanderson@onetel.net.uk

Traditional rural farmhouse on a 200 acre working farm. In a pleasant
rural setting with views over Doune Castle, Ben Ledi and the Campsie
Hills. Convenient for Blair Drummond Safari Park and M9 motorway. A
good touring base for the Trossachs and the Highlands. Private shower
available in bedrooms. A warm welcome awaits you.

1 Twin	1 Priv.NOT ensuite	B&B per person	Open Mar-Oct
1 Double	2 Pub.Bath/Show	from £22.00 Single	
1 Family		from £22.00 Double	

★★★★

B&B

Glenardoch House

Castle Road, Doune, Perthshire, FK16 6EA
Tel:01786 841489

Quality traditional 18th century stone built house by historical Doune
Castle. Set in its own riverside gardens, next to the old bridge. Peaceful
location. Excellent base for exploring the Trossachs and Western
Highlands.

2 Double	All En Suite	B&B per person	Open May-Sep
		from £35.00 Single	
		from £24.00 Double	

Important: Prices stated are estimates and may be subject to amendments

Drymen, Stirlingshire — Map Ref: 1H4

★★★
B&B

The Clachan Inn
2 The Square, Drymen, G63 0BG
Tel:01360 660824

2 Single	1 Priv.NOT ensuite	
1 Double		

B&B per person
from £21.00 Single
from £21.00 Double

Open Jan-Dec excl
Xmas/New Year

The oldest licensed premises in Scotland now has its own Bed & Breakfast adjacent to the Inn. Set in the heart of the village and convenient for the West Highland Way. The village is ideally placed for exploring the east side of Loch Lomond.

★★★
B&B

Easter Drumquhassle Farm
Gartness Road, Drymen, by Loch Lomond, G63 0DN
Tel:01360 660893   Fax:01360 660282
Email:juliamacx.aol.com
Web:http://members.aol.com/juliamacx

1 Twin	All En Suite	
1 Double		
1 Family		

B&B per person
from £28.00 Single
from £19.50 Double

Open Jan-Dec excl
Xmas/New Year
BB & Eve.Meal
from £32.00

Converted granary bedroom and accommodation in the main house, all rooms ensuite and the farmhouse is full of character. Quiet rural location twenty miles from Stirling and Glasgow, one mile from Drymen, the gateway to East Loch Lomond.

★★
B&B

Elmbank B&B
10 Stirling Road, Drymen, Stirlingshire, G63 0BN
Tel:01360 660403
Email:elmbank@amserve.net

1 Single	
3 Twin	
2 Double	

B&B per person
from £25.00 Single
from £20.00 Double

Open Jan-Dec

Self-contained accommodation on first and second floors of traditional stone house in the centre of the village, run personally by the owners who live beneath, on the ground floor. Comfortable relaxed atmosphere.

Dunblane, Perthshire — Map Ref: 2A3

★★★
B&B

Mrs Jean MacGregor
Ciar Mhor, Auchinlay Road, Dunblane, Perthshire
FK15 9JS
Tel:01786 823371

1 Double	All Priv.Fac	
1 Family		

B&B per person
from £20.00 Single
from £18.00 Double

Open Jan-Dec

Modern spacious family home set on the banks of the river Allan, overlooking the park. Set in a peaceful and quiet location on the outskirts of Dunblane within close proximity of the town centre and rail station. Ideal base for touring central Scotland.

Scotland's National Booking and Information Line

Tel: 0845 22 55 121
visitscotland.com

VAT is shown at 17.5%: changes in this rate may affect prices.

Key to symbols is on back flap.

Dunblane, Perthshire

Map Ref: 2A3

★★★★

B&B

Westwood B&B
Doune Road, Kilbryde, Dunblane, Perthshire FK15 9ND
Tel:01786 822579 Fax:01786 825929
Email:lizduncanwestwood@hotmail.com
Web:www.westwoodbandb.co.uk

Ideal base for exploring historic Stirling, the Castle and Wallace Monument. Outdoor activities include golfing, fishing and walking in the beautiful Trossach mountain region. Relaxed and friendly atmosphere in a quiet country setting. Ground floor ensuite room available. Half a mile from A9/M9.

1 Twin	2 En Suite fac	B&B per person	Open Apr-Oct
2 Double	1 Pub.Bath/Show	from £35.00 Single	
		from £22.50 Double	

TV 📺 📶 P 🍵 🔌 ⊁ 🚻 ♿

W V ♿

Dunoon, Argyll

Map Ref: 1F5

★★★★

SMALL
HOTEL

•••

HOME
COOKING

The Anchorage Hotel
Shore Road, Sandbank, by Dunoon, Argyll, PA23 8QG
Tel/Fax:01369 705108
Email:long@anchorage.co.uk
Web:www.anchorage.co.uk

Situated on the shores of the Holy Loch with an immaculate pretty garden. A comfortable lounge and breakfast room take in the stunning lochside scenery. Highland hospitality with homely comfort and individual attention. Luxurious well appointed en-suite bedrooms. Non-smoking throughout. Excellent food using local Scottish produce.

1 Twin	All En Suite	B&B per person	Open Jan-Dec
4 Double		from £35.00 Single	BB & Eve.Meal
		from £30.00 Double	from £45.00

TV 🛏 P 🍵 ⊁ 🍴 📺 🍷

🏧 V ⊙ ♿

★★★★

SMALL
HOTEL

••

RESTAURANT

Enmore Hotel
Marine Parade, Dunoon, Argyll, PA23 8HH
Tel:01369 702230 Fax:01369 702148
Email:enmorehotel@btinternet.com
Web:www.enmorehotel.co.uk

Personal attention assured at this elegant Georgian House set in its own garden overlooking the Firth of Clyde. Each room tastefully decorated and furnished to create a relaxing atmosphere. Award winning restaurant and Taste of Scotland member. Squash courts and four poster rooms, some with double spa baths.

2 Twin	All En Suite	B&B per person	Open mid Feb-mid Dec
6 Double		from £55.00 Single	BB & Eve.Meal
1 Family		from £45.00 Double	from £70.00

TV 📞 🛏 P 🍵 🔌 ⊁ 🍴 📺 🍷

C 🐕 🏧 W V ⊙

🏊 ✏

★★

B&B

Foxbank
Marine Parades, Hunters Quay, Dunoon, Argyll PA23 8HJ
Tel:01369 703858
Email:lawther@foxbank.co.uk

A warm Scottish welcome is assured in this comfortable family home located on the promenade with excellent views over the Firth of Clyde. Hearty breakfasts are provided. Fifteen minutes walk to the town centre and convenient for both ferries. Good selection of hotels and restaurants in the area. A peaceful area for relaxation. Beautiful scenery.

2 Twin	Some En Suite	B&B per person	Open Jan-Dec
1 Family	Ensuite	from £18.00 Single	
		from £22.50 Double	

TV 📺 📶 P 🍵 🔌 ⊁ ♿

C 🐕 V

Scotland's National Booking and Information Line

Tel: 0845 22 55 121
visitscotland.com

Important: Prices stated are estimates and may be subject to amendments

Dunoon, Argyll
Map Ref: 1F5

★★★

SMALL HOTEL

Lyall Cliff Hotel
Alexandra Parade, East Bay, Dunoon, Argyll
PA23 8AW
Tel/Fax:01369 702041
Email:lyallcliff@talk21.com
Web:www.lyallcliff.co.uk

4 Twin	All En Suite	B&B per person	Open Jan-Oct
4 Double		from £25.00 Single	BB & Eve.Meal
2 Family		from £21.00 Double	from £34.00
		from £20.00 Room	
		Only	

Beautifully situated, family-run hotel on the sea-front, with lovely garden
and private car-park. 3 ground-floor bedrooms, marvellous sea-views,
and excellent food. Short breaks and music/themed weekends available
spring and autumn. German spoken.

★★

SMALL HOTEL

Mayfair Hotel
Clyde Street, Kirn, Dunoon, Argyll, PA23 8DX
Tel/Fax:01369 702182
Email:mckellarw@aol.com
Web:www.mayfairhoteldunoon.co.uk

1 Single	All En Suite	B&B per person	Open Jan-Dec excl
2 Twin		from £25.00 Single	Xmas/New Year
3 Double		from £21.00 Double	BB & Eve.Meal
1 Family		from £17.00 Room	from £30.00
		Only	

Family run hotel, all rooms with en suite facilities and some with views to
the Firth of Clyde. Golfing and walking packages. Short break rates
available. Some ground floor accommodation.

Falkirk, Stirlingshire
Map Ref: 2A4

ASHBANK GUEST HOUSE
105 MAIN ST, REDDING, FALKIRK FK2 9UQ
TEL: 01324 716649 FAX: 01324 712431
e.mail: ashbank@guest-house.freeserve.co.uk Web: www.BandBfalkirk.com
Victorian cottage with friendly Scottish welcome. Near M9 motorway and mainline
station. Comfortable individualised bedrooms with great views to hills and river yet
close to all amenities. Off-street parking. Easy access to all major cities and towns in
central Scotland. Ideal touring base for visiting the Trossachs and Loch Lomond.

★★★

GUEST HOUSE

Ashbank Guest House
105 Main Street, Redding, Falkirk, FK2 9UQ
Tel:01324 716649 Fax:01324 712431
Email:ashbank@guest-house.freeserve.co.uk
Web:www.ashbank.falkirkwheel.net

2 Twin	All En Suite	B&B per person	Open Jan-Dec
1 Double		from £30.00 Single	
		from £25.00 Double	

Victorian home - all rooms recently refurbished. Motorway and rail links
very accessible. Ample off street parking. On the outskirts of Falkirk,
junction 5 of M9.

★★★

RESTAURANT WITH ROOMS

Beancross
West Beancross Farm, Polmont, Falkirk
Stirlingshire, FK2 0XS Tel:01324 718333 Fax:01324 718222
Email:mailroom@beancross.com
Web:www.beancross.com

1 Double	All En Suite	B&B per person	Open Jan-Dec
13 Family		£50.00-65.00 Room	
		Only	

Close to Junction 5 on the M9 motorway, we are ideally situated for travel in
central Scotland, and to Glasgow and Edinburgh. Our Millennium individually
designed rooms are popular with corporate guests and tourists alike. Traditional
on the outside, thoroughly modern interpretation on the inside, Beancross
features four stylishly designed dining venues under one roof. Freshly prepared
food served day and night.

VAT is shown at 17.5%: changes in this rate may affect prices. | Key to symbols is on back flap.

Falkirk, Stirlingshire | Map Ref: 2A4

Darroch House
Camelon Road, Falkirk FK1 5SQ
Tel: 01324 623041 Fax: 01324 626288 e.mail: darroch@amserve.net
Exceptionally spacious and comfortable accommodation in Victorian manor peacefully situated in nine acres of grounds yet only ten minutes walk from town centre. Close to canal network and millennium link 'wheel' boatlift. Centrally situated permitting easy day trips to Edinburgh, Glasgow, Stirling, St Andrews, Perth, Trossachs and much more.

★★★★
B&B

Darroch House
Camelon Road, Falkirk, FK1 5SQ
Tel:01324 623041   Fax:01324 626288
Email:darroch@amserve.net

1 Twin	All En Suite	B&B per person	Open Jan-Dec
2 Double		from £45.00 Single	BB & Eve.Meal
		from £25.00 Double	from £45.00

Built in 1838. Family home. Well-proportioned, Victorian manor house, set in 9 acres of garden and woodland in the heart of Falkirk. Traditional Scottish breakfast is served in the original dining room overlooking the donkey pasture.

★★★
B&B

Hawthorndean
Wallacestone Brae, Reddingmuirhead, by Falkirk
Stirlingshire, FK2 0DQ
Tel/Fax:01324 715840
Email:eileenstrain@yahoo.co.uk

1 Single	1 En Suite fac	B&B per person	Open Jan-Dec
1 Twin	1 Priv.NOT ensuite	from £22.00 Single	
1 Double		from £20.00 Double	
		from £18.00 Room	
		Only	

Traditional renovated 19th century 2 storey cottage with log fire. Quiet location in a residential area with interesting garden. Easy access to Motorway links throughout Central Scotland. Ample parking available and Sky Digital TV lounge.

Helensburgh, Argyll | Map Ref: 1G4

★★★★
B&B

Arran View
32 Barclay Drive, Helensburgh, G84 9RA
Tel:01436 673713 Fax:01436 672595
Email:arranview@btinternet.com
Web:www.btinternet.com/~arranview

2 Single	Some En Suite	B&B per person	Open Jan-Dec
1 Twin	1 Pub.Bath/Show	£20.00-25.00 Single	
1 Double		£19.00-22.00 Double	

Welcome, warmth and walks offered at our peaceful hillside home overlooking Firth of Clyde, ten minutes from Loch Lomond, one hour from Stirling, Trossachs and Inverary, half hourly train service to Glasgow. Locally, visit National Trust Hill House, walk, golf, sail and shop. Enjoy seasonal fruit from garden, home made preserves, Scottish bacon, eggs, sausages or fish. Comfortable sitting room available.

★★★★
B&B

Balmillig B&B
64B Colquhoun Street, Helensburgh, nr Loch Lomond G84 9JP
Tel:01436 674922 Fax:01436 679913
Email:theurquharts@sol.co.uk
Web:www.sol.co.uk/t/theurquharts

1 Twin	All En Suite	B&B per person	Open Jan-Dec
1 Double		from £25.00 Single	
		from £25.00 Double	

Although built in 2001, our home has the look of a much older building to match the period of the neighbouring 'Thorndean' which we used to operate as a B&B. Our new home makes great use of natural light and our conservatory is for your use all day but we are sure that with Loch Lomond beckoning you will not have much free time.

Important: Prices stated are estimates and may be subject to amendments

Helensburgh, Argyll

Map Ref: 1G4

★★★

B&B

Bonniebrae B+B
80 Sinclair Street, Helensburgh, Dunbartonshire
G84 8TU
Tel:01436 671469
Email:kbonniebrae@aol.com

Traditional stonebuilt cottage, two minutes walk from centre of town with
its shops and restaurants. Private garden and off road parking. 4 miles
from Loch Lomond. 40 minutes via Erskine Bridge to Glasgow Airport.

1 Twin	All En Suite	B&B per person	Open Jan-Dec excl
1 Family		from £24.00 Single	Xmas/New Year
		from £22.00 Double	

★★★

B&B

Eastbank B&B
10 Hanover Street, Helensburgh, Argyll, G84 7AW
Tel/Fax:01436 673665
Email:enquiries@eastbankscotland.com
Web:www.eastbankscotland.com

1st floor flat conversion with all accommodation on same level. Fine
views from lounge across the Clyde to Greenock. Knitting instruction
available.

| 1 Twin | 1 En Suite fac | B&B per person | Open Jan-Dec |
| 1 Family | | from £18.00 Double | |

★★★

B&B

Ravenswood
32 Suffolk Street, Helensburgh, G84 9PA
Tel/Fax:01436 672112
Email:ravenswoodg84@aol.com
Web:www.stayatlochlomond.com/ravenswood

Relax in the garden or our elegant lounge after breakfasting from an
extensive selection that concentrates on fresh, local produce. The town is
a stroll away and has a range of shops, restaurants and pubs. A sample
selection of menus is kept handy for guests to peruse. Sailing and golf
are available locally. Local walkers and cycle routes are covered in our
extensive area information available to all guests.

2 Single	2 En Suite fac	B&B per person	Open Jan-Dec
1 Twin	1 Priv.NOT ensuite	from £25.00 Single	
1 Double	1 Pub.Bath/Show	from £25.00 Double	

Inversnaid, Stirlingshire

Map Ref: 1G3

★★

B&B

Corriearklet B&B
Inversnaid, Stirling, FK8 3TU
Tel:01877 386208
Email:corriearklet_inversnaid@msn.com

Overlooking Loch Arklet with surrounding hills. Ideal for cyclists, walking,
photography or just relaxing. Good food and congenial hosts. Evening
meal + packed lunches can be arranged.

1 Single	Shared facilities	B&B per person	Open Jan-Dec excl
1 Triple	Bath+Shower	from £30.00 Single	Xmas/New Year
1 Twin		from £25.00 Double	BB & Eve.Meal
		from £20.00 Room	from £35.00
		Only	

Iona, Isle of, Argyll

Map Ref: 1B2

★★

B&B

Finlay Ross (Iona) Ltd
Martyr's Bay, Isle of Iona, Argyll, PA76 6SP
Tel:01681 700357   Fax:01681 700562
Email:finlayross@ukgateway.net

Purpose built rooms some with television all on one level and convenient
for the ferry. Continental breakfast served. Also cottage annexe with TV
lounge.

1 Single	4 En Suite fac	B&B per person	Open Jan-Dec
8 Twin	3 Priv.NOT ensuite	from £27.00 Single	
2 Double	1 Pub.Bath/Show	from £23.50 Double	
2 Family			

VAT is shown at 17.5%: changes in this rate may affect prices.

Key to symbols is on back flap.

Ballygrant, Isle of Islay, Argyll — Map Ref: 1C5

★★★★★

GUEST
HOUSE

●●●●

HOME
COOKING

Kilmeny Country Guest House
Ballygrant, Isle of Islay, PA45 7QW
Tel/Fax:01496 840668
Email:info@kilmeny.co.uk
Web:www.kilmeny.co.uk

Traditional farmhouse approximately 180 years old on 300 acre beef farm. Country house atmosphere with emphasis on a warm welcome and personal service. A fine dining experience in elegant surroundings. The Guest House is ideally situated for days out to the Islands of Jura and Colonsay. Non-smoking house.

1 Twin	All En Suite	B&B per person	Open Jan-Dec excl
2 Double		from £44.00 Double	Xmas/New Year
			BB & Eve.Meal
			from £68.00

Lagavulin, by Port Ellen, Isle of Islay, Argyll — Map Ref: 1C6

★★★

B&B

Tigh na Suil
Lagavulin, by Port Ellen, Isle of Islay, PA42 7DX
Tel/Fax:01496 302483

A warm friendly welcome to our home. Good food. All rooms fully en-suite. Free fly fishing. Peaceful, rural village location. Distillery tours arranged with pleasure.

1 Twin	All En Suite	B&B per person	Open Jan-Dec
1 Double		from £30.00 Single	
		from £22.00 Double	

Port Charlotte, Isle of Islay, Argyll — Map Ref: 1B6

★★★★

SMALL
HOTEL

The Port Charlotte Hotel
Isle of Islay, Argyll, PA48 7TU
Tel:01496 850360   Fax:01496 850361
Email:car1@portcharlottehotel.co.uk
Web:www.portcharlottehotel.co.uk

Restored Victorian hotel offering all modern facilities in an informal, relaxed atmosphere, situated in this picturesque conservation village on the west shore of Loch Indaal. Fresh local seafood, lamb and beef. Distillery visits, fishing and golfing can be arranged.

2 Single	All En Suite	B&B per person	Open Jan-Dec excl
2 Twin		from £59.00 Single	Xmas
5 Double		from £47.50 Double	BB & Eve.Meal
1 Family			from £70.00

Killin, Perthshire — Map Ref: 1H2

FAIRVIEW HOUSE
Main Street, Killin, Perthshire FK21 8UT
Telephone: 01567 820667 Fax: 01567 820667
e.mail: info@fairview-killin.co.uk Web: www.fairview-killin.co.uk

You will receive a warm welcome to our friendly, comfortable guest house set in a picturesque village. Relax by an open fire in the residents lounge with breathtaking views of the central highlands. Excellent off-street parking, good drying facilities, and home-cooked evening meals are also on offer.

★★★

GUEST
HOUSE

●●●

HOME
COOKING

Fairview House
Main Street, Killin, Perthshire, FK21 8UT
Tel:01567 820667
Email:info@fairview-killin.co.uk
Web:www.fairview-killin.co.uk

Family run guest house specialising in home cooking. Excellent touring centre, good walking and climbing area.

1 Single	5 En Suite fac	B&B per person	Open Jan-Dec
1 Twin	2 priv.NOT En Suite	from £25.00 Single	
3 Double		from £22.00 Double	
1 Family			

Important: Prices stated are estimates and may be subject to amendments

Lochearnhead, Perthshire

Map Ref: 1H2

★★★

GUEST HOUSE

Mansewood Country House
Lochearnhead, Perthshire, FK19 8NS
Tel:01567 830213 Fax:01567 830485
Email:katiestalker@aol.com
Web:www.mansewood-country-house.co.uk

This former country manse, which has a great deal of character, has six en-suite bedrooms one of which is on the ground floor. Friendly, cosy atmosphere in the lounges. Ideal for hill walking and the local water sports activities.

1 Twin	All En Suite	B&B per person	Open Jan-Dec
5 Double		from £30.00 Single	
		from £25.00 Double	

Lochgilphead, Argyll

Map Ref: 1E4

★★

SMALL HOTEL

Stag Hotel & Restaurant
Argyll Street, Lochgilphead, Argyll, PA31 8NE
Tel:01546 602496 Fax:01546 603549
Email:staghotel@ukhotels.com
Web:www.staghotel.com

Traditional family run country town hotel offering clean comfortable accommodation with lounge bar/restaurant and public bar areas. Open all year round and ideal for touring, walking, fishing and golfing in Mid-Argyll. Special autumn and winter breaks available on request.

4 Single	All En Suite	B&B per person	Open Jan-Dec
8 Twin		from £39.95 Single	BB & Eve.Meal
6 Double		from £27.50 Double	from £37.50
		from £22.50 Room Only	

---

by Lochgilphead, Argyll

Map Ref: 1E4

SOMERLED

Dunadd View, Bridgend, Kilmichael, Glassary, by Lochgilphead, Argyll PA31 8QA
Tel: 01546 605226 Fax: 01546 605299
e.mail: somerledbridgend@aol.com

Somerled is a new country house set in Kilmartin Glen with views of historic Dunadd Fort and Standing Stones. Also close to Crinan Canal and Kilmartin. Ideal base for touring, walking, fishing.
Spacious accommodation. Price: single from £22. Double twin from £20 pppn.

★★★

B&B

Somerled Bed+Breakfast
Dunadd View, Bridgend
Kilmichael-Glassary, by Lochgilphead, Argyll PA31 8QA
Tel:01546 605226 Fax:01546 605229
Email:somerledbridgend@aol.com

Somerled is a new country house within the village of Bridgend, set in Kilmartin Glen 5 miles from Lochgilphead on the A816. Within walking distance lies Dunadd Fort. We are close to many forest walks and cycle routes. The area is a haven for wildlife and birds and there are many lochs for fishing. We are approximately 2 hours from Glasgow. All bedrooms are ensuite and spacious. Two double and one twin.

1 Twin	All En Suite	B&B per person	Open Jan-Dec excl
2 Double		from £22.00 Single	Xmas/New Year
		from £20.00 Double	
		from £15.00 Room Only	

Lochgoilhead, Argyll

Map Ref: 1F3

★★★★

B&B

Ben Bheula B&B
Lochgoilhead, Argyll & Bute, PA24 8AH
Tel:01301 703508 Fax:01301 703337
Email:benbheula@aol.com

A warm welcome awaits you at our Victorian home set in the heart of Argyll Forest Park. Stunning views over loch and Cowal mountains. Superb walking country. Extensive lochside woodland garden attracts wildlife particularly red squirrels and deer. Many amenities in village include boat hire, fishing and leisure centre with indoor swimming pool, bowls, golf and pony trekking. Relax in tranquil friendly surroundings.

3 Double	2 En Suite fac	B&B per person	Open Mar-Jan excl
	1 Pub.Bath/Show	from £32.50 Single	Xmas/New Year
		from £27.50 Double	

VAT is shown at 17.5%: changes in this rate may affect prices. | Key to symbols is on back flap. |

Luss, Argyll & Bute | Map Ref: 1G4

POLNABEROCH B&B

POLNABEROCH, ARDEN, BY LUSS, LOCH LOMOND G83 8RQ
Telephone/Fax: 01389 850615 e.mail: maclomond@sol.co.uk
Charming country cottage in beautiful gardens amidst lovely
scenery minutes from Loch Lomond golf course. Ideal base
for touring. Guests sitting room and separate dining room.
Tranquil setting surrounded by fields and hills.

★★★★

B&B

Polnaberoch B&B

Arden, By Luss, Loch Lomond, G83 8RQ
Tel/Fax:01389 850615
Email:maclomond@sol.co.uk

1 Twin	All En Suite	B&B per person	Open Apr-Nov
1 Double		£23.00-30.00 Double	

Traditional country cottage in a tranquil rural setting with large, colourful
garden. Short distance from Loch Lomond, golf courses and country
walks. Several eating places within 10 minutes drive. Enjoy beautiful
sunsets from our conservatory.

Shantron Farm

Mobile:
07768 378400

Shantron Farm, Luss, Alexandria G83 8RH
Telephone: 01389 850231 Fax: 01389 850231
e.mail: rjlennox@shantron.u−net.com
Web: www.stayatlochlomond.com/shantron

Enjoy a relaxing break in a spacious bungalow with outstanding views of Loch
Lomond. Our 5,000-acre hill farm is the setting for Morag's croft in "Take the
High Road" thirty minutes from Glasgow Airport. An ideal touring base and for
hillwalking, fishing, watersports, golf. Large garden for guests' enjoyment.

★★★

B&B

Shantron Farm

Shantron Farm, Luss, by Alexandria, Dunbartonshire G83 8RH
Tel/Fax:01389 850231
Email:rjlennox@shantron.u-net.com
Web:www.stayatlochlomond.com

1 Twin	All En Suite	B&B per person	Open Mar-Nov
1 Double		from £22.00 Double	
1 Family			

Cottage in elevated position with panoramic views over Loch Lomond to
the Campsie Fells. Farm is used regularly for filming of 'High Road'. Real
fire in the guests' lounge.

Bunessan, Isle of Mull, Argyll | Map Ref: 1C3

★★★

SMALL
HOTEL

Ardachy House Hotel

Uisken, by Bunessan, Isle of Mull, Argyll
PA67 6DS
Tel:01681 700505 Fax:01681 700797
Email:info@ardachy.co.uk

3 Single	7 En Suite fac	B&B per person	Open Mar-Oct
1 Twin	1 Priv.NOT ensuite	from £35.00 Single	BB & Eve.Meal
3 Double		from £35.00 Double	from £54.50
1 Family			

Small, secluded, personally-run hotel, 7 miles (11 kms) from Iona. Safe
access to white sands of Ardalanish Beach. Spectacular views to Colonsay,
Jura and Islay. 1 room without ensuite. Non-resident dinner available by
prior arrangement.

Important: Prices stated are estimates and may be subject to amendments

Bunessan, Isle of Mull, Argyll　　　　　Map Ref: 1C3

ARDNESS HOUSE
BUNESSAN, ISLE OF MULL, ARGYLL PA67 6DU
TEL/FAX: 01681 700260
e.mail: ardness@supanet.com Web: www.isleofmullholidays.com
Ardness House is a family run Bed & Breakfast situated in a
spectacular location 3 miles from ferries to Iona and Staffa.
En-suite bedrooms are tastefully decorated. Perfect location for
birdwatching, walking, exploring deserted sandy bays, observing
the unique wildlife that roam free in their natural environment.

★★★　B&B

Ardness House
Bunessan, Isle of Mull, Argyll, PA67 6DU
Tel/Fax:01681 700260
Email:ardness@supanet.com
Web:www.isleofmullholidays.com

A well appointed modern bungalow with all bedrooms ensuite. Guests
lounge with panoramic views of Loch Caol and dramatic cliffs beyond.
Three and a half miles from Iona ferry.

1 Twin　All En Suite　B&B per person　Open Easter-Oct
2 Double　　　　　from £18.00 Double

---

by Craignure, Isle of Mull, Argyll　　　　　Map Ref: 1D2

★★★★　B&B

Inverlussa Bed+Breakfast
by Craignure, Isle of Mull, PA65 6BD
Tel:01680 812436 Fax:01680 812137

Personally run modern house in idyllic setting. 6 miles/10 minutes from
Craignure ferry. Ideal base for touring Isle of Mull.

1 Single　1 En Suite fac　B&B per person　Open Apr-Oct
2 Twin　1 Priv.NOT ensuite　from £20.00 Single
2 Double　　　　　from £20.00 Double
1 Family

Dervaig, Isle of Mull, Argyll　　　　　Map Ref: 1C1

★★★　B&B

Achnacraig
Dervaig, Tobermory, Isle of Mull, PA75 6QW
Tel:01688 400309

Winding river, circling buzzards, stone farmhouse, stupendous views.
Dinner available with prior arrangement featuring home grown organic
produce and real cooking. Courtesy mountain bikes available. 4 miles (8
km) from Dervaig.

1 Single　2 Priv.NOT ensuite　B&B per person　Open May-Sep
1 Twin　　　from £20.00 Single　BB & Eve.Meal
1 Double　　　from £20.00 Double　from £34.00

★★★★　B&B

Balmacara
Dervaig, Isle of Mull, PA75 6QN
Tel/Fax:01688 400363
Email:balmacara@mull.com
Web:www.balmacara.mull.com

Modern property set high above Dervaig village with magnificent views
over Glen Bellart and Loch Cuin, framed by the hills and forests of North
West Mull.

2 Twin　2 En Suite fac　B&B per person　Open Jan-Dec excl
1 Double　1 Pub.Bath/Show　from £40.00 Single　Xmas/New Year
　　　from £27.50 Double　BB & Eve.Meal
　　　　　from £42.50

VAT is shown at 17.5%: changes in this rate may affect prices.　　　*Key to symbols is on back flap.*

Dervaig, Isle of Mull, Argyll   Map Ref: 1C1

CUIN LODGE

DERVAIG, ISLE OF MULL PA75 6QL
TEL: 01688 400346 E.MAIL: cuin-lodge@mull.com
WEB: www.cuin-lodge.mull.com

Cuin Lodge is a traditional 19th century former shooting lodge. One mile from Dervaig. You can relax and enjoy views of the Loch and Mull mountains from the conservatory. Ideally situated for walkers and wild life enthusiasts, you can be sure of a warm welcome and good home cooking.

B&B

Cuin Lodge

Dervaig, Isle of Mull, PA75 6QL
Tel:01688 400346
Email:cuin-lodge@mull.com Web:www.cuin-lodge.mull.com

Stone built 19th Century shooting lodge overlooking Loch Chumhainn a mile outside Dervaig. Tastefully modernised, the Conservatory offers panoramic views of Loch and mountains. Cuin Lodge has a secluded position where guests can relax and enjoy meals cooked in the AGA with locally produced ingredients. Ideally situated for ramblers and wild life enthusiasts with Otters in the loch and birdlife both varied and plentiful.

1 Single	2 En Suite fac	B&B per person	Open Mar-Oct
1 Twin	1 Pub.Bath.Show	from £17.50 Single	BB & Eve.Meal
1 Double		from £22.00 Double	from £31.00-35.50

B&B

Inishkea

Dervaig, Isle of Mull, Argyll, PA75 6QW
Tel/Fax:01688 400296
Email:hcwood@compuserve.com

Surrounded by woodland with panoramic views over loch and glen. Emphasis on using local and home grown organic produce. Garden, patio, secure parking.

1 Twin	All En Suite	B&B per person	Open Easter-Nov
2 Double		from £25.00 Double	

Fionnphort, Isle of Mull, Argyll   Map Ref: 1C2

Achaban House

Fionnphort, Isle of Mull PA66 6BL
Tel: 01681 700205 Fax: 01681 700649
e.mail: camilla@achabanhouse.com Web: www.achabanhouse.com

Achaban House, an old manse, is a haven of tranquility, attractively appointed overlooking a fresh water loch, one mile to Fionnphort and the Iona/Staffa ferry. The bedrooms have beautiful views and en-suite facilities. Log fire in the evenings. The area is rich in birdlife, splendid beaches and unique geology.

GUEST HOUSE

Achaban House

Fionnphort, Isle of Mull, PA66 6BL
Tel:01681 700205 Fax: 01681 700649
Email:camilla@achabanhouse.com
Web:www.achabanhouse.com

This is a delightful former manse which is set within its own grounds just a short distance inland from the village of Fionnphort and the ferry to Iona. Peaceful, relaxing away -from-the-road location with views towards Loch Pottie. Your hosts will afford you a very warm welcome and help you to enjoy the very best this beautiful part of Mull has to offer.

1 Single	All En Suite	B&B per person	Open Jan-Dec
2 Twin		from £25	
2 Double			
1 Family			

Important: Prices stated are estimates and may be subject to amendments

Kinlochspelve, Isle of Mull, Argyll — Map Ref: 1D2

★★★★

B&B

The Barn
Barrachandroman, Kinlochspelve, Lochbuie
Isle of Mull, PA62 6AA
Tel:01680 814220 Fax:01680 814247
Email:spelve@aol.com
Web:www.barrachandroman.co.uk

Luxuriously converted barn in secluded lochside location, both rooms with private facilities. Accent on fresh fish and seafood.

2 Double	1 En Suite fac	B&B per person	Open Feb-Dec excl
	1 Prv.Bath/Show	from £20.00 Single	Xmas/New Year
		from £26.00 Double	BB & Eve.Meal
		from £15.00 Room	from £43.00
		Only	

Salen, Aros, Isle of Mull, Argyll — Map Ref: 1D1

★★★

B&B

Callachally Farm
Salen, Aros, Isle of Mull, PA72 6JN
Tel/Fax:01680 300424
Email:macphail@tiscali.co.uk

Comfortable bungalow in peaceful location overlooking surrounding farmland to hills beyond. Short walk to coast and sea views. Ideal for touring, walking, wildlife and bird watching.

| 1 Twin | 1 Priv.NOT ensuite | B&B per person | Open Apr-Oct |
| 1 Double | | from £18.00 Double | |

★★★

B&B

Fascadail
Salen, Aros, Isle of Mull, PA72 6JB
Tel:01680 300444
Email:keivers@tesco.net
Web:www.zynet.co.uk/mull/fascadail

Very comfortable bed and breakfast accommodation in this family home. Located in Salen, centrally situated in Mull for easy exploration of the island. Excellent base for those wishing to experience the delights of the great outdoors.

1 Twin	All En Suite	B&B per person	Open Jan-Dec
2 Double		from £25.00 Single	
		from £20.00 Double	

Tobermory, Isle of Mull, Argyll — Map Ref: 1C1

★★★★

B&B

Glengorm Castle
Tobermory, Isle of Mull, Argyll, PA75 6QE
Tel:01688 302321 Fax:01688 302738
Email:enquiries@glengormcastle.co.uk
Web:www.glengormcastle.co.uk

Spectacularly set overlooking the wild Atlantic breakers to the Western Isles beyond this fairytale Baronial Castle offers a unique experience never to be forgotten. Generous size rooms, log fires in season and a charming hostess along with magnificent breakfasts offering the best of Mull produce.

2 Twin	4 En Suite fac	B&B per person	Open Jan-Dec
3 Double	1 Pub.Bath/Show	from £90.00 Single	
		from £45.00 Double	

Oban, Argyll — Map Ref: 1E2

★★★★

B&B

Aros Ard
Croft Road, Oban, Argyll, PA34 5JN
Tel/Fax:01631 565500
Email:macleanarosad@ukgateway.net
Web:www.oban.org.uk/accommodation/arosard

Set up above the town this modern house offers two very spacious bedrooms occupying the entire first floor. Both with picture windows with beautiful views of Oban Bay. Each room is supplied with TV/video/mini-fridge/tea and coffee tray and hairdryer and comfortable sofa and chairs. Very friendly and hospitable hosts. Ample private parking.

2 Family	All En Suite	B&B per person	Open Mar-Nov
		from £40.00 Single	
		from £22.00 Double	

VAT is shown at 17.5%: changes in this rate may affect prices.

Key to symbols is on back flap.

Important: Prices stated are estimates and may be subject to amendments

Oban, Argyll

Map Ref: 1E2

BRACKER

Polvinister Road, Oban, Argyll PA34 5TN
Telephone: 01631 564302 Fax: 01631 571167
e.mail: cmacdonald@connectfree.co.uk
Web: www.bracker.co.uk

Modern bungalow situated in beautiful quiet residential area within walking distance of town (approx. 8-10 mins.) and the golf course. All bedrooms have private facilities, TV and tea/coffee-making. TV lounge, private parking. Non Smoking.

★★★

B&B

Bracker

Polvinister Road, Oban, Argyll, PA34 5TN
Tel:01631 564302 Fax:01631 571167
Email:cmacdonald@connectfree.co.uk
Web:www.bracker.co.uk

A warm welcome is assured at this modern family bungalow situated in a secluded residential area located a short distance from Oban town centre and all amenities. Private parking. Full en suite.

1 Twin	All En Suite	B&B per person	Open Apr-Oct
2 Double		from £18.00 Single	
		from £18.00 Double	
		from £15.00 Room	
		Only	

★★★★

GUEST HOUSE

Dom-Muir Guest House

Pulpit Hill, Oban, Argyll, PA34 4LX
Tel:01631 564536 Fax:01631 563739
Email:peigi@donmuir.fsnet.co.uk

Set in quiet residential area, high up on Pulpit Hill and close to public transport terminals. A short walk away are 360 degree views of Oban, the bay and its ferries. Parking available.

1 Twin	All En Suite	B&B per person	Open Mar-Oct
3 Double		from £20.00 Double	

★★★

B&B

Drumriggend

Drummore Road, Oban, Argyll, PA34 4JL
Tel:01631 563330 Fax:01631 564217

Detached house in quiet residential area. Situated on the south side of town about 1 mile (2kms) from the centre. All bedrooms comfortably furnished with ensuite facilities, TV's and tea-trays. Separate lounge available for guests' use. Ample private parking.

1 Twin	All En Suite	B&B per person	Open Jan-Dec
1 Double		£17.00-20.00 Double	
1 Family			

★★★★

B&B

Dungrianach

Pulpit Hill, Oban, Argyll, PA34 4LU
Tel/Fax:01631 562840
Email:enquiries@dungrianach.com
Web:www.dungrianach.com

Secluded, in 4 acres of wooded garden on top of Pulpit Hill. Magnificent views over Oban Bay and the islands.

1 Twin	All En Suite	B&B per person	Open Easter-Sep
1 Double		from £35.00 Single	
		from £25.00 Double	

VAT is shown at 17.5%: changes in this rate may affect prices.

Key to symbols is on back flap.

| Oban, Argyll | | | | Map Ref: 1E2 |

B&B ★★

Firgrove Bed+Breakfast
Ardconnel Road, Oban, Argyll, PA34 5DW
Tel/Fax:01631 565250
Email:wilson.catering@tiscali.co.uk
Web:www.accommodation-in-argyll.co.uk

2 Twin	2 Priv.NOT ensuite	B&B per person	Open Jan-Dec
1 Double		from £18.50 Single	
		from £16.00 Double	
		from £13.50 Room	
		Only	

Victorian villa overlooking Oban Bay. Elevated position only 3 minutes walk to town centre and 2 minutes to leisure centre and swimming pool. Oban is an ideal base for visiting all Western Islands and the North of Scotland. Private parking.

GUEST HOUSE ★★★★

Glenburnie House
Esplanade, Oban, Argyll, PA34 5AQ
Tel/Fax:01631 562089
Email:Graeme.Strachan@btinternet.com
Web:www.glenburnie.co.uk

2 Single	All En Suite	B&B per person	Open Mar-Nov
4 Twin		from £28.00 Single	
8 Double		from £28.00 Double	

Convenient for town centre and all amenities, this family run hotel has magnificent views of the bay and islands. Recently refurbished superior rooms.

GREENCOURT GUEST HOUSE

BENVOULLIN LANE, OFF BENVOULLIN ROAD, OBAN, ARGYLL PA34 5EF
TEL: 01631 563987 FAX: 01631 571276
E.MAIL: stay@greencourt-oban.fsnet.co.uk
WEB: www.greencourt-oban.fsnet.co.uk

AA ◆◆◆◆ Guest Accommodation

Experience genuine Highland hospitality, delicious breakfasts featuring local produce, immaculate ensuite rooms and exceptional standards at Greencourt. Peaceful situation, relaxing garden, unique views and ample car parking. All rooms easily accessible on entrance level. Totally non-smoking. Fiddle/accordion-playing hosts Joanie and Michael Garvin even provide a few tunes on request!

GUEST HOUSE ★★★★

Greencourt Guest House
Benvoullin Lane, Benvoullin Road, Oban, Argyll PA34 5EF
Tel:01631 563987 Fax:01631 571276
Email:stay@greencourt-oban.fsnet.co.uk
Web:www.greencourt-oban.fsnet.co.uk

1 Single	5 En Suite fac	B&B per person	Open Jan-Dec
2 Twin	3 Pub.Bath/Show	from £23.00 Single	
5 Double		from £23.00 Double	

Spacious family run property in quiet situation overlooking outdoor bowling green, a short stroll to town centre and adjacent to leisure centre. Attractive rooms, wholesome breakfasts, private parking. Ideal touring base.

B&B ★★★

Harlaw
Glenmore Road, Oban, Argyll, PA34 4ND
Tel:01631 563295

1 Single	2 Priv.Bath/Show	B&B per person	Open Apr-Oct
2 Double		from £18.00 Single	
		from £18.00 Double	

Comfortable accommodation in quiet residential area within walking distance of all amenities. One double and single only let for party of 3.

Important: Prices stated are estimates and may be subject to amendments

Oban, Argyll

Map Ref: 1E2

★★★★

B&B

Hawthorn
Benderloch, Argyll, PA37 1QS
Tel:01631 720452
Email:junecurrie@hotmail.com
Web:www.hawthorn-cottages.co.uk

1 Twin	3 En Suite fac	B&B per person	Open Jan-Dec
2 Double	1 Pub.Bath/Show	from £25.00 Single	BB & Eve.Meal
1 Family		from £18.50 Double	from £30.00

Family bungalow in peaceful rural setting 9 miles (14kms) from Oban and ferry terminals for the islands. 5 minutes walk from the excellent sandy beaches of Tralee Bay. Own restaurant adjacent. Ensuite rooms available.

Hawthornbank Guest House
Dalriach Road, Oban PA34 5JE
Tel: 01631 562041   e.mail: hawthornbank@aol.com
Web: www.SmoothHound.co.uk/hotels/hawthorn.html
Brian and Valerie welcome you to their tastefully refurbished Victorian villa. Immaculate, well-equipped, en-suite rooms. Two feature rooms: Regency with 4-poster and Victorian with brass bed. Beautiful views over Oban Bay. Close to sports centre. Five minutes walk to town centre. Private parking. Non-smoking.

★★★★

GUEST
HOUSE

Hawthornbank Guest House
Dalriach Road, Oban, Argyll, PA34 5JE
Tel:01631 562041
Email:hawthornbank@aol.com
Web:www.SmoothHound.co.uk/hotels/hawthorn.html

1 Single	All En Suite	B&B per person	Open Jan-Dec excl
1 Twin	1 Pub.Bath/Show	from £20.00 Single	Xmas/New Year
6 Double		from £25.00 Double	

Brian and Valerie look forward to welcoming you to Hawthornbank, a tastefully refurbished Victorian villa set in a quiet location yet only a short stroll from the town centre. Comfortable well equipped rooms some with stunning views over Oban Bay. How can you resist?

Scotland's National Booking and Information Line

Tel: 0845 22 55 121
visitscotland.com

VAT is shown at 17.5%: changes in this rate may affect prices.

Key to symbols is on back flap.

Oban, Argyll   Map Ref: 1E2

Kilchrenan House

Corran Esplanade, Oban, Argyll PA34 5AQ
Tel: 01631 562663 Fax: 01631 570021
e.mail: info@kilchrenanhouse.co.uk
Web: www.kilchrenanhouse.co.uk

Spacious Victorian house in excellent seafront location
with uninterrupted views over Oban Bay and the Islands
beyond. The ideal setting for a peaceful break,
Kilchrenan House offers a relaxing atmosphere
combined with modern comforts. All ten bedrooms have
been decorated to a high standard, and each has ensuite
facilities, telephone, television, radio and hospitality trays.
Most offer the delight of waking to a sea view....Read
your book in the sunny bay window of the residents
lounge and watch the boats from the dining room as you
enjoy a tasty breakfast. Private car park. Alison and
Kenny look forward to welcoming you. Open Feb-Nov.

**GUEST
HOUSE**

Kilchrenan House

Corran Esplanade, Oban, Argyll, PA34 5AQ
Tel:01631 562663 Fax:01631 570021
Email:info@kilchrenanhouse.co.uk
Web:www.kilchrenanhouse.co.uk

Assured high standard of service and comfort. Oban town centre and all
amenities within five minutes walk along the esplanade. Sunny position
on Oban's Esplanade - the ideal place to watch the glorious sunsets.

1 Single	All En Suite	B&B per person	Open Feb-Nov
2 Twin		from £25.00 Single	
6 Double		from £25.00 Double	
1 Family			

LA CALA

GANAVAN ROAD, OBAN PA34 5TU
Tel/Fax: 01631 562741 e.mail: lacala@zoom.co.uk
Web: http://pages.zoom.co.uk/lacala
La Cala is a luxuriously appointed two storey Georgian style house situated on the
northern outskirts of Oban. Beautiful situation by the sea with breathtaking
panoramic sea views to the islands. Off street private parking. Single and standard
double rooms let as unit for parties of three sharing. Private bathroom.

B&B

La Cala

Ganavan Road, Oban, Argyll, PA34 5TU
Tel/Fax:01631 562741
Email:lacala@zoom.co.uk
Web:http://pages.zoom.co.uk/lacala

Tastefully appointed Georgian style home set in pleasant gardens.
Beautifully quiet situation by the sea with breathtaking panoramic views
of the sounds of Mull, Kerrera and Lismore. 1.25 miles from Oban centre.
Single and standard double rooms, let as a unit for 3 sharing, private
bathroom.

1 Double	En Suite fac	B&B per person	Open Mar-Oct
1 Double	Shared.Bath/Show	from £28.00 Single	
1 Single	Shared.Bath/Show	£30.00-32.00 Double	

Important: Prices stated are estimates and may be subject to amendments

Oban, Argyll

Map Ref: 1E2

★★★

B&B

Lower Soroba Farmhouse

Lower Soroba, Oban, Argyll, PA34 4SB
Tel:01631 565349
Email:marierjohnston@btopenworld.com

Tastefully refurbished traditional (non-working) farmhouse within a
quiet residential estate on the southern edge of Oban. 1 mile from town
centre and all amenities. Excellent base for touring this beautiful part of
Argyll. Warm welcome. Private parking. Evening meal by arrangement.
Local bus route and hotel nearby.

1 Single	1 Priv.NOT ensuite	B&B per person	Open Jan-Dec
1 Twin	1 Pub.Bath/Show	from £18.00 Single	
1 Double		from £18.00 Double	
1 Family			

OAKBANK

BENVOULIN ROAD, OBAN, ARGYLL PA34 5EF
Tel: 01631 563482 Fax: 01631 570917
e.mail: stay@obansbest.com Web: www.obansbest.com

A small friendly home five minutes from town centre and all amenities including
bus, train and ferry terminals (pick-up on request) panoramic views over Oban
Bay and the Hills of Mull. We don't only offer a warm bed, hearty breakfast and
friendly service, we guarantee value for money.

★★

B&B

Oakbank

Benvoulin Road, Oban, Argyll, PA34 5EF
Tel:01631 563482 Fax:01631 570917
Email:stay@obansbest.com
Web:www.obansbest.com

Small family run bed and breakfast with fine views across Kerrera to the
Isle of Mull, yet only 4 minutes walk from town centre, harbour and
promenade. Visit the nearby sports centre and swimming pool or take a
pleasant walk to McCaigs Tower.

1 Twin	Standard	B&B per person	Open Jan-Dec
2 Double	1 Priv.NOT ensuite	from £22.00 Single	
		from £14.00 Double	

★★★★

GUEST
HOUSE

The Old Manse Guest House

Dalriach Road, Oban, Argyll, PA34 5JE
Tel:01631 564886 Fax:01631 570184
Email:oldmanse@obanguesthouse.co.uk
Web:www.obanguesthouse.co.uk

Victorian detached Villa set in beautiful gardens, with views of sea and
islands. Superior standard of hospitality and comfort. Only minutes walk
to town centre. Private parking. Family suite available.

1 Twin	All En Suite	B&B per person	Open Feb-Nov
3 Double		£20.00-35.00 Double	
1 Family			

Scotland's National Booking and Information Line

Tel: 0845 22 55 121
visitscotland.com

VAT is shown at 17.5%: changes in this rate may affect prices.

Key to symbols is on back flap.

Oban, Argyll — Map Ref: 1E2

B&B ★★★

Rhumor
Drummore Road, Oban, Argyll, PA34 4JL
Tel/Fax:01631 563544
Email:b&b@rhumor.demon.co.uk

1 Twin	All En Suite	B&B per person	Open Feb-Dec excl
1 Double		£18.00-20.00 Double	Xmas/New Year
1 Family			

Traditional bungalow set in a quiet residential area on the outskirts of town. All amenities within 10 minutes walk. Comfortable rooms. Ample parking. Friendly family welcome. Non smoking house.

GUEST HOUSE ★★★★

Roseneath Guest House
Dalriach Road, Oban, Argyll, PA34 5EQ
Tel:01631 562929   Fax:01631 567218
Email:quirkers@aol.com
Web:www.roseneathoban.com

2 Twin	All En Suite	B&B per person	Open Feb-Oct
6 Double		£25.00-30.00 Single	
		£21.00-27.00 Double	

Roseneath, a fine Victorian villa with views over Oban Bay towards the islands of Kerrera and Mull. An ideal touring base for visitors to Lorn and the Isles. Quiet location, yet less than a five minute walk from town centre, train and ferry terminals and convenient to all amenities.

B&B ★★★

The Torrans
Drummore Road, Oban, Argyll, PA34 4JL
Tel:01631 565342   Fax:01631 565342

2 Double	2 En Suite fac	B&B per person	Open Jan-Dec excl
	1 Pub.Bath/Show	from £25.00 Single	Xmas/New Year
		from £16.00 Double	
		from £14.00 Room	
		Only	

Comfortable family home in quiet residential cul-de-sac. 1 mile (2kms) from town centre and all amenities. Excellent views across Oban and the Islands.

B&B ★★★

Verulam
Drummore Road, Oban, Argyll, PA34 4JL
Tel:01631 566115
Email:sandra.scott1@talk21.com

| 2 Double | All En Suite | B&B per person | Open May-Oct |
| | | from £18.00 Double | |

Modern furnished bunglow in quite residential area, close to town centre, restaurants and shops. Ideal base for day trips to the island by ferry. We have private car parking, residential lounge,all bedrooms are ground floor with ensuites, tea and coffee facilities.

---

by Oban, Argyll — Map Ref: 1E2

B&B ★★★★

Invercairn
Musdale Road, Kilmore,by Oban, Argyll, PA34 4XX
Tel/Fax:01631 770301
Email:invercairn.kilmore@virgin.net
Web:www.invercairn.com

| 1 Twin | All En Suite | B&B per person | Open Apr-Sep |
| 2 Double | | from £23.00 Double | |

Warm Scottish welcome assured when you stay in this comfortable home, situated in a tranquil, picturesque Highland Glen. Perfect for touring. Enjoy the magnificent views, comfort and hospitality. Non smoking. Oban, the Gateway to the Isles, only 4 miles away.

Important: Prices stated are estimates and may be subject to amendments

Port of Menteith, Perthshire

Map Ref: 1H3

★★★

B&B

Collymoon Pendicle
Port of Menteith, Stirling, FK8 3JY
Tel:01360 850222
Email:gilliantough@compuserve.com

1 Double	1 Priv.NOT ensuite	B&B per person	Open Apr-Sep
1 Family		from £18.00 Double	BB & Eve.Meal
			from £28.00

Family run modern bungalow beside a traditional working farm in country setting with beautiful panoramic views over surrounding countryside to the Campsie Hills. Home cooking a speciality. All rooms on ground floor. Ideal base for touring the Highlands. Salmon and trout fishing available. Major credit cards accepted.

★★★

B&B

Inchie Farm
Port of Menteith, Perthshire, FK8 3JZ
Tel/Fax:01877 385233
Email:inchiefarm@ecosse.net

1 Twin	1 En Suite fac	B&B per person	Open Mar-Oct
1 Family	1 Priv.Bath/Show	from £23.00 Single	BB & Eve.Meal
		from £19.00 Double	from £29.00

A warm welcome and friendly hospitality at this family farm situated on the shore of Lake of Menteith in a quiet location. Traditional 200 year old stone built house. Home baking and home cooking. Evening meals by arrangement. Non smoking house.

Stirling

Map Ref: 2A4

★★★★★

B&B

Ashgrove House
2 Park Avenue, Stirling, FK8 2LX
Tel:01786 472640
Email:ashgrovehouse@strayduck.com
Web:www.ashgrove-house.com

1 Twin	All En Suite	B&B per person	Open Mar-Oct
2 Double		from £45.00 Single	
		from £30.00 Double	

A warm welcome awaits you at this elegantly restored Victorian villa designed by renowned Scottish architect John Allan. 2 minutes to town centre and within walking distance of historical attractions including Stirling Castle. Ideal base for walking, golfing and exploring Loch Lomond and the Trossachs. Non-Smoking. No children.

Scotland's National Booking and Information Line

Tel: 0845 22 55 121
visitscotland.com

VAT is shown at 17.5%: changes in this rate may affect prices.

Key to symbols is on back flap.

Stirling

Map Ref: 2A4

★★★

B&B

Carseview Bed + Breakfast
16 Ladysneuk Road, Cambuskenneth, Stirling FK9 5NF
Tel/Fax:01786 462235
Email:bandb@carseview.co.uk
Web:www.carseview.co.uk

Comfortable country home evolved from turn of the century stables. In small conservation village within 15 minutes walk of Stirling town centre. Home baked bread served at breakfast.

1 Single	1 Priv.NOT ensuite	B&B per person	Open Jan-Dec
2 Twin		from £18.00 Single	BB & Eve.Meal
		from £18.00 Double	from £28.00

★★★

GUEST
HOUSE

Castlecraig
50 Causewayhead Road, Stirling, Stirlingshire
FK9 5EY
Tel:01786 475452

Purpose-built accommodation adjacent to traditional stone semi-villa, only 5 minutes from Wallace Monument and University. Some ground floor rooms. Full fire certificate.

1 Twin	All En Suite	B&B per person	Open Jan-Dec
1 Double		from £30.00 Single	
1 Family		from £23.00 Double	

★★★

B&B

Mrs M J Dougall
14 Melville Terrace, Stirling, FK8 2NE
Tel/Fax:01786 475361
Email:mjdougall@hotmail.com

Comfortable Georgian Town House located within 5 minutes walk to town centre and Railway Station. Off street parking.

1 Twin	2 En Suite fac	B&B per person	Open Jan-Nov excl
1 Double	1 Pub.Bath/Show	from £25.00 Single	Xmas/New Year
1 Family		from £22.50 Double	

FIRGROVE
13 Clifford Road, Stirling FK8 2AQ
Tel: 01786 475805   Fax: 01786 450733
e.mail: firgrove@stirling.co.uk   Web: www.firgrove.stirling.co.uk

Spacious Victorian home with large comfortable rooms all ensuite. Ample private parking within grounds. Five minutes walk to town centre. Relaxed friendly atmosphere. Non-smoking establishment. Kept to a high standard.

★★★★

B&B

Firgrove B&B
13 Clifford Road, Stirling, Stirlingshire, FK8 2AQ
Tel:01786 475805   Fax:01786 450733
Email:firgrove@stirling.co.uk
Web:www.firgrove.stirling.co.uk

Spacious, elegant family home with large gracious rooms. Excellent parking within leafy grounds. Five minutes walk to town centre, with its array of shops and restaurants. The old town and the Castle are also within walking distance.

1 Twin	All En Suite	B&B per person	Open Jan-Dec excl
2 Double		from £35.00 Single	Xmas/New Year
		from £25.00 Double	

Important: Prices stated are estimates and may be subject to amendments

Stirling

Map Ref: 2A4

★★★★

GUEST HOUSE

Forth Guest House

23 Forth Place, Riverside, Stirling, FK8 1UD
Tel:01786 471020 Fax:01786 447220
Email:loudon@forthguesthouse.freeserve.co.uk
Web:www.forthguesthouse.freeserve.co.uk

Georgian terraced house within 5 minutes walking distance of railway station, town centre and swimming pool. Good location for touring to either Glasgow or Edinburgh by car or train. Close to Stirling Castle and Wallace monument. Private parking.

2 Single	All En Suite
3 Twin	
3 Double	
2 Family	

B&B per person
from £20.00 Single
from £18.00 Double

Open Jan-Dec excl
Xmas/New Year

★★★

GUEST HOUSE

Garfield Guest House

12 Victoria Square, Stirling, Stirlingshire
FK8 2QZ
Tel/Fax:01786 473730

Family run guest house in traditional stone built Victorian house overlooking quiet square close to the town centre, Castle and all local amenities. Ideal base for exploring historic Stirling, Loch Lomond and the Trossachs. Non smoking.

2 Twin	All En Suite
3 Double	
2 Family	

B&B per person
from £22.00 Double

Open Jan-Dec excl
Xmas/New Year

★★★

B&B

Laurinda B&B, Mrs E Paterson

66 Ochilmount, Ochilview, Bannockburn
Stirlingshire, FK7 8PJ
Tel:01786 815612

A warm welcome awaits you at this family home. Modern detached villa in residential area of Bannockburn. Ideal location for touring all main cities and tourist attractions. Parking area. Evening meal by arrangement.

1 Double	1 En Suite fac
1 Family	1 Pub.Bath/Show

B&B per person
from £25.00 Single
from £21.00 Double

Open Jan-Dec
BB & Eve.Meal
from £31.00

★★★★

B&B

Sealladh Ard

Station Brae, Kippen, Stirlingshire, FK8 3DY
Tel:01786 870291
Email:ann@bandbstirling.com
Web:www.bandbstirling.com

Family home on the outskirts of conservation village within 5 mins walk of local hotels. Well laid out and interesting garden, full Scottish breakfast served with home made bread and preserves, sit back and enjoy the spectacular views across the valley.

1 Double	1 En Suite fac
1 Family	1 Priv.NOT ensuite

B&B per person
from £25.00 Single
from £20.50 Double

Open Jan-Dec

Scotland's National Booking and Information Line

Tel: 0845 22 55 121
visitscotland.com

VAT is shown at 17.5%: changes in this rate may affect prices.

Key to symbols is on back flap.

Stirling

Map Ref: 2A4

XI Victoria Square
Stirling, FK8 2RA
Tel:01786 475545
Email:iain.galloway@btinternet.com
Web:www.xivictoriasquare.com

B&B

Victorian house with many original features situated in quiet residential area. 5 minutes walk from town centre, in Kings Park Close to Stirling Castle. One bedroom decorated in Charles Rennie Mackintosh art-deco style; and one spacious family room offering the 'Highland' theme with Tartan drapes.

3 Twin	All En Suite	B&B per person	Open Jan-Dec
3 Double		£45.00-70.00 Single	
1 Family		£30.00-40.00 Double	

West Plean House
Denny Road, Stirling, FK7 8HA
Tel:01786 812208   Fax:01786 480550
Email:west.plean@virgin.net

B&B

200-year-old historic country house on mixed working farm set in extensive grounds with walled garden, duck pond and woodlands walks. Offering warm Scottish farming hospitality. Two rooms en-suite, one with its own private bathroom. Private parking. Near M80/M9, Jnct.9.

1 Single	2 En Suite fac	B&B per person	Open Feb-Dec excl
1 Double	1 Pub.Bath/Show	from £32.00 Single	Xmas/New Year
1 Family		from £25.00 Double	

Whitegables B&B
112 Causewayhead Road, Stirling, FK9 5HJ
Tel/Fax:01786 479838
Email:whitegables@b-j-graham.freeserve.co.uk

GUEST HOUSE

Tudor-style detached house in residential area located midway between Stirling Castle and the Wallace Monument. Easily accessible to motorway links. Private off road car parking available. Non smoking house.

1 Twin	All En Suite	B&B per person	Open Jan-Dec excl
2 Double		from £25.00 Single	Xmas/New Year
1 Family		from £22.00 Double	

Strathyre, Perthshire

Map Ref: 1H3

Coire Buidhe Bed + Breakfast
Main Street, Strathyre, Perthshire, FK18 8NA
Tel:01877 384288
Email:coirebuidhe@amserve.net
Web:www.coirebuidhe.co.uk

B&B

A warm welcome awaits you at this former mill, which is now a B&B offering en suite accommodation, suitable for both couples and families. You can relax in the guests' lounge after spending the day touring, fishing, cycling or walking in the surrounding hills. Lochearnhead with its watersports centre is nearby.

1 Single	3 En Suite fac	B&B per person	Open Jan-Dec excl
1 Twin	1 Priv.NOT ensuite	from £16.00 Single	Xmas
1 Double		from £16.00 Double	
3 Family			

Tarbert, Loch Fyne, Argyll

Map Ref: 1E5

Rhu House
Tarbert, Argyll, PA29 6YF
Tel/Fax:01880 820231
Email:rhuhouse@ukonline.co.uk

B&B

19th Century former shooting lodge situated in 40 acres of woodland on shores of West Loch Tarbert. Closest B & B to Islay ferry. Ideal for bird watchers and central base for touring beautiful Kintyre.

1 Twin	Some En Suite	B&B per person	Open Mar-Nov
2 Double	1 Priv.NOT ensuite	from £20.00 Double	

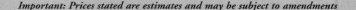

Important: Prices stated are estimates and may be subject to amendments

Tarbert, Loch Fyne, Argyll   Map Ref: 1E5

Glenreasdale House
Whitehouse, by Tarbert,
Loch Fyne, Argyll PA29 6XR
Tel: 01880 730208

*Magnificent views, warm welcome. Quiet location
near to all ferry terminals. Early ferry breakfast.
Evening meal available by arrangement.
Pets welcome. From £18 per person.*

★★

B&B

Glenreasdale House

Whitehouse, by Tarbert, Argyll, PA29 6XR
Tel:01880 730208

2 Single	2 Priv.NOT ensuite	B&B per person	Open Mar-Oct
2 Double		from £18.00 Single	BB & Eve.Meal
1 Family		from £18.00 Double	from £25.00

Friendly B&B with views looking towards Loch Fyne. Ideally located for
walking, fishing, wildlife. Close to Arran, Islay, Jura and Gigha Ferry.

Springside Bed & Breakfast
Pier Road, Tarbert, Loch Fyne, Argyll PA29 6UE
Telephone/Fax: 01880 820413
E.mail: marshall.springside@virgin.net
Web: www.scotland-info.co.uk/springside
Tranquillity of traditional fisherman's cottage situated close to shore, with
excellent views over harbour entrance and five minutes' walk from amenities in
one of the most picturesque Highland fishing villages. We cater for early and all
ferry crossings on beautiful Kintyre Peninsula.
For those who prefer, vegetarian menu is available.

★★

B&B

Springside B&B

Pier Road, Tarbert, Loch Fyne, Argyll, PA29 6UE
Tel/Fax:01880 820413
Email:marshall.springside@virgin.net
Web:www.scotland-info.co.uk/springside

1 Twin	3 En Suite fac	B&B per person	Open Jan-Dec
1 Double	1 Pub.Bath/Show	from £18.00 Single	
2 Family		£18.00-22.00 Double	

Tranquility of traditional fishermans cottage, overlooking the harbour
entrance, within walking distance of village. Convenient for ferries to
Islay, Gigha, Cowal Peninsula and Arran. ¾ hour drive to Campbletown.
Early breakfasts provided.

Tarbet, by Arrochar, Dunbartonshire   Map Ref: 1G3

★★★

B&B

Ballyhennan Toll House

Tarbet, Arrochar, Dumbartonshire, G83 7DA
Tel/Fax:01301 702203
Email:jim@rawle1.freeserve.co.uk
Web:www.oldtollhouse.co.uk

1 Twin	All En Suite	B&B per person	Open Jan-Dec excl
1 Double		from £25.00 Single	Xmas/New Year
1 Family		from £18.00 Double	
		from £15.00 Room	
		Only	

A warm welcome awaits in this comfortable house, convenient for Loch
Lomond.

VAT is shown at 17.5%: changes in this rate may affect prices.   Key to symbols is on back flap.

Tarbet, by Arrochar, Dunbartonshire — Map Ref: 1G3

Bon-Etive
Tarbet, by Arrochar, Dunbartonshire, G83 7DF
Tel:01301 702219

★★★ B&B

1 Twin	1 Priv.NOT ensuite	B&B per person	Open Apr-Oct
1 Double		£17.00-18.00 Double	

Conveniently situated in quiet cul-de-sac close to the A82, with fine views of Loch Lomond and 'The Ben'. Close to station for trains to Glasgow or the scenic route of the West Highland line.

Tillicoultry, Clackmannanshire — Map Ref: 2A3

Westbourne House
10 Dollar Road, Tillicoultry FK13 6PA
Telephone: 01259 750314 Fax: 01259 750642
e.mail: odellwestbourne@compuserve.com
Web: www.westbournehouse.co.uk

Victorian mill owner's mansion set in wooded grounds beneath Ochil Hills. Warm, friendly atmosphere. Delicious breakfasts. Log fires. Croquet lawn. TV/Radio, tea/coffee making facilities in all rooms, one on ground floor. Centrally situated for Edinburgh, Glasgow, Perth, Stirling and Trossachs – motorways fifteen minutes. Secure off-street parking. Single from £25. Double from £22.

Westbourne House
10 Dollar Road, Tillicoultry, FK13 6PA
Tel:01259 750314   Fax:01259 750642
Email:odellwestbourne@compuserve.com
Web:www.westbournehouse.co.uk

★★★ B&B

1 Family	2 En Suite fac	B&B per person	Open Jan-Dec excl
2 Double	1 Pub.Bathroom	from £25.00 Single	Xmas/New Year
		from £22.00 Double	

Victorian mansion, full of character, on the Mill Trail and close to the new Sterling Mills 'Designer Outlet Village', nestling beneath the Ochil Hills. Home baking and cooking. Log fire. Secure off-road parking. E-mail and fax facilities available.

Wyvis B&B
70 Stirling Street, Tillicoultry, Clackmannanshire
FK13 6EA
Tel:01259 751513
Email:wyvis@btopenworld.com

★★★★ B&B

1 Twin	1 En Suite fac	B&B per person	Open Jan-Dec excl
1 Double	1 Pub.Bath/Show	£25.00-28.00 Single	Xmas/New Year
		£23.00-25.00 Double	BB & Eve.Meal
			from £36.00-43.00

Cottage in conservation area overlooking the Ochil Hills and ideally situated for hillwalking. Friendly atmosphere, home cooking and baking. Evening meals by arrangement.

by Glasgow — Map Ref: 1H5

The Westerwood Hotel
1 St Andrews Drive, Cumbernauld, G68 0EW
Tel: 01667 458800 Fax: 01667 455267
E-mail: rooms@morton-hotels.com
Web: www.morton-hotels.com

★★★ HOTEL

55 Double	All En Suite	B&B per person	Open Jan-Dec
42 Twin		from £57.50 per night	D,B&B per person from
3 Suites		Dbl/Twn	£53.50 per night
		from £87.50 Suite per night	

Modern hotel, with recently completed extension, as well as leisure complex, and own championship golf course. The hotel provides a choice of eating and drinking options, including the Old Masters Restaurant and The Clubhouse bar. Conference and function facilities are available.

Important: Prices stated are estimates and may be subject to amendments

Welcome to Scotland

Perthshire, Angus & Dundee and the Kingdom of Fife

Plenty of contrasts here: From the white-walled harbour front houses of the East Neuk fishing villages to the heathery silence of Rannoch Moor, from the arts and culture of Dundee to the tranquillity of the Angus Glens. This area makes a good place for a break, with a little of everything within easy reach.

Rail bridge across the Firth of Tay to Dundee

Perth is an important commercial centre for its hinterland both above and below the Highland line. Another Perthshire speciality are the little resort towns such as Dunkeld, Pitlochry or Aberfeldy, with their good range of visitor attractions such as the Scottish Plant Collectors Garden (Pitlochry) open 2002 and Dewar's World of Whisky at Aberfeldy.

The Kingdom of Fife has plenty of character, with St Andrews noted as Scotland's oldest university and also often called 'the home of golf'. The town offers excellent shopping and is within easy reach of attractive East Neuk villages like Crail southwards and also the city of Dundee across the Tay Bridge to the north.

Dundee is the city of Discovery, with Discovery Point one of Scotland's top attractions while its new Science Centre, 'Sensation' provides the whole family with hands-on fun. The Angus Glens are special places, with roads running deep into the hills through Glens Isla, Prosen, Clova or Esk – great country for walkers, birdwatchers and botanists. The coastline of Angus also offers plenty of interest, with spectacular cliffs and coves and small fishing ports such as Arbroath, home of the 'Arbroath smokie' – a fishy treat! Between hills and coast lie attractions such as Glamis Castle, birthplace of HM Queen Elizabeth the Queen Mother, and Edzell Castle with its unique garden.

Woodland walk at Gannochy near Edzell, Angus

Perthshire, Angus & Dundee and the Kingdom of Fife

Formal gardens at Drummond Castle, Perthshire

Scattered across the whole area are a wide range of other attractions, such as Deep Sea World by North Queensferry (an aquarium featuring the world's largest walk-through tunnel), the birthplace cottage of the playwright J M Barrie in Kirriemuir, and also Scotland's National Garden at Perth and Bells Cherrybank Centre.

Events

Perthshire, Angus & Dundee and the Kingdom of Fife

8 MARCH
Real Ale Festival, Dundee
Tel: 01382 434451
www.cairdhall.co.uk

17-20 MARCH*
StANZA 2003: Scotland's
Poetry Festival
Poetry and education
festival.
Tel: 01333 360491

12-13 APRIL*
City of Dundee Flower Show
Tel: 01382 527527
www.cairdhall.co.uk

16-21 APRIL*
The Links Market, Kirkcaldy
A mile of fairground rides
and attractions.
Tel: 01592 414221
www.standrews.com/fife

3-4 MAY
Central Scotland Horse Trials,
Perth
Tel: 01577 830240
www.scone-palace.co.uk

12-15 MAY*
Fife Golf Classic
Tel: 01292 293040
www.scottishgolfclassics.com

24-30 MAY
Wake Up To Birds Week
Royal Society for the
Protection of Birds. Wide
range of events and activities
at the 60 RSPB reserves across
Scotland. Free entry to all
reserves on one day during
this week.
Tel: 0131 311 6500
www.rspb.org.uk/scotland

25 MAY – 18 AUGUST
Burntisland Summer
Fairground
One of the largest seaside
funfairs.
Tel: 01592 416823

12-13 JULY
Scottish Transport
Extravaganza, Glamis Castle
Comprehensive display of
vintage vehicles.
Tel: 01307 462496
www.glamis-castle.co.uk

8-10 AUGUST*
Auchtermuchty Traditional
Music Festival
Music, ceilidhs, dance and
competitions.
Tel: 01337 828732
www.tmsa.demon.co.uk

9-10 AUGUST*
Arbroath Seafest, Arbroath
A festival celebrating
maritime traditions with
plenty of seafood.
Tel: 01307 473774
www.seafest.co.uk

10 AUGUST
Perth Highland Games
Tel: 01738 627782
www.highlandgames.org.uk

17 AUGUST
Crieff Highland Games
Tel: 01738 627782
www.highlandgames.org.uk

21-24 AUGUST
Bowmore Blair Castle
International Horse Trials
and Country Fair
Tel: 01796 481543
www.blairhorsetrials.co.uk

5-7 SEPTEMBER
Kirriemuir Traditional Music
Festival
Music, ceilidhs, dances and
competitions.
Tel: 01575 540261
www.tmsa.demon.co.uk

7 SEPTEMBER
Blairgowrie Highland Games
Tel: 01828 627253

13 SEPTEMBER
Pitlochry Highland Games
Tel: 01796 473636

13 SEPTEMBER
RAF Leuchars Air Show
Tel: 01334 839000
www.airshow.co.uk

12-14 DECEMBER*
Christmas Craft and Produce
Fair, Dundee
Tel: 01382 527527

** denotes provisional date. Events can be
subject to change, please check before
travelling.*

For up to date events, log on to:
visitscotland.com

Area Tourist Boards
Perthshire, Angus & Dundee and the Kingdom of Fife

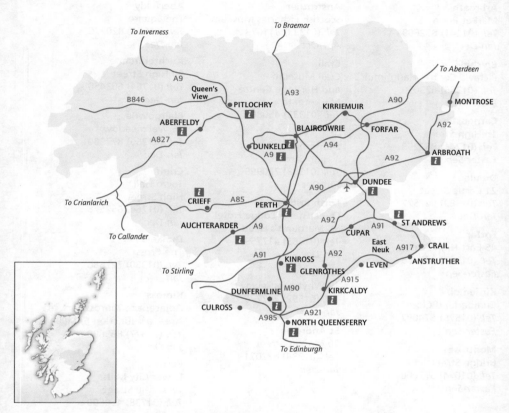

Perthshire Tourist Board
Lower City Mills
West Mill Street
Perth
PH1 5QP

Tel: 01738 450600
Fax: 01738 630416
E-mail: info@perthshire.co.uk
www.perthshire.co.uk

Angus and Dundee Tourist Board
21 Castle Street
Dundee
DD1 3AA

Tel: 01382 527527 (information)
Tel: 01382 527535
(accommodation)
Fax: 01382 527551
E-mail: enquiries@
angusanddundee.co.uk
www.angusanddundee.co.uk

Kingdom of Fife Tourist Board
70 Market Street
St Andrews
KY16 9NU

Tel: 01334 472021 (information)
Tel: 01592 260270
(accommodation)
Fax: 01334 478422
E-mail: standrewsstic@
kftb.ossian.net
www.standrews.com/fife

Tourist Information Centres
Perthshire, Angus & Dundee and the Kingdom of Fife

Angus & City of Dundee Tourist Board

Arbroath
Market Place
Tel: (01241) 872609
Jan-Dec

Brechin
Pictavia Centre, Haughmuir
Tel: (01356) 623050
Easter-Sep

Carnoustie
1b High Street
Tel: (01241) 852258
Easter-Sep

Dundee
21 Castle Street
Tel: (01382) 527527
Jan-Dec

Forfar
45 East High Street
Tel: (01307) 467876
Easter-Sep

Kirriemuir
Cumberland Close
Tel: (01575) 574097
Easter-Sep

Montrose
Bridge Street
Tel: (01674) 672000
Easter-Sep

Kingdom of Fife Tourist Board

Anstruther
Scottish Fisheries Museum
Tel: (01333) 311073
Apr-Oct

Crail
Crail Museum
and Heritage Centre
Marketgate
Tel: (01333) 450869
Apr-Oct

Dunfermline
1 High Street
Tel: (01383) 720999
Jan-Dec

Forth Bridges
Queensferry Lodge Hotel
St. Margaret's Head
Tel: (01383) 417759
Jan-Dec

Kirkcaldy
19 Whytescauseway
Tel: (01592) 267775
Jan-Dec

St Andrews
70 Market Street
Tel: (01334) 472021
Jan-Dec

Perthshire Tourist Board

Aberfeldy
The Square
Tel: (01887) 820276
Jan-Dec

Auchterarder
90 High Street
Tel: (01764) 663450
Jan-Dec

Blairgowrie
26 Wellmeadow
Tel: (01250) 872960
Jan-Dec

Crieff
Town Hall
High Street
Tel: (01764) 652578
Jan-Dec

Dunkeld
The Cross
Tel: (01350) 727688
Jan-Dec

Kinross
Adjacent to Kinross Service
Area, off Junction 6, M90
Tel: (01577) 863680
Jan-Dec

Perth
Lower City Mills
West Mill Street
Tel: (01738) 450600
Jan-Dec

Pitlochry
22 Atholl Road
Tel: (01796) 472215/472751
Jan-Dec

Scotland's National Booking and Information Line
0845 22 55 121

Aberfeldy, Perthshire

Map Ref: 2A1

★★★

B&B

Ardtornish
Kenmore Street, Aberfeldy, Perthshire, PH15 2BL
Tel:01887 820629
Email:ardtornish@talk21.com

1 Double	1 En Suite fac	B&B per person	Open Jan-Dec excl
1 Twin	2 Shared fac	from £18.00 Dbl/Twn	Xmas/New Year
1 Dbl/Twn			

Traditional town house near centre of Aberfeldy. Ideal for touring and all outdoor pursuits. Private parking.

★★★

B&B

Mavisbank B&B (Peter + Nancy Nunn)
Taybridge Drive, Aberfeldy, Perthshire, PH15 2BP
Tel:01887 820223

1 Twin	2 Pub.Bath/Show	B&B per person	Open Mar-Oct
1 Double		£18.00-19.00 Double	

Friendly welcome in peaceful setting on outskirts of small country town. Beautiful views. Convenient for golfing, fishing, walking and birdwatching.

Tigh 'N Eilean
TAYBRIDGE DRIVE, ABERFELDY, PERTHSHIRE PH15 2BP
TEL/FAX: 01887 820109 MOBILE: 07889 472248 and 07753 637967
E.MAIL: info@tighneilean.com WEB: www.tighneilean.com
Elegant Victorian house overlooking the River Tay beautifully decorated ensuite bedrooms one with jacuzzi. Wonderfully comfortable lounge with its open fire creates a warm and friendly atmosphere. Ideal centre for hill-walking, golf, fishing, pony-trekking and exploring beautiful Highland Perthshire. A warm and friendly welcome awaits you.

★★★★

B&B

Tigh'n Eilean
Taybridge Drive, Aberfeldy, Perthshire, PH15 2BP
Tel:01887 820109
Email:info@tighneilean.com
Web:www.tighneilean.com

1 Single	All En Suite	B&B per person	Open Jan-Dec
1 Twin		from £28.00 Single	BB & Eve.Meal
2 Double		from £22.00 Double	from £39.00

Elegant Victorian house overlooking the river. Warm and comfortable, home cooking. One room with jacuzzi.

★★★

B&B

Tighnabruaich
Taybridge Terrace, Aberfeldy, PH15 2BS
Tel:01887 820456 Fax:01887 829254
Email:katesscott123@aol.com

2 Single	2 Priv.NOT ensuite	B&B per person	Open Apr-Oct
1 Twin	1 Pub.Bath/Show	from £18.00 Single	
		from £18.00 Double	

A Victorian stone built house with fine views over the golf course to the hills. Sympathetically furnished retaining the original wood doors and cornices making a comfortable home from home. Off road parking.

VAT is shown at 17.5%: changes in this rate may affect prices.

Key to symbols is on back flap.

Aberfeldy, Perthshire — Map Ref: 2A1

★★ B&B

Tomvale
Tom of Cluny, Aberfeldy, Perthshire, PH15 2JT
Tel/Fax:01887 820171
Email:tomvale@aol.com
Web:www.tomvale.co.uk

Modern bungalow on working farm, with spectacular views over the
Upper Tay Valley. 3 miles (5kms) from Aberfeldy.

1 Double 1 Priv.NOT ensuite	B&B per person
1 Family	from £18.00 Single
	from £18.00 Double

Open Jan-Dec excl
Xmas/New Year
BB & Eve.Meal
from £28.00

P ✕ ◄ ▣

C ✱ W V ♿   ◪ ◪

Abernethy, Perthshire — Map Ref: 2C3

★★★ B&B

Easter Clunie Farmhouse
Newburgh, Fife, KY14 6EJ
Tel:01337 840218   Fax:01337 842226
Email:cluniefarm@aol.com

This 19c farmhouse, on a working farm in a quiet rural setting on the
outskirts of the village, has panoramic views over beautiful countryside to
the River Tay. All the rooms have either private or ensuite facilities.
Guests can also relax in the splendid Victorian walled garden. Convenient
for the main routes to Edinburgh and the Highlands.

2 Twin 1 En Suite fac	B&B per person
1 Family 2 Priv.Bath/Show	from £20.00 Single
	from £20.00 Double

Open Apr-Oct

▦ ▦ P ☕ ⌇ ✗ ▣

C ✪ W V

Anstruther, Fife — Map Ref: 2D3

BEAUMONT LODGE GUEST HOUSE

AA ◆◆◆◆◆

43 Pittenweem Road, Anstruther, Fife KY10 3DT
Telephone/Fax: 01333 310315
e.mail: info@beaumontlodge.co.uk   Web: www.beaumontlodge.co.uk
Only one hour's drive from Edinburgh airport and nine miles from
St. Andrews, this family run guest house offers excellent accommodation
and superb home cooking. This is a quiet guest house where you can
enjoy the best of Scottish hospitality. Private parking. Non smoking.
Children 14+. Evening meals.

★★★★ GUEST HOUSE

Beaumont Lodge Guest House
43 Pittenweem Road, Anstruther, Fife, KY10 3DT
Tel/Fax:01333 310315
Email:info@beaumontlodge.co.uk
Web:www.beaumontlodge.co.uk

Family run guest house, maintained to a very high standard offering
superb accommodation at affordable prices. 2 minutes walk to
Anstruther's 9 hole golf course. Shore and harbour easily accessible.
Private parking. Non-smoking. Children 14 + welcome.

2 Twin All En Suite	B&B per person
2 Double 1 Priv.NOT ensuite	from £30.00 Single
	from £25.00 Double

Open Jan-Dec

TV ▦ P ☕ ⌇ ✗ ✗ ▤

✪ W V ♿

Important: Prices stated are estimates and may be subject to amendments

Anstruther, Fife — Map Ref: 2D3

★★★★
B&B

Far-Reaches B&B
32 Pickford Crescent, Cellardyke, Anstruther, Fife
KY10 3AL
Tel/Fax:01333 310448
Email:far-reaches@demon.co.uk

Modern detached house in quiet residential area of a small fishing village. Excellent views across the Forth Estuary and the Isle of May. Warm welcome & homebaked bread. Plenty of off and on road parking.

1 Twin	2 En Suite fac	B&B per person	Open Mar-Oct
1 Double	1 Priv.NOT ensuite	from £27.00 Single	
1 Family		from £22.00 Double	

★★★
B&B

Invermay Cottage
Common Road, Kilrenny, Anstruther, Fife, KY10 3JQ
Tel:01333 312314
Email:jeremy-ruby@invermay.freeserve.co.uk
Web:www.invermaycottage.co.uk

Renovated 18th century cottage in peaceful location within walled garden. 9 miles from St Andrews. Situated within the East Neuk, between Crail and Anstruther.

1 Double	1 Pub.Bath/Show	B&B per person	Open Mar-Oct
1 Family		from £20.00 Double	
		from £15.00 Room Only	

The Spindrift
Pittenweem Road, Anstruther, Fife KY10 3DT
Tel and Fax: 01333 310573
e.mail: info@thespindrift.co.uk Web: www.thespindrift.co.uk
Set on the western edge of Anstruther, The Spindrift has established a growing reputation for its unique brand of comfort, hospitality, freshly prepared food and service. Convenient for golf, walking, bird watching or exploring the picturesque and historic East Neuk.
Please contact Kenneth and Christine Lawson for reservations.

★★★★
GUEST HOUSE
••
HOME COOKING

The Spindrift
Pittenweem Road, Anstruther, Fife, KY10 3DT
Tel/Fax:01333 310573
Email:info@thespindrift.co.uk
Web:www.thespindrift.co.uk

Stone built Victorian house with wealth of original features, set in fishing village. Short walk from town centre. Ideal touring base. Non smoking. Private parking. Evening meal by arrangement.

2 Twin	7 En Suite fac	B&B per person	Open Jan-Dec excl Xmas
4 Double	1 Pub.Bath/Show	from £26.50 Double	BB & Eve.Meal from £35.00
2 Family			

★★★
B&B

Joyce and Tom Watson
8 Melville Terrace, Anstruther, Fife, KY10 3EW
Tel:01333 310453
Email:tomwatson@beeb.net

Victorian stone-built house near restaurants and harbour in picturesque East Neuk fishing village. Varied and interesting breakfast. Attractive garden with summer house where you can relax with your tea or coffee.

1 Double	1 En Suite fac	B&B per person	Open Apr-Oct
1 Family	1 Priv.NOT ensuite	from £20.00 Double	
	1 Pub.Bath/Show		

Arbroath, Angus   Map Ref: 2D1

BAYVIEW
4 MONKBARNS DRIVE, ARBROATH DD11 2DS
TEL: 01241 879169 FAX: 01241 874037

In an excellent position overlooking the North Sea and West
Links. Gracious house in the west end of town. Parking within the
grounds. Three large letting rooms, two of which have sea views.
Bed and Breakfast prices from £18 per person per night.

★★

B&B

Bayview
4 Monkbarns Drive, Arbroath, Angus, DD11 2DS
Tel:01241 879169   Fax:01241 874037

Situated in quiet residential area. Elevated position with outstanding
views overlooking the River Tay. Private parking. Dogs welcome. All 3
rooms very spacious with own wash-hand basins. Lounge available for
guests use. Only 7-10 mins walk from town centre.

1 Twin	B&B per person	Open Apr-Oct
2 Double	from £18.00 Single	
	from £18.00 Double	

★★★

B&B

Mrs M Fergusson
20 Hillend Road, Arbroath, Angus, DD11 2AR
Tel:01241 873991

Spacious family house in quiet residential area within easy reach of all
facilities in town. Off road parking. Gaelic and Spanish spoken. Non-
smoking house. Hill walking and sea fishing can be arranged.

1 Twin	1 Priv.NOT ensuite	B&B per person	Open May-Sep
1 Double		from £20.00 Single	
		from £18.00 Double	

Auchterarder, Perthshire   Map Ref: 2B3

★★★★

**SMALL
HOTEL**

Cairn Lodge Hotel & Restaurant
Orchil Road, Auchterarder, Perthshire, PH3 1LX
Tel:01764 662634   Fax:01764 664866
Email:email@cairnlodge.co.uk
Web:www.cairnlodge.co.uk

Personally run country house hotel, with large garden and putting green,
on outskirts of Auchterarder. Fine dining, prepared from fresh local
produce.

1 Single	All En Suite	B&B per person	Open Jan-Dec
5 Twin		from £60.00 Single	BB & Eve.Meal
5 Double		from £60.00 Double	from £75.00
5 Family		from £55.00 Room	
		Only	

Scotland's National Booking
and Information Line

Tel: 0845 22 55 121
visitscotland.com

Important: Prices stated are estimates and may be subject to amendments

Auchterarder, Perthshire
Map Ref: 2B3

★★★

B&B

The Parsonage B&B
111 High Street, Auchterarder, Perthshire, PH3 1AA
Tel:01764 662392

2 Twin	1 En Suite fac	B&B per person	Open Jan-Dec
2 Family	2 Priv.NOT ensuite	from £22.00 Single	
		£20.00-22.00 Double	

Personally run guest house in the centre of Auchterarder. Convenient for
golf courses. One room has ensuite facilities and all rooms have colour
TV's and hospitality tray. Residents lounge.

---

by Auchtermuchty, Fife
Map Ref: 2C3

★★★

B&B

Wester Cash Farmhouse B&B
Strathmiglo, By Auchtermuchty, Fife, KY14 7RG
Tel/Fax:01337 860215
Email:info@westercash.co.uk
Web:www.westercash.co.uk

2 Double	All En Suite	B&B per person	Open Mar-Oct
		from £30.00 Single	
		from £25.00 Double	

A warm welcome awaits you on this 400 acre arable farm overlooked by
Lomond Hills in the Heart of Fife. Golfing at Kinross, Ladybank, St
Andrews. Fishing, horse riding, tennis and other leisure pursuits. Central
location for touring.

---

by Ballingry, nr Loch Leven, Fife
Map Ref: 2C3

NAVITIE HOUSE
Ballingry, Nr Loch Leven, Fife KY5 8LR
Telephone: 01592 860295 Fax: 01592 869769
e.mail: navitie@aol.com
Web: http://navitiehouse.co.uk
This period mansion, set in four acres of ground, offers large rooms with ensuite
facilities, home cooking, sauna and excellent views over the Forth Valley.
Situated 4 miles off the M90 and only 30 minutes' drive from Edinburgh.
Many golf courses within a short drive. B&B from £22 per night.
Discounts for children.

★★

GUEST
HOUSE

Navitie House
Nr Loch Leven, By Ballingry, Lochgelly, Fife KY5 8LR
Tel:01592 860295   Fax:01592 869769
Email:navitie@aol.com
Web:http://navitiehouse.co.uk

1 Single	All En Suite	B&B per person	Open Jan-Dec
2 Twin		from £25.00 Single	BB & Eve.Meal
2 Double		from £22.00 Double	from £32.00
2 Family		from £22.00 Room	
		Only	

Detached 200-year-old house in its own grounds overlooking Ballingry
village. Only 4 miles (6kms) from the Edinburgh to Perth motorway.
Centrally located only 30/40 minutes drive from Edinburgh, Stirling,
Perth and St Andrews. Evening meal by arrangement.

Birnam, by Dunkeld, Perthshire
Map Ref: 2B1

★★★★

GUEST
HOUSE

● ● ●
HOME
COOKING

Birnam Wood House
Perth Road, Birnam by Dunkeld, Perthshire, PH8 0BH
Tel:01350 727782 Fax:01350 727196
Email:bob@birnamwoodhouse.co.uk
Web:www.birnamwoodhouse.co.uk

2 Twin	All En Suite	B&B per person	Open Jan-Dec
2 Double		from £24.00 Double	BB & Eve.Meal
			from £44.00

A warm welcome awaits you at Birnam Wood House. After walking in or
touring the beautiful Perthshire countryside, you can relax in the
elegantly furnished lounge before enjoying dinner prepared, where
possible, from fresh local produce.

VAT is shown at 17.5%: changes in this rate may affect prices.

Key to symbols is on back flap.

Blair Atholl, Perthshire — Map Ref: 4C12

★★

B&B

Beechwood

The Terrace, Bridge of Tilt, Blair Atholl
Perthshire, PH18 5SZ
Tel:01796 481379

Bungalow in quiet side street of this picturesque town in rural Perthshire,
surrounded by its magnificent scenery. Centrally situated to all main
tourist routes. Both rooms with en suite.

1 Twin	All En Suite
1 Double	

B&B per person
from £25.00 Single
from £19.00 Double
from £19.00 Room
Only

Open Jan-Dec

T·H·E F·I·R·S
ST. ANDREWS CRESCENT, BLAIR ATHOLL PH18 5TA
Telephone: 01796 481256   Fax: 01796 481661
e.mail: kirstie@firs-blairatholl.co.uk
Web: www.firs-blairatholl.co.uk
Come and stay at our quiet family run guest house in Highland Perthshire.
Set in beautiful scenery, just north of Pitlochry.
Blair Atholl, famous for Blair Castle, offers golf, fishing, mountain bike
hire, pony-trekking and endless walks in spectacular scenery.

★★★

GUEST
HOUSE

The Firs

St Andrews Crescent, Blair Atholl, Pitlochry PH18 5TA
Tel:01796 481256   Fax:01796 481661
Email:kirstie@firs-blairatholl.co.uk
Web:www.firs-blairatholl.co.uk

Friendly country home with half an acre of garden in a tranquil setting.
Well situated in Highland Perthshire, close to Blair Castle and ideal as a
base for either touring or a relaxing holiday.

2 Double	All En Suite
2 Family	

B&B per person
from £20.00 Single
from £19.50 Double
from £19.50 Room
Only

Open Jan-Dec

Blairgowrie, Perthshire — Map Ref: 2B1

DUAN VILLA
Perth Road, Blairgowrie, Perthshire PH10 6EQ
Tel: 01250 873053 e.mail: duanvilla@ukonline.co.uk
Web: www.duanvilla.com
Detached attractive Victorian villa – many original features intact –
providing relaxing atmosphere to enjoy your stay in Blairgowrie.
An ideal base for sight-seeing, touring, walking, golfing, ski-ing or
fishing. There is ample parking and garden for guests' enjoyment.
Situated ten minutes' walk from centre of town.

★★★

B&B

Duan Villa

Perth Road, Blairgowrie, Perthshire, PH10 6EQ
Tel:01250 873053
Email:duanvilla@ukonline.co.uk
Web:www.duanvilla.com

Traditional sandstone detached house retaining original cornices and
wood panelling. On access route to Glenshee.

1 Twin	2 En Suite fac
2 Double	1 Pub.Toilet
1 Family	1 Pub.Bathroom

B&B per person
from £20.00 Single
from £20.00 Double

Open Jan-Dec

Blairgowrie, Perthshire

Map Ref: 2B1

Eildon Bank
118 Perth Road, Blairgowrie, Perthshire, PH10 6ED
Tel/Fax:01250 873648

Comfortable family home, near to town centre, with ample private parking. Television in bedrooms. Good base for touring. Perthshire outdoor activities include walking, skiing, golf and fishing.

1 Twin	2 En Suite fac	B&B per person	Open Jan-Dec excl
2 Double	1 Priv.Bath/Show	from £18.00 Single	Xmas
		from £17.00 Double	

Garfield House B&B
Perth Road, Blairgowrie, Perthshire, PH10 6ED
Tel:01250 872999

Family run Bed and Breakfast, on main road entering Blairgowrie, in the heart of Perthshire. Ideal central base for touring, golfing etc. Off road parking available.

1 Single	2 En Suite fac	B&B per person	Open mid Jan-mid Dec
1 Twin	1 Priv.Bath/Show	from £18.00 Single	
1 Double		from £18.00 Double	

Gilmore House
Perth Road, Blairgowrie, Perthshire, PH10 6EJ
Tel/Fax:01250 872791
Email:J@gilmorehouse.co.uk Web:www.gilmorehouse.co.uk

Comfortable bedrooms in this recently refurbished traditional stone built house on the outskirts of Blairgowrie. The three bedrooms are en suite, have colour TVs, radios, hair driers and hospitality trays. Gilmore House is ideally situated for ski-ing at Glenshee, the whisky and castle trails, fishing on the rivers Ericht and Tay. Plenty golf courses in the area. Private parking.

1 Twin	All En Suite	B&B per person	Open Jan-Dec excl
2 Double		from £18.50 Double	Xmas/New Year

Shocarjen House
Balmoral Road, Blairgowrie, PH10 7AF
Tel:01250 870525
Email:shonaidhbeattie@virgin.net

Newly built house with ground floor rooms. Up to date facilities including videos and fridge. Ideally located adjacent to river Ericht and close to all of Blairgowrie's amenities. Ideal base for touring, golfing, walking, ski-ing, etc. Long or short stays welcome.

1 Twin	All En Suite	B&B per person	Open Jan-Dec
1 Double		from £22.00 Single	
		from £20.00 Double	

---

by Blairgowrie, Perthshire

Map Ref: 2B1

Bankhead
Clunie, Blairgowrie, Perthshire, PH10 6SG
Tel/Fax:01250 884281
Email:ian@ihwightman.freeserve.co.uk

Farmhouse on working family farm between Loch Marlee and Clunie. Central base for touring, local fishing, golfing and skiing, osprey spotting at local Lowes Nature Reserve. Traditional farmhouse cooking and baking.

1 Twin	All En Suite	B&B per person	Open Jan-Dec excl
1 Family		from £20.00 Single	Xmas/New Year
		from £18.00 Double	BB & Eve.Meal
			from £27.00

VAT is shown at 17.5%: changes in this rate may affect prices.

Key to symbols is on back flap.

by Blairgowrie, Perthshire

Map Ref: 2B1

★★★

B&B

Ridgeway B&B
Wester Essendy, by Blairgowrie, Perthshire PH10 6RA
Tel:01250 884734 Fax:01250 884735
Email:Pam.Mathews@btinternet.com
Web:www.ridgewayb-b.co.uk

A warm welcome awaits. Detached bungalow with garden in peaceful
country location. Views overlooking the spectacular scenery of Loch
Marlee and surrounding farmland to the Grampian mountains. Only 3
miles from Blairgowrie. Ideal base for touring, hillwalking, golfing and
fishing.

1 Twin	All En Suite	B&B per person	Open Jan-Dec
1 Double		from £25.00 Single	
		from £25.00 Double	
		from £17.00 Room	
		Only	

Brechin, Angus

Map Ref: 4F12

Blibberhill Farmhouse
MRS WENDY STEWART, BLIBBERHILL FARM, BY BRECHIN, DD9 6TH
TEL: 01307 830323 FAX: 01307 830323
E.MAIL: WendySStewart@aol.com WEB: www.farmhouse-holidays.co.uk
*A warm welcome awaits you to our home on our mixed arable livestock farm. Tastefully
decorated and furnished. En-suite rooms, coal fires, C.H. and electric blankets. Glamis,
Edzell and Dunottar Castles nearby. Centrally situated for golf, fishing, hillwalking,
touring etc. Good home cooking, baking and childrens facilities. Beautiful garden.
Situated near 'Pictavia Centre' between Brechin and Forfar 3 miles along B9134.*

★★★

B&B

Blibberhill Farmhouse
Blibberhill Farm, by Brechin, Angus, DD9 6TH
Tel/Fax:01307 830323
Email:wendySstewart@aol.com
Web:www.farmhouse-holidays.co.uk

Large well-appointed stonebuilt 18th. Century farmhouse peacefully
situated between the glens and coast in the heart of Angus Countryside.
Ideal touring/golfing base. Equestrian centre nearby. Aberdeen and
Perth under 1 hour, Deeside and St.Andrews 40 mins. Homemade
preserves and home cooking and baking. Children very welcome. No
smoking.

1 Twin	3 En Suite fac	B&B per person	Open Jan-Dec
1 Double		from £20.00 Single	
1 Family		from £18.00 Double	

★★★

B&B

Doniford
26 Airlie Street, Brechin, DD9 6JX
Tel:01356 622361
Email:ann@doniford.freeserve.co.uk

A traditional Scottish welcome at this 18th century villa in quiet
residential area. Spacious bedrooms and ensuites. Ideal centre for
touring the glens, fishing, golfing, castles and distilleries. Evening meals
by arrangement. Plenty private parking.

2 Twin	All En Suite	B&B per person	Open Jan-Dec
		from £20.00 Single	
		from £20.00 Double	

Broughty Ferry, Dundee

Map Ref: 2D2

★★★★

B&B

Auchenean
177 Hamilton Street, Broughty Ferry, Dundee
DD5 2RE
Tel:01382 774782

Detached house in quiet cul-de-sac. Residents lounge opening on to
secluded garden. Morning tea served free of charge. 5 minutes from
seafront. Dinner and packed lunches available on request. In close
proximity of Carnoustie and St Andrews Championship Golf Courses.

1 Single	1 Pub.Bath/Show	B&B per person	Open Apr-Nov
1 Twin		from £20.00 Single	BB & Eve.Meal
		from £20.00 Double	from £30.00

Important: Prices stated are estimates and may be subject to amendments

Burntisland, Fife   Map Ref: 2C4

Gruinard

148 Kinghorn Road, Burntisland, Fife KY3 9JU
Tel: 01592 873877 e.mail: gruinard@dircon.co.uk
Web: www.gruinardguesthouse.co.uk

Situated on outskirts of the quiet coastal town of Burntisland, Gruinard offers excellent accommodation set in colourful garden. Overlooking river towards Edinburgh, accessible by train or road in approx 30 minutes. Breakfast includes fresh local produce and is served in conservatory. Warm and friendly stay guaranteed. Sorry, no smoking.

★★★★

B&B

Gruinard

148 Kinghorn Road, Burntisland, Fife, KY3 9JU
Tel:01592 873877
Email:gruinard@dircon.co.uk
Web:www.gruinardguesthouse.co.uk

Very well appointed traditional stone cottage (1904). Have breakfast in our conservatory overlooking the interesting and colourful garden. One room with extensive view across the Firth of Forth to the Edinburgh skyline. 30 minutes from Edinburgh and St Andrew's by car and easy access to Scotland's motorway system.

| 1 Twin | All En Suite | B&B per person | Open Mar-Nov |
| 1 Double | | from £22.00 Double | |

Carnoustie, Angus   Map Ref: 2D2

THE OLD MANOR

PANBRIDE, CARNOUSTIE, ANGUS DD7 6JP
TEL/FAX: 01241 854804
E.MAIL: STAY@OLDMANORCARNOUSTIE.COM
WEB: WWW.OLDMANORCARNOUSTIE.COM

Beautifully restored manse dating from 1765 overlooking the town of Carnoustie and coast of Fife. The large individually decorated en-suite bedrooms are complete with TV, tea, coffee and refreshments. Salmon fishing on the River South Esk and golf tee times on any of the local courses can be arranged.

★★★★

B&B

The Old Manor

Panbride, Carnoustie, DD7 6JP
Tel/Fax:01241 854804
Email:stay@oldmanorcarnoustie.com
Web:www.oldmanorcarnoustie.com

Spacious ensuite rooms in fully restored country house. Peaceful location close to Carnoustie. Convenient for golf, beaches and Angus glens. Non smoking house. Evening meals by arrangement using fresh local produce wherever possible.

2 Twin	4 En Suite fac	B&B per person	Open Jan-Dec
2 Double	1 Pub.Bath/Show	from £35.00 Single	
1 Family		£27.50-35.00 Double	

Scotland's National Booking and Information Line

Tel: 0845 22 55 121
visitscotland.com

VAT is shown at 17.5%: changes in this rate may affect prices.   **Key to symbols is on back flap.**

Carnoustie, Angus   Map Ref: 2D2

AA Selected
◆◆◆◆

PARK HOUSE
12 Park Avenue, Carnoustie, Angus DD7 7JA
Tel/Fax: 01241 852101
e.mail: parkhouse@bbcarnoustie.fsnet.co.uk
Web: www.bbcarnoustie.fsnet.co.uk

Charming smoke-free Victorian villa with private walled garden and parking.
Ensuite bedrooms with sea views. Central location. 3 minutes walk from golf
course and railway station. Ideal base for 30 golf courses (including St Andrews)
all within 45 minutes drive. Discount for longer stays. Warm welcome assured.

★★★★

B&B

Park House
12 Park Avenue, Carnoustie, Angus, DD7 7JA
Tel/Fax:01241 852101
Email:parkhouse@bbcarnoustie.fsnet.co.uk
Web:www.bbcarnoustie.fsnet.co.uk

A detached Victorian house in its own walled garden. Championship golf
course and beach nearby. Private parking. Quiet location.

2 Single	2 En Suite fac	B&B per person	Open Jan-Dec excl
1 Twin	2 Priv.NOT ensuite	from £26.00 Single	Xmas/New Year
1 Double		from £26.00 Double	

Ceres, Fife   Map Ref: 2C3

★★★

INN

Meldrums Hotel
56 Main Street, Ceres, by Cupar, Fife, KY15 5NA
Tel:01334 828286 Fax:01334 828795
Email:info@meldrumshotel.co.uk
Web:www.meldrumshotel.co.uk

Situated in the picturesque village of Ceres, ideal golfing base 6 miles
from St Andrews, the home of golf. Family run country Inn offering fine
food and ale.

1 Single	All En Suite	B&B per person	Open Jan-Dec
5 Twin		from £35.00 Single	
1 Double		from £34.00 Double	

Comrie, Perthshire   Map Ref: 2A2

★★★★

**SMALL
HOTEL**
•
RESTAURANT

The Royal Hotel
Melville Square, Comrie, Perthshire, PH6 2DN
Tel:01764 679200 Fax:01764 679219
Email:reception@royalhotel.co.uk
Web:www.royalhotel.co.uk

A hotel of natural elegance reflecting the simple charm and relaxed
atmosphere of the village of Comrie and the surrounding area.

3 Twin	All En Suite	B&B per person	Open Jan-Dec
8 Double		from £70.00 Single	BB & Eve.Meal
		from £55.00 Double	from £75.00

Crail, Fife   Map Ref: 2D3

★★★

**GUEST
HOUSE**

Selcraig House
47 Nethergate, Crail, Fife, KY10 3TX
Tel:01333 450697 Fax:01333 451113
Email:margaret@selcraighouse.co.uk
Web:www.selcraighouse.co.uk

200-year-old Listed house in quiet street close to seashore. Convenient
for touring the East Neuk of Fife and very close to coastal path walk.
Non-smoking. Ample quiet village parking.

2 Single	Some En Suite	B&B per person	Open Jan-Dec excl
2 Twin		from £20.00 Single	Xmas/New Year
1 Double		from £20.00 Double	
1 Family			

Important: Prices stated are estimates and may be subject to amendments

Crail, Fife

Map Ref: 2D3

CAIPLIE GUEST HOUSE
53 High Street North, Crail, Fife KY10 3RA
Tel: 01333 450564
e.mail: mail@caipliehouse.com Web: www.caipliehouse.com

Attractive guest house in the delightful village of Crail.
Good value accommodation with some en-suite rooms and sea views.
Home cooking a speciality.
Drinks licence and residents lounge.

★★★

**GUEST
HOUSE**

Caiplie House

53 High Street, Crail, Fife, KY10 3RA
Tel:01333 450564
Email:mail@caipliehouse.com
Web:www.caipliehouse.com

Very comfortable and friendly guest house renowned for its home
cooking with restricted table licence. On main street of fishing village
near coastal path and picturesque harbour. Pets welcome by
arrangement.

1 Single	Some En Suite	B&B per person	Open Apr-Nov
2 Twin	2 Priv.NOT ensuite	from £20.00 Single	BB & Eve.Meal
3 Double	1 Pub.Bath/Show	from £18.00 Double	from £28.00
1 Family			

Crieff, Perthshire

Map Ref: 2A2

★★

B&B

Concraig Farmhouse

Muthill Road, Crieff, Perthshire, PH7 4HH
Tel:01764 653237
Email:scott.concraig@tesco.net

Comfortable farmhouse with spacious rooms, including 1 en suite,
peacefully situated just outside Crieff. Ideal location for golfing & touring.

1 Twin	1 En Suite fac	B&B per person	Open all year
1 Double	2 Priv.NOT ensuite	from £25.00 Single	
1 Family		from £18.00 Double	

Galvelmore House
5 Galvelmore Street, Crieff PH7 4BY
Tel: 01764 655721 Fax: 01764 655721
e.mail: katy@galvelmore.co.uk Web: www.galvelmore.co.uk
Situated in a quiet street in the centre of Crieff. Katy and David offer
friendly hospitality, in a relaxed and informal atmosphere.
Our en-suited bedrooms are comfortably furnished, blending Georgian
architecture with contemporary style. The wood-panelled lounge has an open
log fire, and is available for guests use throughout the day.

★★★

B&B

Galvelmore House

Galvelmore Street, Crieff, Perthshire, PH7 4BY
Tel/Fax:01764 655721
Email:katy@galvelmore.co.uk
Web:www.galvelmore.co.uk

You are assured of a warm welcome into this peaceful family home which
is comfortably furnished with a hint of period style. Lounge with warm,
inviting log fire. Close to town centre, in the heart of Strathearn. Evening
meals by prior arrangement. Families welcome.

1 Twin	All En Suite	B&B per person	Open Jan-Dec
2 Double		from £20.00 Single	BB & Eve.Meal
		from £18.00 Double	from £31.00

VAT is shown at 17.5%: changes in this rate may affect prices.

Key to symbols is on back flap.

MERLINDALE

Perth Road, Crieff PH7 3EQ
Tel/Fax: 01764 655205
e.mail: merlin.dale@virgin.net
Web: www.merlindale.co.uk

Merlindale is a luxurious Georgian house situated
close to the town centre. All bedrooms are ensuite
(2 with sunken bathrooms) and have tea/coffee
making facilities. We have a jacuzzi available plus
garden, ample parking and satellite television.

We also have a Scottish library for the use of our
guests. Cordon Bleu cooking is our speciality. A warm
welcome awaits you in this non-smoking house.

★★★★

B&B

Merlindale

Perth Road, Crieff, Perthshire, PH7 3EQ
Tel/Fax:01764 655205
Email:merlin.dale@virgin.net Web:www.merlindale.co.uk

John and Jackie provide a genuinely warm welcome at their comfortable
family home with many touches of luxury. 6 languages spoken. By
advance arrangement we offer a delicious four course dinner (Jackie is
cordon bleu trained) and provide complimentary wine & liqueur.
Extensive library with emphasis on Scotland. Jacuzzi bath. Relax and
enjoy.

1 Twin	All En Suite	B&B per person	Open Feb-Dec
2 Double		from £35.00 Single	BB & Eve.Meal
		from £25.00 Double	from £47.00

"NO 5" ANN COUTTS *AA*

5 DUCHLAGE TERRACE, CRIEFF, PERTHSHIRE PH7 3AS

TEL/FAX: 01764 653516

E.MAIL: number5@ecosse.net WEB: www.number-five.com

Built around 1899, this Victorian terraced house combines style and comfort with a peaceful
and cosy atmosphere. With all bedrooms en-suite, a non-smoking policy and a lounge for the
use of guests throughout the day, NO.5 offers a large breakfast menu with vegetarian alternatives.
Off-road parking is available for 2 cars.

★★★

B&B

No 5

5 Duchlage Terrace, Crieff, Perthshire, PH7 3AS
Tel/Fax:01764 653516
Email:number5@ecosse.net
Web:www.number-five.com

Late Victorian house quietly tucked away from the main thoroughfare,
offering quality ensuite facilities and delicious breakfasts. Easy access to
pubs & restaurants in the centre of the town and well situated for touring
and golfing.

1 Single	1 En Suite fac	B&B per person	Open Jan-Dec excl
1 Twin		from £18.00 Single	Xmas/New Year
1 Family		from £19.00 Double	BB & Eve.Meal
		from £15.00 Room	from £26.00
		Only	

Important: Prices stated are estimates and may be subject to amendments

Crieff, Perthshire　　　　　　　　　　　　　　　**Map Ref: 2A2**

★★★

B&B

Mrs Katie Sloan
Somerton House, Turret Bank, Crieff, Perthshire
PH7 4JN
Tel:01764 653513　Fax:01764 655028
Email:katie@turretbank7.freeserve.co.uk

Friendly bed and breakfast within 15 minutes walk of town centre. All rooms, including the family room, have a remote control TV, radio, hair drier and a hospitality tray. Ideal touring base. Home of the Turretbank Cavalier King Charles spaniels.

1 Twin	All En Suite	B&B per person	Open Jan-Dec excl
1 Double		from £17.00 Single	Xmas/New Year
1 Family		from £16.00 Double	

📺 ♿ 🅿 ☕ 🐾 ✂

© ⓥ

TUCHETHILL HOUSE
TUCHETHILL HOUSE, DOLLERIE, CRIEFF, PERTHSHIRE PH7 3NX
TEL: 01764 653188 FAX: 01764 655836
Situated only three miles from Crieff, Tuchethill House is a new large detached house with ²/₃ acre of garden in rolling countryside, with beautiful views of hills and mountains. There is off-road parking and a ground floor room with disabled facilities. Families are also catered for.

★★★

B&B

Tuchethill House B&B
Dollerie, Crieff, Perthshire, PH7 3NX
Tel:01764 653188　Fax:01764 655836

Joyce and John welcome you to their new home - a large detached house 3 miles from Crieff with panoramic views of the hills, mountains and woods on all sides. There are two ground floor en-suite bedrooms and a first floor family suite with private facilities.

1 Single	Ensuite fac	B&B from	Open Apr-Oct
1 Double	Ensuite fac	£20.00 per person	
1 Family/	Priv.Bathroom		
Suite			

📺 ♿ ♿ 🅿 ☕ 🐾 ✖ ⤵

© ⓥ ♿

🚶 🖼 🖼

★★

B&B

The Vennel
67 East High Street, Crieff, Perthshire, PH7 3JA
Tel:01764 654524
Email:thevennel@talk21.com

Fiona and Robert extend a warm welcome to you at their comfortable home in the centre of Crieff. Both rooms have ensuite facilities, RcTVs, radios, hair driers and hospitality trays. The Vennel is convenient for the shops and a variety of local eating establishments.

1 Twin	All En Suite	B&B per person	Open Jan-Dec excl
1 Double		from £20.00 Single	Xmas/New Year
		from £20.00 Double	

📺 ♿ ☕ 🐾 ✂

🖼 🖼

Scotland's National Booking and Information Line

Tel: 0845 22 55 121
visitscotland.com

VAT is shown at 17.5%: changes in this rate may affect prices. | *Key to symbols is on back flap.*

Culross, Fife — Map Ref: 2B4

B&B ★★★

St Mungos's
Low Causeway, Culross, Fife, KY12 8HJ
Tel:01383 882102
Email:martinpjackson@hotmail.com
Web:www.milford.co.uk/scotland/h-a-1763.html

17c home, with fine views overlooking the Forth. On outskirts of conservation village. Interesting garden. Ideal base for touring. Non smoking and private parking.

1 Twin	1 En Suite fac	B&B per person	Open Jan-Dec excl
1 Double	1 Priv.NOT ensuite	from £20.00 Single	Xmas/New Year
1 Family		from £18.00 Double	

Dalgety Bay, Fife — Map Ref: 2B4

B&B ★★★★

The Coach House
1 Hopeward Mews, Dalgety Bay, Fife, KY11 9TB
Tel:01383 823584 Fax:0870 052 6108
Email:tricia@donibristle.demon.co.uk
Web:www.donibristle.demon.co.uk

Modern family bungalow in superb coastal location with excellent panoramic view south across the Firth of Forth to Edinburgh. Situated on the Fife Coastal Path, only 20 minutes travel from Edinburgh with excellent public transport links. An ideal place to relax and unwind and watch the seals play at the foot of the garden.

1 Single	Some En Suite	B&B per person	Open 3 Jan-21 Dec
1 Twin	1 Priv.NOT ensuite	from £22.00 Single	
2 Double	1 Pub.Bath/Show	from £24.00 Double	
		from £20.00 Room Only	

Dundee, Angus — Map Ref: 2C2

B&B ★★★

Anlast Three Chimneys House
379 Arbroath Road, Dundee, DD4 7SQ
Tel/Fax:01382 456710
Email:angus.three.chimneys@talk21.com
Web:www.visitscotland.com

A warm, friendly welcome awaits you at this attractive large detached villa on the east side of town, only 2 miles from city centre, near to busy bus route. All bedrooms, have private shower/bath, colour TV, central heating and tea/coffee making facilties. A no smoking house, which has private parking, beautiful view and gardens.

3 Twin	2 En Suite fac	B&B per person	Open Jan-Dec
	1 Priv.Bath/Show	£30.00-35.00 Single	
		£22.50-25.00 Double	

B&B ★★★

Ardmoy B&B
359 Arbroath Road, Dundee, Angus, DD4 7SQ
Tel:01382 453249
Email:ardmoy@btopenworld.com

Spacious stone built house in own garden on direct route to centre. Private parking. Close to Discovery and city centre. On tourist route North to Carnoustie and Aberdeen. Evening meal by prior arrangement. En-suite rooms available.

1 Single	2 En Suite fac	B&B per person	Open Jan-Dec
1 Twin	1 Priv.Sharing	from £19.00 Single	BB & Eve.Meal
1 Double		from £19.00 Double	from £26.00
1 Family			

B&B ★★★

Ashvilla
216 Arbroath Road, Dundee, Angus, DD4 7RZ
Tel/Fax:01382 450831
Email:ashvilla_guesthouse@talk21.com

Comfortable detached, stone-built house ideally situated on main route for both city centre and surrounding countryside. Private off-street parking, children welcome. Pets by arrangement. Guests and their children are welcome to relax in our spacious rear garden.

1 Single	1 En Suite fac	B&B per person	Open Jan-Dec excl
1 Twin	1 Priv.NOT ensuite	from £18.00 Single	Xmas/New Year
1 Family		from £18.00 Double	
		from £15.00 Room Only	

Important: Prices stated are estimates and may be subject to amendments

Dundee, Angus   Map Ref: 2C2

DUNTRUNE HOUSE

Main Wing, Duntrune House, Duntrune, Dundee DD4 0PJ
Tel: 01382 350239
e.mail: info@duntrunehouse.co.uk Web: www.duntrunehouse.co.uk
Experience the best of Scottish hospitality within the family
ambience of our historic country home. Share our special
interest in local and family history. Enjoy our lawn and
woodland garden with panoramic views over the Tay Estuary.
A short distance from the city and well worth the trip.

★★★★

B&B

Duntrune House

Main Wing, Duntrune, Dundee, DD4 0PJ
Tel:01382 350239
Email:info@duntrunehouse.co.uk
Web:www.duntrunehouse.co.uk

Superior accommodation in 1820's country house offering superb views
and spacious, well-maintained grounds. Situated in a quiet rural area
close to the city and well located for touring the East of Scotland. Guests
dine with the hosts whose interests include family history, gardening and
antiques.

1 Double	Ensuite Show/Bath	B&B per person	Open Jan-Dec excl
1 Twin	Ensuite Shower	from £30.00 Single	Xmas/New Year
1 Twin	Adj Priv.Show	from £30.00 Double	BB & Eve.Meal
			from £48.00

V

★★★

**GUEST
HOUSE**

Errolbank Guest House

9 Dalgleish Road, Dundee, Angus, DD4 7JN
Tel/Fax:01382 462118

Family run Victorian villa. Comfortable bedrooms with TV, tea trays and
central heating. All double and twin rooms ensuite. Single room with
private facilities adjacent. 1.2 miles east of city centre and Tay Bridge. Off
main road near river and bus routes. Off street parking and garden. No
smoking throughout.

1 Single	5 En Suite fac	B&B per person	Open Jan-Dec excl
3 Twin	1 Priv.Show	from £26.00 Single	Xmas/New Year
2 Double		from £22.00 Double	

C V

★★★★

HOTEL

Hilton Dundee

Earl Grey Place, Dundee, DD1 4DE
Tel:01382 229271 Fax:01382 200072
Email:reservations@dundee.stakis.co.uk
Web:www.hilton.com

Modern hotel with leisure facilities situated on the banks of the River Tay
with views of the Kingdom of Fife. Easy access by road, rail and air.
Conference facilities. Riverside Caffe Cino facility and restaurant and bar
with views of the river. 24 hour room service. 90 Car Parking spaces.

74 Twin	All En Suite	B&B per person	Open Jan-Dec
55 Double		from £54.00 Single	BB & Eve.Meal
		from £68.00 Double	from £69.00-98.00

V   🚶

★★★

B&B

Richmond House

1 Anstruther Road, Stobswell, Dundee, Angus
DD4 7EA
Tel:01382 454090

Spacious, comfortable accommodation overlooking putting green/boating
pond. Easy access to local ring-road/town centre. Excellent bus service.
Two ground floor rooms with shower cubicles. Trouser-press available. On
street parking available.

1 Single	B&B per person	Open Jan-Dec excl
1 Twin	from £20.00 Single	Xmas/New Year
	from £18.00 Double	
	from £16.00 Room	
	Only	

V

VAT is shown at 17.5%: changes in this rate may affect prices. | Key to symbols is on back flap. |

Dunfermline, Fife   Map Ref: 2B4

Glencraig B&B
3 Muirside Grove, Cairneyhill, Dunfermline, Fife
KY12 8RB
Tel:01383 881961
Email:bbhood@glencraig.fsnet.co.uk

Warm friendly welcome assured in this comfortable family home near
Dunfermline. Ideally placed for local attractions and Edinburgh, St
Andrews, Stirling and Perth just a short drive away.

| 2 Twin | 1 Priv.NOT ensuite | B&B per person from £16.00 Double | Open Jan-Dec |

B&B

Hillview House
9 Aberdour Road, Dunfermline, KY11 4PB
Tel/Fax:01383 726278
Email:linda@hillviewhousedunfermline.co.uk
Web:www.hillviewhousedunfermline.co.uk

An attractive detached villa on the outskirts of the town. Close to the
M90, easy access to Edinburgh and Perth. Free private parking. Italian
spoken. All rooms en-suite. Complimentary videos. Benvenuti!

| 2 Single / 1 Twin / 1 Double | All En Suite | B&B per person £25.00-27.00 Single £21.00-23.00 Double £19.00-22.00 Room Only | Open Jan-Dec |

B&B

Hopetoun Lodge
141 Halbeath Road, Dunfermline, Fife, KY11 4LA
Tel:01383 620906
Email:bhast10021@aol.com
Web:www.hopetounlodge.co.uk

1920's bungalow with spacious rooms and Art Deco bathroom.
Conveniently located for access to M90 and only 25 min by train from
Edinburgh. Strictly non-smoking.

| 2 Twin / 1 Family | 1 En Suite fac / 1 Shared Bathroom | B&B per person from £24.00 Single | Open Jan-Dec excl Xmas/New Year |

B&B

Lochfitty B&B
Lochfitty Cottage, Lassodie, Dunfermline, KY12 0SP
Tel:01383 831081
Email:n.woolley@btinternet.com
Web:www.lochfittybandb.com

Rural roadside location, with large natural garden, yet close to all local
amenities and major attractions including Loch Fitty Trout Fishery, water
skiing, numerous golf courses and Knockhill Racing Circuit. 3 kms from
M90 (Junction 3 or Junction 4). Children and pets welcome. Visa and
Mastercard accepted.

| 1 Double / 1 Family | 1 En Suite fac / 1 Pub.Bath/Show | B&B per person from £20.00 Single from £20.00 Double | Open Jan-Dec excl Xmas/New Year |

B&B

Pitfirrane Hotel & Restaurant
Main Street, Crossford, by Dunfermline, Fife KY12 8NJ
Tel:01383 736132 Fax:01383 621760
Email:info@scothotels.com
Web:www.scothotels.com

Large, family run hotel, on main road from Dunfermline to Kincardine
Bridge, but only 2 miles (4kms) from Dunfermline city centre. Large car
park. Golfing breaks are our speciality.

| 10 Single / 15 Twin / 12 Double / 1 Family | All En Suite | B&B per person £31.00-59.00 Single £26.50-36.00 Double | Open Jan-Dec BB & Eve.Meal from £41.00 |

HOTEL

Important: Prices stated are estimates and may be subject to amendments

Dunkeld, Perthshire   Map Ref: 2B1

B&B

The Bridge Bed & Breakfast

10 Bridge Street, Dunkeld, Perthshire, PH8 0AH
Tel/Fax:01350 727068
Web:www.visitscotland.com/thebridge

2 Twin	All En Suite	B&B per person	Open Jan-Dec excl
1 Double		£25.00-30.00 Single	Xmas
		£23.00-26.00 Double	

Welcome to the Bridge a beautiful restored Georgian home situated in the heart of historic Dunkeld. Ideally located for fishing, golf, cycling, walking, weddings, and enjoying the many attractions Perthshire has to offer. We will be happy to advise you. Fresh local produce available for breakfast, with tea, coffee and home baking available all day. All rooms are ensuite. Please note that we are strictly non smoking.

B&B

The Coppers

Inchmagrannachan, Dunkeld, PH8 0JS
Tel:01350 727372

1 Twin	1 En Suite fac	B&B per person	Open Apr-Oct
1 Double	1 Priv.NOT ensuite	£16.00-18.00 Double	

Typical Highland welcome and home baking in this bungalow with one ensuite bedroom. Comfortable lounge/conservatory with TV available for guests use and private parking. Quiet country location, which is easily accessible from the A9. Access to fishing, golf and superb walks. Two minutes from Beatrix Potter's summer residence.

B&B

Elwood Villa

Perth Road, Birnam, Dunkeld, Perthshire, PH8 0BH
Tel:01350 727330
Email:elwood7330@aol.com
Web:www.elwood-villa.co.uk

1 Twin	1 Priv.NOT ensuite	B&B per person	Open Jan-Dec
1 Double		from £18.00 Single	
1 Family		from £18.00 Double	

Edwardian, stone villa in residential area. Close to village amenities and River Tay, with easy access to forest and riverside walks. Friendly Scottish welcome with tea and home bakes. All rooms with wash-hand basins. Off street parking.

B&B

Letter Farm

Loch of the Lowes, Dunkeld, Perthshire, PH8 0HH
Tel:01350 724254   Fax:01350 724341
Email:letterlowe@aol.com
Web:www.letterfarm.co.uk

1 Twin	All En Suite	B&B per person	Open Jan-Dec excl
2 Double		from £32.00 Single	Apr,Xmas,New Year
		from £25.00 Double	BB & Eve.Meal
			from £38.00

This tastefully renovated farmhouse which has en suite bathrooms and 1 ground floor room, is on a working farm 1.5 miles (2.5kms) from the Scottish Wildfowl Trust Reserve and 3 miles (5kms) from Dunkeld. Peaceful location.

Scotland's National Booking and Information Line

Tel: 0845 22 55 121
visitscotland.com

VAT is shown at 17.5%: changes in this rate may affect prices.   *Key to symbols is on back flap.*

Dunkeld, Perthshire

Map Ref: 2B1

★★★★

B&B

●●●
**HOME
COOKING**

The Pend
5 Brae Street, Dunkeld, Perthshire, PH8 0BA
Tel:01350 727586 Fax:01350 727173
Email:molly@thepend.sol.co.uk
Web:www.thepend.com

Situated in the centre of Dunkeld, The Pend is a charming Georgian
house full of character and retaining many original architectural
features. Tastefully decorated and furnished using many fine antiques.
Facilities include wash hand basin, shaver socket, hospitality tray, luxury
bathrobe and colour television. Two large bathrooms.

| 1 Double | 2 Priv.NOT ensuite |
| 2 Family | |

B&B per person
from £30.00 Single
from £30.00 Double

Open Jan-Dec
BB & Eve.Meal
from £50.00

★★★★

B&B

Tigh-na-Braan
Amulree, by Dunkeld, Perthshire, PH8 0BZ
Tel:01350 725247 Fax:01350 725219
Email:tighnabraan@tesco.net

Formerly a manse, this Victorian house is now a comfortable B&B. It has
3 bedrooms - 2 with ensuite bathrooms and 1 with a private bathroom.
Each room has a RcTV, radio and hospitality tray. The house is peacefully
situated in a small village surrounded by hills. This is an ideal base for
touring and walking. Guests can relax in the lounge in front of a real
fire. Non-smoking house.

| 1 Twin | 2 En Suite fac |
| 2 Double | 1 Pub.Bath/Show |

B&B per person
from £22.00 Single
from £22.00 Double

Open Mar-Oct

Dunshalt, Fife

Map Ref: 2C3

★★★

B&B

Rannoch House
Ivy Place, Dunshalt, Fife, KY14 7HA
Tel/Fax:01337 828726
Email:bjcscot@aol.com
Web:www.rannochhouse.com

Traditional house on edge of the picturesque village of Dunshalt, with
both rooms ensuite. Ideal base from which to tour this lovely area,
renowned for its golf courses.

| 2 Twin | All En Suite |
| | 1 Pub.Bath/Show |

B&B per person
from £25.00 Single
from £25.00 Double
from £22.00 Room
Only

Open Jan-Dec
BB & Eve.Meal
from £35.00

Edzell, Angus

Map Ref: 4F12

★★★

B&B

Doune House
24 High Street, Edzell, Angus, DD9 7TA
Tel:01356 648201
Email:johna@cameron21.freeserve.co.uk

Victorian house tastefully upgraded. Welcoming tea/coffee with
homebaking served in lounge. Spacious, comfortable bedrooms. Warm
homely atmosphere. Excellent base for fishing, golfing, walking and
cycling in the Angus Glens.

1 Twin	1 Priv.NOT ensuite
1 Double	1 Pub.Bath/Show
1 Family	

B&B per person
from £17.00 Single
from £17.00 Double

Open Jan-Dec excl
Xmas/New Year

★★★

B&B

Inchcape Bed + Breakfast
High Street, Edzell, Angus, DD9 7TF
Tel:01356 647266
Email:alison.mcm@btinternet.com
Web:www.inchcape.edzell.org.uk

Semi-detached refurbished Edwardian villa on main street of quiet
village, opposite golf course and near bowling green. 4 miles from main
A90.

1 Single	All En Suite
1 Twin	
1 Family	

B&B per person
from £20.00 Single
from £18.00 Double

Open Jan-Dec

Important: Prices stated are estimates and may be subject to amendments

Edzell, Angus

Map Ref: 4F12

★★★

SMALL
HOTEL

Panmure Arms Hotel
52 High Street, Edzell, Angus, DD9 7TA
Tel:01356 648950 Fax:01356 648000
Email:david@panmurearmshotel.co.uk
Web:www.panmurearmshotel.co.uk

A recently refurbished family run hotel with the emphasis on quality and
service. Set in the picturesque village of Edzell with very easy access to
golfing, shooting and fishing. A perfect holiday destination for exploring
the beautiful Angus glens.

2 Single	All En Suite	B&B per person	Open Jan-Dec
5 Twin		from £42.50 Single	BB & Eve.Meal
5 Double		from £30.00 Double	from £40.00
3 Family			

Forfar, Angus

Map Ref: 2D1

Alton Bed and Breakfast
18 Wyllie Street, Forfar, Angus DD8 3DN
Tel: 01307 465193
e.mail: alton@ntlworld.com web: www.welcome2alton.com

Ian and Margaret would like to wish you a warm Scottish welcome to their
19th Century Victorian house, which maintains many original features. These
superior spacious rooms which are all en-suite have colour TV, radio, tea/coffee,
trouser press/iron, hairdryer etc. Town centre 5 minutes walk. Easy access to
A90. Further details and brochure on request.

★★★

B&B

Alton Bed and Breakfast
18 Wyllie Street, Forfar, Angus, DD8 3DN
Tel:01307 465193
Email:alton@ntlworld.com Web:www.welcome2alton.com

Spoil yourselves in the elegance of Alton. Renovated to a high standard
of quality and comfort. Our accommodation consists of lounge, private
dining room, where you may enjoy the breakfast of your choice and our
double room furnishings include a splendid four poster king size bed.
Alton is located in a peaceful residential area and has double glazing
and central heating throughout. Discounts on weekly bookings.

| 1 Twin | All En Suite | B&B per person | Open Jan-Dec |
| 1 Double | | £22.00-24.00 Double | |

★★★

B&B

Atholl Cottage
2 Robertson Terrace, Forfar, DD8 3JN
Tel:01307 465755

Situated in a quiet residential area, yet only 5 minutes walk to town
centre, a warm welcome assured here. Off road parking available. Open
all year.

1 Double	Ensuite fac	B&B per person	Open Jan-Dec
1 Family	Ensuite fac	from £25.00 Single	
		from £20.00 Double	

Scotland's National Booking
and Information Line

Tel: 0845 22 55 121
visitscotland.com

VAT is shown at 17.5%: changes in this rate may affect prices.

Key to symbols is on back flap.

Farmhouse Bed & Breakfast
WEST MAINS OF TURIN, FORFAR DD8 2TE
Telephone: 01307 830229 Fax: 01307 830229
e.mail: cjolly3@aol.com Web: www.s-h-systems.co.uk/hotels/farmho.html

Family run stock farm has a panoramic view over Rescobie Loch. Warm welcome awaits you. Good home cooking and baking ensures guests have an enjoyable stay. Ideal area for golfing (20 mins from Carnoustie), hillwalking, horse-riding, visiting Castles, National Trust properties and gardens. Snooker for evening entertainment.

★★★

B&B

Farmhouse Bed + Breakfast

West Mains of Turin, Forfar, Angus, DD8 2TE
Tel/Fax:01307 830229
Email:cjolly3@aol.com
Web:www.s-h-systems.co.uk/hotels/farmho.html

Farmhouse on working stock farm, 4 miles (6kms) east of Forfar. In elevated position with panoramic views southwards over Rescobie Loch. Evening meals by arrangement. Plenty of golf courses nearby.

1 Single	1 En Suite fac	B&B per person	Open Mar-Oct
1 Double	2 Pub.Bath/Show	£20.00-25.00 Single	BB & Eve.Meal
1 Family		£18.00-20.00 Double	from £30.00-35.00

★★★

B&B

Redroofs Bed + Breakfast

Balgavies, Guthrie, by Forfar, Angus, DD8 2TH
Tel/Fax:01307 830268
Email:redroofs.forfar@virgin.net

A spacious house with all accommodation on the ground floor making this a particularly suitable destination for the more mature traveller. All rooms ensuite with TVs, Tea-trays and fridges. An ideal central base for touring the beautiful Angus glens or the numerous attractions in the area. Less than an hours drive to Aberdeen. Private parking. Children and pets welcome.

1 Twin	All En Suite	B&B per person	Open Jan-Dec excl
1 Double		from £25.00 Single	Xmas/New Year
1 Family		from £22.50 Double	BB & Eve.Meal
			from £27.50

WEMYSS FARM
Montrose Road, Forfar DD8 2TB
Tel/Fax: Forfar 01307 462887 e.mail: Wemyssfarm@hotmail.com

Situated 2½ miles along the B9113, our 190-acre farm has a wide variety of animals. Glamis Castle nearby. Many other castles etc. within easy reach. Ideal touring base for Glens, Dundee (12 miles), Perth, St Andrews, Aberdeen, Edinburgh, Balmoral, Deeside and East Coast resorts. Hillwalking, shooting, golf and fishing nearby. Children welcome.

A warm welcome awaits!

★★★

B&B

Wemyss Farm

Montrose Road, Forfar, DD8 2TB
Tel/Fax:01307 462887
Email:wemyssfarm@hotmail.com

Family farmhouse on working farm. Centrally situated for touring Angus and east coast. Home cooking and baking. Tea/Coffee making facilities available. Children welcome. Several castles and many golf courses within easy reach.

1 Double	1 Pub.Bath	B&B per person	Open Jan-Dec
1 Family	1 Pub.Show	from £23.00 Single	BB & Eve.Meal
		from £18.00 Double	from £30

Important: Prices stated are estimates and may be subject to amendments

Forfar, Angus — Map Ref: 2D1

★★★

B&B

Whinney-Knowe
8 Dundee Street, Letham, Angus, DD8 2PQ
Tel:01307 818288
Email:whinneyknowe@btinternet.com

2 Double	1 En Suite fac	B&B per person	Open Jan-Dec
1 Twin	Shared Bathrm	from £20.00 Single	BB & Eve.Meal
		from £18.00 Double	from £27.50

A warm Scottish welcome awaits you in our home situated in a friendly village. Pub five minutes walk. This is your ideal base for exploring the Angus glens, famous castles and the beauty of the rugged coastline walks.

📺 👶 🅿 👜 ✂️ 🍽️

Ⓒ 🐾 Ⓥ

by Forfar, Angus — Map Ref: 2D1

★★★

B&B

Glencoul House
Justinhaugh,by Forfar, Angus, DD8 3SF
Tel/Fax:01307 860248
Email:glencoul@waitrose.com

1 Twin	2 Priv.NOT ensuite	B&B per person	Open Jan-Dec excl
1 Family		from £20.00 Single	Xmas/New Year
		from £19.00 Double	BB & Eve.Meal
			from £29.00

Former Customs House on South Esk. Fishing available. Quiet and peaceful. Close to glens of Clova and Isla, Forfar, Kirriemuir, Glamis Castle and Dundee. Evening meals available by prior arrangement. A variety of golf courses within easy reach.

📺 🅿 👜 ✂️ 🍽️

Ⓒ 🐾 Ⓥ

Forgandenny, Perthshire — Map Ref: 2B2

★★★★

B&B

Battledown Bed & Breakfast
Off Station Road, Forgandenny, Perthshire, PH2 9EL
Tel/Fax:01738 812471

1 Twin	All En Suite	B&B per person	Open Jan-Dec excl
2 Double		£25.00 Single	Xmas/New Year
		£25.00 Double	

Quiet, comfortable cottage in rural village yet only seven miles from Perth. All 3 bedrooms are on the ground floor and all have en suite facilities, RcTVs, hair driers and hospitality trays. Good local eating establishments. Private parking. Ideal for all outdoor pursuits. No smoking.

📺 👶 🅿 👜 🥤 ✂️

🐾 ♿ Ⓥ ♿

Fortingall, Perthshire — Map Ref: 2A1

★★

B&B

Kinnighallen Farm
Fortingall, Aberfeldy, Perthshire, PH15 2LR
Tel/Fax:01887 830619
Email:a.kininmonth@talk21.com
Web:www.heartlander.scotland.net/home/kinnighallen.htm

1 Twin	1 Pub.Bath/Show	B&B per person	Open Mar-Dec excl
1 Double		from £18.00 Single	Xmas/New Year
		from £18.00 Double	

Farmhouse set in beautiful countryside and woodland. Wide variety of wildlife in this peaceful backwater. Quiet garden for relaxation in the evening.

🅿 🥤 ✂️

Ⓥ

Scotland's National Booking and Information Line

Tel: 0845 22 55 121
visitscotland.com

VAT is shown at 17.5%: changes in this rate may affect prices.

Key to symbols is on back flap.

Glamis, Angus
Map Ref: 2C1

B&B

Mrs Grace Jarron
Hatton of Ogilvy Farm, Glamis, by Forfar, Angus DD8 1UH
Tel/Fax:01307 840229
Email:hattonogilvy@talk21.com

A warm welcome awaits you on our family run farm in a peaceful
picturesque setting. A lovely ensuite room along with sole use of lounge
with TV and beautiful dining room comprises this 4 Star rated
farmhouse. A hearty Scottish breakfast is served and ample spacious
parking is available. Ideal setting for touring Angus, situated only 5 mins
drive from Castle itself.

1 Twin   All En Suite   B&B per person   Open Apr-Oct
from £25.00 Single
£20.00-22.00 Double

Inverkeithing, Fife
Map Ref: 2B4

THE ROODS GUEST HOUSE
16 BANNERMAN AVE, INVERKEITHING KY11 1NG
Telephone/Fax: 01383 415049
e.mail: bookings@theroods.com   Web: www.theroods.com
Quietly situated yet only one minute from railway station. The Roods two ground floor
bedrooms are attractively decorated and offer excellent facilities such as telephones and
mini fridges ensuring guests want for nothing. The luxurious lounge leads onto a dining
conservatory where guests can enjoy breakfast overlooking the garden.

B&B

The Roods Guest House
16 Bannerman Avenue, Inverkeithing, Fife, KY11 1NG
Tel/Fax:01383 415049
Email:bookings@theroods.com
Web:www.theroods.com

Quietly secluded family home. Close to rail station and M90. Well
appointed bedrooms offering mini office and direct dial telephones.
Evening meal by arrangement. Both rooms on ground floor.

1 Twin   All En Suite   B&B per person   Open Jan-Dec
1 Double   from £23.00 Single
from £23.00 Double

Kingsbarns, Fife
Map Ref: 2D3

B&B

The Yards B&B
11 Back Stile, Kingsbarns, Fife, KY16 8ST
Tel:01334 880317
Email:suejaroma@aol.com

Traditional cottage and large garden on the edge of conservation village.
A warm welcome awaits you at this family home (vegetarian and non-
smoking). Only 6 miles to St Andrews and a few miles to the picturesque
fishing villages of the East Neuk. Kingsbarns boasts an award winning
beach. Many golf courses nearby. Free private parking.

1 Double   1 Priv.NOT ensuite   B&B per person   Open Mar-Oct
from £26.00 Single
from £20.00 Double

Scotland's National Booking and Information Line

Tel: 0845 22 55 121
visitscotland.com

Important: Prices stated are estimates and may be subject to amendments

---

Kinloch Rannoch, Perthshire Map Ref: 1H1

BUNRANNOCH HOUSE

Kinloch Rannoch, Perthshire PH16 5QB
Tel/Fax: 01882 632407
e.mail: bun.house@tesco.net Web: www.bunrannoch.co.uk

"A gem of a place". Lovely Victorian house set in 2 acres of grounds on the outskirts of Kinloch Rannoch. A warm welcome awaits you together with a complimentary tea tray of home baking on arrival. Beautiful views, good cooking and log fires. No smoking throughout. Breakfast is a treat!!

★★★

GUEST HOUSE

●●

HOME COOKING

Bunrannoch House

Kinloch Rannoch, Perthshire, PH16 5QB
Tel/Fax:01882 632407
Email:bun.house@tesco.net
Web:www.bunrannoch.co.uk

'A Gem of a Place', set in beautiful surroundings, Bunrannoch House is renowned for its genuine, warm hospitality and excellent food. Explore the hills, where wildlife abounds. Discover castles, antiques, history and folklore. Cycle, walk, fish. Return to log fires, a fresh, home-baked tea tray and peace and relaxation. We would love to welcome you!

2 Twin	5 En Suite fac	B&B per person	Open Jan-Dec excl
3 Double	1 Priv.NOT ensuite	from £22.00 Single	Xmas/New Year
2 Family		from £22.00 Double	BB & Eve.Meal
			from £40.00

Kinross, Perthshire Map Ref: 2B3

★★★★

B&B

Burnbank

79 Muirs, Kinross, Perthshire, KY13 8AZ
Tel:01577 861931   Fax:01577 861931
Email:bandb@burnbank-kinross.co.uk
Web:www.burnbank-kinross.co.uk

This delightful home, formerly a mill shop, is situated at the edge of town and surrounded by open farmland. Restful colours,quality fabrics and linen characterise the rooms. The comfortable ensuite bedrooms are well equipped with TV, video, tea & coffee and have fine outlooks to the Lomond Hills. Fresh fruit and home baked bread add to the enjoyment of the delicious breakfast. Burnbank is an excellent centre for touring.

1 Twin	All En Suite	B&B per person	Open Jan-Dec
1 Double		from £25.00 Single	
1 Family		from £25.00 Double	

★★★★

B&B

Mawcarse House

Milnathort, Kinross-shire, KY13 9SJ
Tel/Fax:01577 862220
Email:wsyoung@farmersweekly.net
Web:www.perthshiresbest.co.uk

Spacious and comfortable family farmhouse with fine open views. Peacefully situated, yet only minutes from M90. Next to designated country walk/cycle route. Golf, fishing, RSPB all nearby.

1 Single	2 En Suite fac	B&B per person	Open Apr-Dec excl
1 Twin	1 Priv.Bath/Show	from £25.00 Single	Xmas/New Year
1 Double		from £25.00 Double	

★★

GUEST HOUSE

Roxburghe Guest House

126 High Street, Kinross, KY13 8DA
Tel/Fax:01577 862498
Email:roxburghe.guesthouse@virgin.net

A warm welcome awaits you from Sandy & Steve at the Roxburghe, which is situated within 0.5hr of the Rosyth Ferry and close to the main tourist routes. Sandy combines the best of Scottish produce with traditional cooking offering a wide choice at breakfast. Evening meals are available, and Sandy will cater for your favourite dish or special diets. The Roxburghe is licensed with snacks and packed lunches available.

1 Twin	1 Priv.NOT ensuite	B&B per person	Open Jan-Dec
1 Double		from £18.00 Single	BB & Eve.Meal
2 Family		from £18.00 Double	from £28.00

VAT is shown at 17.5%: changes in this rate may affect prices.   **Key to symbols is on back flap.**

by Kinross, Perthshire

Map Ref: 2B3

★★★★

B&B

Caplawhead Bed and Breakfast
**by Yetts o' Muckhart, Rumbling Bridge, Kinross
KY13 0QD
Tel:01259 781556
Email:hamish-frances@caplawhead.freeserve.co.uk**

Welcome to Caplawhead. A beautifully restored farmhouse set in the peaceful countryside by Glendevon. Secluded, yet within easy reach of all main tourist routes. Ideal for golfing, fishing, walking, sightseeing or just enjoying the views. Good wholesome Scottish breakfasts with a wide range of delicious alternatives. Organic fare wherever possible.

| 1 Twin | All En Suite |
| 1 Double | |

B&B per person
from £25.00 Single
from £25.00 Double

Open Jan-Dec

Kirkcaldy, Fife

Map Ref: 2C4

★★★

B&B

Arboretum
**20 Southerton Road, Kirkcaldy, Fife, KY2 5NB
Tel:01592 643673
Email:arboretumbb@amserve.net**

Quietly located adjacent to Beveridge Park and close to the centre of Kirkcaldy. Walking distance from shops and railway station. Private and free on-street parking. Double or twin available both en-suite. Not suitable for children under five years.

| 2 Double | All En Suite |

B&B per person
from £22.00 Single
from £19.00 Double

Open Jan-Dec excl
Xmas/New Year

★★★

B&B

Cherrydene
**44 Bennnochy Road, Kirkcaldy, Fife, KY2 5RB
Tel:01592 202147
Email:cherrydene@beeb.net
Web:www.cherrydene.co.uk**

Victorian, end terraced house in quiet residential area, yet within easy reach of all amenities. Private parking. Easy access to A92 (Kirkcaldy West). Ideal base for golfing and touring.

1 Single	2 En Suite fac
1 Double	1 Shared Bath.
1 Family	

B&B per person
from £22.00 Single
from £20.00 Double
from £20.00 Room
Only

Open Jan-Dec excl
Xmas/New Year
BB & Eve.Meal
from £27.50

Scotland's National Booking and Information Line

Tel: 0845 22 55 121
visitscotland.com

Kirkcaldy, Fife — Map Ref: 2C4

North Hall

★★★★ B&B

143 Victoria Road, Kirkcaldy, KY1 1DQ
Tel:01592 268864
Email:cairns@northhall.freeserve.co.uk

Former manse with original oak stairs and doors. Close to town centre. Ideal for touring Fife villages. Edinburgh 26 miles (42kms), 30 minutes by train.

| 1 Twin 1 Double | All En Suite | B&B per person from £22.50 Double | Open Jan-Dec excl Xmas/New Year |

Norview
★★ B&B

59 Normand Road, Dysart, Kirkcaldy, KY1 2XP
Tel:01592 652804 Fax:01592 650801
Email:norviewlinton2000@yahoo.com

Personally run bed and breakfast on main tourist route. Ideal for touring Fife. Golf courses, coastal walks and other amenities close by.

| 2 Twin 1 Double | 2 Priv.NOT ensuite | B&B per person from £17.00 Single from £17.00 Double from £16.00 Room Only | Open Jan-Dec excl Xmas/New Year |

Wemysshof

★★ B&B

69 Lady Nairn Avenue, Kirkcaldy, Fife, KY1 2AR
Tel:01592 652806

Situated in a quiet residential area on the east side of Kirkcaldy. Come and enjoy our chat and stories in our friendly home. Evening meal by request.

| 1 Single 1 Double 1 Family | 1 Priv.NOT ensuite | B&B per person from £16.00 Single | Open Jan-Dec |

Kirkmichael, Perthshire — Map Ref: 4D12

Cruachan
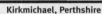
★★★★ B&B

Kirkmichael, Perthshire, PH10 7NZ
Tel:01250 881226
Email:cruachan@kirkmichael.net Web:www.kirkmichael.net

Traditional Victorian country cottage overlooking River Ardle, quiet location close to village amenities. Rooms with ensuite & TVs. Personally run by Alan & Daphne we offer a varied a la carte dinner menu using fresh produce - WINNERS of the 1999 and 2001 Glenturret & Perthshire Tourist Board most enjoyable meal award. An ideal base for touring, with fishing, shooting, riding, walking & many visitor attractions nearby. Pets welcome.

| 1 Twin 1 Double 1 Family | 2 En Suite fac 1 Pub.Bath/Show | B&B per person from £25.50 Single from £21.50 Double | Open Jan-Dec BB & Eve.Meal from £31.50 |

Kirriemuir, Angus　　　　　　　　　　　　　Map Ref: 2C1

★★

B&B

Crepto
Kinnordy Place, Kirriemuir, Angus, DD8 4JW
Tel:01575 572746
Email:davendjessma@bun.com

1 Single	2 Priv.NOT ensuite	B&B per person	Open Jan-Dec
1 Twin		from £23.00 Single	
1 Double		from £23.00 Double	

A friendly welcome at this modern house in quiet cul-de-sac. Only 10 minutes walk from town centre. All rooms with TVs. Guests' lounge and tea-making facilities available. Ample private parking. Gateway to Angus glens.

LOCHSIDE LODGE & ROUNDHOUSE RESTAURANT
Bridgend Of Lintrathen, By Kirriemuir, Angus DD8 5JJ
Tel: 01575 560340 Fax: 01575 560202
e.mail: enquiries@lochsidelodge.com Web: www.lochsidelodge.com
Located alongside Lintrathen Loch, this converted farm steading offers warm and welcoming hospitality with comfortable accommodation. An award winning restaurant provides excellent food with easy bar to relax in. Ideal for walking, cycling or just a relaxing break and the chance to explore the Angus countryside.

★★★★

**RESTAURANT
WITH ROOMS**

●●●

RESTAURANT

Lochside Lodge & Roundhouse Restaurant
Bridgend of Lintrathen, nr Kirriemuir, Angus DD8 5JJ
Tel:01575 560340 Fax:01575 560202
Email:enquiries@lochsidelodge.com
Web:www.lochsidelodge.com

1 Twin	Priv.Bath/Show	B&B per person	Open Jan-Dec
2 Double	all rooms	from £35.00 Single	
1 Family		from £30.00 Double	

Alongside Lintrathen Loch, this converted farm steading offers a fine restaurant and bar, with comfortable accommodation. Modern cuisine of international standard, using fresh local ingredients carefully prepared by chef/proprietor, Graham Riley, a Masterchef of Great Britain.

★★★★

B&B

Purgavie Farm
Lintrathen, by Kirriemuir, Angus, DD8 5HZ
Tel/Fax:01575 560213
Email:purgavie@aol.com

1 Twin	All En Suite	B&B per person	Open Jan-Dec
1 Double		from £25.00 Single	BB & Eve.Meal
1 Family		from £25.00 Double	from £37.00
		from £15.00 Room Only	

A warm welcome in homely accommodation on our farm set in peaceful countryside with excellent views. All rooms have ensuite bathroom, TV and tea-making facilities. Good home cooking providing traditional Scottish Fayre. Fishing on Lintrathen Loch, pony trekking and hill-walking in Glen Isla. Glamis Castle 10 miles. Located 7 miles from Kirriemuir, follow the B951 to Glen Isla, farm signposted at roadside.

Scotland's National Booking and Information Line

Tel: 0845 22 55 121
visitscotland.com

Important: Prices stated are estimates and may be subject to amendments

Letham, Angus

Map Ref: 2D1

Woodville

Heathercroft, Guthrie Street, Letham, by Forfar, Angus DD8 2PS
Tel: 01307 818090

*A warm welcome awaits you. Excellent food and accommodation.
Bedrooms with wash-hand basin, tea facilities, TV. Two twin rooms are available.
Letham is a village set in the middle of Angus. Excellent for touring Glens of Angus,
Royal Deeside and Glamis. It is also near to new Pictavia Centre. Birdwatching,
walks, fishing, golf, pictish interest. Aberdeen, St Andrews, Edinburgh within easy
reach. B&B from £20 pp twin/double. B&B from £22 pp single.*

★★★

B&B

Woodville

**Heathercroft, Guthrie Street, Letham, by Forfar
Angus, DD8 2PS
Tel:01307 818090 Mob:07765 387694**

A warm traditional scottish welcome awaits in modern new house on the
edge of the historic village of Letham. Ideal location for golf, fishing,
walking, glens, castles (Glamis nearby) & birdwatching. Within easy
distance of Dundee, Aberdeen, Edinburgh, Royal Deeside & St Andrews.

2 Twin	2 Priv.NOT ensuite	B&B per person from £22.00 Single from £20.00 Double from £15.00 Room Only pp	Open Jan-Dec BB & Eve.Meal from £32.00

Leven, Fife

Map Ref: 2C3

★★★★★

B&B

Hillpark House

**96 Main Street, Leuchars, by St Andrews, Fife KY16 0HF
Tel/Fax:01334 839280
Email:enquiries@hillparkhouse.com
Web:www.hillparkhouse.com**

Elegant Victorian house refurbished to a high standard. Stylish decor
incorporating many original features including a unique canopy
bath/shower. Cosy and warm with open fire in season. Halfway between
St Andrews and Dundee with golf and beaches nearby.

1 Twin 2 Double	2 En Suite fac 1 Pub.Bath/Show	B&B per person from £32.00 Single from £24.00 Double	Open Jan-Dec

---

Limekilns, Fife

Map Ref: 2B4

★★★★

**GUEST
HOUSE**

Dunclutha Guest House

**16 Victoria Road, Leven, Fife, KY8 4EX
Tel:01333 425515   Fax:01333 422311
Email:pam.leven@dunclutha-accomm.demon.co.uk
Web:www.dunclutha-accomm.demon.co.uk**

Victorian former manse. 2 minutes level walk from centre of Leven. Good
base for golfing enthusiasts and New Fife Coastal Walk. 50 minutes drive
from Edinburgh and 40 minutes from the airport. 7 miles to the nearest
railway station. All bedrooms with either ensuite or private facilities.

1 Twin 1 Double 2 Family	3 En Suite fac 1 Priv.Bath/Show	B&B per person from £26.00 Single from £24.00 Double	Open Jan-Dec

---

★★★

B&B

Breck House

**8 Red Row, Limekilns, Fife, KY11 3HU
Tel:01383 872513**

Ancient, listed building with beach front location. Former customs house
featured in Robert Louis Stevenson's Kidnapped. 4 miles west of M90
(Junction 2) situated in quiet seafront village. Strictly non smoking.

1 Twin 1 Double	1 Priv.NOT ensuite	B&B per person £20.00-22.50 Single £20.00-22.50 Double	Open Jan-Dec

---

VAT is shown at 17.5%: changes in this rate may affect prices.

Key to symbols is on back flap.

Lundin Links, Fife — Map Ref: 2C3

Sandilands
20 Leven Road, Lundin Links, Leven, Fife, KY8 6AH
Tel/Fax:01333 329881
Email:bandb.atsandilands@tesco.net
Web:www.sandilandsfife.co.uk

B&B

2 Twin	2 En Suite fac	B&B per person	Open Jan-Dec
1 Double	1 Pub.Bath/Show	from £23.00 Single	
		from £20.00 Double	

Victorian sandstone villa centrally located in the village of Lundin Links, gateway to the East Neuk of Fife. Several good hotels and pubs nearby. Largo Bay within walking distance. Fife coastal path provides excellent low-level walking. Prime golfing area.

Markinch, Fife — Map Ref: 2C3

Mrs C Craig
Shythrum Farm, Markinch, by Glenrothes, Fife
KY7 6HB
Tel:01592 758372

B&B

1 Family	En Suite	B&B per person	Open Mar-Oct
1 Twin	Priv.Bathroom	from £18.00 Single	
		from £18.00 Double	
		from £13.00 Room Only	

Arable farm adjacent to coaching route used by Mary Queen of Scots. Balgonie Castle 0.5 mile (1km), Falkland Palace 5 miles (8kms). Ideal base for touring the scenic East Neuk of Fife. Easy access to St Andrews, Perth and Dunfermline the birth place of Andrew Carnegie.

Milnathort, by Kinross, Kinross-shire — Map Ref: 2B3

Warroch Lodge Bed & Breakfast
by Milnathort, Kinross-shire, KY13 0RS
Tel:01577 863779

B&B

2 Twin	1 En Suite fac	B&B per person	Open Jan-Dec
	1 Priv.NOT ensuite	from £23.00 Double	

This period lodge, with a large cottage garden, is set in attractive countryside 4 miles (6kms) from Junction 6 of the M90 with easy access to the major towns. Open fire in the lounge. The rooms, which have en suite or private facilities, have radios, hair driers, small fridges and hospitality trays. Evening meal by prior arrangement. Bird watching, golfing, fishing, hill walking, gliding are all nearby as is Knockhill racing circuit.

Montrose, Angus — Map Ref: 4F12

Carlton Hotel & Restaurant
139 High Street, Montrose, DD10 8QN
Tel/Fax:01674 677237
Email:graeme@peelhouse139.freeserve.co.uk

SMALL HOTEL

1 Single	7 En Suite fac	B&B per person	Open Jan-Dec
3 Twin	1 Pub.Bath/Show	from £25.00 Single	
3 Double		from £24.00 Double	
1 Family			

Personally run refurbished restaurant with rooms, in the centre of town. Most rooms with private bathrooms. Varied à la carte menu. Private car park. A good base for touring local castles, distilleries and taking in the Scottish countryside.

Fairfield Bed + Breakfast
24 The Mall, Montrose, Angus, DD10 8NW
Tel/Fax:01674 676386
Email:marlene.scott@tesco.net
Web:www.fairfieldguesthouse.com

B&B

2 Twin	All En suite	B&B per person	Open Jan-Dec
1 Double		from £25.00 Single	
		from £20.00 Double	

Detached Georgian house centrally situated in residential area with ample street parking. Secure cycle parking. All rooms en suite with Tv, Sky Tv, full-size refrigerator and tea-making facilities. Close to Montrose Basin Nature Reserve and an ideal location for walking and golfing.

Important: Prices stated are estimates and may be subject to amendments

Montrose, Angus

Map Ref: 4F12

★★★

GUEST HOUSE

The Limes Guest House
15 King Street, Montrose, Angus, DD10 8NL
Tel:01674 677236 Fax:01674 672798
Email:thelimes@easynet.co.uk
Web:www.thelimesmontrose.co.uk

Family run, centrally situated in quiet, residential part of town. A few minutes walk from the centre, railway station, beach and two golf courses. Private parking.

3 Single	8 En Suite	B&B per person	Open Jan-Dec
4 Twin	4 Priv.Show	from £24.00 Single	
3 Double		from £22.00 Double	
2 Family			

Oaklands Guest House
10 Rossie Island Road, Montrose DD10 9NN
Tel and Fax: 01674 672018   e.mail: oaklands@altavista.net
Web: www.nebsnow.com/oaklands
Comfortable guest house within walking distance of town centre. Excellent breakfast menu. All rooms ensuite with CTV off-street parking. Safe parking for motorcycles in locked garage. Motorcycle tours, golf links and beach nearby. Children welcome. French and Dutch spoken.

★★★

GUEST HOUSE

Oaklands Guest House
10 Rossie Island Road, Montrose, Angus, DD10 9NN
Tel/Fax:01674 672018
Email:oaklands@altavista.net
Web:www.nebsnow.com/oaklands

All rooms ensuite at this comfortable family house, within walking distance of Montrose town centre. Parking. Secure parking for motorcycles and bikes. Evening meals may be available. Please ask on booking.

1 Single	All En Suite	B&B per person	Open Jan-Dec
3 Twin		from £20.00 Single	
2 Double		from £20.00 Double	
1 Family			

---

nr Montrose, Angus

Map Ref: 4F12

★★★★

B&B

Ellington
Station Place, Johnshaven, DD10 0JD
Tel:01561 362756
Email:ellington13@supanet.com
Web:www.ellingtonbandb.co.uk

Modern family home in old fishing village 28 miles south of Aberdeen. Ideally positioned to visit Glen Esk and 14th century Dunnottar Castle. Many well-known golf courses within easy range. Ground floor twin available. Small restaurant in village pub. Warm welcome assured.

1 Twin	All En Suite	B&B per person	Open Jan-Dec excl
1 Double		£20.00-25.00	Xmas/New Year

Scotland's National Booking and Information Line

Tel: 0845 22 55 121
visitscotland.com

VAT is shown at 17.5%: changes in this rate may affect prices.

| Key to symbols is on back flap. |

North Queensferry, Fife | Map Ref: 2B4

★★★★

B&B

Fourteen Falls Bed+Breakfast
Chapel Place, North Queensferry, Fife, KY11 1JT
Tel/Fax:01383 412749
Email:evans@fourteenfalls.com
Web:www.fourteenfalls.com

1 Twin	Bathroom shared with owners.	B&B per person from £22.00 Single from £22.00 Double	Open Jan-Dec

18th Century cottage situated underneath the historic Forth Rail Bridge in conservation village. Secure parking and private garden. Within walking distance of various restaurants. Breakfasts individually catered for.

Perth | Map Ref: 2B2

★★★★

GUEST HOUSE

Ackinnoull Guest House
5 Pitcullen Crescent, Perth, Perthshire, PH2 7HT
Tel:01738 634165
Web:www.ackinnoull.com

1 Twin 2 Double 1 Family	All En Suite	B&B per person from £18.00 Double from £15.00 Room Only	Open Jan-Dec

Beautifully decorated Victorian semi-villa on the outskirts of town. Private parking on premises. 'Perth in Bloom' winners, as picturesque inside as out. Special rates for bookings of 3 days or more.

ALBERT VILLA GUEST HOUSE

63 Dunkeld Road, Perth PH1 5RP
Tel: 01738 622730 Fax: 01738 451182
e.mail: caroline@albertvilla.co.uk
Web: www.albertvilla.co.uk

Spacious and comfortable accommodation on two levels operating with 10 letting bedrooms, 7 having ensuite facilities. 3 ground floor rooms are self-contained offering separate external access and additional privacy. All rooms have been refurbished to a high standard in 2001, each is equipped with hospitality trays, colour TV, and central heating. Ample private parking front/rear.

★★★

GUEST HOUSE

Albert Villa Guest House
63 Dunkeld Road, Perth, Perthshire, PH1 5RP
Tel:01738 622730   Fax:01738 451182
Email:caroline@albertvilla.co.uk
Web:www.albertvilla.co.uk

4 Single 2 Twin 2 Double 2 Family	7 En Suite fac 3 Shared.fac	B&B per person from £20.00 Single from £20.00 Double from £20.00 Room Only	Open Jan-Dec

Caroline and Alistair welcome you to their home which is situated near to the Sports Centre and within walking distance of the city centre with its variety of eating establishments to suit all tastes. Perth is an ideal base for touring scenic Perthshire and enjoying the many outdoor activities available in the area - fishing, golfing, walking but to name a few.

★★★★

GUEST HOUSE

Almond Villa Guest House
51 Dunkeld Road, Perth, PH1 5RP
Tel:01738 629356   Fax:01738 629356
Email:almondvilla@compuserve.com

1 Single 1 Twin 1 Double 1 Family	All En Suite	B&B per person from £23.00 Single from £23.00 Double	Open Jan-Dec

Semi-detached Victorian villa, close to town centre, Gannochy Trust Sports Complex, the North Inch and River Tay. Non smoking house.

Important: Prices stated are estimates and may be subject to amendments

Perth

Perth   Map Ref: 2B2

★★★★

GUEST
HOUSE

Ardfern Guest House
15 Pitcullen Crescent, Perth, PH2 7HT
Tel:01738 637031

1 Twin	2 En Suite fac	B&B per person	Open Jan-Dec
1 Double	1 Pub.Bath/Show	from £20.00 Single	
1 Family		from £20.00 Double	
1 Dbl/Twn			

Victorian semi-villa on outskirts of city within easy access to all amenities.
Non-smoking throughout. Off road parking. Many original features of
the house sympathetically restored and retained.

★★★

B&B

Beeches Guest House
2 Comely Bank, Perth, Perthshire, PH2 7HU
Tel:01738 624486 Fax:01738 643382
Email:enquiries@beeches-guest-house.co.uk
Web:www.beeches-guest-house.co.uk

2 Single	1 En Suite fac	B&B per person	Open Jan-Dec excl
1 Twin		from £20.00 Single	Xmas/New Year
1 Double		from £20.00 Double	

Semi-detached villa, with ample car parking, conveniently situated on
the A94 tourist route. Four of the bedrooms (including singles) have en
suite facilities and all the rooms have a Rc TV, hairdryer and hospitality
tray. The guest's lounge has satellite TV and a video.

★★★★

GUEST
HOUSE

Beechgrove Guest House
Dundee Road, Perth, Perthshire, PH2 7AD
Tel/Fax:01738 636147
Email:beechgroveg.h@sol.co.uk
Web:www.smoothhound.co.uk/hotels/beechgr

1 Single	All En Suite	B&B per person	Open Jan-Dec
2 Twin		from £25.00 Single	
4 Double		from £25.00 Double	
1 Family			

Listed building, former manse (Rectory) set in extensive grounds.
Peaceful, yet only a few minutes walk from the city centre. Non-smoking
establishment.

CLIFTON HOUSE
36 Glasgow Road, Perth PH2 0PB
Telephone: 01738 621997 Fax: 01738 622678
e.mail: clifton_house@hotmail.com
Colin and Margaret Moreland assure you of a warm welcome at their elegant
Victorian House with attractive gardens and extensive private parking.
All bedrooms equipped to a very high standard. Convenient for town centre, bus
and rail stations. Easily accessed from A9 and M90. Non-smoking house.
WINNERS PERTH IN BLOOM.

★★★★

GUEST
HOUSE

Clifton House
36 Glasgow Road, Perth, PH2 0PB
Tel:01738 621997 Fax:01738 622678
Email:clifton_house@hotmail.com

1 Single	3 En suite	B&B per person	Open Jan-Dec excl
2 Twin	1 Priv.NOT En suite	£21.00-24.00 Single	Xmas/New Year
1 Double			

Delightful Victorian house, within easy walking distance of the town
centre with its shops and variety of eating establishments. All bedrooms
have either private or en suite facilities, TVs, hair driers and hospitality
trays. Ample private parking. Ideal location for all leisure facilities.

VAT is shown at 17.5%: changes in this rate may affect prices.   **Key to symbols is on back flap.**

Perth | Map Ref: 2B2

GUEST HOUSE
★★★

Clunie Guest House
12 Pitcullen Crescent, Perth, Perthshire, PH2 7HT
Tel:01738 623625 Fax:01738 623238
Email:ann@clunieguesthouse.co.uk
Web:www.clunieguesthouse.co.uk

A warm welcome awaits you at Clunie Guest House which is situated on
the A94 Coupar Angus road. There is easy access to the city centre with
all its amenities including a variety of eating establishments.
Alternatively, an evening meal can be provided if it is booked in advance.
All rooms ensuite.

1 Single All En Suite
1 Twin
2 Double
3 Family

B&B per person
£19.00-27.00 Single
£19.00-23.00 Double
£18.00-25.00 Room
Only

Open Jan-Dec
BB & Eve.Meal
from £31.00-39.00

B&B
★★★

Comely Bank Cottage
19 Pitcullen Crescent, Perth, PH2 7HT
Tel:01738 631118 Fax:01738 571245
Email:comelybankcott@hotmail.com

Conveniently situated only ½ mile from city centre and all local
amenities. An ideal base for touring Scotland. Friendly welcome assured.

1 Twin All En Suite
1 Double
1 Family

B&B per person
£20.00-25.00 Single
£19.00-20.00 Double
£17.00-18.00 Room
Only

Open Jan-Dec excl
Xmas/New Year

B&B
★★★

Gattaway Farm
Abernethy, Perth, PH2 9LQ
Tel:01738 850746 Fax:01738 850925
Email:tarduff@aol.com
Web:www.smoothhound.co.uk/hotels/gattaway.html

We look forward to welcoming you to our Georgian/Victorian farmhouse
set in a quiet rural location on the outskirts of the village. Lovely views
over Strathearn. All our rooms are en suite - the ground floor twin is
equipped with disabled facilities (category 1). Dinner, if required, and
breakfast are prepared using home or locally produced ingredients
where possible.

1 Twin All En Suite
2 Double

B&B per person
from £27.00 Single
from £22.00 Double

Open Jan-Dec excl
Xmas/New Year
BB & Eve.Meal
from £45.00

GUEST HOUSE
★★★★

Kinnaird Guest House
5 Marshall Place, Perth, Perthshire, PH2 8AH
Tel:01738 628021 Fax:01738 444056
Email:tricia@kinnaird-gh.demon.co.uk
Web:www.kinnaird-guesthouse.co.uk

Georgian house, centrally situated overlooking park. Private parking.
Short walk to town centre and convenient for railway and bus stations.
Personally run. Attentive owners. All rooms have ensuite facilities, TV,
radio, hospitality tray.

1 Single All En Suite
3 Twin
3 Double

B&B per person
from £25.00 Single
from £22.50 Double

Open Jan-Dec excl
Xmas/New Year

Scotland's National Booking and Information Line

Tel: 0845 22 55 121
visitscotland.com

Important: Prices stated are estimates and may be subject to amendments

Perth

Map Ref: 2B2

★★★★

B&B

Ninewells Farmhouse B+B

Woodriffe Road, Newburgh, Fife, KY14 6EY
Tel/Fax:01337 840307
Email:barbara@ninewellsfarm.co.uk
Web:www.ninewellsfarm.co.uk

Traditional farmhouse on operational arable/stock farm. Elevated position with glorious panoramic views over the Tay Valley towards the Perthshire hills. Convenient for Edinburgh, Perth and many golf courses. The lounge is a large conservatory type room with all round views. Visitors are welcomed with tea/coffee and homebaked biscuits or scones. Member of Scotland's Best.

1 Twin	Priv.fac	B&B per person	Open Apr-Oct
1 Triple	Priv.fac	from £30.00 Single	
1 Double	Ensuite fac	from £22.00 Double	

[symbols]

W V

TOPHEAD FARM

TULLYBELTON, STANLEY, BY PERTH PH1 4PT
Telephone and Fax: 01738 828259
e.mail: dowtophead@bosinternet.com
Web: www.tophead-bandb.fsnet.co.uk

Enjoy the panoramic views from the veranda of this welcoming farmhouse which has a relaxing atmosphere and is tastefully furnished. The comfortable spacious bedrooms are bright and airy with SUPERKING BEDS!!

Guests can relax in the comfortable lounge and enjoy interesting breakfasts with home made preserves and local produce in the handsome dining room.

Tophead is an ideal centre for touring Central Scotland, hillwalking, golf, fishing, bird watching, or local sight seeing being situated only 4 miles north of Perth just off the A9 Inverness road.

Edinburgh, St Andrews and Glasgow one hour away, while Crieff, Dundee and Pitlochry only 30 minutes away.

Prices £23-£26 plus £10 single supplement.

COME ON SPOIL YOURSELVES!! **SORRY NO SMOKING.**

★★★★

B&B

Tophead Farm B&B

Tullybelton, Stanley, by Perth, Perthshire, PH1 4PT
Tel/Fax:01738 828259
Email:dowtophead@bosinternet.com
Web:www.tophead-bandb.fsnet.co.uk

A very warm Scottish welcome in this traditional farmhouse on 200 acre dairy farm. Perth 4 miles (6kms). Extensive views over rural Perthshire.

1 Twin	1 En Suite fac	B&B per person
2 Double	1 Priv.NOT ensuite	£33-36 Single
	1 Pub.Bath/Show	£23-26 Double

[symbols]

C [symbols] W V

Perth

Map Ref: 2B2

★★★★

B&B

Westview Bed & Breakfast
49 Dunkeld Road, Perth, Perthshire, PH1 5RP
Tel:01738 627787 Fax:01738 447790

Town house, on the A912 and with private parking, is within easy walking distance of the city centre with its shops and variety of eating establishments. All the rooms are en suite, have RcTV, a radio and hospitality tray. Twin let as a single. Evening meals by prior arrangement.

2 Single	4 En Suite fac	B&B per person	Open Jan-Dec
1 Twin	1 Priv.NOT ensuite	from £20.00 Single	BB & Eve.Meal
2 Double		from £20.00 Double	from £29.00
1 Family		from £15.00 Room Only	

by Perth

Map Ref: 2B2

★★★

B&B

Ann Guthrie
Newmill Farm, Stanley, Perth, Perthshire, PH1 4PS
Tel/Fax:01738 828281
Email:guthrienewmill@sol.co.uk
Web:www.newmillfarm.co.uk

Traditional farmhouse on 330 acre arable farm. Convenient for the A9, 6 miles (10kms) from Perth. Suitable for fishing and other outdoor pursuits. Evening meal by prior arrangement.

1 Twin	All En Suite	B&B per person	Open Feb-Oct
2 Double		from £28-30 Single	
		from £20 Double (sharing)	

★★★★

B&B

The Linn
3 Duchess Street, Stanley, by Perth, PH1 4NF
Tel/Fax:01738 828293
Email:ettalundie@hotmail.com

Etta & Amos would love to welcome you to our home. Five minutes walk to the lovely River Tay. Comfortable bedrooms with many thoughtful extras and touches. Delicious breakfast choice from varied menu. Ideal base for touring, fishing, golf, walking and antiques shopping.

1 Twin	2 En Suite fac	B&B per person	Open Jan-Dec excl
2 Double	1 Pub.Bath/Show	from £20.00 Double	Xmas/New Year
2 Family			

nr Perth

Map Ref: 2B2

Beech-Lea Bed & Breakfast
Beech-Lea House, Strathord, by Stanley, Perth PH1 4PS
Tel: 01738 828715 e.mail: chaslizlin@aol.com
Web: http://members.aol.com/chaslizlin/Index.html
A warm welcome awaits guests at our new luxury comfortable B&B in beautiful quiet countryside. Enjoy an excellent breakfast from our menu overlooking large garden with 9-hole fun putting and wildlife pond. Situated just off A9 ten minutes from Perth. Excellent location – $^{1}/_{2}$ hour Edinburgh, one hour Glasgow, two hours Inverness. Host of local attractions. All rooms ground floor.

★★★★

B&B

Beech-Lea House
Strathord, by Stanley, Perth, PH1 4PS
Tel:01738 828715
Email:chaslizlin@aol.com
Web:http://members.aol.com/chaslizlin/Index.html

A friendly welcome at this family B&B. Situated 6 miles from Perth city centre. 5 mins drive to fishing on the Tay. Approx. 1 hr drive to all major Scottish cities. Many golf courses nearby.

1 Twin	All En Suite	B&B per person	Open Jan-Dec excl
2 Double		from £27.00 Single	Xmas/New Year
		from £20.00 Double	

Important: Prices stated are estimates and may be subject to amendments

Pitlochry, Perthshire | Map Ref: 2A1

GUEST HOUSE
★★★

Annslea
164 Atholl Road, Pitlochry, PH16 5AR
Tel:01796 472430
Email:annsleahouse@aol.com
Web:www.pitlochryguesthouse.com

Victorian house situated within easy walking of town centre. Large garden and private parking. Ideally located for restaurants, Festival Theatre and all other amenities. Some accommodation in annexe cottage in garden.

2 Twin	4 En Suite fac	B&B per person	Open Feb-Nov
4 Double	1 Priv.NOT ensuite	from £21.00 Double	

ATHOLL VILLA
29 Atholl Road, Pitlochry, Perthshire PH16 5BX
Tel: 01796 473820
e.mail: enquiries@athollvilla.co.uk
Web: www.athollvilla.co.uk

Atholl Villa is a family run guesthouse where we offer our guests warm hospitality and friendly service. All our rooms have ensuite facilities, colour television and tea/coffee trays. We have secure off-street parking. There is also a lovely guests conservatory and garden where tea and coffee can be taken. Our high standards and home comforts help make your stay special.

This 10-bedroom Victorian detached stone built house of typical highland construction, built approximately 150 years ago is situated right at the edge of town, close to both rail and bus stations. This area is proud of its tourism traditions, and no thoroughfare sums up these traditions better than Pitlochry's Atholl Road. Here can be found an abundance of restaurants and shops, all offering a wide choice of goods to suit any buyer. Atholl Villa is situated just metres away.
No children. No pets. Totally non-smoking.

GUEST HOUSE
★★★★

Atholl Villa Guest House
29 Atholl Road, Pitlochry, Perthshire, PH16 5BX
Tel:01796 473820
Email:enquiries@athollvilla.co.uk Web:www.athollvilla.co.uk

Lovely refurbished Victorian stone house set in an acre of landscaped garden on Atholl Road just metres from the main shopping centre, and a few minutes walk to the Theatre and the river. All rooms ensuite and a conservatory lounge to enjoy coffee and tea. Private off-street parking to rear. Vegetarian & special diets catered for. Cyclists & walkers most welcome. Secure storage for cycles & motorbikes.

2 Dbl/Twn	All En Suite	B&B per person	Open Jan-Dec
		from £20.00 Double	

GUEST HOUSE
★★★

Bendarroch House
Strathtay, Pitlochry, PH9 0PG
Tel:01887 840420 Fax:01887 840438
Email:bendarrochhouse@netscape.net
Web:www.bendarroch-house.de

Fully refurbished Victorian house set in landscaped grounds with panoramic views of the River Tay which runs past the estate. Situated between Aberfeldy and Pitlochry. Golfing, fishing and canoeing only 2 minutes away, other sports available in the vicinity. Evening meal by prior arrangement, freshly cooked using local produce. Coffee and liqueurs found in the conservatory lounge.

3 Twin	All En Suite	B&B per person	Open Jan-Dec
1 Double		from £30.00 Single	
1 Family		from £25.00 Double	
		from £20.00 Room Only	

VAT is shown at 17.5%: changes in this rate may affect prices.

Key to symbols is on back flap.

Pitlochry, Perthshire

Map Ref: 2A1

★★

B&B

Bridge House B&B
53 Atholl Road, Pitlochry, Perthshire, PH16 5BL
Tel:01796 474062
Email:fionabridgehouse@btopenworld.com
Web:www.bridgehousepitlochry.co.uk

Comfortable family home with the dining room on the first floor
overlooking Pitlochry town centre and the spacious bedrooms on the
second floor with views of the hills to the west of the town. Easy access to
the railway station (5 minutes walk) and close to the town's other
amenities including a variety of eating establishments.

2 Twin	All En Suite	B&B per person	Open Jan-Dec
2 Double		from £18.00 Double	
2 Family		from £15.00 Room	
		Only	

BUTTONBOSS LODGE

25 ATHOLL ROAD, PITLOCHRY, PERTHSHIRE PH16 5BX
Tel/Fax: 01796 472065   Evening Tel: 473000
e.mail: colin@buttonboss.fsnet.co.uk   Web: www.buttonboss.co.uk

Friendly and relaxed atmosphere guaranteed by Colin – P.G.A. golf
professional, and Marleen – former KLM stewardess. This detached villa is
centrally located. French, German and Dutch spoken. Ensuite bedrooms
with TV and hospitality tray. Guest lounge with satellite TV. Ground floor
rooms available. All rooms with thermostatic controlled central heating.
Private parking. Garage for motorbikes and cycles. Prices from £18 B&B.

★★★

**GUEST
HOUSE**

Buttonboss Lodge
25 Atholl Road, Pitlochry, Perthshire, PH16 5BX
Tel/Fax:01796 472065
Email:colin@buttonboss.fsnet.co.uk
Web:www.buttonboss.co.uk

Traditional Victorian house in centre of Pitlochry. Within walking distance
of all facilities. Private parking. Nederlands, Deutch and Francais spoken.

1 Single	7 En Suite fac	B&B per person	Open Jan-Dec
3 Twin	1 Pub.Bath/Show	£20.00-25.00 Single	
4 Double		£18.00-22.00 Double	

Pitlochry, Perthshire   Map Ref: 2A1

Carra Beag Guest House

16 Toberargan Road, Pitlochry, Perthshire PH16 5HG
Tel/Fax: 01796 472835
e.mail: visitus@carrabeag.co.uk
Web: www.carrabeag.co.uk

Carra Beag is a beautiful Victorian villa built in the 1870's as a family home. It still is a family home. These days Helen & Brian open the doors welcoming guests and travellers continuing the long tradition of Highland hospitality. Commanding an elevated position we enjoy magnificent views across the Tummel Valley to the hills beyond. We pride ourselves on offering excellent value, clean and comfortable rooms in a completely non-smoking environment. After parking your vehicle in our private car park, take a stroll through our award winning garden directly onto Pitlochry's main street, visit the famous theatre, or some of Pitlochry's many attractions, dine locally returning home to the open fire in our cosy guests lounge.

GUEST HOUSE

Carra Beag Guest House

16 Toberargan Road, Pitlochry, Perthshire PH16 5HG
Tel/Fax:01796 472835
Email:visitus@carrabeag.co.uk
Web:www.carrabeag.co.uk

Whatever your pursuits a friendly enjoyable stay is assured at Carra Beag. Enjoy magnificent uninterrupted views of the surrounding hills or stroll through our garden directly to Pitlochry's main street. We offer full facilities for walkers and cyclists. Private car park, and value for money.

2 Single	9 En Suite	B&B per person	Open Mar-Nov
3 Twin	1 Pub.Bath/Show	from £17.00 Single	
3 Double		from £17.00 Double	
2 Family			

194

PITLOCHRY

E

**PERTHSHIRE, ANGUS AND DUNDEE
AND THE KINGDOM OF FIFE**

Pitlochry, Perthshire

Map Ref: 2A1

Craigroyston House

2 Lower Oakfield, Pitlochry PH16 5HQ
Telephone/Fax: 01796 472053
**e.mail: reservations@craigroyston.co.uk
Web: www.craigroyston.co.uk**

A Victorian country house set in own grounds with views
of the surrounding hills. Centrally situated, there is
direct pedestrian access to the town centre.
★ All rooms have private facilities, some with 4-posters
   and are equipped to a high standard.
★ Residents' lounge with real log fire.
★ Safe private parking.
★ Dining room with separate tables.
★ Colour TV, welcome tray, central heating.
★ Craigroyston is a non-smoking guest house.
Bed & Breakfast from £20 per person.

AA
SELECTED
◆◆◆◆

★★★★

GUEST
HOUSE

Craigroyston House
2 Lower Oakfield, Pitlochry, Perthshire, PH16 5HQ
Tel/Fax:01796 472053
Email:reservations@craigroyston.co.uk
Web:www.craigroyston.co.uk

Quietly situated in its own grounds with views of the surrounding hills.
Offering safe off street parking and direct access to the town centre. The
spacious bedrooms are well equipped with attention to detail and
tastefully decorated with period furniture.

2 Twin	All En suite	B&B per person	Open Jan-Dec
5 Double		from £20.00 Double	
1 Family			

★★★

GUEST
HOUSE

Dalshian House
Old Perth Road, Pitlochry, PH16 5TD
Tel:01796 472173
Email:dalshian@haworth7.fsnet.co.uk

A warm welcome awaits you at this listed property situated on outskirts
of Pitlochry. Set in picturesque parkland. An 18th century farmhouse
retaining its original style but with all bedrooms en-suite and well
equipped.

1 Twin	All En Suite	B&B per person	Open Jan-Dec
4 Double		from £20.00 Single	BB & Eve.Meal
2 Family		from £20.00 Double	from £32.00

**Scotland's National Booking
and Information Line**

**Tel: 0845 22 55 121
visitscotland.com**

Important: Prices stated are estimates and may be subject to amendments

Pitlochry, Perthshire   **Map Ref: 2A1**

Derrybeg Guest House

18 Lower Oakfield, Pitlochry PH16 5DS
Tel: 01796 472070 Fax: 01796 472070
e.mail: marion@derrybeg.fsnet.co.uk
Web: www.derrybeg.co.uk

★★★★
GUEST HOUSE

Both of DERRYBEG's adjoining buildings are set in a quiet location only a few minutes' walk from the town centre, enjoying magnificent views of the Vale of Atholl. The resident proprietors, Derek and Marion Stephenson, ensure only the finest hospitality, comfort, and good home cooking.
● All bedrooms with private facilities.
● Colour television and welcome tea/coffee tray in all bedrooms.
● Open all year for B&B or D,B&B. Unlicensed, but guests welcome to supply own table wine.
● Full central heating throughout.
● Comfortable lounge and dining room.
● Food Hygiene Excellent Award.
● Ample parking in the grounds.
● Leisure activities can easily be arranged, i.e. theatre bookings, golf, fishing, pony-trekking, etc.
Colour brochure/tariff and details of weekly reductions available on request.

★★★★

GUEST HOUSE

Derrybeg
18 Lower Oakfield, Pitlochry, PH16 5DS
Tel/Fax:01796 472070
Email:marion@derrybeg.fsnet.co.uk
Web:www.derrybeg.co.uk

Privately owned detached house, with large south facing garden, in quiet but central location. Elevated position with uninterrupted views across Tummel Valley and surrounding hill sides. Three annexe rooms. Ample off road parking. Four course evening meal available and guests welcome to supply their own table wine.

2 Single	All En Suite	B&B per person	Open Jan-Nov
2 Twin		£18-28 Single	plus Xmas/New Year
6 Double		£18-28 Double	BB & Eve.Meal
1 Family			£33-43
3-2 bdrm Apts			

★★

B&B

Donavourd Farmhouse
Pitlochry, Perthshire, PH16 5JS
Tel:01796 472254
Email:donavourd@compuserve.com
Web:www.donavourd.cx

200 year old stonebuilt farmhouse with wonderful views down the Tummel Valley. Offering fresh farm foods and homebaking.

1 Twin	All En Suite	B&B per person	Open Feb-Nov
1 Double		from £17.00 Single	BB & Eve.Meal
		from £17.00 Double	from £25.00

Pitlochry, Perthshire — Map Ref: 2A1

DUNDARAVE HOUSE

Strathview Terrace, Pitlochry PH16 5AT Tel/Fax: 01796 473109
e.mail: dundarave.guesthouse@virgin.net
Web: www.theaa.com/hotels/11251.html

*Dundarave Guest House, the ideal place for your overnight stay or longer.
A relaxed atmosphere in this traditional home in a quiet location with stunning
views, a short walk from the town. Ensuite facilities. A comfortable lounge.
Non-smoking. Private parking. From £18 pppn.*

AA SELECTED ♦♦♦♦   ★★★ GUEST HOUSE

★★★

**GUEST
HOUSE**

Dundarave House

Strathview Terrace, Pitlochry, Perthshire PH16 5AT
Tel/Fax:01796 473109
Email:dundarave.guesthouse@virgin.net
Web:www.theaa.com/hotels/11251.html

Victorian built, late nineteenth century by local craftsmen, and set in its
own half acre of formal grounds. Dundarave is a house of great charm,
character and serene atmosphere.

2 Single	5 En Suite fac	B&B per person	Open Jan-Dec excl
2 Twin	2 Pub.Bath/Show	from £18.00 Single	Xmas/New Year
2 Double		from £18.00 Double	BB & Eve.Meal
1 Family			from £30.00

EASTER DUNFALLANDY COUNTRY HOUSE B&B

PITLOCHRY, PERTHSHIRE PH16 5NA   ★★★★ **B&B**

*Tel: 01796 474128
e.mail: sue@dunfallandy.co.uk   Web: www.dunfallandy.co.uk*

Quietly situated country house enjoying wonderful views just 1 mile from
Pitlochry and within easy reach of the areas many attractions. All 3
bedrooms are ensuite. Decor and furnishing are high quality throughout.
Afternoon tea on arrival and gourmet breakfast. Online booking.
Top 20 B&B "Which" Good B&B Guide.

★★★★

B&B

Easter Dunfallandy Country House

Logierait Road, Pitlochry, Perthshire, PH16 5NA
Tel:01796 474128 Fax:01796 474446
Email:sue@dunfallandy.co.uk
Web:www.dunfallandy.co.uk

A large Victorian country house retaining many original features
regaining its period charm. Situated in elevated position with panoramic
views over the Vale of Atholl. 1.5 miles south of Pitlochry on quiet
country road. Large country garden. Non-smoking house. Evening meals
by prior arrangement.

2 Twin	All En Suite	B&B per person	Open Jan-Dec excl
1 Double		from £38.00 Single	Xmas/New Year
		from £28.00 Double	BB & Eve.Meal
			from £43.00

Scotland's National Booking and Information Line

Tel: 0845 22 55 121
visitscotland.com

Important: Prices stated are estimates and may be subject to amendments

Pitlochry, Perthshire | Map Ref: 2A1

Ferrymans Cottage ★★★★ B&B

Port-na-Craig, Pitlochry, Perthshire PH16 5ND
Tel: 01796 473681 Fax: 01796 473681
e.mail: kath@ferrymanscottage.fsnet.co.uk

Enjoy quality en-suite rooms in our cosy 250-year-old listed cottage surrounded by flowers in an idyllic tranquil setting beside the River Tummel. Relax and watch the salmon fishermen. Perfectly situated below the Festival Theatre dam and fish ladder, yet only minutes into town. *Phone/fax Kath Sanderson 01796 473681.*

★★★★

B&B

Ferrymans Cottage

Port-na-Craig, Pitlochry, Perthshire, PH16 5ND
Tel/Fax:01796 473681
Email:kath@ferrymanscottage.fsnet.co.uk

Our cosy home was once the Ferryman's Cottage serving the quiet, picturesque hamlet of Port-na-Craig, on the banks of the River Tummel. Perfectly situated below the Festival Theatre, dam and fish ladder, yet only a short walk into town.

1 Family	All En Suite	B&B per person	Open Jan-Nov excl
1 Dbl/Twn		from £22.00 Double	New Year

📺 🛁 🅿 ☕ 🍳 ⌂ 🐾

C W V

★★★

B&B

Gardeners Cottage

Faskally, Pitlochry, Perthshire, PH16 5LA
Tel:01796 472450

Original gardeners cottage dating from mid 19th century. Adjoining Faskally wood and overlooking the Loch. Ground floor bedroom available.

1 Twin	1 Priv.NOT ensuite	B&B per person	Open Jan-Dec
2 Double	1 Pub.Bath/Show	from £23.00 Single	
		from £18.00 Double	

📺 🅿 ☕ 🍳 ⌂ ♿

🐾 V ♿

★★★

B&B

Holzhafen

5 Windsor Gardens, Pitlochry, Perthshire, PH16 5BE
Tel:01796 473562 Fax:01796 470054
Email:croemmele@aol.com
Web:www.highland-gateway.com

Family run B&B within walking distance of town centre. Ideal base for touring this beautiful part of Perthshire. Great walking, fishing and theatre. Families and pets most welcome.

1 Single	1 En Suite fac	B&B per person	Open Easter-Nov
1 Twin	1 Priv.NOT ensuite	from £18.00 Single	
1 Double		from £16.00 Double	

📺 🛁 🅿 ☕ 🍳 ⌂

C 🐾 W V

★★★★

GUEST HOUSE

Kinnaird House

Kirkmichael Road, Pitlochry, Perthshire, PH16 5JL
Tel/Fax:01796 472843
Email:enquiries@kinnaird-house.co.uk
Web:www.kinnaird-house.co.uk

Enjoying an elevated position 1.5 miles above the delightful small town of Pitlochry this stone built Victorian villa has magnificent views of the surrounding hills, and glen. Very comfortable accommodation, a super home cooked breakfast and a warm welcome awaits you.

3 Double	En Suite	B&B per person	Open Easter-Oct
1 Double	Priv.facilities	£35.00-50.00 Single	
1 Twin	En Suite	£25.00-30.00 Double	

📺 🛁 🚿 🅿 ☕ 🍳 ⌂

💳 V ♿

VAT is shown at 17.5%: changes in this rate may affect prices. | Key to symbols is on back flap.

Pitlochry, Perthshire

Map Ref: 2A1

★★★

B&B

Lavalette
Manse Road, Moulin, Pitlochry, Perthshire
PH16 5EP
Tel:01796 472364

A warm welcome awaits you at 'Lavalette', a bungalow on the edge of the conservation village of Moulin which has its own hotel - a former staging post. Pitlochry town centre with its shops and a variety of eating establishments is within walking distance.

1 Single	Some En Suite	B&B per person
1 Double		from £16.50 Single
1 Family		from £17.50 Double

Open Apr-Oct

★★

B&B

Lonaig
28 Lettoch Terrace, Pitlochry, Perthshire
PH16 5BA
Tel:01796 472422

Semi detached house, with most attractive, well-tended, colourful garden. Set in a peaceful cul-de-sac with some views over the town. Non-smoking house.

2 Double	1 Priv.NOT ensuite

B&B per person from £15.50 Double

Open Easter-Oct

NUMBER 10
10 Atholl Road, Pitlochry PH16 5BX
Tel: 01796 472346 Fax: 01796 473519
e.mail: fran.norris@btinternet.com Web: www.pitlochry-guesthouse.co.uk

We invite you to experience our comfortable, clean, relaxing "home from home" where we guarantee the highest of standards. Number 10 is a splendid Victorian villa, within strolling distance of shops, restaurants and Pitlochry theatre. Set in lovely gardens the house is beautifully decorated with care and attention to detail.

★★★★

GUEST HOUSE

Number 10
10 Atholl Road, Pitlochry, Perthshire, PH16 5BX
Tel:01796 472346   Fax:01796 473519
Email:fran.norris@btinternet.com
Web:www.pitlochry-guesthouse.co.uk

The relaxed warm atmosphere and friendly hospitality of experienced hosts Fran and Alan will make you want to return regularly to this cosy retreat. The guest house has comfortable bedrooms, a snug bar, quiet lounge and a dining room serving only fresh food based on Scottish produce. In easy walking distance of the town centre, with a lovely ten minute walk over the river to Pitlochry Theatre.

3 Twin	9 En Suite fac	B&B per person
4 Double	1 Priv.NOT ensuite	£22.00-32.00 Double
2 Family		£18.00-27.00 Room Only

Open Feb-Dec excl Xmas/New Year

★★★

B&B

Pooltiel
Lettoch Road, Pitlochry, Perthshire, PH16 5AZ
Tel/Fax:01796 472184
Email:ajs@pooltiel.freeserve.co.uk
Web:www.pooltiel.freeserve.co.uk

Located in an elevated position overlooking Pitlochry, with views of the surrounding hills this is an excellent base from which to enjoy numerous outdoor activities and explore Perthshire and the Southern Highlands. "Which" recommended.

1 Twin	1 Bath/Shower	B&B per person
1 Double	for guests	from £17.50 Double
1 Family		

Open Apr-Oct

Pitlochry, Perthshire

Map Ref: 2A1

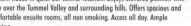

SUNNYBANK

19 LOWER OAKFIELD, PITLOCHRY PH16 5DS
TEL/FAX: 01796 473014
E.MAIL: k.ellson@btinternet.com WEB: www.scenicscotland.net/1/sunnybank.htm

Sunnybank is a comfortable modern house centrally located in a quiet residential street a few minutes walk from the town centre. Ample parking available. We offer 3 spacious, tastefully furnished en-suite B & B rooms: 2 doubles, 1 family (TV, Tea/Coffee making facilities). Non-smoking house. German spoken. £18 to £22 pp.

★★★

B&B

Sunnybank

19 Lower Oakfield, Pitlochry, Perthshire, PH16 5DS
Tel:01796 473014
Email:k.ellson@btinternet.com
Web:www.scenicscotland.net/1/sunnybank.htm

Modern house in quiet but central location. Enjoys elevated position with view over the Tummel Valley and surrounding hills. Offers spacious and comfortable ensuite rooms, all non smoking. Access all day. Ample parking.

| 2 Double | All En Suite | B&B per person | Open Jan-Dec |
| 1 Family | | £18.00-22.00 Single | |

Wester Knockfarrie

Knockfarrie Road, Pitlochry PH16 5DN
Tel: 01796 472020 Fax: 01796 474407

Victorian home quietly situated in woodlands only minutes walk from town centre. Beautiful views over Tummel Valley. Woodland walks, peaceful garden. Private parking. Individually designed bedrooms with fully fitted private facilities. TV and tea/coffee tray. A full Scottish breakfast is served in our elegant dining room. Contact Sally Spaven.

★★★★

B&B

Wester Knockfarrie

Knockfarrie Road, Pitlochry, Perthshire, PH16 5DN
Tel:01796 472020 Fax:01796 474407

Wester Knockfarrie, a Victorian home quietly situated in woodlands on the outskirts of Pitlochry, yet only a few minutes walk from the town. Beautiful views over the Tummel Valley and the hills beyond, a peaceful garden to relax in with woodland strolls and forest trails close by. Individually designed non smoking bedrooms with fully fitted private facilities. A full Scottish breakfast is served in the elegant dining room. Private parking.

| 1 Twin | All En Suite | B&B per person | Open Mar-Nov |
| 1 Double | | from £20.00 Double | |

Scotland's National Booking and Information Line

Tel: 0845 22 55 121
visitscotland.com

VAT is shown at 17.5%: changes in this rate may affect prices.

Key to symbols is on back flap.

Pitlochry, Perthshire

Map Ref: 2A1

★★★

B&B

Woodburn House
Ferry Road, Pitlochry, Perthshire, PH16 5DD
Tel/Fax:01796 473818
Email:info@woodburnhouse.co.uk
Web:www.woodburnhouse.co.uk

Friendly family run Bed and Breakfast. Situated within 3 minutes
walking distance to the town centre and Festival Theatre.

| 1 Twin | 2 En Suite fac | B&B per person | Open Jan-Dec |
| 2 Double | 1 Pub.Bath/Show | £19.00-25.00 Double | BB & Eve.Meal from £30.00-37.50 |

TV 📶 📶 P ☕ 🍴 ✂

C 🐕 V

St Andrews, Fife

Map Ref: 2D2

★★

B&B

38 Chamberlain Street
St Andrews, Fife, KY16 8JF
Tel:01334 473749

Quietly located 10 minutes walk from town centre. Local bus route to all
amenities. Ideal base to explore the picturesque fishing villages on the
East Neuk, only about 10 miles away. Bed & Breakfast within walking
distance to all golf courses.

| 1 Twin | 1 Priv.NOT ensuite | B&B per person from £22.00 Single from £20.00 Double | Open Jan-Dec excl Xmas/New Year |

TV P ☕ 🍴

V

ABBEY COTTAGE
ABBEY WALK, ST ANDREWS, FIFE KY16 9LB
Telephone: 01334 473727
e.mail: coull@lineone.net Web: www.abbeycottage.co.uk
COTTAGE DATING FROM 1791 BUILT AGAINST ABBEY
WALL WITH COTTAGE GARDEN. NEAR HARBOUR,
CATHEDRAL AND EAST SANDS. PRIVATE PARKING.

★★

B&B

Abbey Cottage
Abbey Walk, St Andrews, Fife, KY16 9LB
Tel:01334 473727
Email:coull@lineone.net
Web:www.abbeycottage.co.uk

Listed property dating from 18c with walled cottage garden. Close to
centre of St. Andrews. Fantail doves and pet hens. Parking.

| 1 Twin | Some En Suite | B&B per person from £27.00 Single from £22.00 Double | Open Jan-Dec |
| 1 Double | 1 Pub.Bath/Show | | |

TV 📶 📶 P ☕ ✂

W V 🛏

★★

B&B

Ardmore
1 Drumcarrow Road, St Andrews, Fife, KY16 8SE
Tel:01334 474574

Family house in quiet residential area, within walking distance of town
centre. Convenient for all amenities. You are welcome to borrow the use
of our hairdryer and ironing facilities. Free on-street parking.

| 2 Twin | 1 Priv.NOT ensuite | B&B per person from £17.50 Double | Open Jan-Dec excl Xmas/New Year |

TV P ✂

V 🛏

Important: Prices stated are estimates and may be subject to amendments

St Andrews, Fife

Map Ref: 2D2

★★★★

GUEST
HOUSE

Aslar Guest House
120 North Street, St Andrews, Fife, KY16 9AF
Tel:01334 473460   Fax:01334 477540
Email:enquiries@aslar.com
Web:www.aslar.com

Victorian family run terraced house furnished to a high standard with
period features. Centrally situated for shops, golf courses, restaurants
and cultural pursuits.

1 Single	All En Suite	B&B per person	Open Jan-Dec excl
2 Twin		from £30.00 Single	Xmas/New Year
2 Double		from £30.00 Double	

AWAITING
INSPECTION

Birchlea
8 Horseleys Park, St Andrews, Fife, KY16 8RZ
Tel/Fax:01334 472698

1 Twin	All En Suite	B&B per person	Open Jan-Dec excl
1 Double		from £35.00 Single	Xmas/New Year
		from £25.00 Double	

★★★★

B&B

Bramley House
10 Bonfield Road, Strathkiness, St Andrews KY16 9RP
Tel/Fax:01334 850362
Email:heather@bramleyguesthouse.com
Web:www.bramleyguesthouse.com

Beautifully situated 2.5 miles west of St Andrews, this elegant country
house is for that special break away. The attractive bedrooms are
spacious, well furnished and offer all the expected amenities. Your
hostess, Heather McQueen, has a renowned reputation for her relaxed
country house atmosphere, enjoyable home cooking and early bird
golfing breakfast.

1 Twin	All En Suite	B&B per person	Open Jan-Dec
1 Double		from £25.00 Double	
1 Family			

★★★

GUEST
HOUSE

Burness House Guest House
Murray Park, St Andrews, Fife, KY16 9AW
Tel/Fax:01334 474314
Email:marie@burnesshouse.com
Web:www.burnesshouse.com

Under new ownership, and with the personal supervision of Marie and
David Skinner, an enjoyable and comfortable stay is assured. Golfing can
be arranged.

1 Single	All En Suite	B&B per person	Open Jan-Dec
3 Twin		£37.00-42.00 Single	
4 Double		£27.00-37.00 Dbl/Twn	

★★★★

GUEST
HOUSE

Craigmore Guest House
3 Murray Park, St Andrews, Fife, KY16 9AW
Tel:01334 472142   Fax:01334 477963
Email:enquiries@standrewscraigmore.com
Web:www.standrewscraigmore.com

Victorian stone built guest house in centre of St Andrews. Short walk
from town centre, beaches and 'Old Course'. Ground floor room. Non
smoking. Relax in the comfortable lounge/dining room after a days golf
and sightseeing.

2 Twin	All En Suite	B&B per person	Open Jan-Dec
2 Double		from £30.00 Double	
3 Family			

VAT is shown at 17.5%: changes in this rate may affect prices.

Key to symbols is on back flap.

St Andrews, Fife

Map Ref: 2D2

★★★★

B&B

Dykes End B&B
5 Kinburn Place, Double Dykes Road, St Andrews
Fife, KY16 9DT
Tel/Fax:01334 474711
Email:seygolf@aol.com Web:www.seygolf.com

A friendly welcome awaits you in superior quality home in prime
residential area only 5 minutes walk from town centre, golf courses,
beach and bus station. All bedrooms are non-smoking and have full
ensuite or private facilities. Private parking is available and golf can be
arranged.

1 Twin	1 En Suite fac	B&B per person	Open Jan-Dec
1 Double	2 Priv.Bath/Show	from £39.00 Single	
1 Family		from £25.00 Double	

Easter Craigfoodie
Dairsie, Cupar, Fife KY15 4SW
Telephone: 01334 870286

Comfortable farmhouse with wonderful views over
bay only 6 miles from St Andrews. Residents' lounge
with TV. Ample parking. Ideal golf or touring base.

★★★

B&B

Easter Craigfoodie
Dairsie, Cupar, Fife, KY15 4SW
Tel:01334 870286

Traditional, Victorian farmhouse with panoramic views across Fife to Firth
of Tay and Angus coast. 7 miles (11kms) from St Andrews. Ideal golf and
touring base.

1 Twin	B&B per person	Open Jan-Dec excl
1 Double	from £20.00 Single	Xmas/New Year
	from £18.00 Double	

★★

B&B

Hawthorne House
33 Main Street, Strathkinness, St Andrews, Fife
KY16 9RY
Tel:01334 850855
Email:hawthornehouse@onetel.net.uk

Friendly family run bed and breakfast in attractive village only five
minutes drive or approx 2.5 miles from the world famous 'Old Course'
and the 'Old Grey Town' of St Andrews. Situated in a picturesque village.
Free private parking. All rooms ensuite.

1 Twin	All En Suite	B&B per person	Open Jan-Dec
2 Double		from £25.00 Single	
		from £18.00 Double	

★★★

SMALL
HOTEL

Hazelbank Hotel
28 The Scores, St Andrews, Fife, KY16 9AS
Tel/Fax:01334 472466
Email:michael@hazelbank.com
Web:www.hazelbank.com

Refurbished elegant Victorian townhouse. Overlooking St Andrews Bay
and golf courses. A drive and a wedge from the 18th on the Old Course.
3 minutes walk to University and historic town centre.

2 Single	All En Suite	B&B per person	Open Jan-Dec excl
8 Dbl/Twn		from £45.00 Single	Xmas/New Year
		from £36.50 Double	

Important: Prices stated are estimates and may be subject to amendments

"THE LARCHES"

7 River Terrace, Guardbridge, By St. Andrews KY16 0XA
Tel/Fax: 01334 838008   e.mail: thelarches@aol.com

"The Larches" is a beautiful former old Memorial Hall, situated in Guardbridge on the A919 between St. Andrews (3 miles) and Dundee (6 miles), convenient for golf, riding, glorious countryside and beaches. All rooms are ensuite or private bathroom, with colour TV, hairdryer, tea/coffee facilities, shaver points, hospitality tray, use of trouser press and ironing facilities, centrally heated throughout. Residents lounge with VCR and large selection of films, satellite TV. Conservatory recently built for residents use – available at all times. Children welcome, cot and high chair available at no extra charge. Come and sample our fantastic breakfasts!
Every home comfort!

★★★★

B&B

The Larches B&B

7 River Terrace, Guardbridge, St Andrews, Fife
KY16 0XA
Tel/Fax:01334 838008
Email:thelarches@aol.com

A beautiful old memorial hall, now converted into a family home, near centre of Guardbridge and R.A.F. Leuchars. 4 miles (6kms) from St. Andrews. Free private parking. Strictly non-smoking house.

2 Twin	All En Suite
1 Double	

B&B per person
from £28.00 Single
from £20.00 Double

Open Jan-Dec

★★

GUEST HOUSE

Nethan House

17 Murray Park, St Andrews, KY16 9AW
Tel:01334 472104

In town centre, close to Old Course, University and all amenities.

2 Single	Some En Suite
1 Double	
2 Family	

B&B per person
from £28.00 Single
from £28.00 Double

Open Jun-Sep

Scotland's National Booking and Information Line

Tel: 0845 22 55 121
visitscotland.com

VAT is shown at 17.5%: changes in this rate may affect prices.

Key to symbols is on back flap.

St Andrews, Fife   Map Ref: 2D2

Old Fishergate House

North Castle Street, St Andrews, Fife, KY16 9BG
Tel/Fax:01334 470874
Email:themitchells@oldfishergatehouse.fsnet.co.uk

2 Twin	All En Suite	B&B per person from £30.00 Double	Open Jan-Dec excl Xmas/New Year

★★★★

B&B

17th century town house in the oldest part of historic St Andrews. 100 yards from the castle and 2 mins walk to town centre and University. 5 mins walk to the Old Course. Fully refurbished to high modern standards which retain its comforting original features.

THE PADDOCK

Sunnyside, Strathkinness, By St Andrews, Fife KY16 9XP
Tel: 01334 850888 Fax: 01334 850870
e.mail: thepaddock@btinternet.com Web: www.thepadd.co.uk
*Comfortable family run Bed & Breakfast in large
modern bungalow in rural village with panoramic
views over surrounding countryside to St Andrews,
which is a five minute drive. Private parking.
All rooms ensuite. Warm welcome assured.*

The Paddock

Sunnyside, Strathkinness, by St. Andrews, Fife KY16 9XP
Tel:01334 850888   Fax:01334 850870
Email:thepaddock@btinternet.com
Web:www.thepadd.co.uk

1 Twin 2 Double	All En Suite	B&B per person from £21.00 Double	Open Feb-Nov

★★★★

B&B

Modern bungalow furnished to a high standard, in a semi-rural location on the edge of Strathkinness village, having open outlook to farmland to the rear. St Andrews is three miles away, with easy access to golf courses, beach, shops and cultural buildings. Craigtoun Country Park is within one and a half miles.

Rockmount Cottage

Dura Den Road, Pitscottie, by St Andrews KY15 5TG
Tel/Fax:01334 828164
Email:annmreid@rockmount1.freeserve.co.uk
Web:www.rockmount-1.co.uk

1 Single 1 Double 1 Family	2 Priv.NOT ensuite 1 Pub.Bath/Show	B&B per person £21.00-28.00 Single £21.00-28.00 Double	Open Jan-Dec excl Xmas/New Year

★★★

B&B

Easy to find in the centre of Pitscottie and well placed for touring the Kingdom of Fife and beyond. Modernised traditional Scottish cottage with south facing garden and car parking area. Bath and shower rooms fully equipped for ambulant disabled.

St Nicholas Farmhouse

East Sands, St Andrews, Fife, KY16 8LD
Tel:01334 473090

2 Family	All En Suite	B&B per person from £25.00 Single from £17.50 Double	Open Jan-Dec

★★

B&B

Traditional farmhouse set amidst modern housing on the eastern edge of St Andrews. East Sands beach is only about 400 metres away. Free Parking. Both rooms en-suite. Facilities for children, pets and non-smokers.

Important: Prices stated are estimates and may be subject to amendments

PERTHSHIRE, ANGUS AND DUNDEE
AND THE KINGDOM OF FIFE

E

205

ST ANDREWS

St Andrews, Fife

Map Ref: 2D2

Spinkieden

13 Cairnsden Gardens, St. Andrews KY16 8SQ
Telephone/Fax: 01334 475303
e.mail: welcome@spinkieden.co.uk
Web: www.spinkieden.co.uk

The beautiful historic town of St. Andrews, the home of golf, is the perfect location to explore the East Neuk of Fife and well beyond. We offer you comfortable, friendly accommodation with central heating, TV/videos and tea/coffee facilities in all rooms to make your stay as enjoyable as possible.

★★★

B&B

Spinkieden B&B

13 Cairnsden Gardens, St Andrews, Fife, KY16 8SQ
Tel/Fax:01334 475303
Email:welcome@spinkieden.co.uk
Web:www.spinkieden.co.uk

Be assured of a very warm welcome at this attractive bungalow where you'll find comfortable, ground floor accommodation with a home from home atmosphere. Situated in a quiet residential area. The town centre is only three minutes by car or easily accessible by a scenic stroll along the Lade Braes.

1 Twin	1 Priv.NOT ensuite	B&B per person	Open Jan-Nov
2 Double	1 En Suite	£20.00-25.00 Single	
	1 Priv.Bath/Show	£18.00-22.00 Double	

SPINKSTOWN FARMHOUSE

St Andrews, Fife KY16 8PN
Tel/Fax: 01334 473475
e.mail: anne@spinkstown.com Web: www.spinkstown.com

Two miles from St Andrews on A917 to Crail this bright uniquely designed farmhouse furnished to a high standard has spacious bedrooms, ensuite bathrooms (bath and shower) comfortable lounge dining room where substantial breakfast sets you up for the day. Historic St Andrews famous Old Course, fishing villages, National Trust properties nearby.

★★★★

B&B

Spinkstown Farmhouse

St Andrews, Fife, KY16 8PN
Tel/Fax:01334 473475
Email:anne@spinkstown.com
Web:www.spinkstown.com

A warm welcome awaits at this uniquely designed farmhouse, only 2 miles (3km) east of St Andrews. Some rooms with sea views and surrounding countryside. Bright and spacious. Plenty free parking on site. Abundant wildlife in peaceful surroundings.

1 Twin	All En Suite	B&B per person	Open Jan-Dec excl
2 Double		from £25.00 Single	Xmas/New Year
		from £23.00 Double	

Scotland's National Booking and Information Line

Tel: 0845 22 55 121
visitscotland.com

VAT is shown at 17.5%: changes in this rate may affect prices.

Key to symbols is on back flap.

Stravithie Country Estate

STRAVITHIE, ST ANDREWS, FIFE KY16 8LT

Tel: 01334 880251 Fax: 01334 880297

Bed and Breakfast on a beautiful old Scottish
Country Estate with 30 acres of wooded
grounds and gardens. Rooms within east wing
of Castle. Facilities within the grounds include
trout-fishing, open-air badminton, table-tennis,
golf practice (9-holes), nature trail, launderette
and telephone.

**HOW TO FIND US: 3 miles from St Andrews
on the Anstruther road (B9131).**

B&B FROM £32 per person per night.

★★★

B&B

Stravithie Country Estate

Stravithie, St Andrews, Fife, KY16 8LT
Tel:01334 880251   Fax:01334 880297

Bed & breakfast within 19c castle set in 30 acres of peaceful grounds,
with nature walks, golf practice (9 holes), trout stream, riding,
badminton. St Andrews 3 miles (5kms). Come and experience the
atmosphere of a fine old Scottish country estate. Large sitting room style
bedrooms with own kitchen. Buffet breakfast.

1 Twin	All En Suite	B&B per person	Open May-Sep
1 Double		from £32	
1 Family			

TODHALL HOUSE

DAIRSIE, BY ST ANDREWS, FIFE KY15 4RQ

Tel: 01334 656344   Fax: 01334 650791

e.mail: todhallhouse@ukgateway.net

Web: www.todhallhouse.com

At Todhall our aim is to provide quality accommodation, traditional fare and warm,
personal service. Come! Explore historic St Andrews (7 miles) and the many varied
attractions in the Kingdom of Fife and beyond, or simply relax in peaceful surroundings.
Excellent train service to Edinburgh – I hour.

AA ◆◆◆◆◆ Member of Scotland's Best B&B's.

★★★★★

B&B

Todhall House

Dairsie, by St Andrews, Fife, KY15 4RQ
Tel:01334 656344   Fax:01334 650791
Email:todhallhouse@ukgateway.net
Web:www.todhallhouse.com

Refurbished to a high standard this traditional Scottish country house is
peacefully located amidst extensive lawns and rosebeds, with panoramic
view across the Eden valley. Tastefully appointed bedrooms, one with 4
poster bed. You can be assured of a warm welcome from Gill and John
Donald. Please note this is a non-smoking house.

2 Twin	All En Suite	B&B per person	Open Mar-Oct
2 Double		from £35.00 Single	BB & Eve.Meal
		from £28.00 Double	from £48.00

Important: Prices stated are estimates and may be subject to amendments

St Andrews, Fife

Map Ref: 2D2

★★

B&B

West Mains Farmhouse
West Mains, Peat Inn, Cupar, Fife, KY15 5LF
Tel/Fax:01334 840313

1 Twin	1 Priv.NOT ensuite	B&B per person	Open Apr-Oct
1 Double		from £18.00 Double	

Mixed farm with open views of countryside. Good base for touring, golfing and visiting the East Neuk of Fife. 7 miles (11kms) from St Andrews. Tea, coffee and home baking served in front of an open fire in the evening.

★★★

GUEST HOUSE

West Park House
5 St Marys Place, Market Street, St Andrews, Fife KY16 9UY
Tel:01334 475933   Fax:01334 476634
Email:rosemary@westparksta.freeserve.co.uk
Web:www.westpark-standrews.co.uk

1 Twin	3 En Suite fac	B&B per person	Open Jan-Nov
3 Double	2 Pub.Bath/Show	from £26.00 Double	
1 Family			

Beautiful Listed Georgian house c1830 in heart of historic town. Close to Old Course and all amenities. Sandy beaches close by and within easy reach of the pretty East Neuk fishing villages (approx 10 miles).

---

nr St Andrews, Fife

Map Ref: 2D2

★★★★

B&B

Cambo House
nr St Andrews, Fife, KY16 8QD
Tel:01333 450054 Fax:01333 450987
Email:cambo@camboestate.com
Web:www.camboestate.com

1 Double	1 En Suite fac	B&B per person	Open Jan-Dec excl
1 Family	1 Pub.Bath/Show	from £42.00 Single	Xmas/New Year
		from £42.00 Double	BB & Eve.Meal
		from £34.00 Room	from £78.00
		Only	

Elegant Victorian mansion on wooded coastal estate, close to St Andrews adjacent to Kingsbarns Golf Links. With handsome four poster bed in principal guest bedroom. Evening meal by prior arrangement.

Scone, by Perth, Perthshire

Map Ref: 2B2

BLACKCRAIGS FARMHOUSE
Blackcraigs, Scone, Perthshire PH2 7PJ
Tel/Fax: 01821 640254
e.mail: millar@blackcraigs.fsworld.co.uk Web: www.blackcraigs.com
18th century farmhouse where a warm welcome awaits you. Good touring area. Ideally situated for pursuing a wide range of activities including golf, fishing, horseriding, hill-walking. Also many interesting castles to visit. Fine restaurants and pubs locally. You will find us on the A94 four miles from Perth.

★★★

B&B

Blackcraigs Farmhouse
Blackcraigs Farm, Scone, Perthshire, PH2 7PJ
Tel/Fax:01821 640254
Email:millar@blackcraigs.fsworld.co.uk
Web:www.blackcraigs.com

1 Twin	2 En Suite fac	B&B per person	Open Jan-Dec excl
2 Double	1 Pub.Bath/Show	from £23.00 Single	Xmas/New Year
		from £20.00 Double	

A warm welcome at this comfortable farmhouse peacefully situated on 260 acre mixed farm, 4 miles (6kms) from Perth.

Strathkinness, by St Andrews, Fife — Map Ref: 2D3

★★★

B&B

Brig-a-Doon
6 High Road, Strathkinness, by St Andrews
KY16 9XY
Tel:01334 850268
Email:emms0@tesco.net

Extensive views from the lounge across the Eden Estuary and St Andrews Bay. South facing garden with colourful planting and seating area in summer. 3 miles from St Andrews and its famous golf courses and easy access to Scotland's tourist routes.

1 Twin	1 Priv.NOT ensuite	B&B per person	Open Apr-Sep
1 Double	1 Pub.Bath/Show	from £30.00 Single	
		from £20.00 Double	

Tayport, Fife — Map Ref: 2D2

★★★

B&B

Forgans B&B
23 Castle Street, Tayport, Fife, DD6 9AE
Tel/Fax:01382 552682
Email:m.forgan@talk21.com Web:www.forgan.ukf.net/

Truly Scottish welcome awaits you here. Situated in centre of Tayport, just a short walk from picturesque harbour. Easy commuting to Dundee and St Andrews. Good bus service. Near to Dundee and Leuchars Railway Station. Many golf courses nearby. 1 hour drive from Edinburgh. Good home cooking. Full Scottish breakfast. Special diets catered for. Children free when sharing with adults.

2 Twin	2 Priv.NOT ensuite	B&B per person	Open Jan-Dec
1 Double		from £20.00 Single	
		from £17.00 Double	
		from £16.00 Room	
		Only	

by Glasgow — Map Ref: 1H5

★★★

HOTEL

The Westerwood Hotel
1 St Andrews Drive, Cumbernauld, G68 0EW
Tel: 01667 458800 Fax: 01667 455267
E-mail: rooms@morton-hotels.com
Web: www.morton-hotels.com

Modern hotel, with recently completed extension, as well as leisure complex, and own championship golf course. The hotel provides a choice of eating and drinking options, including the Old Masters Restaurant and The Clubhouse bar. Conference and function facilities are available.

55 Double	All En Suite	B&B per person	Open Jan-Dec
42 Twin		from £57.50 per night	D,B&B per person from
3 Suites		Dbl/Twn	£53.50 per night
		from £87.50 Suite per	
		night	

Scotland's National Booking and Information Line

Tel: 0845 22 55 121
visitscotland.com

Important: Prices stated are estimates and may be subject to amendments

Welcome to Scotland

Aberdeen and Grampian Highlands – Scotland's Castle and Whisky Country

Between the granite of the high Cairngorms and a dramatic unspoilt coastline, lie hills, moors and wooded farmlands, river valleys and characterful towns, as well as Aberdeen, Scotland's third city, noted for its unique silver granite architecture and its floral displays.

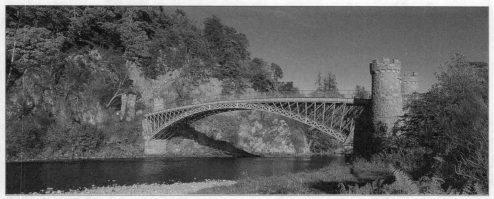

The Telford Bridge near Craigellachie, Moray

Aberdeen offers plenty for visitors: museums, art gallery, great shopping plus an expanding range of leisure attractions along its extensive promenade. The city is also the gateway to Royal Deeside, noted not just for Balmoral Castle and royal family connections, but beautiful scenery with plenty of walking, climbing and castles to visit nearby, plus Royal Lochnagar Distillery. The new Old Royal Station at Ballater portrays the areas association with Queen Victoria.

Malt whisky is most strongly associated with Moray and its unique Malt Whisky Trail, offering a wide choice of distilleries to visit many of which are located along the beautiful birchwood setting of the River Spey. The third major river in this area, the River Don, is associated with the Castle Trail, where

some of the finest castles in Scotland are linked in a signposted trail, which range from the medieval fortress of Kildrummy to the Adam revival grandeur of Haddo House.

The coastline offers yet more delights, not just in the coastal links golf courses, endless beaches and spectacular cliffs and coves, but also in a further range of visitor attractions, including the unique Museum of Scottish Lighthouses at Fraserburgh, the site of Scotland's first lighthouse, and also the equally unique displays at Macduff Marine Aquarium, where a natural kelp reef – seen through one of the largest viewing windows in any British aquarium – shelters a community of fish and other sea creatures usually only seen by divers.

Aberdeen and Grampian Highlands –
Scotland's Castle and Whisky Country

Crovie, Moray

Aberdeen and Grampian Highlands – Scotland's Castle and Whisky Country

Duthie Park, Aberdeen

Grampian is certainly full of surprises – including the chance to see Britain's largest resident colony of bottle-nose dolphins, which turn up close to land anywhere on the Moray Firth coast between Findhorn and Banff.

Events

Aberdeen and Grampian Highlands – Scotland's Castle and Whisky Country

7-9 MARCH
Braemar Telemark Festival
Scotland's largest
international ski event with
competitions, fun skiing and
apres ski events.
Tel: 01339 741242

2-5 MAY*
Spirit of Speyside Whisky
Festival
Enjoy tastings, distillery visits,
music and themed events.
Tel: 01343 542666
www.spiritofspeyside.com

24-30 MAY
Wake Up To Birds Week
Royal Society for the
Protection of Birds. Wide
range of events and activities
at the 60 RSPB reserves across
Scotland. Free entry to all
reserves on one day during
this week.
Tel: 0131 311 6500
www.rspb.org.uk/scotland

7 JUNE*
Taste of Grampian, Inverurie
Festival celebrating the
richness and diversity of
Grampian's larder.
Tel: 01467 623760
www.tasteofgrampian.co.uk

1-8 JUNE
Spirit of Speyside
Environment Festival, Moray
Walks, trails, badger, otter
and dolphin watching.
Tel: 01343 820339
www.wildlifefestival.co.uk

30 JULY – 9 AUGUST*
Aberdeen International
Youth Festival
International multi arts
festival.
Tel: 020 8946 2995
www.aiyf.org

7-10 AUGUST
Speyfest, Fochabers
A pan celtic festival of
traditional music, arts and
crafts.
Tel: 01343 829022
www.speyfest.co.uk

23 AUGUST
The Lonach Gallery,
Strathdon
Traditional highland games.
Tel: 01975 651233

6 SEPTEMBER
Braemar Gathering
One of the most famous
Highland games, featuring
traditional events.
Tel: 01339 755377
www.braemargathering.org

29 SEPTEMBER – 2 OCTOBER*
Speyside Golf Classic
Tel: 01292 293040
www.scottishgolfclassics.com

31 DECEMBER
Stonehaven Fireball Festival
Dramatic and traditional
New Year display.
Tel: 01569 764009
www.hogmanay.net

** denotes provisional date. Events can be
subject to change, please check before
travelling.*

For up to date events, log on to:
visitscotland.com

Area Tourist Boards

Aberdeen and Grampian Highlands – Scotland's Castle and Whisky Country

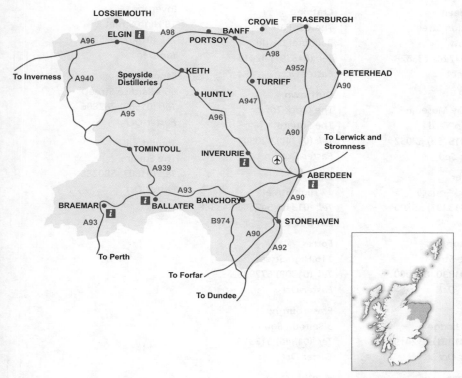

**Aberdeen and Grampian
Tourist Board**
27 Albyn Place
Aberdeen
AB10 1YL

Tel: 01224 288828
(information)
Tel: 01224 288825
(accommodation)
Fax: 01224 581367
E-mail:
info@castlesandwhisky.com
www.castlesandwhisky.com

Tourist Information Centres

Aberdeen and Grampian Highlands – Scotland's Castle and Whisky Country

**Aberdeen and Grampian
Tourist Board**

Aberdeen
23 Union Street
Shiprow
Tel: (01224) 288828
Jan-Dec

Alford
Railway Museum
Station Yard
Tel: (019755) 62052
Easter-Sep

Ballater
Station Square
Tel: (013397) 55306
Jan-Dec

Banchory
Bridge Street
Tel: (01330) 822000
Easter-Oct

Banff
Collie Lodge
Tel: (01261) 812419
Easter-Oct

Braemar
The Mews
Mar Road
Tel: (013397) 41600
Jan-Dec

Crathie
The Car Park
Balmoral Castle
Tel: (013397) 42414
Easter-Oct

Dufftown
The Clock Tower
The Square
Tel: (01340) 820501
Easter-Oct

Elgin
17 High Street
Tel: (01343) 542666/543388
Jan-Dec

Forres
116 High Street
Tel: (01309) 672938
Easter-Oct

Fraserburgh
3 Saltoun Square
Tel: (01346) 518315
Easter-Oct

Huntly
9a The Square
Tel: (01466) 792255
Easter-Oct

Inverurie
18 High Street
Tel: (01467) 625800
Jan-Dec

Stonehaven
66 Allardice Street
Tel: (01569) 762806
Easter-Oct

Tomintoul
The Square
Tel: (01807) 580285
Easter-Oct

Scotland's National Booking and Information Line
0845 22 55 121

Aberdeen   **Map Ref: 4G10**

ABERDEEN NICOLL'S GUEST HOUSE
63 SPRINGBANK TERRACE, FERRYHILL, ABERDEEN AB11 6JZ
Tel: 01224 572867 Fax: 01224 572867
e.mail: aberdeennicollsguesthouse@btinternet.com
Web: www.aberdeennicollsguesthouse.com
Family run, friendly, tastefully decorated, comfortable accommodation in
city centre. Convenient for bus/rail stations, Duthie Park Winter Garden, the
beautiful river Dee, beach, carnival, swimming pools, shops, theatre and
restaurants. Within 5 miles radius of 6 golf courses. Ideal base for touring the
Highlands and whisky trails. Private parking.

★★★
GUEST HOUSE

Aberdeen Nicoll's Guest House
63 Springbank Terrace, Ferryhill, Aberdeen AB11 6JZ
Tel/Fax:01224 572867
Email:aberdeennicollsguesthouse@btinternet.com
Web:www.aberdeennicollsguesthouse.com

Family run, friendly Victorian granite terraced Guest House in Aberdeen's
city centre. 1/4 mile (1/2km) from shops, theatre & restaurants. Ideal
base for touring the Highlands etc. 6 Golf courses nearby. Limited off
street parking.

3 Twin	3 En Suite fac	B&B per person	Open Jan-Dec excl
3 Family	2 Priv.NOT ensuite	from £25.00 Single	Xmas/New Year
		from £17.50 Double	

★
GUEST HOUSE

Antrim Guest House
157 Crown Street, Aberdeen, AB11 6HT
Tel/Fax:01224 590987

Situated close to city centre, railway and bus stations. Private parking.

2 Single	3 Pub.Show	B&B per person	Open Jan-Dec excl
1 Twin		from £22.00 Single	Xmas/New Year
1 Double		from £17.00 Double	
1 Family			

★★★
GUEST HOUSE

Arkaig Guest House
43 Powis Terrace, Aberdeen, AB25 3PP
Tel:01224 638872 Fax:01224 622189
Email:pat@arkaig.biz
Web:www.arkaig.biz

Traditional granite house, city centre 1/2 mile (1km). Convenient to places
of interest, station, harbour, airport, university, Aberdeen College (ASET)
and hospitals.

3 Single	7 En Suite fac	B&B per person	Open Jan-Dec excl
2 Twin	1 Priv.NOT ensuite	from £25.00 Single	Xmas/New Year
3 Double		from £25.00 Double	BB & Eve.Meal
1 Family			from £37.50

★★
GUEST HOUSE

Balvenie Guest House
9 St Swithin Street, Aberdeen, AB10 6XB
Tel:01224 322559 Fax:01224 325064
Email:balvenieguesthouse@aol.com

Late Victorian granite built house in residential area in West End, close
to city centre. Parking. Convenient for local and airport buses.

2 Single	2 Priv.NOT ensuite	B&B per person	Open Jan-Dec
2 Twin		from £20.00 Single	BB & Eve.Meal
1 Double		from £16.00 Double	from £23.50

VAT is shown at 17.5%: changes in this rate may affect prices. | *Key to symbols is on back flap.* |

Aberdeen   **Map Ref: 4G10**

★★★

B&B

33 Carden Place
Aberdeen, AB10 1UN
Tel:01224 645191

1 Single	1 Priv.NOT ensuite	B&B per person
2 Twin		from £20.00 Single
		from £20.00 Double

Open Jan-Dec excl
Xmas/New Year

Victorian terraced house in west end of city. Within easy walking distance of city centre. Garden breakfast room in summer. Non smoking house.

★

**GUEST
HOUSE**

Four Bees Guest House
356 Holburn Street, Aberdeen, AB10 7GX
Tel:01224 585110

2 Twin	1 En Suite fac	B&B per person
2 Double	2 Priv.NOT ensuite	from £20.00 Single
2 Family		from £16.00 Double
		from £18.00 Room
		Only

Open Jan-Dec excl
Xmas/New Year

Traditional granite house with long garden, set back from the road. Convenient for city centre and all amenities. On main bus routes.

FURAIN GUEST HOUSE
North Deeside Road, Peterculter, Aberdeen AB14 0QN
Telephone: 01224 732189 Fax: 01224 739070
e.mail: furain@btinternet.com

FURAIN GUEST HOUSE, on the A93, 8 miles west of Aberdeen centre, close to several historic castles and convenient for touring some of the most beautiful countryside in the UK. We give a full Scottish breakfast with choice, special diets catered for.

★★★

**GUEST
HOUSE**

Furain Guest House
92 North Deeside Road, Peterculter, Aberdeen
AB14 0QN
Tel:01224 732189   Fax:01224 739070
Email:furain@btinternet.com

1 Single	All En Suite	B&B per person
3 Twin		from £30.00 Single
2 Double		from £20.50 Double
2 Family		from £28.00 Room
		Only

Open Jan-Dec excl
Xmas/New Year
BB & Eve.Meal
from £45.00

Late Victorian house built of red granite. Family run. Convenient for town, Royal Deeside and the Castle Trail. Private car parking. Dinner available on Wednesday, Friday and Saturday.

★★★

B&B

V Millers B&B
5 Cairnvale Crescent, Kincorth, Aberdeen, AB12 5JB
Tel/Fax:01224 874163

1 Single	1 Pub.Bath/Show	B&B per person
1 Double		£18.00-20.00 Single
		£18.00-20.00 Double

Open Jan-Dec

Set in a quiet residential area, a semi detached family house offering bed and breakfast of a high standard. Cosy and very neat, convenient for access to South Deeside and routes south to Stonehaven and Dundee. 2 miles from the city centre. On main bus route.

Important: Prices stated are estimates and may be subject to amendments

Aberdeen

Map Ref: 4G10

★★★

B&B

Manorville

252 Great Western Road, Aberdeen, AB10 6PJ
Tel/Fax:01224 594190
Email:manorvilleabz@aol.com

Granite dwelling house in close proximity to town centre. On main bus route to Deeside. All rooms ensuite.

1 Single	All En Suite	B&B per person	Open Jan-Dec
1 Twin		from £25.00 Single	
1 Family		from £21.00 Double	

Scottish Agricultural College

CRAIBSTONE ESTATE, BUCKSBURN, ABERDEEN AB21 9TR
Tel: 01224 711195   Fax: 01224 711298
e.mail: s.may@ab.sac.ac.uk Web: www.craibstone.com

Situated in quiet rural location within large woodland estate only 5 miles from Aberdeen with own 18-hole golf course, it is the ideal venue for touring the north east of Scotland, playing the many golf courses or just relaxing.
Whatever your needs we will give you a warm welcome.

★★

**CAMPUS
ACCOMMODATION**

Scottish Agricultural College

Craibstone Estate, Bucksburn, Aberdeenshire AB21 9TR
Tel:01224 711195   Fax:01224 711298
Email:s.may@ab.sac.ac.uk
Web:www.craibstone.com

Halls of Residence, set in extensive country estate with new 18 hole golf course on outskirts of Aberdeen, with easy access to all amenities.

36 Single	60 En Suite fac	B&B per person	Open Apr,Jul-Sep
20 Twin	12 Priv.NOT ensuite	from £20.00 Single	BB & Eve.Meal
	5 Pub.Bath/Show		from £26.75

St ELMO

64 HILTON DRIVE, ABERDEEN AB24 4NP
Telephone: 01224 483065 e.mail: StElmoBandB@aol.com
Web: http://home.aol.com/StElmoBandB/

This comfortable, smoke-free, family accommodation is ideal for guests looking for a small quiet place to stay, yet on a city centre bus route, close to airport, university and hospital. CTV, courtesy tray, microwave and fridge facilities in bedrooms; full Scottish breakfast; special multinight rates; off-street parking available.

★★★

B&B

St Elmo Bed + Breakfast

64 Hilton Drive, Aberdeen, AB24 4NP
Tel:01224 483065
Email:StElmoBandB@aol.com
Web:http://home.aol.com/StElmoBandB/

A detached bungalow in residential area with off road parking. Totally non-smoking, with additional TV/videos mini-fridges, microwaves, crockery and cutlery for restricted self-catering in evenings. Scottish breakfast provided. City centre 2 miles. Situated on main bus route.

1 Twin	1 Priv.NOT ensuite	B&B per person	Open Jan-Dec
1 Double		from £22.00 Single	
1 Family		from £20.00 Double	

VAT is shown at 17.5%: changes in this rate may affect prices.

Key to symbols is on back flap.

Aboyne, Aberdeenshire | Map Ref: 4F11

★★★★★

B&B

Struan Hall
Ballater Road, Aboyne, Aberdeenshire, AB34 5HY
Tel/Fax:013398 87241
Email:struanhall@zetnet.co.uk
Web:www.struanhall.co.uk

Peacefully situated in the two acres of mature gardens, this substantial
family home has been sensitively restored to provide a traditional and
very comfortable holiday base. Royal Deeside offers a vast range of
outdoor and heritage attractions.

2 Twin	All En Suite	B&B per person	Open Jan-Oct excl
1 Double		from £27.50 Single	New Year
		from £27.50 Double	

Alford, Aberdeenshire | Map Ref: 4F10

★★★

B&B

Bydand Bed & Breakfast
18 Balfour Street, Alford, Aberdeenshire, AB33 8NF
Tel:019755 63613

A warm welcome in this family B&B set in quiet residential area yet only
5 minutes walk from village centre. Ideal location for Castle and Whisky
trails. Plenty of outdoor activities within village including dry ski slope
and 18 hole golf course.

1 Twin	All En Suite	B&B per person	Open Jan-Dec
1 Double		from £20.00 Single	
		from £20.00 Double	
		from £17.00 Room	
		Only	

★★★

B&B

Lethenty
Tullynessle, Alford, Aberdeenshire, AB33 8DB
Tel/Fax:019755 63402
Email:lethentyout@freenet.co.uk

Enjoy the unique atmosphere of the beautiful part of the Vale of Alford,
with glorious views of the hills. Lethenty Farm House is set on a working
farm of 400 acres of land. It is an ideal base for wildlife, walking,
climbing or just relaxing yet only 3 miles from Alford. Ground floor
accommodation.

1 Twin	2 En Suite fac	B&B per person	Open Jan-Dec
2 Double	1 Pub.Bath/Show	from £21.50 Single	
		from £19.50 Double	

Ballater, Aberdeenshire | Map Ref: 4E11

★★★

B&B

East Bank B&B
50 Albert Road, Ballater, AB35 5QU
Tel:013397 55742   Fax:013397 55795
Email:reynard12@aol.com
Web:www.strathdee/ballater/eastbank

Traditional stone built house offering very comfortable accommodation in
a peaceful residential area of this Royal Deeside village. Two minute
walk to golf course, tennis courts and bowling green with nearby shops
and restaurants. Victorian Trail, Balmoral, hillwalking, climbing, pony
trekking, fishing and skiing amongst others are all close by.

1 Single	1 Priv.Show	B&B per person	Open Jan-Dec excl
1 Twin	1 Priv.Show	from £25.00 Single	Xmas/New Year
1 Double	1 En suite Show	from £22.00 Double	

Scotland's National Booking
and Information Line

Tel: 0845 22 55 121
visitscotland.com

Important: Prices stated are estimates and may be subject to amendments

Ballater, Aberdeenshire
Map Ref: 4E11

★★★★

B&B

Inverdeen House
11 Bridge Square, Ballater, AB35 5QJ
Tel:013397 55759 Fax:013397 55993
Email:info@inverdeen.com Web:www.inverdeen.com

We offer a splendid selection of great breakfasts featuring pancakes with genuine Canadian maple syrup, Venison sausage and home-made jam. Inverdeen House faces the A93 (at the Dee Bridge). There is easy access to such attractions as hillwalking, mountain climbing, orienteering, cycling, skiing, pony trekking, fishing, gliding, 4x4 driving, bird watching, Archaeolink and the Whisky, Castle and Stone Circle trails.

1 Twin	Ensuite fac	B&B per person	Open Jan-Dec
1 Family	Ensuite fac	from £22.50 pppn	
1 Double	Priv.Shower		

★★★

HOTEL

●●

RESTAURANT

Loch Kinord Hotel
Ballater Road, Dinnet, Royal Deeside
Aberdeenshire, AB34 5JY
Tel:013398 85229 Fax:013398 87007
Email:stay@lochkinord.com Web:www.lochkinord.com

Under the enthusiastic new ownership of Jenny and Andrew Cox the hotel has undergone public areas refurbishment featuring some 4 poster bedrooms with all modern facilities. Situated in the centre of this small village it makes a great base for exploring Royal Deeside, skiing, walking, and playing golf. Non-residents very welcome and popular in the area for excellent food from their AA rosette restaurant.

1 Single	15 En Suite fac	B&B per person	Open Jan-Dec
3 Twin	2 Priv.NOT ensuite	from £30.00 Single	BB & Eve.Meal
11 Double		from £35.00 Double	from £45.00
2 Family			

★★★★

Morvada House
28 Braemar Road, Ballater AB35 5RL
Tel/Fax: 013397 56334
e.mail: morvada@aol.com Web: www.morvada.com
Allan and Thea Campbell welcome you to the beautiful village of Ballater. This peaceful village is well situated for walking (Lochnagar and Glen Muick), visiting castles (Balmoral and Braemar), or distilleries (Royal Lochnagar and Glenlivet). Warmth, personal service, absolute cleanliness, trust, a laugh, and acknowledgement are assured during your stay.

★★★★

GUEST
HOUSE

Morvada House
28 Braemar Road, Ballater, AB35 5RL
Tel/Fax:013397 56334
Email:morvada@aol.com
Web:www.morvada.com

A friendly family run Victorian house offering traditional highland hospitality with modern en-suite facilities and a guests lounge. Furnished to a high standard with tea and coffee including herbal tea and hot chocolate in the bedrooms. A quiet location close to the village centre and golf course with shops and wide choice of restaurants nearby.

1 Twin	All En Suite	B&B per person	Open Feb-Nov
5 Double		from £21.00 Double	

Banchory, Aberdeenshire
Map Ref: 4F11

★★★★

B&B

Mrs J Robb
Ardconnel, 6 Kinneskie Road, Banchory, AB31 5TA
Tel:01330 822478
Email:jsrobb@talk21.com

Very comfortable modern bungalow in quiet spot overlooking local golf course. 3 minutes from town centre, and all amenities. Ground floor bedrooms, one with en suite, the other a private bathroom facility.

1 Twin	1 En Suite fac	B&B per person	Open Mar-Oct
1 Double	1 Priv.Bath/Show	£30.00 Single	
		from £20.00 Double	

VAT is shown at 17.5%: changes in this rate may affect prices.

Key to symbols is on back flap.

Important: Prices stated are estimates and may be subject to amendments

by Banchory, Aberdeenshire

Map Ref: 4F11

B&B ★★★★

Dorena Bed+Breakfast
Strachan, By Banchory, Kincardineshire, AB31 6NL
Tel/Fax:01330 822540

Modern bungalow on edge of quiet village, with views across the fields and woods. Private parking. Only 3 miles from Banchory. Excellent hospitality assured.

1 Twin	All En Suite	B&B per person	Open Jan-Dec excl
2 Double		from £20.00 Double	Xmas/New Year

MONTHAMMOCK FARM

DURRIS, BY BANCHORY AB31 6DX

Tel/Fax: 01330 811421 e.mail: g&tlaw@ic24.net

Magnificent panoramic views. Converted steading in tranquil country setting. Modern comfortable accommodation. Convenient for sightseeing and country pursuits. Traditional home cooking.

B&B ★★★

Monthammock Farm
Durris, by Banchory, AB31 6DX
Tel/Fax:01330 811421
Email:g&tlaw@ic24.net

Tranquility and a warm welcome at this sympathetically converted steading, with spectacular views over Deeside.

1 Twin	Some En Suite	B&B per person	Open Jan-Dec excl
1 Double	1 Priv.NOT ensuite	from £25.00 Single	Xmas/New Year
	1 Pub.Bath/Show	from £20.00 Double	BB & Eve.Meal
			from £34.00-39.00

Banff

Map Ref: 4F7

MORAYHILL

Bellevue Road, Banff AB45 1BJ
Tel: 01261 815956   e.mail: morayhill@aol.com
Fax: 01261 818717 Web: www.morayhill.co.uk

Situated in a residential area close to central amenities, this detached Victorian house offers a warm welcome. Close by are many golf courses including the highly rated Duff House Royal. The comfortable accommodation offers a relaxing lounge with log fire and a dining room overlooking the garden. Off road parking.

B&B ★★★★

Morayhill
Bellevue Road, Banff, Aberdeenshire, AB45 1BJ
Tel:01261 815956 Fax:01261 818717
Email:morayhill@aol.com
Web:www.morayhill.co.uk

Large Victorian house, centrally situated for town, golf, and fishing. Warm and friendly welcome assured. Private Parking. Many places of interest locally including Duff House and MacDuff Aquarium.

2 Twin	2 En Suite fac	B&B per person	Open Jan-Dec
1 Double	1 Pub.Bath/Show	from £25.00 Single	
		from £21.00 Double	
		from £15.00 Room	
		Only	

VAT is shown at 17.5%: changes in this rate may affect prices.

 Key to symbols is on back flap.

Braemar, Aberdeenshire | Map Ref: 4D11

★★★

GUEST HOUSE

Clunie Lodge Guest House
Cluniebank Road, Braemar, Aberdeenshire, AB35 5ZP
Tel:013397 41330
Email:ClunieLodge@hotmail.com

Victorian former manse house peacefully located close to village centre and short drive to golf course. Ideal base for walking, touring, golfing and ski-ing.

1 Triple	3 En Suite fac	B&B per person	Open Jan-Dec excl
3 Double	2 Priv.Bath/Show	from £28.00 Single	Xmas/New Year
1 Family		from £24.00 Double	

★★★

B&B

Mayfield Bed+Breakfast
11 Chapel Brae, Braemar, Aberdeenshire, AB35 5YT
Tel:013397 41238
Email:info@mayhouse.co.uk
Web:www.mayhouse.co.uk

Situated in a quiet, peaceful situation with views over the site of the Royal Highland gathering to the mountains beyond. A guest house since Victorian times the present owners continue the family tradition with highland hospitality and all modern comforts.

1 Single	2 Priv.NOT ensuite	B&B per person	Open Mar-Nov
1 Twin		from £19.00 Single	
2 Double		from £19.00 Double	
1 Family			

SCHIEHALLION HOUSE

GLENSHEE ROAD, BRAEMAR, ABERDEENSHIRE AB35 5YQ
Telephone: 013397 41679

Combining mountain splendour with village charm, Schiehallion House lies in the very heart of the Scottish Highlands. Your hosts, Julie and Steve Heyes, welcome you with courteous, friendly and personal service. Why not make this your base to explore the delights of Royal Deeside. Private parking. Village centre 400 metres.

★★★

GUEST HOUSE

Schiehallion Guest House
10 Glenshee Road, Braemar, Aberdeenshire, AB35 5YQ
Tel:013397 41679

Comfortable, tastefully decorated, Victorian house with attractive garden at gateway to Royal Deeside. Offering personal service and log fires. One ground floor annexe room. All nationalities welcome.

1 Single	5 En Suite fac	B&B per person	Open Jan-Sep excl
3 Twin	1 Priv.NOT ensuite	from £20.00 Single	New Year
3 Double		from £19.00 Double	
2 Triple			

Scotland's National Booking and Information Line

Tel: 0845 22 55 121
visitscotland.com

Important: Prices stated are estimates and may be subject to amendments

Buckie, Banffshire | Map Ref: 4E7

★★★★

B&B

Rosemount B&B
62 East Church Street, Buckie, Banffshire
AB56 1ER
Tel/Fax:01542 833434
Email:rosemount_bck@btinternet.com

Modernised Victorian detached house, centrally situated overlooking
Moray Firth. Ideal for fishing, golf, Malt Whisky Trail, and at the start of
the Spey Way Walk.

2 Twin	2 En Suite fac
1 Double	1 Priv.Bath/Show

B&B per person
from £25.00 Single
from £20.00 Double

Open Jan-Dec excl
Xmas/New Year

Cullen, Moray | Map Ref: 4E7

★★★

B&B

Alesund
13 Ogilvie Park, Cullen, Moray, AB56 4XZ
Tel:01542 840017
Email:bobmaur@phimister.fsnet.co.uk

Modern detached bungalow with garden, overlooking Cullen and the
Moray Firth. Short walk to all amenities.

1 Twin	1 Priv.NOT ensuite
1 Double	

B&B per person
from £18.00 Single
from £18.00 Double

Open May-Sep

Dufftown, Banffshire | Map Ref: 4E9

★★★

B&B

Bed+Breakfast
11 Conval Street, Dufftown, Banffshire, AB55 4AE
Tel:01340 820818
Email:ukn0000107308@freedomland.co.uk

Warm welcome at quiet modern bungalow, off main street 18 miles (29
kms) south of Elgin. On Whisky Trail.

1 Twin	1 Priv.NOT ensuite
1 Double	

B&B per person
from £20.00 Single
from £18.00 Double

Open Jan-Dec

★★★

B&B

Davaar
Church Street, Dufftown, Keith, AB55 4AR
Tel:01340 820464
Email:davaar@cluniecameron.co.uk
Web:www.davaardufftown.co.uk

Comfortable and personally run accommodation. Close to Whisky and
Castle Trails.

1 Twin	All En Suite
2 Double	

B&B per person
from £18.00 Single
from £20.00 Double

Open Jan-Dec

Dufftown, Banffshire

Map Ref: 4E9

GOWANBRAE

19 Church Street, Dufftown AB55 4AR
Tel/Fax: 01340 820461
e.mail: gowanbrae@breathemail.net Web: www.gowanbrae-dufftown.co.uk
Family run bed and breakfast in Speyside town of Dufftown the whisky
capital. Ideal for touring castle and whisky trails and walking. Fully
ensuite, meals, cycle hire.

★★★

B&B

Gowan Brae
19 Church Street, Dufftown, AB55 4AR
Tel/Fax:01340 820461
Email:gowanbrae@breathemail.net
Web:www.gowanbrae-dufftown.co.uk

Family run bed & breakfast in small Speyside town. Ideal location for
touring the whisky trail, touring and walking.

1 Twin	All En Suite	B&B per person	Open Jan-Dec excl
2 Double		from £16.00 Double	Xmas
1 Family			BB & Eve.Meal
			from £24.00

Elgin, Moray

Map Ref: 4D8

ARDGYE HOUSE

Elgin, Moray IV30 8UP Tel/Fax: 01343 850618
e.mail: ardgyehouse@hotmail.com Web: www.scottish-holidays.net
ARDGYE HOUSE is a gracious Edwardian mansion in its own extensive
grounds situated close to main Aberdeen to Inverness road (3.5 miles west of
Elgin). Superb accommodation in quiet surroundings. Central position ideal
for beaches, golf, riding, fishing, castles and distilleries. Recommended by
Holiday Which. *For full details contact Carol and Alistair McInnes.*

★★★★

GUEST HOUSE

Ardgye House
Elgin, Moray, IV30 8UP
Tel/Fax:01343 850618
Email:ardgyehouse@hotmail.com
Web:www.scottishholidays.net

Gracious Edwardian mansion in own extensive grounds easily accessible
from A96. 3 miles (5kms) from Elgin. Recommended by Holiday Which.

1 Single	6 En Suite fac	B&B per person	Open Jan-Dec
2 Twin	4 Pub.Bath/Show	from £14.00 Single	
3 Double		from £14.00 Double	
4 Family			

Scotland's National Booking and Information Line

Tel: 0845 22 55 121
visitscotland.com

Important: Prices stated are estimates and may be subject to amendments

Elgin, Moray   Map Ref: 4D8

CARRICK HOUSE
13 SOUTH GUILDRY STREET, ELGIN, MORAY 1V30 1QN
TEL: 01343 569321
E.MAIL: kevin@scotbandb.co.uk WEB: www.scotbandb.co.uk

This fine Georgian house is the most comfortable of starting points for
exploring the Highlands of Scotland. All our guest rooms are of a very high
standard and evening meals are available. We are situated near the centre
of old Elgin in an ideal location for all local amenities.

★★★★

B&B

Carrick House

13 South Guildry Street, Elgin, Moray, IV30 1QN
Tel:01343 569321
Email:kevin@scotbandb.co.uk
Web:www.scotbandb.co.uk

Fully restored Georgian house in residential street close to railway
station. Property is decorated throughout to a very high standard in a
modern style while retaining some of the original features.

| 1 Twin
2 Double | Some En Suite
1 Priv.NOT ensuite | B&B per person
from £24.00 Single
from £20.00 Double
from £18.00 Room
Only | Open Jan-Dec
BB & Eve.Meal
from £32.00 |

★★★★

GUEST HOUSE

The Pines Guest House

East Road, Elgin, Moray, IV30 1XG
Tel:01343 552495 Fax:01343 552495
Email:thepines@talk21.com
Web:www.thepinesguesthouse.com

Victorian elegance with modern comforts. Friendly atmosphere, freshly
prepared food. Convenient for golf, fishing, Whisky and Castle Trails.

| 1 Twin
4 Double
1 Family | All En Suite | B&B per person
from £30.00 Single
from £22.00 Double | Open Jan-Dec excl
Xmas/New Year |

★★★

B&B

Richmond

Moss Street, Elgin, Morayshire, IV30 1LT
Tel:01343 542561
Email:richmond@clara.co.uk

Friendly, family home with garden close to town centre and all amenities.
Ensuite rooms available.

| 1 Single
2 Twin
2 Double
1 Family | Some En Suite
1 Pub.Bath/Show | B&B per person
from £18.00 Single
from £18.00 Double | Open Jan-Dec excl
Xmas/New Year |

---

by Elgin, Moray   Map Ref: 4D8

★★★

B&B

Foresters House

Newton, by Elgin, Moray, IV30 8XW
Tel:01343 552862
Email:goodwin@forestershouse.fsnet.co.uk
Web:http://mysite.freeserve.com/goodbb

Traditional stone built house in the middle of open countryside. 3 miles
(5kms) west of Elgin on A96. Turn right on to the B9013 and Foresters
House is 400m on the right hand side. A traditional Scottish welcome
awaits you.

| 1 Double
1 Family | Limited En Suite
1 Pub.Bath/Show | B&B per person
from £17.00 Single
from £15.00 Double | Open Jan-Dec |

VAT is shown at 17.5%: changes in this rate may affect prices.   Key to symbols is on back flap.

by Elgin, Moray   Map Ref: 4D8

Parrandier, The Old Church of Urquhart
Meft Road, Urquhart, by Elgin, Moray IV30 8NH
Tel & Fax: 01343 843063   e.mail: parrandier@freeuk.com
Web: www.oldkirk.co.uk

Find your own little island of peace in this perpendicular Scottish
Church surrounded by a sea of stormy farmland. Discover a distinctly
DIFFERENT PLACE to explore secret Scotland. Relax in your spacious
lounge in a real special atmosphere and enjoy good food and a taste of
whisky. Guest lounges and open fire. Gardens for guest use.

★★★★

B&B

Parrandier, The Old Church of Urquhart
Meft Road, Urquhart, by Elgin, Morayshire IV30 8NH
Tel/Fax:01343 843063
Email:parrandier@freeuk.com
Web:www.oldkirk.co.uk

1 Twin	2 En Suite fac	B&B per person	Open Jan-Dec
1 Double	1 Pub.Bath/Show	from £27.00 Single	BB & Eve.Meal
1 Family		from £22.00 Double	from £32.00
		from £18.00 Room	
		Only	

Perched on a hill top this beautiful rural setting offers uninterrupted
views across surrounding farmland. Built in 1843 the church is recently
converted into a unique family home. The character of the church has
been retained encompassing arched windows and beamed ceilings. Guest
lounges and fire. Dinner available.

---

nr Elgin, Moray   Map Ref: 4D8

★★

B&B

Carsewell Farmhouse
Alves, Nr Eglin, Morayshire, IV30 3UR
Tel:01343 850201
Email:carsewell@lineone.net
Web:www.carsewell.co.uk

2 Double	1 Priv.NOT ensuite	B&B per person	Open Apr-Oct
		from £16.00 Single	
		from £15.00 Double	

Traditional stone-built farmhouse just off A96 in village of Alves, midway
between Elgin & Forres. Short walk to local pub & restaurant. Bedrooms
can be accessed by stairlift.

Findhorn, Moray   Map Ref: 4C7

HEATH HOUSE
HEATH HOUSE, FINDHORN, MORAY IV36 3WN
Tel/Fax: 01309 691082 e.mail: elizabeth-tony.cowie@talk21.com
Web: www.aboutscotland.com/moray

Set in seaside village of Findhorn, one minute from the sea,
this ranch type home in quiet cul-de-sac offers friendly
comfortable accommodation. Handy for golf courses, castles,
distilleries and nature reserve. Boating trips organised.

★★★

B&B

Heath House
Findhorn, Moray, IV36 3WN
Tel/Fax:01309 691082
Email:elizabeth-tony.cowie@talk21.com
Web:www.aboutscotland.com/moray

1 Twin	1 Priv.NOT ensuite	B&B per person	Open Jan-Dec excl
1 Double	1 Pub.Bath/Show	from £20.00 Single	Xmas/New Year
		from £20.00 Double	

Modern bungalow in secluded cul-de-sac on outskirts of Findhorn close to
beach. 4 miles (7km) to Forres. Walking, ornithology, various golf
courses, the famous whisky trail and newly created trails

Important: Prices stated are estimates and may be subject to amendments

Forres, Moray
           Map Ref: 4C8

★★★

B&B

April Rise Bed + Breakfast
16 Forbes Road, Forres, Moray, IV36 1HP
Tel:01309 674066

Traditional Scottish hospitality in friendly family home. 2 rooms ensuite. Short walk to town and all amenities.

1 Single	Some En Suite	B&B per person	Open Jan-Dec excl
1 Twin	1 Priv.NOT ensuite	from £20.00 Single	Xmas/New Year
1 Family		from £18.50 Double	

★★★

B&B

Caranrahd
Sanquhar Road, Forres, Moray, IV36 1DG
Tel:01309 672581

Traditional Scottish hospitality in friendly family home, within quiet residential area. Ideal touring base.

2 Double	2 Priv.NOT ensuite	B&B per person	Open Jan-Dec excl
1 Family		from £17.00 Single	Xmas/New Year
		from £17.00 Double	

★★★★

B&B

Milton of Grange Farmhouse B&B
Milton of Grange Farm, Forres, Morayshire IV36 2TR
Tel/Fax:01309 676360
Email:hildamassie@aol.com
Web:www.forres-accommodation.co.uk

Beautifully appointed recently converted farmhouse on working farm, with all rooms ensuite. With Forres only 2 miles away, an ideal base for touring the whisky and castle trails or playing golf. Nearby is the historic village of Findhorn, popular with bird-watchers and boating enthusiasts. A warm welcome is assured here.

1 Double	All En Suite	B&B per person	Open Jan-15 Dec excl
2 Twin/		£20.00-30.00 Single	Xmas/New Year
Family		£20.00-22.50 Double	
		from £18.00 Room Only	

★★★

B&B

Morven
Caroline Street, Forres, Moray, IV36 0AN
Tel/Fax:01309 673788
Email:morven2@globalnet.co.uk
Web:www.getpersgreenlees.com/morven/

Victorian house offering bed and breakfast in a warm friendly family atmosphere, with all conveniences. Town centre location.

3 Twin	2 En Suite fac	B&B per person	Open Jan-Dec
	2 Priv.NOT ensuite	from £19.00 Single	
	1 Pub.Bath/Show	from £19.00 Double	

★★★★

B&B

Sherston House
Hillhead, Forres, Moray, IV36 0QT
Tel:01309 671087 Fax:01343 850535

Tastefully restored stone built house, 1 mile (2km) from Forres and beside main A96. Garden area available. Dinner by prior arrangement. Wonderful gardens in Forres and Findhorn village and foundation also nearby.

3 rooms	All En Suite	B&B per person	Open Jan-Dec excl
each		from £25.00 Single	Xmas/New Year
Dbl/Twn/		from £20.00 Double	BB & Eve.Meal
Fam		from £18.00 Room Only	from £32.50

VAT is shown at 17.5%: changes in this rate may affect prices.   **Key to symbols is on back flap.**

Forres, Moray
Map Ref: 4C8

Springfield B&B
Croft Road, Forres, Moray, IV36 3JS
Tel:01309 676965 Fax:01309 673376
Email:catherinebain@tinyworld.co.uk
Web:www.scotland-
index.co.uk/moray/forres/springfield/bed_and_breakfast

Large, comfortable, modern home, set in own grounds. Short stroll to town centre, restaurants and all amenities. From Elgin on A96, left at roundabout first right (Findhorn Rd) first left to the bottom. From Inverness A96 over the first roundabout to next, take the right into Forres then as above.

1 Double	All En Suite	B&B per person	Open Jan-Dec
1 Family		from £19.50 Single	
		from £19.50 Double	
		from £20.00 Room	
		Only	

by Forres, Moray
Map Ref: 4C8

Mrs Flora Barclay
Moss-side Farmhouse B&B, Rafford, Forres, IV36 2SL
Tel:01309 672954

Traditional farmhouse with modern extension set in 28 acres on the outskirts of Forres. Ideal for golf, fishing and walking. On the Whisky and Castle Trails. Home cooking and baking. A quiet place for a relaxing holiday.

1 Twin	1 Priv.NOT ensuite	B&B per person	Open Apr-Oct
1 Double		from £16.00 Single	
1 Family		from £16.00 Double	
		from £10.00 Room	
		Only	

The Old Kirk
Dyke, By Forres, IV36 2TL
Tel:01309 641414 Fax:01309 641057
Email:oldkirk@gmx.net Web:www.oldkirk.co.uk

A warm welcome awaits you at this distinctly different Bed & Breakfast. This former Scottish church has been converted into a stylish family home with high quality standards. The Old Kirk is perfectly situated for exploring Moray tourist attractions as well as having a relaxing short break in the beautiful countryside. Choose your favourite breakfast variety from the delicious choice of our menu.

1 Twin	2 En Suite fac	B&B per person	Open Jan-Dec
2 Double	1 Pub.Bath/Show	from £30.00 Single	
		from £20.00 Double	
		from £18.00 Room	
		Only	

Fyvie, Aberdeenshire
Map Ref: 4G9

Bed + Breakfast (Mrs Marjory Wyness)
Meikle Camaloun, Fyvie, Aberdeenshire, AB53 8JY
Tel/Fax:01651 891319
Email:w.wyness@btinternet.com

Large comfortable farmhouse, with inviting garden and superb views over rolling farmland. Ideal for Whisky and Castle Trails. Close to Fyvie Castle.

1 Twin	1 En Suite fac	B&B per person	Open Jan-Dec excl
1 Double	1 Pub.Bath/Show	from £25.00 Single	Xmas/New Year
		£22.00-25.00 Double	

Important: Prices stated are estimates and may be subject to amendments

Gardenstown, Banffshire

Map Ref: 4G7

★★★

B&B

Bankhead Croft
Gamrie, Banff, AB45 3HN
Tel/Fax:01261 851584
Email:Lucinda@bankheadcroft.freeserve.co.uk
Web:www.bankheadcroft.freeserve.co.uk

Enjoy friendly welcoming hospitality in our modern country cottage in peaceful surroundings. 2 miles (3 kms) from coast. 6 miles (10 kms) East of Banff. Evening meals available using home produce. Special diets catered for and packed lunches available. Ideal for all outdoor pursuits. 'Welcome'.

1 Twin	All En Suite	B&B per person	Open Jan-Dec
1 Double	1 Priv.NOT ensuite	from £20.00 Single	BB & Eve.Meal
1 Family		from £18.50 Double	from £28.50
		from £12.00 Room Only	

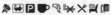

★★★

B&B

The Palace Farm
Gamrie, Banff, AB45 3HS
Tel:01261 851261 Fax:01261 851401
Email:palace@gamrie.com Web:www.gamrie.com

A warm welcome awaits you at Palace farm a 18th century farmhouse, on a mixed arable farm. Excellent home cooking from a qualified cook using fresh farm produce and local fish. Just a few miles away from Gardenstown built virtually on a cliff face, reach Crovie by a narrow foot path, and visit Pennan. Certificate of excellence and member of Scotlands Best.

1 Twin	All En Suite	B&B per person	Open Jan-Dec excl
1 Double		£22.00-25.00 Single	Xmas/New Year
1 Family		£20.00-22.00 Double	BB & Eve.Meal
		from £20.00 Room Only	from £33.00

Glenkindie, Aberdeenshire

Map Ref: 4E10

★★★

B&B

The Smiddy House
Glenkindie, Aberdeenshire, AB33 8SS
Tel:01975 641216 Fax:01975 641279
Email:jones.thesmiddy@btclick.com
Web:www.visitscotland.net

Friendly bed and breakfast on Highland Route and Castle Trail. Set in pleasant surroundings. A good variety of wild birds to be seen in the garden.

1 Twin	All En Suite	B&B per person	Open Mar-Nov
1 Double		from £18.00 Double	BB & Eve.Meal
			from £25.00

Scotland's National Booking and Information Line

Tel: 0845 22 55 121
visitscotland.com

VAT is shown at 17.5%: changes in this rate may affect prices. | *Key to symbols is on back flap.*

Glenlivet, Banffshire   Map Ref: 4D9

RIVERSTONE COTTAGE

Glenlivet, Ballindalloch AB37 9DA
Tel/Fax: 01807 590766
e.mail: anne@dundasa.freeserve.co.uk
Web: www.riverstonecottage.co.uk
Relax and enjoy a warm friendly welcome with comfortable accommodation, good food. Excellent fishing available on the Rivers Spey, Avon and Livet. Many walks to explore. Bird watchers can see an abundance of species. Photographers will be spoilt for choice. You can visit many distilleries, castles and historic sights.

★★★

B&B

Riverstone Cottage

Glenlivet, Ballindalloch, Banffshire, AB37 9DA
Tel/Fax:01807 590766
Email:anne@dundasa.freeserve.co.uk
web:www.riverstonecottage.co.uk

Riverstone cottage is situated in the heart of Glenlivet, and provides a relaxed base to explore this part of Scotland. Castles including Drumin, Ballindalloch, Crown Estates, Speyside Way for walkers. Fishing on Spey, Avon and Livet. Whisky Trail, and much more for you to discover. Packed lunches available.

2 Twin	1 En Suite fac	B&B per person	Open Jan-Dec
1 Double	1 Priv.NOT ensuite	from £20.00 Single	BB & Eve.Meal
		from £25.00 Double	from £35.00

Roadside Cottage

Tomnavoulin, Glenlivet, Ballindalloch, Banffshire AB37 9JL
Telephone: 01807 590486   Fax: 01807 590486
Awake to bird-song, the aroma of a traditional breakfast, a stunning view from your window. Every guest is a VIP in this land of moor and hills, rivers and ski-slopes, birds and wildlife – and whisky! This is the good life! Finalist Millennium Thistle Awards.
Member of Pride of Moray.

★★★

B&B

Roadside Cottage Bed + Breakfast

Tomnavoulin, Ballindalloch, Banffshire, AB37 9JL
Tel/Fax:01807 590486

Traditional stone built cottage situated in this beautiful Highland glen in the heart of malt whisky country. Warm and friendly welcome, a relaxed atmosphere, real fires. Home cooking with fresh local produce. Children and pets welcome. Excellent base for walking the Speyside Way; lots of local walks and cycling trails on the Crown Estate.

1 Single	2 Shared fac	B&B per person	Open Jan-Dec
1 Double		from £16.00 Single	BB & Eve.Meal
1 Family		from £16.00 Double	from £26.00
		from £10.00 Room Only	

Huntly, Aberdeenshire   Map Ref: 4F9

★★★

**GUEST
HOUSE**

Greenmount Guest House (Mrs E Manson)

43 Gordon Street, Huntly, Aberdeenshire, AB54 8EQ
Tel:01466 792482

c1854 town house with annexe. Friendly personal attention. Private parking. In town centre but quiet. On Castle and Whisky Trails, ideal touring base. Popular area for salmon and sea trout.

2 Single	4 En Suite fac	B&B per person	Open Jan-Dec excl
4 Twin	1 Priv.NOT ensuite	from £17.00 Single	Xmas/New Year
2 Family	1 Pub.Bath/Show	£17.00-20.00 Double	

Important: Prices stated are estimates and may be subject to amendments

by Huntly, Aberdeenshire — Map Ref: 4F9

★★★

B&B

Mrs Alice J Morrison
Haddoch Farm, by Huntly, Aberdeenshire, AB54 4SL
Tel:01466 711217
Email:alice.morrison@tinyworld.co.uk

1 Single	2 Priv.NOT ensuite	B&B per person	Open Apr-Oct
1 Double		from £17.00 Single	BB & Eve.Meal
1 Family		from £16.00 Double	from £26.00

Mixed stock/arable farm near River Deveron, on B9022, 3 miles (5kms) from Huntly and 15 miles (24kms) from coast. Fine views of countryside. Home cooking. Ideal touring base for castle and Whisky Trail. A warm welcome awaits you.

⊇ ⊒ ⊒ ✕ ⊒ ✂

C V

Inverurie, Aberdeenshire — Map Ref: 4G9

★★★★

B&B

Fridayhill B&B
Kinmuck, Inverurie, Aberdeenshire, AB51 0LY
Tel/Fax:01651 882252
Email:fergusmcgh@aol.com
Web:www.b-and-b-scotland.co.uk/fridayhill.htm

2 Double	1 En Suite fac	B&B per person	Open Jan-Dec
	1 Priv.Bath/Show	from £26.00 Double	

High standard of accommodation, with ensuite/private facilities. In rural surroundings, with fine views, yet within easy access to all amenities. Only 7 miles from Dyce airport. Roam in the beautiful garden with rockeries and fish pond, and watch the interesting variety of wild birds.

⊞ ⊞ P ⊒ ⊒ ✕ ⊒

⊞ V ⚲

by Inverurie, Aberdeenshire — Map Ref: 4G9

★★★

B&B

Broadsea (Mrs E Harper)
Burnhervie, Inverurie, Aberdeenshire, AB51 5LB
Tel:01467 681386
Email:elizharper@broadsea99.freeserve.co.uk

1 Family	All En Suite	B&B per person	Open Jan-Dec
		from £26.00 Single	BB & Eve.Meal
		£19.00-22.00 Double	from £32.00

Accommodation of a high standard on this family farm of 200 acres. Inverurie 5 miles. Aberdeen 20 miles. Bennachie is very close by. Ideally situated for Archaeolink, Castle and Whisky Trails. Evening meal by arrangement.

C 🐾 V ⚲

Keith, Banffshire — Map Ref: 4E8

★★★

GUEST HOUSE

The Haughs Farm Guest House
The Haughs, Keith, Banffshire, AB55 3QN
Tel/Fax:01542 882238
Email:jiwjackson@aol.com

1 Twin	All En Suite	B&B per person	Open Apr-Oct
1 Double		from £25.00 Single	
1 Family		from £19.00 Double	

Traditional farmhouse on 165 acre farm. Just off main road and near the town. On Whisky Trail. Many local sports including golf available at numerous courses.

⊞ ⊞ P ⊒ ✕ ⊒ (⊞

V ⚲

Scotland's National Booking and Information Line

Tel: 0845 22 55 121
visitscotland.com

VAT is shown at 17.5%: changes in this rate may affect prices.

Key to symbols is on back flap.

Lossiemouth, Moray — Map Ref: 4D7

★★★

B&B

Carmania
45 St Gerardine's Road, Lossiemouth, Moray
IV31 6JX
Tel:01343 812276

Modern detached bungalow with large garden. In residential area on south side of town centre. Within walking distance of beach, golf and bowling.

| 1 Twin | 1 En Suite fac | B&B per person | Open Apr-Oct |
| 1 Double | 1 Priv.Bath/Show | from £18.00 Double | |

Methlick, Aberdeenshire — Map Ref: 4G9

★★

B&B

Sunnybrae Farm
Gight, Methlick, Ellon, Aberdeenshire, AB41 7JA
Tel:01651 806456 Fax:01651 806456
Email:sunnybrae-farm@talk21.com

Comfortable accommodation on a working farm, in a quiet peaceful location with superb views. Close to Castle and Whisky Trails. Dogs welcome.

1 Single	2 En Suite fac	B&B per person	Open Jan-Dec
1 Twin		from £18.00 Single	
1 Double		from £18.00 Double	

Oldmeldrum, Aberdeenshire — Map Ref: 4G9

CROMLET HILL
SOUTH ROAD, OLDMELDRUM, ABERDEENSHIRE AB51 0AB
Telephone: 01651 872315   Fax: 01651 872164

A superb listed building overlooking *Bennachie* and the *Grampian Hills* beyond. Recently restored, the original features are retained inside and out and the house is furnished in sympathetic and luxurious style. Set in beautiful secluded gardens including a large Victorian conservatory. Private parking. Aberdeen city centre 30 minutes.

★★★★

B&B

Cromlet Hill Guest House
South Road, Oldmeldrum, Aberdeenshire, AB51 0AB
Tel:01651 872315 Fax:01651 872164

Spacious, elegant, Listed Georgian mansion, in large secluded gardens within conservation area. Airport 20 minutes. On the castle trail and close to many well known National Trust properties. Including Fyvie Castle, Haddo House and Pitmedden Gardens.

1 Twin	All En Suite	B&B per person	Open Jan-Dec excl
1 Double		from £30.00 Single	Xmas
1 Family		from £24.00 Double	

Scotland's National Booking and Information Line

Tel: 0845 22 55 121
visitscotland.com

Important: Prices stated are estimates and may be subject to amendments

Oldmeldrum, Aberdeenshire

Map Ref: 4G9

The Redgarth
Kirk Brae, Oldmeldrum, Aberdeenshire, AB51 0DJ
Tel:01651 872353
Email:redgarth1@aol.com

INN

Family run inn enjoying magnificent views of surrounding countryside.
Non-smoking rooms. Home cooking including vegetarian choices and a
selection of cask ales.

1 Twin	2 En Suite fac	B&B per person	Open Jan-Dec excl
2 Double	1 Pub.Bath/Show	from £45.00 Single	Xmas/New Year
		from £27.50 Double	

Peterhead, Aberdeenshire

Map Ref: 4H8

Carrick Guest House
16 Merchant Street, Peterhead, Aberdeenshire
AB42 1DU
Tel/Fax:01779 470610

GUEST
HOUSE

Comfortable accommodation, centrally situated for all amenities. Two
minutes walk from main shopping centre, harbour and beach.
Convenient for maritime museum, lighthouse museum and several
nearby golf courses. Certificate of Excellence.

1 Single	All En Suite	B&B per person	Open Jan-Dec excl
2 Twin		from £22.00 Single	Xmas/New Year
1 Double		from £22.00 Double	
2 Family			

Pond View B&B
Brucklay, Maud, Peterhead, AB42 4QN
Tel:01771 613675/07929 594168
Email:mhepburn@lineone.net
Web:www.pondview.uk

B&B

Our house is now six years old. Just one mile from the village of Maud,
15 mls from both Peterhead and Fraserburgh. Lovely picturesque view
surrounded by trees and a pond 100 yds down in field. On the National
Route, Number 1. Cycle.

1 Twin	Priv.Bathrrom	B&B per person	Open Jan-Dec
1 Double	En Suite fac	from £22.00 Single	
		from £20.00 Double	

by Peterhead, Aberdeenshire

Map Ref: 4H8

The Old Bank House
6 Abbey Street, Old Deer, Peterhead, Aberdeenshire
AB42 5LN
Tel:01771 623463
Email:linda.rhind@btinternet.com

B&B

Originally village Bank, now comfortable family home, tastefully
refurbished. In centre of quiet historic village, close to Aden Country
Park. Non-smoking. Peterhead 9 miles. High teas available.

1 Twin	All En Suite	B&B per person	Open Jan-Dec excl
1 Double		£22.00-25.00 Single	Xmas/New Year
		£20.00-22.00 Double	

nr Portsoy, Aberdeenshire

Map Ref: 4F7

Academy House
School Road, Fordyce, Aberdeenshire, AB45 2SJ
Tel:01261 842743
Email:academy_house@hotmail.com
Web:www.fordyceaccommodation.com

B&B

Scottish hospitality in stylish country home set in beautiful conservation
village. Quality cooking with local produce. Well located for touring. 2
miles from Portsoy.

1 Twin	1 En Suite fac	B&B per person	Open Jan-Dec excl
1 Double	1 Pub.Bath/Show	from £28.00 Single	Xmas/New Year
		from £24.00 Double	BB & Eve.Meal
			from £37.00

VAT is shown at 17.5%: changes in this rate may affect prices.

Key to symbols is on back flap.

| Stonehaven, Kincardineshire | | | | Map Ref: 4G11 |

B&B

4 Urie Crescent
Stonehaven, Kincardineshire, AB39 2DY
Tel:01569 762220

Victorian semi-detached house in a quiet residential area at the top of the town. Easy walking distance of town centre and eating places. Stonehaven is well known for its picturesque harbour, and the magnificent site of Dunottar Castle.

1 Single
1 Double
1 Family

1 Priv.NOT ensuite

B&B per person
from £18.00 Single
from £18.00 Double
from £16.00 Room Only

Open Jan-Dec excl Xmas/New Year

GUEST HOUSE

Alexander Guest House
36 Arduthie Road, Stonehaven, Kincardineshire AB39 2DP
Tel:01569 762265   Fax:0870 1391045
Email:marion@alexanderguesthouse.com
Web:www.alexanderguesthouse.com

Family run guest house situated five minutes walk from town centre, beach, stonebuilt harbour, restaurant and shops. TV lounge, license, and some ensuite rooms available. Non-smoking household.

2 Single
2 Double
3 Family

5 En Suite fac
2 Priv.NOT ensuite

B&B per person
£20.00-30.00 Single
£20.00-30.00 Double

Open Jan-Dec excl Xmas/New Year

★★★★

B&B

Dunnottar Mains Farmhouse
Dunnotter Mains Farm, Stonehaven, Kincardineshire AB39 2TL
Tel/Fax:01569 762621
Email:dunnottar@ecosse.net
Web:www.dunnottarmains.co.uk

Traditional farmhouse welcome at this working farm, overlooking Dunnottar Castle on the coast.

2 Double

Some En Suite

B&B per person
from £24.00 Single
£20.00-£22.00 Double

Open Apr-Oct

B&B

Tewel Farmhouse
Tewel Farm, Stonehaven, Kincardineshire, AB39 3UU
Tel:01569 762306   Fax:01569 760386
Mobile: 07815 167404

Traditional farmhouse in quiet location on the outskirts of Stonehaven. With lovely views of surrounding countryside, on Auchenblae Road.

1 Dbl/Fam
1 Twin

All En Suite

B&B per person
from £23.00 Single
from £20.00 Double

Open Jan-Dec

GUEST HOUSE

Woodside of Glasslaw
Stonehaven, AB39 3XQ
Tel/Fax:01569 763799
Email:douton@globalnet.co.uk
Web:www.woodsideofglasslaw.co.uk

Modern bungalow in rural setting, yet within easy access of main routes and Deeside. Ample parking. All rooms ensuite. Warm welcome assured.

1 Single
2 Twin
2 Double
1 Family

All En Suite

B&B per person
from £22.00 Single
from £20.00 Double

Open Jan-Dec

Important: Prices stated are estimates and may be subject to amendments

Strathdon, Aberdeenshire
Map Ref: 4E10

★★★

B&B

Buchaam Farmhouse Bed+Breakfast
Strathdon, Aberdeenshire, AB36 8TN
Tel/Fax:01975 651238
Email:e.ogg@talk21.com

1 Twin	2 Pub.Bath/Show	B&B per person from £17.00	Open Apr-Oct
1 Double			
1 Family			

Large farmhouse on 600 acre mixed farm with sporting facilities, including badminton, table tennis (June-September only) and putting green. Free river fishing.

P ⊁ ◄

C ♿

★★

SMALL HOTEL

The Colquhonnie Hotel
Strathdon, Aberdeenshire, AB36 8UN
Tel:019756 51210
Email:mail@colquhonnie.co.uk
Web:www.colquhonnie-hotel.co.uk

1 Single	7 En Suite fac	B&B per person	Open Jan-Dec
1 Twin	1 Pub.Bath/Show	from £30.00 Single	BB & Eve.Meal
4 Double		from £27.50 Double	from £35.00
2 Family		from £23.50 Room Only	

The 200-year-old Colquhonnie Hotel in Strathdon overlooks the Aberdeenshire Don Valley from a South facing elevated site. This friendly hotel offers 7 ensuite rooms and a family suite with private bathroom. Children are very welcome and have outdoor adventure play area to entertain them.

TV 🛁 🛁 P 🍵 ⊁ 🍽 🎦 🍷

C 🚭 V

Tomintoul, Banffshire
Map Ref: 4D10

★★★

B&B

Auchriachan Farmhouse
Mains of Auchriachan, Tomintoul
Ballindalloch, Banffshire, AB37 9EQ
Tel:01807 580416
Email:irene.duffus@btinternet.com
Web:www.auchriachan.btinternet.co.uk

1 Twin	2 En Suite fac	B&B per person	Open Jan-Dec excl
1 Double	1 Priv.Bath/Show	£20.00-25.00 Single	Xmas
1 Family		£16.00-18.00 Double	

Traditional farmhouse 1 mile (2kms), from Tomintoul village. Ideal for outdoor activities, including skiing, Whisky and Castle Trails. One ground floor bedroom.

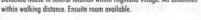
TV 🛁 P 🍵 🏹 ⊁ ◄

C 🐕 W V ♿

★★★

B&B

Bracam House B&B
32 Main Street, Tomintoul, Ballindalloch, AB37 9EX
Tel/Fax:01807 580278
Email:camerontomintoul@compuserve.com
Web:www.aplacetostay.uk

1 Single	1 En Suite fac	B&B per person	Open Jan-Dec
1 Twin	1 Priv.NOT ensuite	from £15.00 Single	
1 Double		from £16.00 Double	

Detached house in central location within Highland village. All amenities within walking distance. Ensuite room available.

TV 🛁 P 🍵 ⊁ ◄

C 🐕 W V

Scotland's National Booking and Information Line

Tel: 0845 22 55 121
visitscotland.com

VAT is shown at 17.5%: changes in this rate may affect prices.

Key to symbols is on back flap.

Tomintoul, Banffshire

Map Ref: 4D10

★★

B&B

Croughly Farmhouse
Tomintoul, Banffshire, AB37 9EN
Tel/Fax:01807 580476
Email:johnannecroughlyf@tinyworld.co.uk

18th century listed farmhouse, overlooking the River Conglass with
stunning views of the Cairngorms. 2 miles (3kms) from Tomintoul.

| 1 Family | All En Suite
1 Pub.Bath/Show | B&B per person
from £20.00 Single
from £18.00 Double | Open Apr-Oct |

★★★★

B&B

Findron Farm
Tomintoul, Ballindalloch, AB37 9ER
Tel/Fax:01807 580382
Email:elmaturner@talk21.com
Web:www.findronfarmhouse.co.uk

Comfortable farmhouse on working farm with new conservatory dining
area and offering a warm and friendly welcome, situated 1 mile (2 kms)
from Tomintoul. 4 miles (7 km) from the Lecht ski-slopes.

| 1 Twin
1 Double
1 Family | 2 En Suite fac
1 Pub.Bath/Show | B&B per person
£16.00-18.00 Single
£16.00-18.00 Double | Open Jan-Dec excl
Xmas/New Year |

★★

B&B

Livet House
34 Main Street, Tomintoul, Banffshire, AB37 9EX
Tel:01807 580205
Email:michele@livetcottage.co.uk
Web:www.tghh.ukgateway.net/page6.html

Family run accommodation in the centre of Tomintoul. One of the oldest
houses in the village, shop which specialises in whisky next door. The
Lecht and whisky trails can all be easily accessed. Walking, mountain
biking, fishing all nearby. Plenty of eating places within a short walking
distance.

| 2 Twin
2 Double
2 Family | 1 En Suite fac
1 Priv.NOT ensuite | B&B per person
from £18.00 Single
from £16.00 Double | Open Jan-Dec |

by Turriff, Aberdeenshire

Map Ref: 4F8

★★

B&B

Lower Plaidy
by Turriff, Aberdeenshire, AB53 5RJ
Tel:01888 551679 Fax:01888 551747
Email:lowplaidy@aol.com
Web:www.lowerplaidy.co.uk

Traditional working farm. Certificate of excellence holder assuring a
warm welcome. Convenient for castle, whisky and coastal trails with golf
courses, beaches and marine aquarium nearby, on the national cycle
route (Sustran). 7 miles south of Banff and 4 miles north of Turriff.

| 1 Single
1 Twin
1 Double | | B&B per person
from £18.00 Single
from £18.00 Double
from £15.00 Room
Only | Open Jan-Dec excl
Xmas/New Year |

Scotland's National Booking
and Information Line

Tel: 0845 22 55 121
visitscotland.com

Important: Prices stated are estimates and may be subject to amendments

Welcome to Scotland

The Highlands and Skye

Scenic variety is the keynote in this area – from the soaring craggy heights of Glencoe to the wide-skies and glittering lochans of the flow country of Caithness in the north. East-west contrasts are just as spectacular. This area takes in both the sunny, sandy shores of the inner Moray Firth around Nairn, with its coastal links golf courses, and the dazzling white beaches around Morar in the west, with the small isles filling the horizon.

Cuillins, Isle of Skye

With the Torridon mountains, Kintail and the peaks of Sutherland all adding to the spectacle, this area has more than simply scenic grandeur. There are substantial towns with everything for the visitor and the city of Inverness, sometimes called 'the capital of the Highlands' is a natural gateway to the northlands. At the western end of the Great Glen is Fort William, in the shadow of Britain's highest mountain, Ben Nevis.

This town is another busy location, a natural route centre and meeting place with a whole range of facilities and attractions.

The eastern seaboard also has plenty of interesting towns: picturesque Cromarty, with the air of an old-time Scottish burgh, Dornoch with its cathedral and famous championship golf course. Tain with Glenmorangie Distillery on its outskirts. Helmsdale with its evocation of Highland life in the Timespan Heritage Centre and Art Gallery. Further north, Wick and Thurso are major centres.

The Highlands and Skye

Steam train on the viaduct near Glenfinnan

The Highlands and Skye

Loch Torridon, Wester Ross

The Isle of Skye is famed for the spectacle of the Cuillin Hills with their craggy ridges offering a serious climbing challenge. However, there are plenty of less active pursuits. Armadale Castle and the Museum of the Isles, Dunvegan Castle and the Aros Experience all tell the fascinating story of the island.

Events
The Highlands and Skye

25-26 JANUARY
Sled Dog Rally, Aviemore
Teams of sled dogs compete in timed trials.
Tel: 01908 609796
www.siberianhuskyclub.com

22 FEBRUARY – 15 MARCH
Inverness Music Festival
Tel: 01463 716616

5-8 MAY*
Highland Golf Classic
Tel: 01292 293040
www.scottishgolfclassics.com

23 MAY – 7 JUNE
Highland Festival
Music, theatre, visual arts, dance and street events to celebrate Highland culture.
Tel: 01463 711112
www.highland-festival.co.uk

24-30 MAY
Wake Up To Birds Week
Royal Society for the Protection of Birds. Wide range of events and activities at the 60 RSPB reserves across Scotland. Free entry to all reserves on one day during this week.
Tel: 0131 311 6500
www.rspb.org.uk/scotland

16-20 JUNE*
Caithness Golf Classic
Tel: 01292 293040
www.scottishgolfclassics.com

21-26 JULY*
Inverness Tattoo
A spectacular display of pipe band music and more.
Tel: 01463 242915

6 AUGUST
Skye Highland Games, Portree
Traditional Highland Games and 3 day piping competition commencing on the 4th August.
Tel: 01463 612540
www.highlandgames.community.skye.co.uk

19-23 SEPTEMBER
Skye and Lochalsh Food Festival
Tel: 01599 534999
www.skyefood.co.uk

EARLY OCTOBER
Highland Food and Drink Festival, various venues, Highlands
A celebration of local produce.
www.highlandfeast.co.uk

* denotes provisional date. Events can be subject to change, please check before travelling.

For up to date events, log on to:
visitscotland.com

Area Tourist Boards
The Highlands and Skye

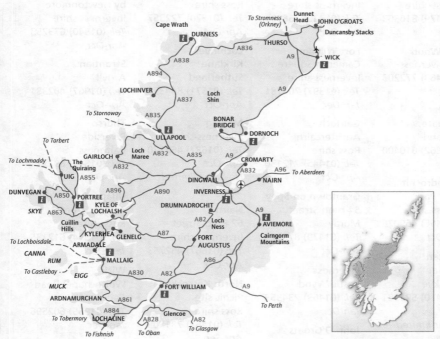

To Stromness (Orkney)
Dunnet Head
JOHN O'GROATS
Duncansby Stacks
Cape Wrath
DURNESS
THURSO
A836
A9
WICK
A838
A894
A9
LOCHINVER
A837
Loch Shin
BONAR BRIDGE
A835
DORNOCH
To Stornoway
ULLAPOOL
Loch Maree
A832
A835
A9
CROMARTY
To Tarbert
GAIRLOCH
A832
A832
A96
To Aberdeen
To Lochmaddy
The Quiraing
UIG
A855
A896
A890
DINGWALL
INVERNESS
NAIRN
DUNVEGAN
A850
PORTREE
DRUMNADROCHIT
A9
SKYE
A863
KYLE OF LOCHALSH
A82
Loch Ness
AVIEMORE
Cuillin Hills
KYLERHEA
GLENELG
A87
FORT AUGUSTUS
Cairngorm Mountains
To Lochboisdale
ARMADALE
CANNA
RUM
MALLAIG
A86
A9
To Castlebay
EIGG
A830
A82
MUCK
ARDNAMURCHAN
A861
FORT WILLIAM
To Perth
A884
Glencoe
To Tobermory
LOCHALINE
A828
A82
To Glasgow
To Fishnish
To Oban

The Highlands of Scotland Tourist Board
Peffery House
Strathpeffer
Ross-shire
IV14 9HA

Tel: 0845 22 55 121
Fax: 01506 832 222
E-mail: info@visitscotland.com
www.highlandfreedom.com

Tourist Information Centres
The Highlands and Skye

**The Highlands of
Scotland Tourist
Board**

Aviemore
Grampian Road
Inverness-shire
Tel: (01479) 810363
Jan-Dec

Daviot Wood
A9 by Inverness
Tel: (01463) 772203
Apr-Oct

Dornoch
The Square
Sutherland
Tel: (01862) 810400
Jan-Dec

Drumnadrochit
The Car Park
Inverness-shire
Tel: (01456) 459076
Easter-Oct

Dunvegan
2 Lochside
Isle of Skye
Tel: (01470) 521581
Apr-Oct
*Nov-Mar limited
opening*

Durness
Sango
Sutherland
Tel: (01971) 511259
Jan-Dec
*Oct-Mar Mon-Fri
only*

Fort Augustus
Car Park
Inverness-shire
Tel: (01320) 366367
Apr-Oct

Fort William
Cameron Square
Inverness-shire
Tel: (01397) 703781
Jan-Dec

Gairloch
Auchtercairn
Ross-shire
Tel: (01445) 712130
Apr-Oct

Grantown on Spey
54 High Street
Moray
Tel: (01479) 872773
Apr-Oct

Inverness
Castle Wynd
Tel: (01463) 234353
Jan-Dec

John O'Groats
County Road
Caithness
Tel: (01955) 611373
Apr-Oct

Kilchoan
Pier Road
Argyll
Tel: (01972) 510222
Easter-Oct

Lochcarron
Main Street
Ross-shire
Tel: (01520) 722357
Apr-Oct

Lochinver
Kirklane
Sutherland
Tel: (01571) 844330
Apr-Oct

Mallaig
Inverness-shire
Tel: (01687) 462170
Apr-Oct
*Nov-Mar limited
opening*

Nairn
62 King Street
Inverness-shire
Tel: (01667) 452753
Apr-Oct

North Kessock
Picnic site
Ross-shire
Tel: (01463) 731505
Apr-Sep

Portree
Bayfield House
Bayfield Road
Isle of Skye
Tel: (01478) 612137
Jan-Dec

Ralia
A9 Northbound
by Newtonmore
Inverness-shire
Tel: (01540) 673253
Apr-Oct

Strontian
Argyll
Tel: (01967) 402381
Apr-Oct

Thurso
Riverside
Caithness
Tel: (01847) 892371
Apr-Oct

Ullapool
Argyle Street
Ross-shire
Tel: (01854) 612135
Jan-Dec

Wick
Whitechapel Road
Caithness
Tel: (01955) 602596
Jan-Dec

Scotland's National Booking and Information Line
0845 22 55 121

Alness, Ross-shire
Map Ref: 4B7

★★★

B&B

Averon Bank Cottages B&B
Ardross Road, Alness, Ross-shire, IV17 0QA
Tel:01349 882392

3 Twin	All En Suite	B&B per person	Open Jan-Dec
	1 Priv.NOT ensuite	from £25.00 Single	
		from £23.00 Double	

Detached cottage with a private garden area, on the edge of Alness. It provides comfortable accommodation, whether for just a short stay or for a longer break, and is an ideal base for day trips to the North and West Highlands, as well as the coastal towns and villages of the area. This is a no smoking house.

Ardgay, Sutherland
Map Ref: 4A6

★★

B&B

B&B
Corvost, Ardgay, Sutherland, IV24 3BP
Tel/Fax:01863 755317

1 Single	1 Bathroom Wc	B&B per person	Open Jan-Dec excl
1 Twin	1 Shower Wc	from £15.00 Single	Xmas/New Year
1 Double		from £15.00 Double	BB & Eve.Meal
			from £22.00

Set in a beautiful and historical Highland Strath, this modern bungalow on working croft is homely and central for touring. Golfing, fishing, hillwalking and birdwatching all available in area.

Ardnamurchan, Argyll
Map Ref: 3E12

Feorag House
Glenborrodale, Acharacle, Argyll PH36 4JP
Tel: 01972 500248 Fax: 01972 500285
e.mail: admin@feorag.co.uk
Web: www.feorag.co.uk

Feorag House, a haven of comfort, peace, warmth, good food and good friends located in the village of Glenborrodale on the Ardnamurchan Peninsula, the most westerly point of mainland Britain. Set amongst 13 acres of private grounds and only 50 yards from the secluded shoreline, the house enjoys breathtaking views from all ensuite rooms.
The excellent cuisine is a sheer delight using mostly local produce. Most activities are readily available with fishing, walking, stalking, sailing and golf all close by. Wildlife abounds from otters, seals and porpoise to pinemartens, wildcats, red deer and golden eagles.

1997 THISTLE AWARD WINNER
The perfect relaxing holiday.

★★★★★

**GUEST
HOUSE**

●●●●
**HOME
COOKING**

Feorag House
Glenborrodale, Acharacle, Argyll, PH36 4JP
Tel:01972 500248 Fax:01972 500285
Email:admin@feorag.co.uk
Web:www.feorag.co.uk

1 Twin	All En Suite	DB&B per person	Open Jan-Dec
2 Double		£69.00	

Delightful country house on the shores of Loch Sunart. Peace and tranquility, warm and friendly atmosphere with imaginative cuisine. Ideal central location for exploring Ardnamurchan. Unlicensed, but you are welcome to bring your own wine.

VAT is shown at 17.5%: changes in this rate may affect prices.

Key to symbols is on back flap.

Arisaig, Inverness-shire — Map Ref: 3F11

★★★
B&B

Leven House Bed+Breakfast
Borrodale, Arisaig, Inverness-shire, PH39 4NR
Tel:01687 450238
Email:ejmacmillan@aol.com
Web:www.thelevenhouse.co.uk

Recently built modern, family home offering two comfortable ensuite bedrooms with TV's and tea-trays. Situated in peaceful setting just off the A830 road to the isles. Lovely beaches within a short stroll, ideal for relaxing break or as a base for walking, driving or sailing to the small isles of Eigg, Muck, Rhum. Scenic 9-hole golf-course only 6 miles.

2 Family	All En Suite	B&B per person from £30.00 Single from £22.00 Double	Open Jan-Dec excl Xmas/New Year

Aultbea, Ross-shire — Map Ref: 3F6

★★★★
GUEST HOUSE

Cartmel
Birchburn Road, Aultbea, Ross-shire, IV22 2HZ
Tel:01445 731375
Email:margaretm@cartmelguesthouse.com
Web:www.cartmelguesthouse.com

Comfortable bungalow guest house set in 1.5 acres of mature garden. Personally run. Evening meals by prior arrangement and vegetarians very welcome. Regret no smoking.

2 Twin 2 Double	2 En Suite fac	B&B per person from £26.00 Single £21.00-25.00 Double	Open Mar-Oct BB & Eve.Meal from £34.00-38.00

★★★★
GUEST HOUSE

Mellondale Guest House
47 Mellon Charles, Aultbea, Ross-shire, IV22 2JL
Tel/Fax:01445 731326
Email:mellondale@lineone.net
Web:www.mellondale.co.uk

Comfortable family guest house set in 4 acres, with open views of Loch Ewe. 9 miles (14.4 Kms) from Inverewe Gardens. Ideal walking centre.

2 Twin 2 Double	All En Suite 1 Pub.Bath/Show	B&B per person from £24.00 Double	Open Feb-Nov BB & Eve.Meal from £38.00

★★★
B&B

Tranquility
21 Mellon Charles, Aultbea, Ross-shire, IV22 2JN
Tel/Fax:01445 731241

Small comfortable family home surrounded by open croftland and with superb views over the Torridons and The Minches. Tea and biscuits on arrival. Evening meals available. Private parking. Birdwatching, walking, fishing all close by. Peace and quiet on the spot. Close to Inverewe gardens .

1 Single 1 Double 1 Family	2 En Suite fac 1 Priv.Bath/Show	B&B per person from £20.00 Single from £20.00 Double	Open Jan-Dec excl Xmas/New Year

Aviemore, Inverness-shire — Map Ref: 4C10

★★★
HOTEL

Aviemore Inn
Aviemore, Inverness-shire, PH22 1PH
Tel:01479 811811   Fax:01479 811309
Email:reservations_coylumbridge@hilton.com
Web:www.hilton.com

Situated in the heart of the Aviemore Centre, this modern hotel offers comfortable accommodation.

52 Twin 10 Double	All En Suite		Open Jan-Dec BB & Eve.Meal from £39.00-59.00

Important: Prices stated are estimates and may be subject to amendments

Aviemore, Inverness-shire | Map Ref: 4C10

CAIRN EILRIG

Mrs Mary Ferguson, Cairn Eilrig, Glenmore, Aviemore PH22 1QU
Telephone: 01479 861223 e.mail: mary@cairneilrig.fsnet.co.uk

Warm welcome in this small peaceful bed and breakfast situated in Glenmore Forest Park. Ideal base for exploring, walking, ski-ing, water sports, bird watching and relaxing. Tea/coffee and biscuits available in conservatory which provides panoramic views of the Cairngorms as do the bedrooms. Funicular Railway/Ski-lifts – two miles.

★★★

B&B

Cairn Eilrig
Glenmore, Aviemore, Inverness-shire, PH22 1QU
Tel:01479 861223
Email:mary@cairneilrig.fsnet.co.uk

Cairn Eilrig is situated just behind Cairngorm Reindeer Centre, in Glenmore Forest Park with superb open views of the Cairngorms. Warm Highland hospitality guaranteed. Ski lifts 2 miles (3 kms).

1 Twin	1 Shared Bthrm
1 Family/	
Double	

B&B per person
from £18.00 Single
from £18.00 Double

Open Jan-Dec

★★

GUEST HOUSE

Cairngorm Guest House
Grampian Road, Aviemore, Inverness-shire, PH22 1RP
Tel/Fax:01479 810630
Email:conns@lineone.net
Web:www.aviemore.co.uk/cairngormguesthouse

Peter and Gail welcome you to our lovely Victorian House, 5 min walk from centre.

3 Twin	All En Suite
5 Double	1 Pub.Bath/Show
1 Family	

B&B per person
£20.00-32.00 Single
£20.00-28.00 Double

Open Jan-Dec

★★★

B&B

Dunroamin Bed+Breakfast
Craig-Na-Gower Avenue, Aviemore, PH22 1RW
Tel:01479 810698
Email:lorraine.sheffield@virgin.net

Family run bed and breakfast accommodation close to the centre of Aviemore. Many activities and attractions in the area, to keep the whole family occupied: walking, cycling, golf, play areas and much more.

1 Double	All En Suite
2 Family	

B&B per person
from £20.00 Single
from £18.00 Double

Open Jan-Dec

VAT is shown at 17.5%: changes in this rate may affect prices. | Key to symbols is on back flap.

ERISKAY

Craig-na-Gower, Aviemore PH22 1RW
Tel: 01479 810717 Fax: 01479 812312
e.mail: eriskay@cali.co.uk

Eriskay is situated within the village of Aviemore and offers quiet comfortable en suite accommodation. Ideal for walking, bird-watching, cycling, pony trekking and touring. With its friendly and relaxed atmosphere Eriskay is the perfect base for winter and summer pursuits.

★★★★

B&B

Eriskay

Craig-na-Gower Avenue, Aviemore, Inverness-shire
PH22 1RW
Tel:01479 810717 Fax:01479 812312
Email:eriskay@cali.co.uk

Situated in quiet location only a short walk from all of Aviemore's extensive facilities. A comfortable and friendly place to stay.

1 Twin	All En Suite	B&B per person
2 Double		£25.00-30.00 Single
		£20.00-25.00 Double

Open Jan-Dec

★★★

B&B

Junipers

5 Dellmhor, Aviemore, Inverness-shire, PH22 1QW
Tel:01479 810405 Fax:01479 812850
Email:junipers@dellmhor.fsnet.co.uk

Comfortable home with large sun room and Alpine garden, midway between Aviemore and Coylumbridge.

1 Twin	1 En Suite fac	B&B per person
1 Double	1 Priv.NOT ensuite	from £20.00 Single
2 Family		from £18.00 Double

Open Jan-Dec

★★

GUEST
HOUSE

Kinapol Guest House

Dalfaber Road, Aviemore, PH22 1PY
Tel/Fax:01479 810513
Email:kinapol@ecosse.net
Web:www.aviemore.co.uk/kinapol

Friendly welcome at modern house, set in large garden with views of Cairngorms. Quiet location but only 5 minutes walk to the town centre.

1 Twin	2 Priv.NOT ensuite	B&B per person
1 Double		from £18.00 Single
1 Family		from £16.00 Double
		from £10.00 Room
		Only

Open Jan-Dec

Scotland's National Booking and Information Line

Tel: 0845 22 55 121
visitscotland.com

Important: Prices stated are estimates and may be subject to amendments

Aviemore, Inverness-shire   Map Ref: 4C10

★★

INN

Mackenzies Highland Inn
125 Grampian Road, Aviemore, PH22 1RL
Tel:01479 810672 Fax:01479 810595
Email:mackhotel@aol.com

'Mackenzies' is the ideal base to sample all that the Highlands and the
Strathspey valley have to offer, with friendly and helpful staff to make
your stay one you'll never forget.

4 Twin	All En Suite	B&B per person	Open Jan-Dec excl
4 Double		from £20.00 Double	Xmas
			BB & Eve.Meal
			from £35.00

★★

GUEST HOUSE

Ravenscraig Guest House
141 Grampian Road, Aviemore, Inverness-shire PH22 1RP
Tel:01479 810278 Fax:01479 810210
Email:ravenscrg@aol.com
Web:www.aviemoreonline.com

Ravenscraig is centrally located, close to all Aviemore's amenities and
bus/rail links. All rooms recently refurbished some with magnificent
views over the Cairngorm Mountains. We also offer ground floor rooms
in the garden annexe. A great base for exploring the beauty of the
Highlands or discovering the many attractions and activities here on our
doorstep.

1 Single	All En Suite	B&B per person	Open Jan-Dec
4 Twin		from £20.00 Single	
5 Double		from £20.00 Double	
2 Family			

VERMONT GUEST HOUSE
Grampian Road, Aviemore, Inverness-shire PH22 1RP
Tel: 01479 810470 e.mail: vermont@amserve.net
Located in the heart of Aviemore the ideal base to tour
The Highlands. Most rooms have en-suite, TV and
hospitality trays. Full Scottish breakfast and friendly
atmosphere. Car parking at rear of house. Five minute walk to
restaurants and hotels. Payphone in hallway.

★★

GUEST HOUSE

Vermont Guest House
Grampian Road, Aviemore, PH22 1RP
Tel:01479 810470
Email:vermont@amserve.net

Situated in centre of Aviemore, all bedrooms with some en suite facilities.
Ideally placed for touring Spey Valley, and access to Cairngorm ski area.

2 Twin	3 En Suite fac	B&B per person	Open Jan-Dec
3 Double	1 Priv.NOT ensuite	from £17.00 Double	
1 Family	1 Pub.Bath/Show		

★★★

B&B

Waverley Bed + Breakfast
35 Strathspey Avenue, Aviemore, Inverness-shire
PH22 1SN
Tel:01479 811226
Email:maggie.fraser@talk21.com

Bungalow situated in quiet cul-de-sac within easy access to all of towns
amenities. Accommodation all on one level.

1 Twin	Priv. Bath/Show	B&B per person	Open Jan-Dec
1 Double	En Suite	£22.00-25.00 Single	
		£18.00-22.00 Double	

VAT is shown at 17.5%: changes in this rate may affect prices. | *Key to symbols is on back flap.*

Ballachulish, Argyll | Map Ref: 1F1

Ballachulish Home Farm ★★★★
BALLACHULISH, ARGYLL PH49 4JX
B&B

A warm welcome awaits you at our modern farmhouse, situated on an elevated site amid naturally wooded parkland, giving a sense of peace and quietness. Accommodation includes 2 rooms - 1 twin, 1 double, all ensuite, bright spacious lounge, separate dining room and drying facilities. Very central for touring West Highlands. Newly built 9 hole golf course (par 68) on farm.

For details contact Mrs J McLauchlan. Tel/Fax: 01855 811792.

★★★★

B&B

Ballachulish Home Farm

Ballachulish, Argyll, PH49 4JX
Tel/Fax:01855 811792
Web:www.host.co.uk

1 Twin	All En Suite	B&B per person	Open Apr-Oct
1 Double		from £30.00 Single	
		from £25.00 Double	

New, traditional style farmhouse, situated on an elevated site amid naturally wooded parkland, giving a sense of peace and quietness. Open view across Loch Leven. Non-smoking house with large spacious bedrooms. Newly built nine hole pay-and-play golf course and club house on farm.

★★★

GUEST HOUSE

Craiglinnhe House

Lettermore, Ballachulish, Argyll, PH49 4JD
Tel/Fax:01855 811270
Email:info@craiglinnhe.co.uk
Web:www.craiglinnhe.co.uk

2 Twin	All En Suite	B&B per person	Open Feb-Dec
3 Double		from £22.00 Double	BB & Eve.Meal
			from £37.00

Lochside Victorian villa amid spectacular mountain scenery offering period charm with modern comfort. Warm, friendly atmosphere, good food and wine. Ideal base for exploring the Western Highlands.

FERN VILLA GUEST HOUSE
Loanfern, Ballachulish, Argyll PH49 4JE
Telephone: 01855 811393 Fax: 01855 811727
e.mail: BB4@fernvilla.com Web: www.fernvilla.com

A welcoming drink on arrival refreshes you as you start what should be a memorable stay. All rooms en-suite. Comfortable guest lounge. Home made Natural Cooking of Scotland menus. Fine wines and malts. Weekly rates available. Non-smoking. AA ◆◆◆◆. For walking, climbing, touring, relaxing - **The perfect base for the great outdoors.**

★★★

GUEST HOUSE

Fern Villa Guest House

Loanfern, Ballachulish, PH49 4JE
Tel:01855 811393 Fax:01855 811727
Email:bb4@fernvilla.com
Web:www.fernvilla.com

2 Twin	All En Suite	B&B per person	Open Jan-Dec
3 Double		from £23.00 Double	BB & Eve.Meal
			from £35.00

A warm welcome awaits you in this fine Victorian granite built house in the lochside village amidst spectacular scenery. One mile from Glencoe, convenient for Fort William. Home baking and Natural Cook of Scotland features on our dinner menu. Table licence. The perfect base for walking, climbing or touring in the West Highlands. Private parking.

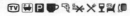

Ballachulish, Argyll
Map Ref: 1F1

Riverside House
East Laroch, Ballachulish, Argyll, PH49 4JE
Tel/Fax:01855 811473

Modern family house, in quiet location in centre of village. 1 mile from
Glencoe, 15 miles (24 kms) from Fort William. Ideal base for touring and
outdoor pursuits. Some bedrooms with view over our garden to the loch
and surrounding area. Spacious lounge with TV and video for wet days.
Ample private parking. Within walking distance of village centre, hotel,
pub, bus-stop etc. Two bedrooms ensuite. Non-smoking house.

★★★ B&B

1 Twin, 2 Double | 2 En Suite fac, 1 Pub.Bath/Show | B&B per person £18.00-20.00 Double | Open Easter-Oct

Beauly, Inverness-shire
Map Ref: 4A8

Cruachan
Wester Balblair, Beauly, IV4 7BQ
Tel:01463 782479 Fax:01463 783574
Email:isabella679@aol.com

Comfortable Bed & Breakfast in quiet location yet within easy reach of
Beauly and its restaurants, shops and walks. 10 miles from Inverness
convenient for Glen Affric and touring the Highlands.

★★★ B&B

2 Double | All En Suite | B&B per person £16.00-18.00 Single | Open Jan-Dec excl Xmas/New Year

Mrs MacKay
Ellangowan, Croyard Road, Beauly, IV4 7DJ
Tel:01463 782273

Comfortable, centrally heated home near Priory. Ideal base for touring
the Highlands of Scotland and Great Glen. A short walk to Beauly's
shops, banks and restaurants. Off road parking.

★★ B&B

1 Twin, 1 Double, 1 Family | Some En Suite, 1 Priv.NOT ensuite | B&B per person £14.00-18.00 Double | Open Apr-Oct

Rheindown Farm Holidays
Rheindown, Beauly, Inverness-shire, IV4 7AB
Tel:01463 782461

Farmhouse on working farm, in elevated position overlooking Beauly
and the Firth beyond.

★★ B&B

1 Double, 1 Family | 1 Priv.NOT ensuite | B&B per person from £17.00 Single from £15.50 Double | Open Mar-Nov

by Beauly, Inverness-shire
Map Ref: 4A8

Broomhill
Kiltarlity, Beauly, Inverness-shire, IV4 7JH
Tel:01463 741447 Fax:01463 741773
Email:broomhill@cali.co.uk
Web:www.cali.co.uk/freeway/broomhill

Edwardian manse set in own grounds surrounded by open countryside 11
miles (18kms) from Inverness & 4 miles (6km) from Loch Ness. Large,
warm comfortable rooms. Award-winning home cooking. Ideal touring
base for the Highlands. Prices remain the same throughout the year.

★★★ B&B

1 Twin, 1 Double | 1 Priv.NOT ensuite | B&B per person from £15.00 Single from £15.00 Double | Open Jan-Dec excl Xmas/New Year BB & Eve.Meal from £23.00

VAT is shown at 17.5%: changes in this rate may affect prices. Key to symbols is on back flap.

Boat of Garten, Inverness-shire	Map Ref: 4C10

★★★

GUEST HOUSE

Avingormack Guest House
Boat of Garten, Inverness-shire, PH24 3BT
Tel:01479 831614   Fax:01479 831344
Email:avin.gormack@ukgateway.net
Web:www.scotland2000.com/avingormack

Rural guest house, 4 miles from Aviemore with stunning views. Within easy reach of all attractions. Award winning traditional and vegetarian breakfasts.

1 Twin   2 En Suite
2 Double
1 Family

B&B per person
from £21.00 Double

Open Jan-Dec

★★★

B&B

Burnside
Drumuillie, Boat of Garten, Inverness-shire
PH24 3BX
Tel/Fax:01479 831396
Email:anne@burnside-scotland.co.uk

Comfortable 108 year old modernised detached house, set back from A95 5 miles (8km) from Aviemore. Ideal for touring Spey Valley. Magnificent open views to front.

1 Single   1 Pub Bath/Show
1 Twin

B&B per person
from £15.00 Single
from £15.00 Double
from £10.00 Room
Only

Open Jan-Dec

★★★★

B&B

Chapelton Steading Bed + Breakfast, Mrs Smyth
Boat of Garten, Inverness-shire, PH24 3BU
Tel:01479 831327
Email:chapelton@btinternet.com
Web:www.boatofgarten.com/chapelton

This converted and extended barn comfortably accommodates 6 guests and features privacy and independence. Handcrafted furnishings, a log fire, home-baking, interesting collections of books and paintings all add to the friendly atmosphere of this family home. The rural setting and traditional country garden are enhanced by the views to the Cairngorm mountains.

1 Twin   All En Suite
2 Double

B&B per person
from £28.00 Single
from £23.00 Double

Open Mar-Oct

★★★

GUEST HOUSE

Granlea Guest House
Deshar Road, Boat of Garten, PH24 3BN
Tel:01479 831601
Email:dixon@granlea.freeserve.co.uk
Web:www.granlea.freeserve.co.uk

Stone built Edwardian house, in village centre, close to Osprey reserve and golf course. Ideal touring base. Evening meal by arrangement.

1 Twin   Some En Suite
2 Double   1 Priv.NOT ensuite
1 Family

B&B per person
from £22.00 Single
from £22.00 Double

Open Jan-Dec excl
Xmas/New Year
BB & Eve.Meal
from £36.00

Scotland's National Booking and Information Line

Tel: 0845 22 55 121
visitscotland.com

Important: Prices stated are estimates and may be subject to amendments

Boat of Garten, Inverness-shire — Map Ref: 4C10

MOORFIELD HOUSE

"Great place, Great food .... Great!!!" KB. UK
"This has been our best B&B experience! Thanks" EJQ. USA
"Wish you were closer, we'd move in for good." PW. UK

Deshar Road, Boat of Garten, Inverness-shire PH24 3BN   Tel: 01479 831646
e.mail: enquiries@moorfieldhouse.com Web: www.moorfieldhouse.com

★★★★

GUEST HOUSE

Moorfield House

Deshar Road, Boat of Garten, Inverness-shire PH24 3BN
Tel:01479 831646
Email:enquiries@moorfieldhouse.com
Web:www.moorfieldhouse.com

Informality is the key to this luxuriously furnished Victorian house.
Ideally suited to those seeking relaxed and peaceful surroundings. A
friendly welcome, comfortable beds and a hearty breakfast await. Fully
non smoking. Evening meal by arrangement.

2 Twin	All En Suite	B&B per person	Open Mar-Oct
4 Double		from £31.00 Single	
		from £25.00 Double	

Brackla, Loch Ness-side, Inverness-shire — Map Ref: 4A9

★★★

HOTEL

Loch Ness Clansman Hotel

Brackla, Loch Ness Side, Inverness-shire, IV3 8LA
Tel:01456 450326 Fax:01456 450845
Email:lochnessclansman@aol.com
Web:www.lochnessclansman.com

Family run hotel situated on the west shores of Loch Ness. 9 miles from
Inverness, and 4 miles from Drumnadrochit. Wheelchair access to all
public areas. Many attractions within 90 minutes drive, including the Isle
of Skye and the Whisky Trail. Historic Sites such as Culloden Battlefield
and Cawdor Castle, plus numerous Golf courses. Short break packages
available, whether you are travelling by plane, train or by car.

2 Single	All En Suite	B&B per person	Open Jan-Dec excl
3 Twin		from £39.50 Single	Xmas
14 Double		from £29.50 Double	BB & Eve.Meal
4 Family		from £25.00 Room	from £39.00
		Only	

Brora, Sutherland — Map Ref: 4C6

AR DACHAIDH
BADNELLAN, BRORA, SUTHERLAND KW9 6NQ

Tel / Fax: 01408 621658 e.mail: badnellan@madasafish.com
Web: http://www.robbins-associates.co.uk/brora/

Traditional croft house in quiet crofting area. Ideal stop for
touring the whole of the north. Ideal location for walking,
birdwatching, golf, fishing, cycling, motorcycling or just sitting on
the miles of quiet beaches. Home cooked meals a speciality.
Treat yourself to a romantic stay in a four poster bed.

★★

B&B

Ar Dachaidh

Badnellan, Brora, Sutherland, KW9 6NQ
Tel/Fax:01408 621658
Email:badnellan@madasafish.com
Web:www.robbins-associates.co.uk/brora/

Traditional 19c croft house, very quietly situated behind the village of
Brora. Friendly welcome, home cooked evening meals, B&B Certificate of
Excellence. Motorcycle friendly.

1 Single	1 Priv.NOT ensuite	B&B per person	Open Mar-Nov
1 Twin		from £17.50 Single	BB & Eve.Meal
1 Double		from £17.50 Double	from £27.50

VAT is shown at 17.5%: changes in this rate may affect prices.   **Key to symbols is on back flap.**

Brora, Sutherland   Map Ref: 4C6

★★

B&B

Clynelish Farm (Mrs J Ballantyne)
Brora, Sutherland, KW9 6LR
Tel/Fax:01408 621265
Email:jane@clynelish.fsnet.co.uk

1 Twin   2 En Suite fac   B&B per person   Open Easter-Oct
2 Double   1 Pub.Bath/Show   £20.00-25.00 Single
                               £18.00-22.50 Double

Listed house circa 1865 on family run working livestock farm in quiet
location about a mile (2kms) from Brora and beaches. Golfing and
fishing available locally. Open Easter to October or by arrangement.

GLENAVERON   AA ♦♦♦♦♦

Golf Road, Brora, Sutherland KW9 6QS
Tel/Fax: 01408 621601
e.mail: glenaveron@hotmail.com   Web: www.glenaveron.co.uk
Glenaveron is a luxurious Edwardian house with extensive mature gardens.
Only a short walk to Brora golf club and lovely beaches. A 25 minute drive
to the Royal Dornoch golf club. An ideal base for touring The Northern
Highlands and Orkney. All rooms are en-suite. Non smoking.

★★★★

B&B

Glenaveron
Golf Road, Brora, Sutherland, KW9 6QS
Tel/Fax:01408 621601
Email:glenaveron@hotmail.com Web:www.glenaveron.co.uk

1 Twin   All En Suite   B&B per person   Open Jan-Dec excl
1 Double   from £28.00 Single   Xmas/New Year
1 Family   from £26.00 Double

Spacious stone built family home, set in mature gardens, in a peaceful
area of Brora. A few minutes walk from the golf course; several others,
including Royal Dornoch in the area. Other sporting and leisure facilities
nearby, as are sandy beaches, historic sites, eating establishments.
Excellent base for exploring the far north of Scotland; ideal stopover en
route to Orkney.

★★★

B&B

Rockpool Guest House
Rosslyn Street, Brora, Sutherland, KW9 6NY
Tel/Fax:01408 621505
Email:ghrockpool@netscape.net

1 Single   2 Priv.NOT ensuite B&B per person   BB & Eve.Meal
1 Twin   £20.00-22.00 Single   from £37.00-40.00
2 Double   £22.00-25.00 Double

Heather and Graham have restored this traditional stone built house to a
warm cosy and stylish Bed & Breakfast home. Enthusiastic hospitality,
evening meals by arrangement and a very comfortable TV lounge with
Sky Channels. Salmon and sea trout available on the Brora River behind,
with golf and sea fishing packages available.

★★★★

B&B

Tigh Fada
18 Golf Road, Brora, Sutherland, KW9 6QS
Tel/Fax:01408 621332
Email:clarkson@tighfada.fsnet.co.uk
Web:www.tighfada.fsnet.co.uk

2 Twin   1 En Suite fac   B&B per person   Open Jan-Dec excl
1 Double   2 Priv.Bath/Show from £25.00 Single   Xmas/New Year
                             £20.00-25.00 Double

Fine sea views and open peat fires, home baking and a real Highland
welcome. Ideal half way house between Inverness and John O'Groats, or
if catching a ferry to Orkney. Why not stay longer and visit Dunrobin
Castle, the Timespan Heritage Centre, or go fishing or golfing. Explore
beautiful Sutherland, and take a day trip to the rugged West Coast.

Important: Prices stated are estimates and may be subject to amendments

Carrbridge, Inverness-shire

Map Ref: 4C9

★★★
B&B

Birchwood
12 Rowan Park, Carrbridge, PH23 3BE
Tel/Fax:01479 841393
Email:normanwhitehall@lineone.net
Web:www.carrbridge.com

Modern bungalow in quiet Highland village, warm welcome assured.
Ideal base for touring, bird watching, hillwalking and cycling.

1 Twin	1 En Suite fac	B&B per person	Open Jan-Dec excl
1 Double	1 Pub.Bath/Show	from £19.00 Single	Xmas/New Year
		from £19.50 Dbl.ens	
		from £17.50 Twin	

★★★
INN

The Cairn Hotel
Carrbridge, Inverness-shire, PH23 3AS
Tel:01479 841212   Fax:01479 841362
Email:cairn.carrbridge@lineone.net
Web:www.smoothhound.co.uk/hotels/cairnhotel.html

Enjoy the country pub atmosphere, log fire, malt whiskies, real ales and
affordable food in this family owned village centre hotel. Close to the
historic bridge a perfect base for touring the Cairngorms, Whisky Trail
and Loch Ness.

2 Single	4 En Suite fac	B&B per person	Open Jan-Dec
1 Twin		from £19.00 Single	
2 Double		from £22.00 Double	
2 Family			

★★★
GUEST HOUSE

Craigellachie Guest House
Main Street, Carrbridge, Inverness-shire, PH23 3AS
Tel/Fax:01479 841641
Email:e.pedersen@virgin.net

Craigellachie provides quiet and relaxing accommodation in the centre of
this Highland Village. Dinners are available using fresh produce;
alternatively there is a choice of eating establishments within walking
distance. Excellent base for bird watching, cycling or walking trips, or just
unwinding in front of a real fire.

1 Single	3 En Suite fac	B&B per person	Open Jan-Dec
2 Twin	2 Shared/Public	from £17.00 Single	BB & Eve.Meal
2 Double		from £17.00 Double	from £30.00
2 Family			

Cawdor, Nairnshire

Map Ref: 4C8

★★★
B&B

Cawdor Stores & Post Office
West End House, Cawdor, Nairn, IV12 5XP
Tel:01667 404201

A delightful traditional stone built family house at the heart of this quiet
highland village. Comfortable accommodation and excellent Scottish
breakfast

2 Double	1 Pub.Bath/Show	B&B per person	Open May-Sep
		from £25.00 Single	
		from £22.50 Double	

★★★
B&B

Fairview
Balinrait, Cawdor, Inverness-shire, IV12 5QY
Tel:01667 404459 Fax:01667 454382
Email:irislapham@aol.com

Spacious, attractive bungalow situated in rural setting overlooking open
countryside. Close to Cawdor Castle, and lovely woodland walks. Culloden
Moor and Fort George close by.

1 Twin	Priv.fac	B&B per person	Open Jan-Dec excl
1 Family	Ensuite	from £20.00 Single	Xmas/New Year
		from £18.00 Double	
		from £12.00 Room	
		Only	

VAT is shown at 17.5%: changes in this rate may affect prices.

Key to symbols is on back flap.

Contin, Ross-shire | Map Ref: 4A8

Hideaway B&B

Contact: Mrs Janet Greathead
Hideaway, Craigdarroch Drive, Contin, Ross-shire IV14 9EL
Telephone/Fax: 01997 421127 e.mail: hideaway@bushinternet.com
Web: www.visithideaway.co.uk

Hideaway rests beside a peaceful tree-lined driveway in an area where well stocked trout lochs, forest walks and mountain scenery abound. The central location is perfect for exploring the Northern Highlands. A warm welcome and good food await you in our comfortable home.

★★★

B&B

Hideaway B&B
Craigdarroch Drive, Contin, Ross-shire, IV14 9EL
Tel/Fax:01997 421127
Email:hideaway@bushinternet.com
Web:www.visithideaway.co.uk

Modern bungalow in quiet setting, one mile from Contin village. Near to Falls of Rogie. Centrally situated for touring the Northern Highlands. Good base for bird watching, walking or just relaxing.

1 Twin	All En Suite	B&B per person	Open Jan-Dec excl
2 Double		£18.00 Single	Xmas/New Year
		£16.00 Double	

★★★★

B&B

Nayrendah
Craigdarroch Drive, Contin, by Strathpeffer
Ross-shire, IV14 9EL
Tel/Fax:01997 421408
Email:nayrendah@amserve.net
Web:www.SmoothHound.co.uk/hotels/nayrendah.html

Comfortable, en-suite accommodation in modern detached bungalow in an attractive woodland setting. Close to Contin and the Victorian spa town of Strathpeffer incorporating the Museum of Childhood. Plenty to see and do. Inverness only 18 miles distance.

1 Twin	All En Suite	B&B per person	Open Jan-Dec
1 Double		£16.00-20.00 Single	
		£15.00-18.00 Double	

Corpach, by Fort William, Inverness-shire | Map Ref: 3G12

★★★

GUEST HOUSE

The Neuk
Corpach, Fort William, Inverness-shire, PH33 7LR
Tel:01397 772244

A warm friendly welcome awaits you at this detached villa on Mallaig road (A830) with panoramic views over the Mamore Mountains, Ben Nevis and Loch Linnhe. Within few mins walk of Canal Bank and Neptunes Staircase. Evening meals by arrangement. Ideal base for touring surrounding area or walking, cycling and skiing. Featured in Scotland's essential guide to the high roads.

1 Single	4 En Suite fac	B&B per person	Open Jan-Dec excl
1 Twin		from £30.00 Single	New Year
1 Double		from £20.00 Double	BB & Eve.Meal
2 Family			from £34.00

Important: Prices stated are estimates and may be subject to amendments

---

Cromarty, Ross-shire   Map Ref: 4B7

★★★★

B&B

Beechfield House

4 Urquhart Court, Cromarty, Ross-shire, IV11 8YD
Tel/Fax:01381 600308
Email:faericketts@btinternet.com

Built with guests comfort in mind, this large modern house with a
conservatory and garden is situated on the outskirts of the lovely 18c
town of Cromarty. Off street parking, non smoking house, credit cards
accepted. Activities available in the area include golfing, walking and
dolphin watching trips.

1 Twin	All En Suite	B&B per person	Open Mar-Oct
1 Double		from £25.00 Single	
1 Family		from £20.00 Double	

---

by Cromarty, Ross-shire   Map Ref: 4B7

★★★★

B&B

Newfield

Newhall Bridge, Poyntzfield, by Dingwall, IV7 8LQ
Tel:01381 610325
Email:jean.munro@tesco.net
Web:www.newfield-bb.co.uk

Comfortable bed & breakfast in a traditional cottage set amidst peaceful
farming country on the Black Isle. 18 miles from Inverness and 6 miles to
Cromarty. An ideal location for touring the East, North and West Coast of
the Highlands. Udale Bay Bird Sanctuary 1 mile away. Dolphin trips
available at Cromarty and Avoch.

1 Single	1 En Suite fac	B&B per person	Open Feb-Nov
1 Double	1 Pub.Bath/Show	from £20.00 Single	
1 Family		from £20.00 Double	

---

nr Cromarty, Ross-shire   Map Ref: 4B7

Braelangwell House

Balblair, Ross-shire IV7 8LT
Tel: 01381 610353 Fax: 01381 610467
e.mail: Braelangwell@btinternet.com
Web: www.btinternet.com/~braelangwell

A fine Georgian house of the late 18th-century situated
in fifty acres of beech woodland and gardens including
the original walled garden where you can play croquet
on the lawn. Choose from three bedrooms –
The Garden Room, a double room with a four poster
bed; The Chinese Room, another double bed;
The Henrietta Room with twin beds. All rooms have
an ensuite or private bathroom, television, radio and
tea/coffee making facilities. Enjoy breakfast in the
elegant diningroom and relax in the library,
conservatory or upstairs hall with lovely views over the
garden to the Cromarty Firth.

★★★★

B&B

Braelangwell House

Balblair, by Dingwall, Ross-shire, IV7 8LT
Tel:01381 610353   Fax:01381 610467
Email:braelangwell@btinternet.com
Web:www.btinternet.com/~braelangwell

Fine Georgian house dating from the late 18th Century, situated in 5
acres of garden and 50 acres of woodland. 7 miles from Cromarty.
Convenient for road and air links from the south. Ideal base for
exploring the northern Highlands.

1 Twin	1 En Suite fac	B&B per person	Open Mar-Oct
2 Double	2 Pub.Bath/Show	from £35.00 Single	
		from £25.00 Double	

VAT is shown at 17.5%: changes in this rate may affect prices.   **Key to symbols is on back flap.**

Culloden Moor, Inverness-shire — Map Ref: 4B8

★★★

B&B

Bayview
West Hill, Inverness, IV2 5BP
Tel/Fax:01463 790386
Email:bayview.guest@lineone.net
Web:www.bayviewguest.com

Quiet, comfortable house in pleasant country surroundings with
magnificent views over the Moray Firth. Evening meals by arrangement,
home cooking. Two nights or more.

1 Twin	2 En Suite fac	B&B per person	Open Apr-Oct
2 Double	1 Pub.Bath/Show	from £22.00 Double	BB & Eve.Meal
			from £32.00

★★★

B&B

Culdoich Farm
Culloden Moor, Inverness, IV2 5EL
Tel:01463 790268

18c farmhouse built the year after the Battle of Culloden on mixed
arable and livestock farm. On hillside near Culloden Battlefield and
Clava Stones. Home baking always available.

1 Family	1 Shared.Bath	B&B per person	Open May-Nov
1 Dbl/Twn	1 Pub.Toilet	from £20.00 Single	
		from £18.00 Double	

★★

B&B

Westhill House
Westhill, Inverness, IV2 5BP
Tel:01463 793225 Fax:01463 792503
Email:j.honnor@bigfoot.com
Web:www.scotland-info.co.uk/westhill.htm

Set in lovely rural surroundings, this modern family home offers
traditional Bed & Breakfast accommodation resting within its own
peaceful grounds and pretty garden. 1 mile from historic Culloden
Battlefield and a central base to explore Inverness, Loch Ness and the
Highlands. Approx 3 miles to rail station and 5 miles to airport.

1 Single	Some En Suite	B&B per person	Open Mar-Nov
1 Twin	1 Pub.Bath/Show	£18.00-22.00 Single	
1 Family		from £20.00 Double	

Dalcross, by Inverness, Inverness-shire — Map Ref: 4B8

★★★★

B&B

Easter Dalziel Farmhouse
Easter Dalziel Farm, Dalcross, Inverness, IV2 7JL
Tel/Fax:01667 462213
Email:stb@easterdalzielfarm.co.uk
Web:www.easterdalzielfarm.co.uk

Bob and Margaret invite you to stay in our Victorian farmhouse home
with beautiful gardens on stock/arable farm. Panoramic views to open
countryside, friendly atmosphere, log fire in lounge and home baking.
Inverness 7 miles (11 kms). Culloden 5 miles (8 kms). Evening meals by
prior arrangement.

1 Twin	2 Pub.Bath/Show	B&B per person	Open Jan-Dec excl
2 Double		from £18.00 Double	Xmas/New Year
			BB & Eve.Meal
			from £30.00

Dingwall, Ross-shire — Map Ref: 4A8

★★★★

B&B

Averon House
Wester Toberchurn, Culbokie, by Dingwall
Ross-shire, IV7 8LS
Tel/Fax:01349 877179
Email:averon@lineone.com
Web:www.smoothhound.co.uk/hotels/averonhouse

Set into the hillside above the Cromarty Firth, Averon House commands
excellent views of the Firth and the hills and mountains beyond. Quiet
peaceful location, yet within 10 minutes of the A9, providing easy access
to Inverness and for touring the Highlands.

1 Twin	All En Suite	B&B per person	Open Feb-Nov
1 Double		from £20.00 Double	
1 Family			

Important: Prices stated are estimates and may be subject to amendments

Dornie, by Kyle of Lochalsh, Ross-shire   Map Ref: 3G9

Castle View

Upper Ardelve, By Dornie, Kyle of Lochalsh IV40 8EY
Telephone and Fax: 01599 555453
e.mail: rosemary@castleview-scotland.co.uk
Web: www.castleview-scotland.co.uk *or*
www.eileandonancastleview.co.uk

The countryside surrounding Eilean Donan Castle is of exceptional beauty and grandeur with magnificent mountain, loch and forest scenery. Rich in wildlife, the area offers fascinating rewards for observant nature lovers. There are otters, seals, wild goats and deer, whilst overhead may be seen buzzards, falcons and the magnificent golden eagle.

★★★

B&B

Castle View Bed+Breakfast

Upper Ardelve, By Dornie, Kyle of Lochalsh
Ross-shire, IV40 8EY
Tel/Fax:01599 555453
Email:rosemary@castleview-scotland.co.uk
Web:www.castleview-scotland.co.uk

Warm welcome assured in new croft house with breathtaking views to Eilean Donan Castle, Loch Duich and the Sisters of Kintail. Evening meal available by arrangement. Reserved for total non-smokers only.

1 Twin	All En Suite	B&B per person	Open Jan-Dec excl
2 Double		£23.00-25.00 Double	Xmas/New Year
			BB & Eve.Meal
			from £35.00-37.00

★★★

B&B

Fasgadale

2 Sallachy, Dornie, Kyle, Ross-shire, IV40 8DZ
Tel:01599 588238

Modern bungalow on working croft. An elevated position with views across Loch Long. Gaelic spoken.

1 Twin	1 Priv.NOT ensuite	B&B per person	Open Easter-Oct
1 Double		from £15.00 Single	
		from £15.00 Double	

★★★

B&B

Sealladh Mara

Ardelve, Dornie,by Kyle of Lochalsh, Ross-shire
IV40 8AY
Tel/Fax:01599 555250

Modern family home, looking over Loch Duich and Eilean Donan Castle towards Kintail mountains. Handy for touring to Skye and Wester Ross. Ideal for walking.

1 Twin	1 En Suite fac	B&B per person	Open Jan-Dec
2 Double		from £20.00 Single	
		from £16.00 Double	

Scotland's National Booking and Information Line

Tel: 0845 22 55 121
visitscotland.com

VAT is shown at 17.5%: changes in this rate may affect prices.

Key to symbols is on back flap.

Dornoch, Sutherland   Map Ref: 4B6

Auchlea

Mrs F Garvie, Auchlea, Dornoch IV25 3HY
Tel: 01862 811524   e.mail: fionamgarvie@yahoo.com
Web: www.milford.co.uk/go/auchlea.html
*Luxury bungalow with beautiful views of mountains and sea.
Accommodation 3 ensuite bedrooms, one with jacuzzi. Excellent evening
meals served in a warm friendly atmosphere. Cosy log fire in comfortable
lounge. One mile from historic cathedral town of Dornoch. Miles of
sandy beaches and Royal Dornoch golf course.*

★★★

B&B

●

**HOME
COOKING**

Auchlea Guest House
Auchlea, Dornoch, Sutherland, IV25 3HY
Tel:01862 811524
Email:fionamgarvie@yahoo.com
Web:www.milford.co.uk/go/auchlea.html

Purpose built bungalow set in a large garden with ample parking and beautiful
views of mountains and sea. Built in 1998, having accommodation comprising 3
en-suite bedrooms, one of which has a jacuzzi. Excellent evening meals cooked
on an Aga cooker in a warm and friendly atmosphere. Cosy log fire in
comfortable lounge. 1 mile from historic Cathedral town of Dornoch with miles of
sandy beaches as well as Royal Dornoch Golf Course.

3 Twin	All En Suite	B&B per person from £22.00 Single from £20.00 Double	Open Jan-Dec excl Xmas/New Year

---

★★★★

B&B

Hillview
Evelix Road, Dornoch, IV25 3RD
Tel:01862 810151
Email:hillviewbb@talk21.com

Hillview is a double fronted bungalow situated in rural woodland setting.
3 mins from Dornoch, double room with private bathroom & lounge.
Private parking. Dornoch boasts breathtaking walks & views nearby.
Award winning beach. Two golf courses one of which is a championship
course.

1 Double	1 Pub.Bath/Show	B&B per person from £24.00 Single from £20.00 Double	Open Jan-Dec

★★★★

HOTEL

●

RESTAURANT

The Royal Golf Hotel
1st Tee, Dornoch, Sutherland, IV25 3LG
Tel: 01667 458800 Fax: 01667 455267
E-mail: rooms@morton-hotels.com
Web: www.morton-hotels.com

Previously a family mansion, the hotel overlooks the golf course and the
Dornoch Firth. 5 minutes walk to town. Taste of Scotland. Special breaks
available. Local attractions include Dunrobin Castle, Falls of Shin,
Hunters of Brora, Dornoch Cathedral and gold panning.

5 Single 18 Twin 2 Double	All En Suite Suites avail	B&B per person from £89.00 Single from £55.50 Dbl/Twn	Open Jan-Dec

★★★

B&B

Tordarroch
Castle Street, Dornoch, Sutherland, IV25 3SN
Tel/Fax:01862 810855
Email:rose@tordarroch72.freeserve.co.uk

18th century town House, full of character, set in large enclosed gardens
in the centre of the historic Royal Burgh of Dornoch. Close to the
Cathedral, founded in the 13th Century. Royal Dornoch Golf Club and
sandy beaches nearby.

1 Single 1 Twin 1 Double	Some En Suite 1 Pub.Bath/Show	B&B per person from £20.00 Single from £21.00 Double	Open Easter-Nov

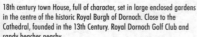

Important: Prices stated are estimates and may be subject to amendments

by Dornoch, Sutherland

Map Ref: 4B6

★★

B&B

Corven
Station Road, Embo, Dornoch, Sutherland, IV25 3PR
Tel:01862 810128 Mobile 07986 214823

1 Twin	1 En Suite fac	B&B per person	Open Mar-Oct
1 Double	1 Priv.NOT ensuite	from £20.00 Single	
		from £17.00 Double	

Small detached bungalow with fine views across the Golspie/Helmsdale Rogart, Dornoch Bay/Lochfleet to hills beyond. Sandy beaches and golf courses nearby. Non-smoking throughout. All rooms on one level.

Drumnadrochit, Inverness-shire

Map Ref: 4A9

★★★

B&B

Allanmore Farm
Drumnadrochit, Inverness-shire, IV63 6XE
Tel:01456 450247

1 Twin	1 Priv.NOT ensuite	B&B per person	Open Easter-Oct
2 Double		£17.00-18.00 Double	

16th Century farmhouse on stock and arable farm in peaceful setting. 10 minutes walk to village.

DRUMBUIE FARM

DRUMBUIE FARM, LOCH NESS-SIDE, DRUMNADROCHIT IV63 6XP
Telephone: 01456 450634 Fax: 01456 450595
e.mail: drumbuie@amserve.net
Custom built luxury farmhouse on working farm. Drumbuie sits on an elevated site overlooking Loch Ness and surrounding hills with spectacular views. The farm boasts a herd of "hairy" Highland cattle as well as sheep, lambs, other cattle breeds and also grows its own animal feeds. All rooms ensuite. Four poster bed. No smoking.

★★★★

B&B

Drumbuie Farm B&B
Loch Ness, Drumnadrochit, Inverness-shire IV63 6XP
Tel:01456 450634 Fax:01456 450595
Email:drumbuie@amserve.net
Web:www.lochnessfarmb&b.com

1 Twin	All En Suite	B&B per person	Open Jan-Dec
2 Double		from £19.00 Double	

Modern farmhouse, with all rooms ensuite, on an elevated site overlooking Loch Ness and surrounding farmland. Own herd of Highland cattle. Non-smoking household.

★★★

B&B

Gillyflowers
Drumnadrochit, Inverness-shire, IV63 6UJ
Tel/Fax:01456 450641
Email:gillyflowers@cali.co.uk
Web:www.cali.co.uk/freeway/gillyflowers

1 Twin	Some En Suite	B&B per person	Open Jan-Dec
2 Double		from £15.00 Double	

Renovated farmhouse of character and charm. Countryside location close to Loch Ness. Hospitality assured.

VAT is shown at 17.5%: changes in this rate may affect prices.

Key to symbols is on back flap.

Drumnadrochit, Inverness-shire | Map Ref: 4A9

GLEN ROWAN HOUSE
WEST LEWISTON, DRUMNADROCHIT IV63 6UW
Tel: 01456 450235 Fax: 01456 450817
e.mail: info@glenrowan.co.uk Web: www.glenrowan.co.uk

*Comfortable, friendly guest house in tranquil village setting close to Loch Ness,
Urquhart Castle and other tourist attractions. All accommodation appointed to a
high standard with guest lounge overlooking large riverside garden. Ideal location
for touring, walking, fishing or just relaxing. Ample off-road parking. Non-smoking,
no dogs (except guide/support dogs).*

**AWAITING
INSPECTION**

Glen Rowan House

West Lewiston, Drumnadrochit, Inverness-shire IV63 6UW
Tel:01456 450235 Fax:01456 450817
Email:info@glenrowan.co.uk
Web:www.glenrowan.co.uk

Modern house with large garden running down to river in a quiet village
by Loch Ness between Drumnadrochit and Urquhart Castle. Boat trips
and horse riding close by. Non-smoking establishment. Ample off road
parking. All rooms comfortably furnished with bedrooms on ground floor.
Evening meal by prior arrangement.

2 Twin	All En Suite	B&B per person	Open All Year
1 Double		from £25.00 Single	
		from £17.50 Double	

Kilmore Farmhouse
Drumnadrochit, Inverness-shire IV63 6UF
**Telephone: 01456 450524 e.mail: kilmorefarm@supanet.com
Web: www.olstravel.com/guest/kilmore/**

Modern, luxury custom-built family run farmhouse peacefully situated at walking
distance from Loch Ness. An ideal base for hillwalking and touring the Highlands.
All rooms are ground-floor and tastefully decorated. Guests' lounge with log fire.
A friendly and warm welcome and home cooking provides value for money.
Evening meal available. See Highland cattle.
Non-smoking. *Major credit cards accepted*

★★★★

B&B

Kilmore Farmhouse

Drumnadrochit, IV63 6UF
Tel:01456 450524
Email:kilmorefarm@supanet.com
Web:www.host.co.uk

Modern farmhouse peacefully situated with splendid views of
surrounding hills. Site of Special Scientific Interest. Highland Cattle.

2 Double	All En Suite	B&B per person	Open Jan-Dec
1 Family		from £18.00 Double	BB & Eve.Meal
			from £28.00

★★★

B&B

Westwood

Lower Balmacaan, Drumnadrochit, Loch Ness, IV63 6WU
Tel/Fax:01456 450826
Email:sandra@westwoodbb.freeserve.co.uk
Web:www.westwoodbb.freeserve.co.uk

Comfortable modern bungalow with beautiful views of the surrounding
hills. Quiet location in popular highland village. Loch Ness, Urquhart
Castle and the 'Nessie' exhibitions are close by. Westwood is the ideal
centre for exploring the highlands, high and low level hiking, or just
relaxing and enjoying our wonderful highland air.

1 Single	2 En Suite fac	B&B per person	Open Jan-Dec
1 Twin	1 Priv.NOT ensuite	from £18.00 Single	
1 Double		from £18.00 Double	

Important: Prices stated are estimates and may be subject to amendments

Drumnadrochit, Inverness-shire
Map Ref: 4A9

WOODLANDS

East Lewiston, Drumnadrochit, Inverness-shire IV63 6UJ
Tel/Fax: 01456 450356
e.mail: enquiry@woodlandsbandb.net Web: www.woodlandsbandb.net
A warm welcome awaits you in our modern, comfortable, non-smoking home
set in over an acre of garden with panoramic views of the surrounding hills.
Close to Loch Ness and Urquhart Castle. Ideally situated for touring the
Highlands and only 15 miles from Inverness.
Sorry no children.

★★★★

B&B

Woodlands

East Lewiston, Drumnadrochit, Inverness-shire IV63 6UJ
Tel/Fax:01456 450356
Email:enquiry@woodlandsbandb.net
Web:www.woodlandsbandb.net

Comfortable modern home, newly refurbished in peaceful location with
panoramic views of the surrounding hills. Non smoking establishment for
the comfort of our guests.

1 Twin	All En Suite	B&B per person	Open Mar-Nov
2 Double		from £30.00 Single	
		from £22.00 Double	

Dunbeath, Caithness
Map Ref: 4D4

TORMORE FARM

TORMORE FARM, DUNBEATH, CAITHNESS KW6 6EH
Telephone & Fax: 01593 731240
Comfortable friendly accommodation is offered on this family
cattle and sheep farm. Situated in beautiful location on the main
A9. Well situated for walking and birdwatching. Highland cattle on
view. Traditional farmhouse cooking. Tea and home baking
served on arrival and in evening.

★★

B&B

Tormore Farm

Dunbeath, Caithness, KW6 6EH
Tel/Fax:01593 731240

Warm Highland hospitality on this traditional working farm. Dinner
available on request. One ground floor bedroom. Extensive sea view
from the farm, clifftop walks, including varied bird species & especially
puffins.

1 Twin	1 Priv.NOT ensuite	B&B per person	Open May-Oct
1 Double	1 Pub.Bath/Show	from £17.00 Single	BB & Eve.Meal
1 Family		from £15.00 Double	from £23.00

Dundonnell, Ross-shire
Map Ref: 3G7

★★★

B&B

4 Camusnagaul

Dundonnell, by Garve, Ross-shire, IV23 2QT
Tel:01854 633237 Fax:01854 633382

Ideal for walkers and climbers, being close to the An Teallach Mountain
Range. Warm welcome assured on working croft.

1 Twin	Some En Suite	B&B per person	Open Jan-Dec
2 Double	1 Priv.NOT ensuite	from £17.00 Double	
1 Family			

VAT is shown at 17.5%: changes in this rate may affect prices. | *Key to symbols is on back flap.*

Dundonnell, Ross-shire   Map Ref: 3G7

BADRALLACH B&B
Croft 9, Badrallach, Dundonnell, Ross-shire IV23 2QP
Tel: 01854 633281
e.mail: michael.stott2@virgin.net Web: www.badrallach.com
Dinner bed and breakfast in the old byre with peat stove, gas lighting and crisp linen sheets is truly special. The tranquil lochshore location on this working croft overlooking Anteallach is magnificent. You can walk, sleep, boat, fish, view orchids, otters, porpoises, golden eagles or just do nothing.

★★★★

B&B

Badrallach B&B
Croft 9, Badrallach, Dundonnell, Ross-shire IV23 2QP
Tel:01854 633281
Email:michael.stott2@virgin.net
Web:www.badrallach.com

Traditional croft B&B in the Old Byre with peat stove, gas lighting, crisp linen sheets in a magnificent remote lochshore setting. Ullapool and Gairloch nearby.

1 Twin	All En Suite	B&B per person from £16.00 Single from £16.00 Double from £11.00 Room Only	Open Jul-Aug plus by appointment BB & Eve.Meal from £32.00

Durness, Sutherland   Map Ref: 4A3

★★

B&B

Orcadia (Bed + Breakfast)
Lerin, Durness, Sutherland, IV27 4QB
Tel:01971 511336   Fax:01971 511382
Email:morrison.orcadia@lineone.net

Bungalow offering comfortable accomodation with open views, and very close to famous Smoo caves. Ideal base for exploring the rugged North of Scotland, with its glorious beaches.

2 Double 1 Family	1 Priv.NOT ensuite	B&B per person £18.00-22.00 Single £16.00-18.00 Double	Open Jan-Dec excl Xmas/New Year

---

★★★

B&B

Puffin Cottage
Durness, Sutherland, IV27 4PN
Tel/Fax:01971 511208
Email:puffincottage@aol.com
Web:www.puffincottage.com

A friendly welcome awaits you at this comfortable cottage. En-suite room has sea views. Close to the village, yet in a quiet location. Golf course and beaches only a short distance away. Smoo Cave 2 miles away. Hillwalking, bird and wildlife in abundance.

2 Double	1 En Suite fac 1 Priv.NOT ensuite	B&B per person from £18.00 Double	Open Apr-Oct

Scotland's National Booking and Information Line

Tel: 0845 22 55 121
visitscotland.com

Important: Prices stated are estimates and may be subject to amendments

Durness, Sutherland

Map Ref: 4A3

★★★

B&B

Smoo Falls

Durness, Sutherland, IV27 4QA
Tel/Fax:01971 511228
Email:joey@smoofalls.com
Web:www.smoofalls.com

Extended croft house situated near to Smoo Cave. Ideal touring base for
Northern coast, its beaches, and its other attractions.

1 Twin	Ensuite	B&B per person	Open Apr-Oct
1 Twin	Pub Bath/Show	from £20.00 Double	
1 Double	Ensuite		
1 Family	Ensuite		

Fort Augustus, Inverness-shire

Map Ref: 4A10

★★★

B&B

Cartref

Fort William Road, Fort Augustus, Inverness-shire
PH32 4BH
Tel:01320 366255 Fax:01320 366782
Email:cartref@hotmail.com

Local stone built house situated in the village and with hotels and
restaurants close by. Within walking distance of Loch Ness and
Caledonian Canal. Ideal base for touring the Highlands and the Great
Glen.

1 Twin	1 En Suite fac	B&B per person	Open Mar-Nov
2 Double	2 Pub.Bath/Show	from £18.00 Double	

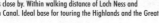

★★★

B&B

Lorien House

Station Road, Fort Augustus, Loch Ness, PH32 4AY
Tel:01320 366736 Fax:01320 366263
Email:lorienhouse@aol.com
Web:www.lochness-accommodation.co.uk

A luxurious home with views of Loch Ness in the centre of a picturesque
village right in the heart of the Highlands. Perfect touring base for Skye,
Ben Nevis, Aonach Mor ski range and Inverness. Ideal too for Great Glen
walk. Qualified alternative therapies available to help you unwind.

1 Twin	1 En Suite fac	B&B per person	Open Jan-Dec excl
1 Double		£20.00-30.00 Single	Xmas/New Year
1 Family		£20.00-25.00 Double	

★★★★

B&B

Sonas

Inverness Road, Fort Augustus, Inverness-shire PH32 4DH
Tel/Fax:01320 366291
Email:servicesonas@bushinternet.com
Web:www.nessaccom.co.uk/sonas

Comfortable modern house in elevated position on the northern edge of
the village, with excellent views of surrounding hills. Attractive garden
available for guests. Good parking.

1 Twin	All En Suite	B&B per person	Open Jan-Dec excl
1 Double		from £20.00 Single	Xmas/New Year
1 Family		from £15.00 Double	
		from £13.00 Room	
		Only	

★★★

B&B

Thistle Dubh

Auchterawe Road, Fort Augustus, Inverness-shire
PH32 4BN
Tel:01320 366380
Email:thistledubh@supanet.com

Very comfortable rooms in large modern home set in peaceful
surroundings on edge of natural woodlands. 10 minutes walk to village,
shops, restaurants and canal side.

1 Twin	All En Suite	B&B per person	Open Mar-Nov
2 Double		from £20.00 Single	
		from £20.00 Double	

VAT is shown at 17.5%: changes in this rate may affect prices.

Key to symbols is on back flap.

Fort Augustus, Inverness-shire   **Map Ref: 4A10**

TIGH NA MAIRI

Canalside, Fort Augustus PH32 4BA
Tel/Fax: 01320 366766
e.mail: suecallcutt@talk21.com

Situated on the bank of the Caledonian Canal, an ideal base for walking, cycling, touring or Nessie hunting! Alternatively, just relax and watch the boats and swans glide by. Heaven has a tough act to follow! A warm welcome awaits you.

★★

B&B

Tigh Na Mairi

Canalside, Fort Augustus, Inverness-shire
PH32 4BA
Tel/Fax:01320 366766
Email:suecallcutt@talk21.com

Detached traditional cottage with outstanding views on the banks of the Caledonian Canal. On the Great Glen cycle route, horseriding, canoeing and boat trips available locally. Vegetarians catered for.

1 Twin	1 Priv.NOT ensuite	B&B per person	Open Jan-Dec excl
2 Double		from £20.00 Single	Xmas
		from £18.00 Double	
		from £15.00 Room	
		Only	

Fort William, Inverness-shire   **Map Ref: 3H12**

Alt-An Lodge

Achintore Road, Fort William PH33 6RN Tel: 01397 704546
e.mail: altanlodge@bushinternet.com
Web: www.visitscotland.com

Quality accommodation enjoying superb location on the banks of Loch Linnhe. Ensuite rooms with loch/mountain views. Private parking. All facilities including hearty breakfast. Enjoy the picturesque 1 mile stroll to the town centre along the loch side. Ideal base for mountain walks or touring.
"A really nice place to stay".

★★★

B&B

Alt-An Lodge

Achintore Road, Fort William, Inverness-shire
PH33 6RN
Tel:01397 704546
Email:altanlodge@bushinternet.com

Comfortable en-suite / private accommodation in friendly B&B overlooking Loch Linnhe. Private parking. Traditional Scottish breakfast and hospitality awaits you.

| 1 Twin | 2 En Suite fac | B&B per person | Open Jan-Dec excl |
| 2 Double | 1 Priv.Bath/Show | from £18.00 Double | Xmas/New Year |

★★★★

B&B

Balcarres

Seafield Gardens, Fort William, Inverness-shire PH33 6RJ
Tel:01397 702377 Fax:01397 702232
Email:balcarres@btinternet.com
Web:www.scotland2000.com/balcarres

Modern newly-built family home in quiet area. Excellent views across the loch. Close to the town centre.

1 Twin	All En Suite	B&B per person	Open Jan-Dec
1 Double		from £21.00 Double	
1 Family			

Important: Prices stated are estimates and may be subject to amendments

Fort William, Inverness-shire | Map Ref: 3H12

Ben Nevis View
Station Road, Corpach, by Fort William
Inverness-shire, PH33 7JH Tel:01397 772131
Email:bennevisview@amserve.net
Web:www.bennevisview.co.uk

Modern house situated on the Road to The Isles near the beginning of
the Caledonian Canal. Only 3 miles from the centre of Fort William.
Beautiful view of Ben Nevis and surrounding hills. Ample private
parking. Local restaurants/pubs within walking distance. Comfortable
guests lounge with Sky tv.

★★★ B&B

1 Double   All En Suite   B&B per person   Open All Year
1 Family   £18.00-22.00 Double

BLYTHEDALE
SEAFIELD GARDENS, FORT WILLIAM, INVERNESS-SHIRE PH33 6RJ
TEL: 01397 705523
Modern detached villa situated 1 mile from Fort William town centre.
Train and bus stations nearby. Set back from main A82 road in quiet
surroundings. Guests enjoy fine views of Loch Linnhe and Ardgour Hills.
Comfortable well equipped rooms, all en-suite. Colour TVs,
private car parking. Guests lounge. Open all year.

Blythedale
Seafield Gardens, Fort William, Inverness-shire
PH33 6RJ
Tel:01397 705523

★★★★ B&B

Blythedale is a modern detached villa situated approx 1 mile from Fort
William town centre. Set back and above the main A82 road in quiet
surroundings. Guests enjoy a fine view of Loch Linnhe, Loch Eil and the
Ardgour Hills. Full Scottish breakfast and a separate lounge for guests to
relax in.

1 Twin   All En Suite   B&B per person   Open Jan-Dec
2 Double   from £25.00 Single
                         from £20.00 Double

Scotland's National Booking and Information Line

Tel: 0845 22 55 121
visitscotland.com

VAT is shown at 17.5%: changes in this rate may affect prices.   *Key to symbols is on back flap.*

Corrieview

Corrieview, Lochyside
Fort William PH33 7NX
Telephone: 01397 703608
e.mail: corrieview@hotmail.com
Traditional detached house in quiet
residential area close to all amenities. All
rooms with private facilities. Open views
of Ben Nevis range and Mamore
mountains. Well appointed and
comfortable rooms and residents lounge.
Ample private parking. Excellent base for
touring the Highlands of Scotland.

★★★

B&B

Corrieview
Lochyside, Fort William, PH33 7NX
Tel:01397 703608
Email:corrieview@hotmail.com

Detached family home in quiet residential area 2 miles (3kms) from Fort
William. Convenient for touring West Coast. Ideal base for walkers/skiers
and tourers. Ample off-street parking. Drying facilities available.

1 Twin	2 En Suite	B&B per person	Open Jan-Dec excl
2 Double	1 Priv.NOT En Suite	from £22.00 Single	Xmas/New Year
		from £18.00 Double	

**Scotland's National Booking
and Information Line**

**Tel: 0845 22 55 121
visitscotland.com**

"CROLINNHE"

"Crolinnhe", Grange Road, Fort William PH33 6JF
Telephone: 01397 702709 Fax: 01397 700506
e.mail: crolinnhe@yahoo.com
Web: www.crolinnhe.co.uk

Spoil yourself with the elegance of Crolinnhe where this grand Victorian house stands proudly overlooking Loch Linnhe. Relax in the tastefully furnished rooms where the attention to detail is clearly visible. Start the day with a varied menu for breakfast in the charming dining room overlooking the loch and the hills beyond. Relax on cooler evenings by log fire with complementary sherry. The town of Fort William is only a 10 minute walk away where you may shop, take a boat trip on Loch Linnhe and more. Ben Nevis, Scotland's highest peak, invites you to a challenging but attainable climb.

Prices from £37.50-£60.00 per person per night.

★★★★★

B&B

Crolinnhe

Grange Road, Fort William, PH33 6JF
Tel:01397 702709   Fax:01397 700506
Email:crolinnhe@yahoo.com
Web:www.crolinnhe.co.uk

Family run detached Victorian villa c1880, refurbished to a high standard. Friendly and welcoming atmosphere. Large colourful garden. Superb views. Short walk from town centre and all amenities.

1 Twin	All En Suite	B&B per person	Open Easter-Oct
2 Double		from £37.50 Double	

V

★★★★

GUEST HOUSE

Distillery House

Nevis-Bridge, Fort William, Inverness-shire PH33 6LR
Tel:01397 700103   Fax:01397 702980
Email:disthouse@aol.com
Web:www.fort-william.net/distillery-house

Distillery house at old Glenlochy Distillery in Fort William beside A82, road to the Isles. Situated at the entrance to Glen Nevis just 5 minutes from the town centre. Distillery House has been upgraded to high standards. Set in the extensive grounds of the Glenlochy Distillery with views over the River Nevis. All bedrooms are ensuite with TV, telephone and hospitality tray.

1 Single	All En Suite	B&B per person	Open Jan-Dec
2 Twin		from £25.00 Single	
3 Double		from £22.50 Double	
1 Family			

C £ W V

Fort William, Inverness-shire | Map Ref: 3H12

Glendevin

★★

B&B

Righ Crescent, Inchree, Onich, Fort William PH33 6SG
Tel:01855 821330 Fax:01855 821578
Email:info@glendevin.com
Web:www.glendevin.com

Comfortable and relaxing family home, situated between Fort William
and Glencoe. Quiet location, close to forest walks and the waterfalls at
Inchree.

1 Twin	1 En Suite fac	B&B per person	Open Jan-Dec
1 Double	2 Pub.Bath/Show	£20.00-26.00 Single	
1 Family		£38.00-46.00 Double	

Glenlochy Guest House

Nevis Bridge, Fort William,
Inverness-shire PH33 6PF
Telephone: 01397 702909
e.mail: glenlochy1@aol.com
Web: www.glenlochyguesthouse.co.uk
Situated in its own spacious grounds within
walking distance of town centre and Ben Nevis.
At entrance to Glen Nevis. Recommended by
"Which Best B&B Guide". Special rates for 3 or
more nights. Large private car park. 8 of 10
bedrooms are ensuite. Phone for reservation or
colour brochure. B&B from £18.

Glenlochy Guest House

★★★

**GUEST
HOUSE**

Nevis Bridge North Road, Fort William
Inverness-shire, PH33 6PF
Tel:01397 702909
Email:glenlochy1@aol.com
Web:www.glenlochyguesthouse.co.uk

Detached house with garden situated at Nevis Bridge, midway between
Ben Nevis and the town centre. 0.5 miles (1km) to railway station. 2
annexe rooms.

3 Twin	8 En Suite fac	B&B per person	Open Jan-Dec
5 Double	2 Priv.NOT ensuite	from £20.00 Single	
2 Family		from £18.00 Double	

Innishfree

★★★★

B&B

Lochyside, Fort William, PH33 7NX
Tel:01397 705471
Email:mburnsmaclean@aol.com
Web:www.innshfree.co.uk

A warm highland welcome awaits you at this modern detached house
with attractive landscaped garden located in quiet residential area.
Breakfast served in conservatory with panoramic views towards Ben Nevis
and Aonach Mor. All rooms ensuite with colour TV. Private parking. Ideal
base to explore the areas glens and lochs.

| 1 Double | 2 En Suite fac | B&B per person | Open Jan-Dec |
| 1 Family | | £19.00-25.00 Double | |

Important: Prices stated are estimates and may be subject to amendments

Fort William, Inverness-shire		Map Ref: 3H12

★★

B&B

Mrs E Kennedy
4 Perth Place, Fort William, Inverness-shire
PH33 6UL
Tel:01397 706118
Email:elzakennedy@aol.com

Detached house in quiet residential area with picturesque views over Loch Linnhe to the Ardgour Hills.

2 Double 1 Priv.NOT ensuite B&B per person £18.00-22.00 Single £16.00-18.00 Double Open Jan-Dec excl Xmas/New Year

★★

B&B

Kismet Villa
Heathercroft, Fort William, Inverness-shire
PH33 6RS
Tel:01397 703654
Email:kismetvilla@bushinternet.com

A warm welcome awaits you at our bed & breakfast 10 minutes walk from town centre. Comfortable bedrooms with tea trays and TVs. Walkers, skiers and tourers welcome. Ideal base for touring Fort William and Lochaber area. Ample private parking.

3 Twin 2 Priv.NOT ensuite B&B per person 1 Double from £16.00 Double Open Jan-Dec

LAWRIESTONE GUEST HOUSE

Achintore Road, Fort William,
Inverness-shire PH33 6RQ
Tel/Fax: 01397 700777
e.mail: susan@lawriestone.co.uk
Web: www.lawriestone.co.uk

Treat yourself to a break in this beautifully maintained fully refurbished elegant Victorian townhouse built in 1885. Situated in its own grounds only 5 minutes walk from the town centre, this family run guest house offers a high standard of accommodation, a friendly Scottish welcome and excellent Scottish breakfasts. Fort William is an ideal touring base with Oban, Mallaig, Isle of Skye, Inverness and Speyside all within easy reach for a day's outing. Non-smoking. Private car park. Sorry no pets.

★★★★

B&B

Lawriestone Guest House
Achintore Road, Fort William, Inverness-shire PH33 6RQ
Tel/Fax:01397 700777
Email:susan@lawriestone.co.uk
Web:www.lawriestone.co.uk

A warm welcome awaits you at Lawriestone. Our main concern is your comfort and well being. The beautifully furnished rooms are all en-suite with colour TV and tea/coffee making etc. At breakfast a varied selection, including Scottish or vegetarian breakfasts, is available. Come and experience our hospitality and our beautiful location by Loch Linnhe and surrounding hills. Walking, fishing, golf, skiing etc are available locally.

1 Twin All En Suite B&B per person 2 Double from £20.00 Double Open Jan-Dec excl Xmas/New Year

VAT is shown at 17.5%: changes in this rate may affect prices. | *Key to symbols is on back flap.* |

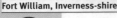
Fort William, Inverness-shire   **Map Ref: 3H12**

★★★

B&B

Leasona Bed + Breakfast
Torlundy, Fort William, PH33 6SW
Tel:01397 704661
Email:leasona@hotmail.com

Friendly, highland welcome awaits you in our modern family home.
Situated in a beautiful Glen setting with outstanding views of Ben Nevis
and Aonach Mor ski area. Only 2 1/2miles from Fort William town
centre. Excellent base for hill-walking, skiing, pony trekking and touring.
Private parking.

1 Twin	2 En Suite fac	B&B per person	Open Jan-Dec excl
2 Double	1 Pub.Bath/Show	£22.00-25.00 Single	Xmas/New Year
		£16.00-20.00 Double	

★★★★

GUEST HOUSE

Lochan Cottage Guest House
Lochyside, Fort William, Inverness-shire, PH33 7NX
Tel/Fax:01397 702695
Email:lochanco@supanet.com
Web:www.fortwilliam-guesthouse.co.uk

Lochan Cottage Guest House is situated in 1 acre of gardens with
panoramic views of Ben Nevis, the highest mountain in Great Britian,
and the ski slopes of Aonach Mor. Traditional Scottish, vegetarian or
continental breakfast is served in the bright conservatory. Relax over a
bottle of wine or a fine Scottish malt in our cosy lounge.

1 Twin	All En Suite	B&B per person
5 Double		from £25.00 Double

★★★

GUEST HOUSE

Lochview House
Heathercrfoft, Argyll Terrace, Fort William
Inverness-shire, PH33 6RE
Tel:01397 703149   Fax:01397 706138
Email:info@lochview.co.uk
Web:www.lochview.co.uk

Situated in a quiet, hillside location above the town giving panoramic
views over Loch Linnhe and the Ardgour Hills. Non-smoking house. Only
10 minutes walk from town centre. Ample private parking, Self catering
apartment also available.

1 Single	All En Suite	B&B per person	Open May-Sep
1 Twin		from £25.00 Single	
4 Double		from £20.00 Double	

Scotland's National Booking and Information Line

Tel: 0845 22 55 121
visitscotland.com

Important: Prices stated are estimates and may be subject to amendments

MELANTEE
ACHINTORE ROAD, FORT WILLIAM, INVERNESS-SHIRE PH33 6RW
TEL: 01397 705329 FAX: 01397 700453
E.MAIL: floracookmelantee@yahoo.co.uk

Melantee is a comfortable bungalow with picturesque views of Loch Linnhe and the Ardgour Hills. Situated only 1.5 miles south of Fort William town centre, it is near all local amenities, and makes an ideal base for touring the lochs, glens and surrounding highland area.

★★

B&B

Melantee

Achintore Road, Fort William, Inverness-shire
PH33 6RW
Tel:01397 705329 Fax:01397 700453

Bungalow 1.5 miles (3kms) from town centre, overlooking the shores of Loch Linnhe and the Ardgour hills and on the main A82 road.

1 Single	2 Pub Toilet/Show	B&B per person	Open Jan-Dec excl
1 Twin		from £16.50 Single	Xmas/New Year
1 Double		from £16.50 Double	
1 Family		from £14.00 Room Only	

★★★★

HOTEL

●

RESTAURANT

The Moorings Hotel

Banavie, Fort William, PH33 7LY
Tel:01397 772797 Fax:01397 772441
Email:reservations@moorings-fortwilliam.co.uk
Web:www.moorings-fortwilliam.co.uk

Privately owned hotel situated beside the Caledonian Canal and Neptune's Staircase. Many rooms have views of the Ben Nevis mountain range and canal locks. Meals are served in the restaurant, or in the Upper Deck, providing a good range of dining options, both formal and informal. Ten superior rooms with extra sized beds.

2 Single	All En Suite	B&B per person	Open Jan-Dec excl
5 Twin		£46.00-60.00 Single	Xmas
19 Double		£36.00-55.00 Double	BB & Eve.Meal
1 Family			from £59.00-78.00
1 Triple			

★★

HOTEL

Nevis Bank Hotel & Apartments

Belford Road, Fort William, Inverness-shire PH33 6BY
Tel:01397 705721 Fax:01397 706275
Email:info@nevisbankhotel.co.uk
Web:www.nevisbankhotel.co.uk

Privately owned hotel situated on A82 at Glen Nevis access road. Ideally situated for touring and business. Some annexe accommodation. Walkers and cyclists welcome (limited cycle storage space).

6 Single	All En Suite	B&B per person	Open Jan-Dec
10 Twin		from £30.00 Single	BB & Eve.Meal
16 Double		from £25.00 Double	from £35.00
5 Family		from £20.00 Room Only	

VAT is shown at 17.5%: changes in this rate may affect prices.   *Key to symbols is on back flap.*

Fort William, Inverness-shire | **Map Ref: 3H12**

QUAICH COTTAGE
Upper Banavie, Fort William PH33 7PB
Tel & Fax: 01397 772799
e.mail: MacDonald@quaichcottage.fsnet.co.uk
Our modern detached home on an elevated rural site offers spacious accommodation
and a warm friendly welcome. All rooms have uninterrupted views across the Great
Glen and Caledonian Canal to Ben Nevis and ski area.
The peaceful atmosphere will recharge the batteries.
A Taste of Scotland restaurant close by.

B&B

Quaich Cottage

Upper Banavie, Fort William, Inverness-shire PH33 7PB
Tel/Fax:01397 772799
Email:macdonald@quaichcottage.fsnet.co.uk
Web:www.visitscotland.com

Modern villa nestling in the hills with spectacular views towards Ben
Nevis and Nevis Range. Ideal base for skiers, walkers and climbers and
touring North West Highlands. All rooms ensuite. Ample parking. Wide
choice for breakfast - both traditional and continental. Easy access to
Caledonian Canal. Fort William 4 miles. Banavie 1.5 miles. Drying
facilities available.

1 Twin	All En Suite	B&B per person	Open Jan-Dec
1 Double		from £20.00 Single	
1 Family		from £20.00 Double	

B&B

Rhiw Goch

Banavie, Fort William, PH33 7LY
Tel/Fax:01397 772373
Email:kay@rhiwgoch.co.uk Web:www.rhiwgoch.co.uk

Situated at the top of Neptune's Staircase, 3 miles from Fort William, our
ensuite bedrooms have superb views overlooking the Caledonian Canal
and beyond to Ben Nevis. We will happily share our knowledge of the
area with you. Enjoy the outdoor actvities on offer or simply take in the
magnificent scenery. We also hire out mountain bikes and Canadian
canoes.

| 3 Twin | All En Suite | B&B per person | Open Jan-Dec excl |
| | | £20.00-25.00 Twin | Xmas/New Year |

Scotland's National Booking and Information Line

Tel: 0845 22 55 121
visitscotland.com

Important: Prices stated are estimates and may be subject to amendments

RUSHFIELD HOUSE
Tomonie, Banavie, Fort William PH33 7LX
Tel: 01397 772063 Fax: 01397 772063
e.mail: rushbb0063@aol.com
Web: www.members.aol.com/rushbb0063/index.html

Modern house with excellent views of Ben Nevis situated within 3 miles of Fort William.
All rooms ensuite. TVs, hospitality trays and ample parking. Non-smoking residence. Amenities close by include "Neptunes Staircase" on the Caledonian Canal, "Treasures of the Earth" Museum.
Ten minute drive will find you Aonach Mor ski resort and restaurant with some excellent views also in the summer months. The "Jacobite Steam Train" enthusiasts will be able to view the train on its journey to Mallaig from bridge nearby. Fort William centre has many bars/restaurants or within walking distance we also have various bars/restaurants.
Open February–October.

★★★

B&B

Rushfield House
Tomonie, Banavie, Fort William, PH33 7LX
Tel:01397 772063
Email:rushbb0063@aol.com
Web:www.members.aol.com/rushbb0063/index.html

Modern bungalow with ground floor bedroom in quiet residential area, close to the canal and Neptune's staircase. Open views of Ben Nevis and Glen Nevis. Good selection of hotels and restaurants within a short distance. Excellent base for exploring the Western Highlands.

| 1 Double | All En Suite | B&B per person | Open Feb-Oct |
| 2 Family | | from £18.00 Double | |

★★★

B&B

●●
TEA ROOM

Seangan Croft
Seangan Bridge, Banavie, Fort William, PH33 7PB
Tel:01397 772228

Modern croft house within 5 miles of bustling Fort William, surrounded by open countryside, woodland, hills and moorland. Hours of relaxed hillwalking and a wealth of wildlife. Stroll along the nearby Caledonian Canal towpath or enjoy a leisurely meal in our Taste of Scotland restaurant.

1 Twin	All En Suite	B&B per person	Open Apr-Oct
2 Double		from £28.00 Single	
		from £20.00 Double	

★★

B&B

Stobahn
Fassifern Road, Fort William, PH33 6BD
Tel/Fax:01397 702790
Email:boggi@supanet.com

Detached house, situated close to the town centre and just a few minutes walk from the High Street, and the railway station.

1 Single	All En Suite	B&B per person	Open Jan-Dec
1 Twin		£15.00-22.00 Single	BB & Eve.Meal
1 Double		£15.00-22.00 Double	from £25.00-32.00
1 Family		£15.00-19.00 Room Only	

VAT is shown at 17.5%: changes in this rate may affect prices.   Key to symbols is on back flap.

Fort William, Inverness-shire

Map Ref: 3H12

★★★

GUEST HOUSE

Stronchreggan View Guest House
Achintore Road, Fort William, Inverness-shire PH33 6RW
Tel:01397 704644/704707 Fax:01397 704644
Email:patricia@apmac.freeserve.co.uk
Web:www.stronchreggan.co.uk

Stronchreggan View is family run by Archie and Pat McQueen. Modern
double glazed house overlooking Loch Linnhe with views of the Ardgour
Hills and surrounding countryside. Excellent centre for visiting Oban,
Mull, Skye, Aviemore and many other spots.

1 Twin	All En Suite
2 Double	
2 Family	

B&B per person
from £19.00 Double

Open Mar-Oct
BB & Eve.Meal
from £29.00

★★

B&B

Taormina
Banavie, Fort William, PH33 7LY
Tel:01397 772217

Taormina is in a quiet situation in Banavie Village close to Neptune's
Staircase on the Caledonian Canal. Ben Nevis and Aonach Mor can be
seen from the large garden. Banavie Scotrail station and bus halt are
five minute's walk away. Several good hotels and pubs locally.

1 Single	1 Priv.NOT ensuite
1 Twin	
1 Double	
1 Family	

B&B per person
from £16.00 Single
from £16.00 Double
from £12.00 Room
Only

Open Mar-Oct

THISTLE COTTAGE
TORLUNDY, FORT WILLIAM PH33 6SN
Telephone: 01397 702428
e.mail: m.a.matheson@amserve.net Web: www.thistlescotland.co.uk
In a rural area 3 miles north of Fort William in a beautiful quiet
valley below Aonach Mor ski centre. Central for touring the
Highlands. TV, tea/coffee making facilities in all rooms.
Ample parking. Pets welcome. Warm friendly welcome.

★★★

B&B

Thistle Cottage
Torlundy, Fort William, PH33 6SN
Tel:01397 702428
Email:m.a.matheson@amserve.net
Web:www.thistlescotland.co.uk

A warm highland welcome awaits you in our modern house in quiet
location close to Nevis Range. Good base for touring all west coast
attractions ski-ing, climbing and walking. Close to golf course. Ample
parking. 3 miles from Fort William.

1 Twin	All En Suite
1 Double	
1 Family	

B&B per person
from £22.00 Single
from £17.50 Double

Open Jan-Dec

★★★

B&B

Torlinnhe
Achintore Road, Fort William, Inverness-shire
PH33 6RN
Tel/Fax:01397 702583

Friendly family run guest house with ample car parking situated 1 mile
south of the town centre,on main A82 road. Views of Loch Linnhe and
the hills beyond. All rooms en suite or with private bathrooms. Ideal base
for touring, walking, climbing and ski-ing.

1 Single	5 En Suite fac
1 Twin	1 Pub.Bath/Show
2 Double	
2 Family	

B&B per person
£22.00-25.00 Single
£22.00-25.00 Double

Open Jan-Dec

Important: Prices stated are estimates and may be subject to amendments

Fort William, Inverness-shire | Map Ref: 3H12

Voringfoss B&B
★★★★
B&B

5 Stirling Place, Fort William, Inverness-shire
PH33 6UW
Tel:01397 704062 Fax:01397 706151
Email:voringfoss@lineone.net

Highland hospitality at its best for those who prefer a quiet situation
within one mile of the town centre. Landscaped garden affords
panoramic views to surrounding hills. An ideal centre from which to
explore the West Highlands. Special diets catered for.

1 Twin	All En Suite	B&B per person	Open Jan-Dec
2 Double		from £25.00 Single	
		from £25.00 Double	

West End Hotel
★★★
HOTEL

Achintore Road, Fort William, PH33 6ED
Tel:01397 702614 Fax:01397 706279
Email:welcome@westend-hotel.co.uk
Web:www.westend-hotel.co.uk

Family run hotel in the centre of Fort William overlooking Loch Linnhe.
Ideal base for touring the West Highlands.

9 Single	All En Suite	B&B per person	Open Feb-Dec excl
20 Twin		from £25.00 Single	Xmas/New Year
16 Double		from £25.00 Double	BB & Eve.Meal
5 Family			from £35.00

WOODLAND HOUSE

Torlundy, Fort William PH33 6SN
Tel: 01397 701698/700250 Fax: 01397 700433
e.mail: woodlandhouse@btinternet.com
Web: www.woodlandscotland.co.uk

A modern house situated in a beautiful quiet residential area 3 miles north of Fort
William on A82. Ensuite rooms available. TV, tea/coffee facilities in all rooms. Central
for touring the Highlands. Warm and friendly welcome. Designed for the disabled. Pets
welcome by arrangement. Ample parking. Children welcome.
From £24 single and from £18 - £22 pppn.

Woodland House
★★★
B&B

Torlundy, Fort William, Inverness-shire, PH33 6SN
Tel:01397 701698/700250
Email:woodlandhouse@btinternet.com
Web:www.woodlandscotland.co.uk

Friendly welcome from all the Matheson family at this modern detached
home only 10 minutes drive from Fort William town centre. Semi rural
location, nestling at foot of Aonoch Mhor and along from Ben Nevis.
Ideal base for walkers, climbers, skiers, in fact anyone, including pets.
Level access and Category 1 grade awarded for facilities, plus accessibility
makes this an ideal place to stay for disabled guests.

1 Twin	All En Suite	B&B per person	Open Jan-Dec excl
1 Double		from £24.00 Single	Xmas/New Year
1 Family		from £18.00 Double	

Scotland's National Booking and Information Line

Tel: 0845 22 55 121
visitscotland.com

VAT is shown at 17.5%: changes in this rate may affect prices. | Key to symbols is on back flap.

by Fort William, Inverness-shire | Map Ref: 3H12

B&B

Clintwood

23 Hillview Drive, Corpach, Fort William, PH33 7LS
Tel:01397 772680 Fax:01397 772476
Email:clintwoodhouse@amserve.com

Clintwood is situated within a residential area of the village of Corpach. 4 miles (6 kms) from Fort William, off the road to the Isles. You can be sure of a warm, Highland welcome from your hosts Christine and Ian. Relax in our spacious lounge with fine views of Ben Nevis and surrounding mountains. Ideal base for walks, cruises, golf, fishing and pony trekking or touring the Highlands. We wish to make your stay with us truly memorable.

1 Twin	All En Suite	Open Easter-Oct
2 Double		

B&B per person
from £35.00 Single
from £25.00 Double

📺 🍴 P ☕ 🦴 ✕ 🚗 📞

B&B

Dailanna Guest House

Kinlocheil, Fort William, Inverness-shire PH33 7NP
Tel/Fax:01397 722253
Email:flo@dailanna.co.uk
Web:www.dailanna.co.uk

Detached bungalow with large garden in elevated, peaceful position with fine views southwards over Loch Eil to the hills of Ardgour. Enjoy the colourful sunset skies from our spacious lounge. The Isle of Skye, Morvan and Moidart are all easily accessible along the 'Road to the Isles'.

1 Twin	All En Suite	Open May-Oct
1 Double		
1 Family		

B&B per person
£22.50-30.00 Double

🍴 P ☕ 🦴 ✕ 🚗 📞

Ⓥ ♿

nr Fort William, Inverness-shire | Map Ref: 3H12

SPRINGBURN FARM HOUSE

STRONABA, SPEAN BRIDGE, INVERNESS-SHIRE PH34 4DX
Telephone/Fax: 01397 712707
e.mail: info@stronaba.co.uk Web: www.stronaba.co.uk
Family home in farm grounds with wonderful views of the Highlands.
Spacious rooms with all facilities and lots of homely touches.
Come and relax and be spoilt or help comb the highland cows.
A truly unique place for a holiday. Hill walkers and cyclists welcome.

B&B

Springburn Farm House

Spean Bridge, Inverness-shire, PH34 4DX
Tel/Fax:01397 712707
Email:info@stronaba.co.uk
Web:www.stronaba.co.uk

Family home in own grounds with panoramic views of Ben-Nevis and surrounding hills. Bedrooms with all facilities and comfortable lounge for relaxing after a days touring in the area. Why not spend the evening feeding the Highland Cows?

1 Twin	All En Suite	Open Jan-Dec
2 Double		

B&B per person
from £20.00 Single
from £20.00 Double

📺 🍴 P ☕ 🦴 ✕ 🚗 📞

Ⓒ 💳 Ⓥ ♿

Scotland's National Booking and Information Line

Tel: 0845 22 55 121
visitscotland.com

Important: Prices stated are estimates and may be subject to amendments

Gairloch, Ross-shire | Map Ref: 3F7

DUISARY

Strath, Gairloch, Ross-shire IV21 2DA Tel/Fax: 01445 712252
e.mail: isabel@duisary.freeserve.co.uk
Web: www.duisary.freeserve.co.uk

Comfortable accommodation and a true Highland welcome awaits you in modernised croftbouse on the outskirts of village where Gaelic is spoken and a little French and German. Superb views of sea and Torridon Hills. TV and central beating in bedrooms. Close to famous Inverewe Gardens. Idyllic setting with beaches, golf course, swimming and leisure centre nearby. Ideal for hill-walking, bird-watching, fishing or just relaxing.

★★★

B&B

Duisary

24 Strath, Gairloch, Ross-shire, IV21 2DA
Tel/Fax:01445 712252
Email:isabel@duisary.freeserve.co.uk
Web:www.duisary.freeserve.co.uk

Traditional stone built croft house on edge of village, with fine views across Gairloch to the hills of Torridon. 6 miles from Inverewe Gardens, safe sandy beaches within easy reach. Ideal spot for hill walking, bird watching, fishing or just relaxing.

1 Twin	1 En Suite fac	B&B per person	Open Apr-Oct
1 Double	1 Priv.NOT ensuite	from £18.00 Single	
1 Family	1 Pub.Bath/Show	from £18.00 Double	

★★★

B&B

Dunedin

42 Strath, Gairloch, Ross-shire, IV21 2DB
Tel:01445 712050
Email:kendunedin@aol.com

A true Highland welcome awaits you at our peaceful home, which enjoys an elevated position in a secluded area on the edge of the village. Our lounge offers a panoramic view over the sea, ranging from Skye to the Torridon mountains. 8 miles from Inverewe Gardens. Many opportunities for fishing and walking, and the attractive 9-hole Golf Course and golden sands are only 2 miles away.

2 Double	1 En Suite fac	B&B per person	Open May-Sep
	1 Priv.Bath/Show	from £22.00 Single	
		from £18.00 Double	

HEATHERDALE

Charleston, Gairloch IV21 2AH
Tel/Fax: 01445 712388 e.mail: brochod1@aol.com

A warm welcome awaits at Heatherdale, situated on the outskirts of Gairloch, overlooking the harbour and bay beyond. Within easy walking distance of golf course and sandy beaches. Ideal base for hill-walking. All rooms en-suite facilities, some with seaview. Excellent eating out facilities nearby. Ample parking. Residents lounge with open fire.

★★★★

B&B

Heatherdale

Charleston, Gairloch, Ross-shire, IV21 2AH
Tel/Fax:01445 712388
Email:Brochod1@aol.com

Modern detached house on hill on outskirts of Gairloch and overlooking the harbour. Ideal base for a relaxing holiday. Ample space for parking. All bedrooms now ensuite. A warm welcome assured.

1 Twin	All En Suite	B&B per person	Open Feb-Nov
2 Double		from £22.00 Double	

VAT is shown at 17.5%: changes in this rate may affect prices. | *Key to symbols is on back flap.*

Map Ref: 3F7

KERRYSDALE HOUSE

GAIRLOCH, ROSS-SHIRE IV21 2AL
TEL/FAX: 01445 712292
E.MAIL: mac.kerr@btinternet.com   WEB: www.kerrysdalehouse.co.uk

Make Kerrysdale House, built in 1790, your base to explore beautiful Wester Ross. Warm tastefully decorated rooms, with private facilities, and a hearty breakfast await you. Peacefully situated one mile from harbour on A832, 20 minutes from Inverewe Garden. Contact Marie Macrae for brochure or visit website.

★★★

B&B

Kerrysdale House

Gairloch, Rosshire, IV21 2AL
Tel/Fax:01445 712292
Email:Mac.Kerr@btinternet.com
Web:www.kerrysdalehouse.co.uk

18c farmhouse recently refurbished and tastefully decorated. Modern comforts in a peaceful setting. 1 mile (2kms) south of Gairloch.

1 Twin	2 En Suite fac	B&B per person	Open Feb-Nov
2 Double	1 Pub.Bath/Show	£20.00-25.00 Single	
		£20.00-25.00 Double	

★★★

B&B

Mrs Maclean

Strathlene, 45 Strath, Gairloch, Ross-shire IV21 2DB
Tel:01445 712170
Email:info@strathlene.com
Web:www.strathlene.com

Cosy bedrooms in this modern family home with views over Gairloch Bay to the Torridon Hills and Skye. No smoking house. Private parking. Tea tray and TV in bedrooms.

| 1 Double | All En Suite | B&B per person | Open Mar-Nov |
| 1 Family | | from £17.50 Double | |

★★

GUEST HOUSE

The Mountain Restaurant and Lodge

Strath Square, Gairloch, Ross-shire, IV21 2BX
Tel:01445 712316

In Gairloch's main square. Unique themed restaurant and lodge. Views across bay to mountains. 4 poster bed and ocean views. Mountaineering memorabilia donated by Chris Bonnington and others. Evening meals during H/S. Daytime speciality coffee shop featuring cappucino and espresso drinks and over 60 different teas and coffees. Mountain style home baking, snacks and lunches. All in an informal atmosphere. Lochside sun terrace. Nature Shop/Bookstore.

1 Twin	All En Suite	B&B per person	Open Mar-Dec
2 Double		from £30.00 Single	
		from £19.95 Double	

★★★

GUEST HOUSE

Whindley Guest House

Auchtercairn Brae, Gairloch, Ross-shire, IV21 2BN
Tel/Fax:01445 712340
Email:bill@whindley.co.uk
Web:www.whindley.co.uk

Modern bungalow with large garden in elevated position, with fine views overlooking Gairloch Bay, and across to Skye. Beach and golf course nearby. Evening meals by arrangement. Non smoking house.

1 Twin	All En Suite	B&B per person	Open Jan-Dec excl
1 Double		from £20.00 Single	Xmas/New Year
1 Family		from £20.00 Double	BB & Eve.Meal
			from £35.00

Important: Prices stated are estimates and may be subject to amendments

Garve, Ross-shire   Map Ref: 4A8

Mossford Cottages

Mr & Mrs S. Doyle, Lochluichart, Garve, Ross-shire IV23 2QA
Tel: 01997 414334

e.mail: sealochluichart@aol.com   Web: www.mossford-cottages.co.uk
Mossford Cottages are a small B&B overlooking Loch Luichart.
The station is nearby on the famous and beautiful Inverness-Kyle line.
Ideal for visiting the varied places nearby of Ullapool, Gairloch and Inverewe.
The emphasis is on a friendly, relaxed atmosphere.
Dinner is available on request.

★★★

B&B

Mossford Cottage

Lochluichart, Garve, Ross-shire, IV23 2QA
Tel:01997 414334
Email:sealochluichart@aol.com
Web:www.mossford-cottages.co.uk

A warm welcome awaits you at Mossford cottages, formerly 2 workers cottages, with panoramic views across Loch Luichart. Close to Lochluichart railway station and 29 miles from Inverness or 36 miles to Ullapool. An ideal base for walking holidays and exploring Ross-shire. Evening meal available by prior arrangement.

1 Single	2 En Suite fac	B&B per person	Open Jan-Dec excl
1 Twin	1 Pub.Bath/Show	from £18.00 Single	Xmas/New Year
1 Double		from £18.00 Double	BB & Eve.Meal
1 Family			from £28.00

Glencoe, Argyll   Map Ref: 1F1

★★★

GUEST HOUSE

Dunire Guest House

Glencoe, Argyll, PH49 4HS
Tel:01855 811305 Fax:01855 811671

Modern bungalow in centre of Glencoe Village. Ideal base for touring, climbing and hill walking, in fact all outdoor pursuits. All bedrooms tastefully furnished with TV's, radio's and tea-making facilities. Cosy guests lounge. Ample private parking. Drying facilities for walkers.

2 Twin	All En Suite	B&B per person	Open Jan-Dec excl
3 Double		from £17.00 Double	Xmas

★★★★

B&B

Gleann-Leac-Na-Muidhe

Glencoe, Argyll, PH49 4LA Tel/Fax:01855 811598
Email:jeffanna@namuidhe.freeserve.co.uk
Web:www.namuidhe.freeserve.co.uk

Experience the mountains from the doorstep. A warm welcome awaits you at this peaceful highland retreat situated 1 mile along a private road in the heart of the glen with stunning views all around. Feel the history, being a short distance from the remains of Maclains summer house where the chief of the MacDonald Clan met his death in the Glencoe Massacre of 1692. An ideal base for tourists, walkers and climbers alike. Vegetarians welcome.

2 Double	1 En Suite fac	B&B per person	Open Jan-Dec excl
	1 Priv.Bath/Show	from £40.00 Single	Xmas/New Year
		from £25.00 Double	

★★

SMALL HOTEL

Glencoe Hotel

Glencoe Village, West Highlands, PH49 4HW
Tel:01855 811245 Fax:01855 811687
Email:glencoehotel@hotmail.com
Web:www.GlencoeHotel-Scotland.com

In the same family for over 70 years this hotel offers a warm and friendly atmosphere with superb views over Loch Leven and beyond.

2 Single	All En Suite	B&B per person	Open Jan-Dec excl
4 Twin	1 Pub.Bath/Show	from £36.00 Single	Xmas
6 Double		from £24.00 Double	BB & Eve.Meal
3 Family		from £35.00 Room	from £39.00
		Only	

VAT is shown at 17.5%: changes in this rate may affect prices. | Key to symbols is on back flap. |

Glencoe, Argyll   Map Ref: 1F1

★★★

B&B

Parkview
18 Park Road, Ballachulish, Argyll, PH49 4JS
Tel:01855 811560
Email:db.macaskill@talk21.com
Web:www.glencoe-parkview.co.uk

A traditional Highland welcome awaits you at this family run B&B, situated in the centre of Ballachulish village with views of Meall Mhor and The Pap of Glencoe. Ideal base for walkers and climbers in the Glencoe area. Fort William 14 miles to north. Glencoe 3 miles. In wet weather relax in our cosy TV lounge or read from our selection of local interest books. Drying facilities and parking available.

1 Twin	2 Priv.NOT ensuite	B&B per person	Open Jan-Dec excl
2 Double		from £20.00 Single	Xmas/New Year
		£16.00-20.00 Double	

SCORRYBREAC GUEST HOUSE
GLENCOE,   ARGYLL   PH49   4HT
Tel/Fax: 01855 811354
e.mail: info@scorrybreac.co.uk
Web: www.scorrybreac.co.uk
Scorrybreac is a comfortable well-appointed guest house in beautiful woodland surroundings managed by the resident owners. We are a no-smoking establishment. It is an ideal base for exploring the Glencoe and Ben Nevis area or for a shorter stay on a more extended tour of the Highlands.

★★★

GUEST
HOUSE

Scorrybreac Guest House
Glencoe, Argyll, PH49 4HT
Tel/Fax:01855 811354
Email:info@scorrybreac.co.uk
Web:www.scorrybreac.co.uk

Scorrybreac is a comfortable single storey guest house in beautiful woodland surroundings, overlooking Loch Leven, in a quiet secluded location on the edge of village, near local forest walks. Ideal base for exploring Glencoe and Ben Nevis area or for a shorter stay on a more extended tour of the Highlands. Colourful garden. Ample parking.

3 Twin	5 En Suite	B&B per person	Open 26 Dec-Oct
3 Double	1 Priv.Bath/Show	from £20.00 Single	
		from £18.00 Double	

★★★

GUEST
HOUSE

Strathassynt Guest House
Loan Fern, Ballachulish, Argyll, PH49 4JB
Tel:01855 811261   Fax:01855 811914
Email:info@strathassynt.com
Web:www.strathassynt.com

Comfortable family run licenced guest house in a small village amidst superb loch & mountain scenery. Excellent facilities for walkers and cyclists including skiing, canoeing and bike hire. Home baking and cooking using fresh local produce. Family room available. French/German spoken. Evening meal by prior arrangement.

1 Single	All En Suite	B&B per person	Open Jan-Dec
2 Twin		from £20.00 Single	BB & Eve.Meal
2 Double		from £18.00 Double	from £28.00
1 Family			

Grantown-on-Spey, Moray   Map Ref: 4C9

★★★★

GUEST
HOUSE

An Cala
Woodlands Terrace, Grantown on Spey, Moray PH26 3JU
Tel:01479 873293   Fax:01479 870297
Email:ancala@globalnet.co.uk
Web:www.ancalahouse.co.uk

A traditional stone built villa on the outskirts of Grantown, but within easy walking distance of the town centre. Fish on the Spey, walk the hills, play the golf courses, watch the wildlife, sample the whisky and enjoy the comfort of our home. Tea on arrival, evening meals available and the house is totally non-smoking.

1 Twin	All En Suite	B&B per person	Open Jan-Dec
2 Double		from £30.00 Single	BB & Eve.Meal
		from £23.00 Double	from £34.00

Important: Prices stated are estimates and may be subject to amendments

Grantown-on-Spey, Moray | Map Ref: 4C9

Ardconnel House

Woodlands Terrace, Grantown-on-Spey, Moray PH26 3JU
Tel/Fax: 01479 872104 e.mail: enquiry@ardconnel.com
Web: www.ardconnel.com

An elegant and comfortable Victorian house furnished with antiques and pine.
All bedrooms are ensuite offering colour TV, hairdryer and hospitality tray.
Dinner by arrangement prepared by owner/chef. Licensed.
No smoking throughout. 2001/2002 AA Guest Accommodation of the Year for Scotland.

AA ◆◆◆◆◆ RAC ◆◆◆◆◆

GUEST HOUSE

Ardconnel House

Woodlands Terrace, Grantown-on-Spey, Moray PH26 3JU
Tel/Fax:01479 872104
Email:enquiry@ardconnel.com
Web:www.ardconnel.com

Splendid Victorian villa with private car parking. All rooms ensuite. No smoking throughout. Taste of Scotland selected member. Warm welcome assured. Peaceful friendly ambience.

1 Single	All En Suite	B&B per person	Open Apr-Oct
2 Twin		from £28.00 Single	BB & Eve.Meal
3 Double		from £28.00 Double	from £46.00

Bank House

1 The Square, Grantown-on-Spey, Moray PH26 3HG
Tel/Fax: 01479 873256 e.mail: farleys@breathemail.net

Centrally situated. A few minutes walk from the renowned River Spey and golf course. Ideal for the whisky trail, bird watching, fishing, golfing, walking and horse riding. The Bank House offers very spacious family rooms, comfortably heated with TV, tea/coffee facilities and armchairs. Cot and high chair provided. Children welcome. Full Scottish breakfast.

B&B

Bank House

1 The Square, Grantown-on-Spey, Morayshire
PH26 3HG
Tel:01479 873256

Centrally situated, very spacious and comfortable accommodation. Ideal touring base. Warm and friendly welcome assured. Centrally situated for whisky trail, golfing, fishing, bird watching and skiing. Children welcome, cot and high chair provided.

1 Twin	1 En Suite fac	B&B per person	Open Jan-Dec
1 Double	2 Pub.Bath/Show	from £20.00 Single	BB & Eve.Meal
1 Family		from £20.00 Double	from £30.00

HOTEL

Ben Mhor Hotel

53-57 High Street, Grantown on Spey, PH26 3EG
Tel:01479 872056 Fax:01479 873537
Email:christine@benmhorhotel.co.uk
Web:www.benmhorhotel.co.uk

Personally run, friendly town centre hotel; choice of bars, bistro dining and function room all available. Live music some nights. Good base for the business or leisure traveller. Parking at rear of hotel.

3 Single	All En Suite	B&B per person	Open Jan-Dec
9 Twin		from £29.50 Single	BB & Eve.Meal
10 Double		from £29.50 Double	from £45.00
2 Family			

VAT is shown at 17.5%: changes in this rate may affect prices. | *Key to symbols is on back flap.*

Brooklynn

Grant Road, Grantown-on-Spey PH26 3LA
Tel: **01479 873113**
e.mail: **brooklynn@woodier.com** *Web:* **www.woodier.com**
Brooklynn is an elegant and unusually decorated late Victorian house, ideally situated for your Highland holiday. Many outdoor activities can be enjoyed, from golf, walking and fishing to the Malt Whisky Trail. Our rooms are spacious and comfortable; our home-cooked food delicious accompanied by modestly priced wines and spirits.

★★★★

GUEST HOUSE

••

HOME COOKING

Brooklynn
Grant Road, Grantown on Spey, PH26 3LA
Tel:01479 873113
Email:brooklynn@woodier.com
Web:www.woodier.com

A warm welcome and friendly personal service await you at Brooklynn. We use locally sourced or homegrown food wherever possible for our delicious dinners;sample a Speyside Malt and finally, sleep well in our comfortable spacious bedrooms. Enjoy our pretty gardens too.

2 Single	5 Ensuite fac	B&B per person	Open Jan-Dec
2 Twin	1 Pub.Bath/Show	from £20.00 Single	BB & Eve.Meal
3 Double		from £22.00 Double	from £35.00

Culdearn House

PPP GOLD   AA ★★

Woodlands Terrace, Grantown-on-Spey PH26 3JU
Tel: 01479 872106 Fax: 01479 873641
e.mail: culdearn@globalnet.co.uk Web: www.culdearn.com
Elegant country house with friendly Scottish hosts. Comfortable rooms with every facility. Log fires. Excellent cuisine with fine wine list and 80 malt whiskies. Taste of Scotland recommended. Superb location for all manner of activities including whisky and castle trails. 3 and 7 day breaks available. *AA/RAC ★★.*
Please contact Isobel and Alasdair Little for reservations.

★★★★

SMALL HOTEL

•••

RESTAURANT

Culdearn House
Woodlands Terrace, Grantown-on-Spey, Morayshire PH26 3JU
Tel:01479 872106   Fax:01479 873641
Email:culdearn@globalnet.co.uk
Web:www.culdearn.com

Elegant Victorian house, retaining many original features and caringly restored to include all modern comforts. Warm and friendly atmosphere. All rooms ensuite facilities. Taste of Scotland member. Award winning kitchen. Interesting wine list and unique collection of malt whisky.

1 Single	All En Suite	B&B per person	Open Mar-Oct
3 Twin		from £45.00 Single	BB & Eve.Meal
5 Double		from £45.00 Double	from £70.00

PPP

Important: Prices stated are estimates and may be subject to amendments

Grantown-on-Spey, Moray   Map Ref: 4C9

FIRHALL GUEST HOUSE

Grant Road, Grantown-on-Spey, Morayshire PH26 3LD
Tel/Fax: 01479 873097
e.mail: info@firhall.com Web: www.firhall.com

A warm friendly welcome awaits you at Firhall. Situated in the heart of the Highlands, Grantown is ideally placed for the malt whisky trail, historic castles, golf, fishing and the breathtaking local scenery. The town centre, golf course, forest trails and River Spey are just a short walk away.

GUEST HOUSE

Firhall Guest House

Grant Road, Grantown-on-Spey, Moray, PH26 3LD
Tel:01479 873097   Fax:01479 873097
Email:info@firhall.com
Web:www.firhall.com

Firhall is a fine example of Victorian elegance, retaining much of the original character of this period. Particular features include the beautifully preserved pitched pine woodwork, ornate cornices and marble fireplaces. Home cooking. Family run.

1 Single	3 En Suite fac	B&B per person	Open Jan-Dec excl
1 Twin	1 Priv.NOT ensuite	from £18.00 Single	Xmas
1 Double	1 Pub.Bath/Show	from £18.00 Double	BB & Eve.Meal
3 Family			from £29.00

GUEST HOUSE

Parkburn Guest House

High Street, Grantown-on-Spey, PH26 3EN
Tel:01479 873116

Semi detached Victorian villa standing back from main road with ample parking available. Fishing and fishing tuition can be arranged.

2 Single	5 En Suite fac	B&B per person	Open Jan-Dec
1 Twin	1 Pub.Bath/Show	from £20.00 Single	
3 Double		from £20.00 Double	

GUEST HOUSE

Rosegrove Guesthouse

Skye of Curr, Dulnain Bridge, Grantown on Spey, Inverness-shire
PH26 3PA
Tel/Fax:01479 851335
Email:info@rosegroveguesthouse.com
Web:www.rosegroveguesthouse.com

Modern house, personally run. Home cooking. A short distance from Dulnain Bridge.

1 Single	Some En Suite	B&B per person	Open Jan-Dec
2 Twin		from £18.00 Single	BB & Eve.Meal
2 Double		from £20.00 Double	from £32.50
1 Family		from £12.00 Room	
		Only	

VAT is shown at 17.5%: changes in this rate may affect prices.

Key to symbols is on back flap.

Grantown-on-Spey, Moray   Map Ref: 4C9

ROSSMOR GUEST HOUSE
WOODLANDS TERRACE, GRANTOWN-ON-SPEY PH26 3JU
Tel/Fax: 01479 872201
e.mail: johnsteward.rossmor@lineone.net   Web: www.rossmor.co.uk
Splendid Victorian villa, with many original features, where a warm
welcome with personal friendly service awaits you. Spacious and
comfortable guest rooms, all ensuite. A non-smoking house.
Ideal location for touring the many distilleries, castles, Moray Firth coast,
Cairngorms and RSPB reserves. **Proprietors: John & Julia Steward.**

★★★★

GUEST
HOUSE

Rossmor Guest House

Woodlands Terrace, Grantown on Spey, Moray PH26 3JU
Tel/Fax:01479 872201
Email:johnsteward.rossmor@lineone.net
Web:www.rossmor.co.uk

Spacious Victorian detached house with original features and large
garden. A warm welcome. Parking. Panoramic views. No smoking
throughout.

2 Twin	All En Suite	B&B per person
2 Double		from £25.00 Single
2 Family		from £23.00 Double

Open Jan-Dec

Helmsdale, Sutherland   Map Ref: 4C5

★★★

B&B

Broomhill House

Navidale Road, Helmsdale, Sutherland, KW8 6JS
Tel/Fax:01431 821259
Email:asblance@aol.com
Web:www.host.co.uk

Victorian stone built house with turret. Magnificent panoramic view over
Helmsdale to the sea. Local heritage centre and art gallery in the village.
Harbour nearby. Ideal base for exploring the far north, or for stopping
off en-route to Orkney. Golf, tennis, squash, indoor bowls, sea and river
angling available nearby.

1 Twin	All En Suite	B&B per person
1 Double		from £18.00 Double

Open Jan-Dec excl
Xmas/New Year
BB & Eve.Meal
from £30.00

Invergarry, Inverness-shire   Map Ref: 3H11

FOREST LODGE
South Laggan, Invergarry, by Spean Bridge, Inverness-shire PH34 4EA
Tel: 01809 501219   Fax: 01809 501476
e.mail: info@flgh.co.uk   Web: www.flgh.co.uk
Staying one night or more, Ian and Janet Shearer's comfortable
home offers pleasant ensuite accommodation, relaxed surroundings
and home cooking served with friendly attention. Forest Lodge is
conveniently situated in the centre of the Great Glen and is ideal for
touring or participating in outdoor pursuits.

★★★

GUEST
HOUSE

Forest Lodge

South Laggan, Invergarry, Spean Bridge, PH34 4EA
Tel:01809 501219   Fax:01809 501476
Email:info@flgh.co.uk
Web:www.flgh.co.uk

Staying in the Great Glen for one night or more? Situated where the
Caledonian Canal joins Loch Lochy and Oich. We offer pleasant, ensuite
accommodation and home cooking in our relaxed and friendly home.
Open all year for touring, walking or just to relax. Please call for a
brochure.

2 Twin	6 En Suite fac	B&B per person
2 Double	1 Pub.Bath/Show	from £20.00 Double
3 Family		

Open Jan-Dec excl
Xmas/New Year
BB & Eve.Meal
from £32.00-38.00

Important: Prices stated are estimates and may be subject to amendments

Invergordon, Ross-shire

Map Ref: 4B7

★★★

GUEST
HOUSE

Craigaron Guest House

17 Saltburn, Invergordon, Ross & Cromarty IV18 0JX
Tel:01349 853640 Fax:01349 853619
Email:jobrown@craigaron.co.uk
Web:www.craigaron.co.uk

19th century converted fisherman's cottage overlooking the sea. Five minute drive from town centre. 20+ golf courses within an hours drive. Dolphins and other sea and birdlife. Many visiting cruise liners including the QE2.

1 Single	2 En Suite fac	B&B per person	Open Jan-Dec excl
4 Twin	1 Priv.NOT ensuite	from £20.00 Single	Xmas/New Year
		from £19.00 Double	
		from £16.00 Room	
		Only	

Invermoriston, Inverness-shire

Map Ref: 4A10

★★★★

B&B

Court Green

Invermoriston, Inverness-shire, IV63 7YA
Tel:01320 351287
Email:courtgreen@supanet.com
Web:www.host.co.uk

Very comfortable bed and breakfast accommodation with attractive bedrooms all en-suite. Situated near the shores of Loch Ness. Ideal location for walking, fishing, cycling, golf and touring the Highlands. Restaurant and pub nearby.

1 Twin	Ensuite fac	B&B per person	Open Mar-Oct
1 Double	Ensuite fac	from £22.50 Single	
1 Double	Priv.Bath/Show	from £20.00 Double	

Inverness

Map Ref: 4B8

ABERFELDY LODGE GUEST HOUSE

11 SOUTHSIDE ROAD, INVERNESS IV2 3BG

Telephone: 01463 231120 Fax: 01463 234741
e.mail: class@algh.freeserve.co.uk
Web: www.SmoothHound.co.uk/hotels/aberfeld.html

Within a five minute walk from the city centre. We are ideally situated to take in all that Inverness has to offer. Come and enjoy your stay with us in a relaxed and informal atmosphere. All rooms en-suite. From only £19.50 pppn including a hearty breakfast.

★★★

GUEST
HOUSE

Aberfeldy Lodge Guest House

11 Southside Road, Inverness, Inverness-shire IV2 3BG
Tel:01463 231120 Fax:01463 234741
Email:class@algh.freeserve.co.uk
Web:www.SmoothHound.co.uk/hotels/aberfeld.html

Comfortable Guest House close to city centre. All rooms ensuite. Hearty breakfast, vegetarians catered for and children welcome. Private car park.

1 Single	All En Suite	B&B per person	Open Jan-Dec
2 Twin		from £25.00 Single	
3 Double		from £19.50 Double	
2 Family			

★★★★

B&B

Advie Lodge

31 Crown Drive, Inverness, IV2 3QQ
Tel:01463 237247
Email:june.inverness@talk21.com

Traditional town house in quiet residential area of Inverness, offering ensuite rooms and private parking. Within walking distance of the town centre and River Ness.

1 Single	2 En Suite fac	B&B per person	Open Jan-Dec excl
1 Twin	1 Pub.Bath/Show	£20.00-23.00 Single	Xmas/New Year
1 Double		£20.00-23.00 Double	

VAT is shown at 17.5%: changes in this rate may affect prices.

Key to symbols is on back flap.

Inverness		Map Ref: 4B8	

★★★

B&B

Amulree
40 Fairfield Road, Inverness, IV3 5QD
Tel:01463 224822
Email:amulree@supanet.com

Warm and friendly welcome in Victorian house within easy walking distance of town centre and all facilities. Close to Eden Court Theatre and the Aquadome.

2 Single	3 En Suite fac	B&B per person	Open Jan-Dec excl
1 Twin	1 Priv.Bath/Show	from £19.00 Single	Xmas
1 Double		from £20.00 Double	

★★★

GUEST HOUSE

Ardmuir House Hotel
16 Ness Bank, Inverness, Inverness-shire, IV2 4SF
Tel/Fax:01463 231151
Email:hotel@ardmuir.com
Web:www.ardmuir.com

Family run guest house on the bank of the River Ness close to town centre and Ness Islands. Conveniently situated for exploring the Highlands.

1 Single	All En Suite	B&B per person	Open Jan-Dec excl
2 Twin		£33.00-36.00 Single	Xmas/New Year
5 Double		£27.00-33.00 Double	
2 Family			

AWAITING INSPECTION

Aros
5 Abertarff Road, Inverness, IV2 3NW
Tel:01463 235674
Email:aros@5abertarff.fsnet.co.uk

1 Double	All En Suite	B&B per person	Open Jan-Dec excl
2 Family		from £22.00 Double	Xmas/New Year

Atherstone Guest House
42 Fairfield Road, Inverness IV3 5QD
Telephone: 01463 240240

Enjoy a warm Highland welcome at this Victorian home just minutes from town centre. Ensuite rooms, central heating, tea/coffee trays and parking. The friendly atmosphere and personal attention from Alex and Jenny Liddell make Atherstone the ideal place to relax after a day touring Loch Ness and the Highlands.

★★★

B&B

Atherstone
42 Farifield Road, Inverness, IV3 5QD
Tel:01463 240240

Attractively decorated and comfortably furnished with a homely atmosphere. All rooms ensuite. Private parking. 10 minutes walk from town centre. Ideal touring base, most of the Highlands can be visited within a day.

2 Single	All En Suite	B&B per person	Open Jan-Dec excl
2 Double		from £22.00 Single	Xmas/New Year
		from £22.00 Double	

Important: Prices stated are estimates and may be subject to amendments

Inverness   Map Ref: 4B8

★★

B&B

Balcroydon
6 Broadstone Park, Inverness, IV2 3LA
Tel:01463 221506

1 Single	2 En Suite fac	B&B per person	Open Jan-Dec excl
1 Family	1 Pub.Bath/Show	from £21.00 Single	Xmas/New Year
1 Dbl/Twn		from £20.00 Double	
		from £17.00 Room Only	

Semi-detached house in quiet residential road, 5 minutes walk from
town centre, bus and railway station. Off road parking.

BALLIFEARY HOUSE HOTEL
10 BALLIFEARY ROAD, INVERNESS IV3 5PJ
Tel: 44 01463 235572 Fax: 01463 717583
e.mail: info@ballifearyhousehotel.co.uk Web: www.ballifearyhousehotel.co.uk
A lovely Victorian villa built circa 1876. Professionally run by owners. All rooms
with en-suite facilities and tastefully decorated. Warm, friendly, relaxed atmosphere
and No Smoking throughout. Awarded highest quality grade of "5 diamonds" from
AA and "5 stars Guest House" from STB. Private car park and nice gardens.
Minimum age 15 years. A 10 minute picturesque walk to the town centre.

★★★★★

GUEST HOUSE

Ballifeary House Hotel
10 Ballifeary Road, Inverness, IV3 5PJ
Tel:01463 235572 Fax:01463 717583
Email:info@ballifearyhousehotel.co.uk
Web:www.ballifearyhousehotel.co.uk

Attractive detached Victorian villa situated in quiet residential area, and just a
short walk to the Eden Court Theatre, River Ness and many excellent restaurants.
The house is tastefully decorated and furnished throughout and has a very
relaxed and friendly atmosphere. Lovely sitting room with wealth of tourist
information. Large car park in the grounds. Establishment not suitable for
families as minimum age is 15 years.

2 Twin	All En Suite	B&B per person	Open Jan-Dec excl
3 Double		£36.00-39.00 Double	Xmas/New Year

BALTHANGIE B&B
37 Ballifeary Lane, Inverness IV3 5PH
Telephone: 01463 237637 Fax: 01463 224780
e.mail: lesdavidson@tiscali.co.uk
Situated in a quiet residential area with off-street parking only ten
minutes walk from town centre, close to River Ness, Eden Court
Theatre, The Aquadome & Sports Centre and Caledonian Canal.
Balthangie makes a perfect base for touring Loch Ness and the
Highlands. A warm friendly welcome with personal service is assured.

★★★★

B&B

Balthangie B&B
37 Ballifeary Lane, Inverness, IV3 5PH
Tel:01463 237637 Fax:01463 224780
Email:lesdavidson@tiscali.co.uk

Modern family home in quiet residential area, within walking distance of
town centre and all amenities. All the rooms are ensuite and on the
ground floor. Close to Eden Court Theatre, Sports Centre and Aquadome.

1 Twin	All En Suite	B&B per person	Open Jan-Dec
2 Double		from £23.00 Double	

VAT is shown at 17.5%: changes in this rate may affect prices. | Key to symbols is on back flap. |

'Bonnieview'

**Tower Brae (North), Westhill,
Inverness IV2 5FE Tel: 01463 792468
Mobile: 0774 0082464**

At 'Bonnieview' experience a special warmth and hospitality
rare in its sincerity – look out from the dining room with
marvellous views stretching over the Beauly and Moray Firths,
whilst enjoying highly acclaimed home cooking and baking.
Excellent as a touring base for day trips around the
Highlands. Complete ensuite in all rooms. You can relax with
tea and conversation in the lounge beside a soothing coal fire
on those chilly days.
A fine welcome awaits you all.
**B&B £23 per person, £12 dinner.
Only twin/double for 2003.**   ★★★
OPEN ALL YEAR.

Details from *Marjory O'Connor.*

★★★

B&B

Bonnie View

**Towerbrae North, Westhill, Inverness-shire
IV2 5FE
Tel:01463 792468**

Friendly welcome at this modern house quietly located overlooking the
Moray Firth. 2 miles (3kms) from Culloden Moor, 4 miles (6kms) from
Inverness. Evening meal on request.

1 Twin	All En Suite	B&B per person	Open Jan-Dec
1 Double		from £23.00 Double	BB & Eve.Meal
			from £35.00

★★★

B&B

Braehead

**5 Crown Circus, Inverness, IV2 3NH
Tel:01463 224222
Email:ian.mackenzie@tinyworld.co.uk**

Traditional stone built Victorian villa in residential area of Inverness with
easy access to city centre and all amenities. Non-smoking.

1 Double	1 En Suite fac	B&B per person	Open Jan-Dec excl
1 Family	1 Pub.Bath/Show	from £25.00 Single	Xmas/New Year
		from £20.00 Double	

★★★★

**SMALL
HOTEL**

●●●

RESTAURANT

Bunchrew House Hotel

**Bunchrew, Inverness, IV3 8TA
Tel:01463 234917 Fax:01463 710620
Email:welcome@bunchrew-inverness.co.uk
Web:www.bunchrew-inverness.co.uk**

Country house hotel set in 20 acres of woodland on the edge of the
Beauly Firth and yet only 4 miles (6kms) from Inverness.

4 Twin	All En Suite	B&B per person	Open Jan-Dec excl
8 Double		from £80.00 Single	Xmas
2 Family		from £60.00 Double	BB & Eve.Meal
			from £70.00

Important: Prices stated are estimates and may be subject to amendments

Inverness   Map Ref: 4B8

CLACH MHUILINN
7 HARRIS ROAD, INVERNESS IV2 3LS
TEL: 01463 237059 FAX: 01463 242092
E.MAIL: stay@ness.co.uk WEB: www.ness.co.uk

Clach Mhuilinn, a 5 star B&B has two delightful en-suite
bedrooms, one double and one king/twin bedded suite with own
sitting room. Every facility and many extra touches to enhance
your stay. Delicious breakfasts served overlooking the beautiful
garden. No smoking. Convenient for golf course, Loch Ness,
Culloden, Cawdor Castle etc.

★★★★★

B&B

Clach Mhuilinn
7 Harris Road, Inverness, IV2 3LS
Tel:01463 237059   Fax:01463 242092
Email:stay@ness.co.uk
Web:www.ness.co.uk

Excellent, welcoming B&B hospitality, in modern detached home, in
Inverness residential area. Two charming bedrooms: one double, one
twin suite, each with en-suite shower room, and many extra touches to
make your stay special. Small friendly and unpretentious. Delicious
breakfast served overlooking colourful, mature gardens.

1 Double	All En Suite	B&B per person	Open Mar-Nov
1 Twin/		from £30.00 Double	
King Suite			

Craigside Lodge
**4 GORDON TERRACE
INVERNESS IV2 3HD
TEL: 01463 231576
FAX: 01463 713409
E.MAIL:
craigsidelodge@amserve.net**

Delightfully situated overlooking the
River Ness and enjoying panoramic
views of Cathedral, Castle and town,
this Georgian house offers comfortable
ensuite bedrooms, spacious lounge
and yet just a few minutes walk to
town centre, bus and railway stations.
Guests can be sure of a real Highland
welcome.

★★★

**GUEST
HOUSE**

Craigside Lodge
4 Gordon Terrace, Inverness, IV2 3HD
Tel:01463 231576   Fax:01463 713409
Email:craigsidelodge@amserve.net
Web:http://guesthouses.co.uk/

Delightfully situated Georgian house overlooking the River Ness, and
enjoying panoramic views from the lounge towards the cathedral, castle
and the city, with distant hills beyond. Within a few minutes walk of all
the amenities of the highland capital.

2 Twin	All En Suite	B&B per person	Open Jan-Dec
3 Double		from £25.00 Single	
		from £22.00 Double	

Scotland's National Booking
and Information Line

Tel: 0845 22 55 121
visitscotland.com

VAT is shown at 17.5%: changes in this rate may affect prices. | Key to symbols is on back flap. |

Inverness

Map Ref: 4B8

GUEST HOUSE

★★★

Dalmore Guest House
101 Kenneth Street, Inverness, IV3 5QQ
Tel:01463 237224 Fax:01463 712249
Email:dalmoreguesthouse@amserve.net

Comfortable family run guest house close to the centre of Inverness and all facilities. Private parking. Ground floor room available. Credit cards accepted.

2 Single	4 En Suite fac	B&B per person	Open Jan-Dec
1 Twin	2 Pub.Bath/Show	from £25.00 Single	
1 Double		from £23.00 Double	
2 Family			

EASTER MUCKOVIE FARMHOUSE
Mr & Mrs J Maclellan, Inverness IV2 5BN
Tel: 01463 791556   e.mail: cullodenbb@talk21.com
Web: www.cullodenbb.com
Ideally situated for visiting many historical sites. Scenic views of Moray Firth and Black Isle from grounds. Many golf courses within twenty miles. Well tended garden in which guests can relax. Tastefully decorated bedrooms. A varied and substantial breakfast is cooked and served by owners.

B&B

★★★★

Easter Muckovie Farmhouse
Westhill, Inverness, IV2 5BN
Tel:01463 791556
Email:cullodenbb@talk21.com
Web:www.cullodenbb.com

Extended farmhouse on edge of town, with easy access to main routes, and all of local amenities. Culloden battlefield, Cawdor Castle and many other historic sites in the area. Excellent base for exploring the Highlands and the Moray coast.

2 Family	1 En Suite fac	B&B per person	Open Jan-Dec excl
	1 Pub.Bath/Show	from £25.00 Single	Xmas/New Year
		from £18.00 Double	

GUEST HOUSE

★★

Fairways Guest House
72 Telford Road, Inverness, IV3 8HN
Tel:01463 224934
Email:janenestor@ecosse.net

Friendly welcome in our family run modernised guest house in quiet residential area. Close to town centre and all amenities. Children and pets welcome.

4 Twin	2 En Suite fac	B&B per person	Open Jan-Dec excl
2 Double	2 Priv.NOT ensuite	from £20.00 Single	Xmas/New Year
		from £18.00 Double	
		from £16.00 Room Only	

B&B

★★

Furan Cottage
100 Old Edinburgh Road, Inverness, IV2 3HT
Tel:01463 712094
Email:furancottage@talk21.com

Family home on main road, 1 mile (2kms) from town centre. Private parking. No smoking house. Evening meals by prior arrangement.

2 Single	3 Priv.NOT ensuite	B&B per person	Open Jan-Dec excl
1 Double	1 Pub.Bath/Show	from £15.00 Single	Xmas/New Year
1 Family		from £15.00 Double	BB & Eve.Meal from £25.00

Important: Prices stated are estimates and may be subject to amendments

Inverness | Map Ref: 4B8

B&B ★★★

Handa
56 Lochalsh Road, Inverness, IV3 8HW
Tel:01463 236530 Fax:01463 229575
Email:handa@bun.com
Web:www.handaguesthouse.co.uk

Family home in residential area with all rooms on ground floor. 15 minute walk to city centre and all amenities. Transport to/from Rail and Bus stations and airport available by prior arrangement.

1 Single	2 Priv.NOT ensuite	B&B per person	Open Jan-Dec
1 Twin		from £18.00 Single	BB & Eve.Meal
2 Double		from £18.00 Double	from £25.00

Highfield House
62 Old Edinburgh Road, Inverness IV2 3PG
Telephone/Fax: 01463 238892
e.mail: highfieldhouse62@talk21.com

Highfield House is a family home offering quality accommodation and warm Scottish hospitality. We are situated in a quiet residential area with off-road private parking yet only 10 minutes walk from the town centre. One double room with ensuite shower room, one family/double/twin room with private shower room. Price for 2003 – £22 per person family/double/twin with private shower, £24 per person for en-suite double room.

★★★★
B&B

Highfield House
62 Old Edinburgh Road, Inverness, IV2 3PG
Tel/Fax:01463 238892
Email:highfieldhouse62@talk21.com

Warm friendly welcome in spacious detached house standing in its own grounds in a quiet residential area but only 0.5 miles (1km) from the city centre.

1 Double	Show En Suite	B&B per person	Open Feb-Oct
1 Family	Priv.Show	from £30.00 Single	
		from £24.00 Double	

★★
B&B

J A Jamieson
The Linn, Inshes, Inverness, IV2 5BG
Tel:01463 231260
Email:alanjmsn@aol.com
Web:www.visitscotland.net

Large detached property (all rooms ground floor), in a quiet location set in 2 acres of grounds and garden. 1 mile from town centre.

2 Twin	1 En Suite fac	B&B per person	Open Apr-Nov
	1 Pub.Bath/Show	£22.00-25.00 Single	BB & Eve.Meal
		£22.00-25.00 Double	from £35.00

★★★
GUEST HOUSE

Larchfield House
15 Ness Bank, Inverness, IV2 4SF
Tel:01463 233874 Fax:01463 711600
Email:info@larchfieldhouse.com
Web:www.larchfieldhouse.com

Peacefully situated on the banks of the River Ness and yet within five minutes pleasant walk to the city centre, rail and coach terminals. Larchfield House offers quality accommodation at a reasonable price. All rooms are fully ensuite and prices include a traditional cooked breakfast. All produce is sourced locally.

1 Single	All En Suite	B&B per person	Open Jan-Dec excl
1 Twin		from £25.00 Single	Xmas/New Year
3 Double		from £25.00 Double	
1 Family			

VAT is shown at 17.5%: changes in this rate may affect prices.

Key to symbols is on back flap.

Inverness   Map Ref: 4B8

★★★★

B&B

Lorne House
40 Crown Drive, Inverness, IV2 3QG
Tel:01463 236271

Victorian detached house in quiet residential area, close to town centre
and railway station. Guest car parking. Ensuite facilities.

1 Twin 1 Double	All En Suite	B&B per person from £23.00 Double	Open Jan-Dec excl Xmas/New Year

---

★★★

B&B

Lynver
30 Southside Road, Inverness, IV2 3BG
Tel:01463 242906
Email:lynver@talk21.com

Extremely comfortable modern detached villa in quiet residential area
within five minutes walk of city centre and easy strolling distance of a
wide range of cafes, bars and restaurants, yet within easy access of all
major road networks to and from Inverness. An excellent base for
exploring the beauty of the Highlands. Private parking available on site.

1 Twin 2 Double	All En Suite	B&B per person from £25.00 Single from £20.00 Double from £17.00 Room Only	Open Jan-Dec excl Xmas/New Year

---

MALVERN
54 KENNETH STREET, INVERNESS IV3 5PZ
Tel/Fax: 01463 242251   e.mail: malvern.guesthouse@virgin.net
Web: http://freespace.virgin.net/raymond.mackenzie

Large Victorian house situated ten minutes from city centre offering comfortable
bedrooms complete with hospitality tray, TV, ensuite, separate dining room and
extensive breakfast menu, conservatory and guest lounge. Enclosed car park. Airport,
rail, bus links readily accessible. Cinemas, restaurants, theatre, sports facilities close
by. Excellent base for day trips. Non-smoking. Payment may be made by credit card.

★★★

**GUEST
HOUSE**

Malvern Bed + Breakfast
54 Kenneth Street, Inverness, IV3 5PZ
Tel/Fax:01463 242251
Email:malvern.guesthouse@virgin.net
Web:http://freespace.virgin.net/raymond.mackenzie

Victorian detached house in central location in Inverness. Off-street
parking. All rooms are ensuite.

1 Twin 3 Double 3 Family	All En Suite	B&B per person from £20.00 Double	Open Jan-Dec

---

★★★

**GUEST
HOUSE**

Melrose Villa
35 Kenneth Street, Inverness, IV3 5DH
Tel:01463 233745
Email:info@melrosevilla.com
Web:www.melrosevilla.com

Warm and frienldly, family run guest house within a few minutes walk of
the town centre. Close to Eden Court Theatre, Sports Centre and
Swimming Pool. Many places offering good food nearby.

3 Single 1 Twin 3 Double 2 Family	7 En Suite fac 1 Pub Show	B&B per person from £20.00 Single from £20.00 Double	Open Jan-Dec excl Xmas

---

Important: Prices stated are estimates and may be subject to amendments

Inverness

Map Ref: 4B8

★★★★★

B&B

Millwood House
36 Old Mill Road, Inverness, IV2 3HR
Tel:01463 237254 Fax:01463 719400

3 Double	Some En Suite
	1 Pub.Bath/Show

B&B per person
from £50.00 Single
from £35.00 Double
from £65.00 Room
Only

Open Mar-Dec excl
Xmas/New Year

A warm friendly welcome in comfortable family home with cosy
traditional cottage style bedrooms. Large secluded garden, in pleasant
residential area close to town centre.

MOYNESS HOUSE
6 BRUCE GARDENS, INVERNESS IV3 5EN
Telephone/Fax: 01463 233836
e.mail: stay@moyness.co.uk   Web: www.moyness.co.uk
*This fine Victorian villa has been sympathetically restored with elegant
decoration and furnishings enhancing the many beautiful original features.
The delightful bedrooms (all en-suite) offer modern comfort and period charm.
All are no smoking. Pretty garden and ample parking.
Located in quiet area near town centre, theatre and lovely riverside.*
Brochure from Jenny and Richard Jones or book on 01463 233836.

★★★★★

GUEST
HOUSE

Moyness House
6 Bruce Gardens, Inverness, IV3 5EN
Tel/Fax:01463 233836
Email:stay@moyness.co.uk
Web:www.moyness.co.uk

1 Single	All En Suite
2 Twin	
3 Double	
1 Family	

B&B per person
£33.00-37.00 Single
£33.00-37.00 Double

Open Jan-Dec excl
Xmas/New Year

Gracious Victorian villa with attractive walled garden. Family run, in
quiet area. Short walk to town centre, river, Eden Court Theatre and
many sporting amenities. Moyness House is totally non-smoking.

★★★★

B&B

Sealladh Sona
3 Whinpark, Canal Road, Muirtown, Inverness IV3 8NQ
Tel/Fax:01463 239209
Email:cooksona@aol.com
Web:http://members.aol.com/cooksona

2 Twin	All En Suite
1 Double	

B&B per person
£31.00-36.00 Single
£26.00-31.00 Double

Open Jan-Dec excl
Xmas/New Year

A Scottish couple welcome you to their modernised but traditional-style
120 year old home, peacefully situated overlooking the Caledonian Canal
and Inverness, but only 10 minutes from the city centre. Vegetarian
breakfasts available. Homemade biscuits on the hospitality tray. Private
parking.

Scotland's National Booking and Information Line

Tel: 0845 22 55 121
visitscotland.com

VAT is shown at 17.5%: changes in this rate may affect prices.

Key to symbols is on back flap.

Inverness				Map Ref: 4B8		

GUEST HOUSE
★★★

Strathmhor Guesthouse
99 Kenneth Street, Inverness, IV3 5QQ
Tel:01463 235397

1 Single
2 Family

1 Pub.Bath/Show

Bed+Breakfast
£22.00-26.00 Single
£38.00-44.00 Dbl/Twn
£48.00-60.00 Triple
£50.00-65.00 Fam

Open Jan-Dec

Scottish hospitality in friendly family home. 10 minutes walk from town centre.

Sunnyholm

12 MAYFIELD ROAD, INVERNESS IV2 4AE
Telephone: 01463 231336 Fax: 01463 715788
e.mail: ago7195587@aol.com
Web: www.invernessguesthouse.com

This well-appointed, traditionally built Scottish bungalow of the early 1930s is situated in a large, mature, secluded garden in a very pleasant, residential area and has ample private parking. It is within 6-7 minutes walking distance of the town centre, castle, Tourist Information Centre Office and other essential holiday amenities.

B&B
★★★

Sunnyholm
12 Mayfield Road, Inverness, IV2 4AE
Tel:01463 231336   Fax:01463 715788
Email:ago7195587@aol.com
Web:www.invernessguesthouse.com

2 Twin
2 Double

All En Suite

B&B per person
from £25.00 Single
from £20.00 Double

Open Jan-Dec excl
Xmas/New Year

Bungalow situated in quiet residential area close to town centre and castle. All bedrooms ensuite and on ground floor. Private car park.

B&B
★★★★

Taigh Na Teile
6 Island Bank Road, Inverness, Inverness-shire
IV2 4SY
Tel:01463 222842 Fax:01463 713760
Email:jenny@islandbank.co.uk
Web:www.islandbank.co.uk

1 Twin
2 Double

All En Suite

B&B per person
£20.00-30.00 Single
£20.00-25.00 Double

Open Jan-Dec excl
Xmas/New Year

Bed and Breakfast in a comfortable home. Situated in a quiet location with views over River Ness yet only a short walk to town centre and all its amenities. Eden Court Theatre close by.

B&B
★★★

Tamarue
70a Ballifeary Road, Inverness, Inverness-shire
IV3 5PF
Tel:01463 239724

1 Twin
1 Double

1 En Suite fac
1 Priv.NOT ensuite

B&B per person
£15.00-25.00 Single
£15.00-20.00 Double
from £16.00 Room
Only

Open Jan-Dec excl
Xmas/New Year

Situated in quiet residential area, close to town centre, River Ness, golf course, Eden Court Theatre, Aquadome and Sports Centre. Off street parking.

Important: Prices stated are estimates and may be subject to amendments

Inverness   Map Ref: 4B8

STONEA

3A RESAURIE, SMITHTON, BY INVERNESS IV2 7NH
Telephone: 01463 791714 e.mail: mbmansfield@uk2.net
Web: www.mansfieldhighlandholidays.f2s.com
3 miles east of Inverness. We are in a small residential area adjacent
to farmland overlooking Moray Firth, Ross-shire Hills, Ben Wyvis.
Ground floor double and twin sharing bathroom. Double ensuite.
High tea, dinner by arrangement. Ample parking. Great Britain Cycle
Route 7 passes us. Non-smoking. Public transport nearby.

★★
B&B

Stonea

3a Resaurie, Smithton, Inverness, IV2 7NH
Tel:01463 791714
Email:mbmansfield@uk2.net
Web:www.mansfieldhighlandholidays.f2s.com

Modern house set in quiet residential area 4 miles (6kms) from Inverness
with panoramic views across the Moray Firth. Warm and friendly stay
assured. Non-smoking. Home-cooked evening meals by arrangement.

1 Twin	1 En Suite fac	B&B per person	Open Jan-Dec excl
2 Double	1 Priv.NOT ensuite	from £17.00 Double	Xmas/New Year
			BB & Eve.Meal
			from £29.00

John o'Groats, Caithness   Map Ref: 4E2

★★★
B&B

Bayview

Post Office, Canisbay, nr John o'Groats, KW1 4YH
Tel/Fax:01955 611213
Email:john-o-groats@ukf.net
Web:www.john-o-groats.ukf.net

100 year old Post Office house. Panoramic views of Pentland Firth, close
to John O'Groats and Orkney Ferries. Personally run. Extensive breakfast
menu.

1 Twin	Priv.fac	B&B per person	Open Easter-Sep
1 Double	Ensuite	from £25.00 Single	
		from £22.00 Double	

★★★
B&B

Bencorragh House

Upper Gills, Canisbay, Caithness, KW1 4YD
Tel/Fax:01955 611449
Email:bartonsandy@hotmail.com
Web:www.bencorraghhouse.com

A working croft with Jacobs sheep, Highland cattle and Jersey cows,
horses, chickens and other animals. Excellent outlook over the Pentland
Firth towards the island of Stroma. Comfortable and spacious
accommodation; a warm welcome and relaxing atmosphere. Excellent
base for unwinding, while you explore this fascinating coastline and
beyond.

1 Twin	All En Suite	B&B per person	Open Mar-Nov
1 Double		from £25.00 Single	Winter by
1 Family		from £22.00 Double	arrangement
			BB & Eve.Meal
			from £34.50

★★
**GUEST
HOUSE**

Caber Feidh Guest House

John O'Groats, Wick, Caithness, KW1 4YR
Tel:01955 611219

Centrally situated in John O' Groats and 2 miles (3kms) from Duncansby
Head. It is well situated for exploring the north east, including the north
coast of Sutherland, the inland Flow Country, and more. Day trips to
Orkney are a popular choice.

2 Single	7 En Suite fac	B&B per person	Open Jan-Dec
4 Twin		from £18.00 Single	BB & Eve.Meal
3 Double		from £17.00 Double	from £28.00
5 Family			

VAT is shown at 17.5%: changes in this rate may affect prices.   Key to symbols is on back flap.

John o'Groats, Caithness | Map Ref: 4E2

★★

B&B

The Hawthorns
Mey, Thurso, Caithness, KW14 8XH
Tel:01847 851710
Email:hawthorns.scotland@btinternet.com
Web:www.hawthorns.scotland.btinternet.co.uk

Spacious modern house, situated in the quiet village of Mey, on the north coast of Scotland. Open outlook towards Dunnet Head and across the Pentland Firth. Excellent base for exploring this fascinating corner of Scotland.

| 3 Double | All En Suite | B&B per person from £20.00 Single from £20.00 Double from £15.00 Room Only | Open Jan-Dec BB & Eve.Meal from £32.00 |

★★

B&B

Mill House
John O'Groats, Caithness, KW1 4YR
Tel:01955 611239

Traditional farmhouse, with all rooms on the ground floor; situated on working mixed stock farm, 0.5 mile from John O' Groats and the Orkney passenger ferry, also from Gill Bay car ferry. Views over the Pentland Firth towards Stroma and Orkney. Duncansby Head, famous for its cliffs, Stacks and seabirds, is a short distance away. Much more to see and do in the area.

| 1 Twin
2 Double | 1 Priv.NOT ensuite
1 Pub.Bath/Show | B&B per person from £25.00 Single £17.00-18.50 Double | Open May-Oct |

Kincraig, by Kingussie, Inverness-shire | Map Ref: 4C10

★★★

GUEST
HOUSE

Braeriach Guest House
Braeriach Road, Kincraig, by Kingussie
Inverness-shire, PH21 1QA
Tel/Fax:01540 651369
Web:www.braeriachgh.com

Former manse situated on the banks of the River Spey with picturesque garden extending to private jetty. Dinners available using home grown vegetables and free range eggs.

| 1 Twin
1 Double
1 Family | All En Suite | B&B per person from £25.00 Single from £22.50 Double | Open Jan-Dec BB & Eve.Meal from £40.00 |

INSH HALL LODGE
Kincraig, Inverness-shire PH21 1NU
Telephone: 01540 651272 Fax: 01540 651208
e.mail: office@lochinsh.com   Web: www.lochinsh.com
Superb 14-acre woodland setting bordering scenic Loch Insh, RSPB, Cairngorms. Part of Loch Insh Watersports. Free watersports (set times/min 2 nights). En-suite B&B 150m from beach and Boathouse Restaurant/Bar. TV lounges, sauna, minigym. Children's adventure areas, lochside walk, ski slope, mountain bikes. 7 miles south of Aviemore. Dec-Apr downhill/snowboard packages.

★

GUEST
HOUSE

Insh Hall Lodge
Kincraig, Inverness-shire, PH21 1NU
Tel:01540 651272 Fax:01540 651208
Email:office@lochinsh.com Web:www.lochinsh.com

Family ensuite accommodation just 150m from the beach of scenic Loch Insh. Licensed Boathouse restaurant overlooking the activities on the water. Free watersports (set times) for guests staying 2 nights. Sauna, minigym, laundry, TV lounges. Dry ski slope, archery, mountain bikes, interpretation trail, children's adventure area. Dec - April downhill ski hire/instruction.

| 2 Single
6 Twin
5 Double
7 Family | All En Suite | B&B per person from £24.50 Single from £19.50 Double | Open Jan-Dec BB & Eve.Meal from £34.50 |

Important: Prices stated are estimates and may be subject to amendments

Kincraig, by Kingussie, Inverness-shire

Map Ref: 4C10

★★★

GUEST HOUSE

Insh House Guesthouse

Kincraig, by Kingussie, Inverness-shire, PH21 1NU
Tel:01540 651377
Email:inshhouse@btinternet.com
Web:www.kincraig.com/inshhouse.htm

Set in spacious grounds, this C listed Telford designed Manse, c1827, has all the original charm of a traditional Highland home. In good walking country, it is close to Glenfeshie & Loch Insh and equidistant from Kingussie & Aviemore. Birdwatching, watersports and skiing nearby.

2 Single	2 En Suite fac	B&B per person	Open Boxing Day –
1 Twin	1 Pub.Bath/Show	from £19.00 Single	end Oct
1 Double		from £20.00 Double	BB & Eve.Meal
1 Family			from £30.00

★★★

B&B

Kirkbeag B&B

Kincraig, Kingussie, Inverness-shire, PH21 1ND
Tel/Fax:01540 651298
Email:kirkbeag@kincraig.com
Web:www.kincraig.com

19c church, in quiet location converted to family home. Spiral staircase and craft workshop. Craft courses available. Aviemore 5 Miles (8 kms). Smokers welcome.

1 Twin	2 Pub Bath/Show	B&B per person	Open Jan-Dec
1 Double		from £21.00 Single	
		from £19.50 Double	

Kingussie, Inverness-shire

Map Ref: 4B11

ARDEN HOUSE

Newtonmore Road, Kingussie, Inverness-shire PH21 1HE
Tel/Fax: 01540 661369
e.mail: ardenhouse@tiscali.co.uk Web: www.kingussie.co.uk/ardenhouse

Arden House provides real home comfort in elegant surroundings. Feature bedrooms for that special occasion with full range of extras. Log fire in season in comfortable lounge featuring books and newspapers. Excellent traditional and vegetarian breakfasts. Offering great value for weekend breaks, main holidays, touring or business.

★★★

GUEST HOUSE

Arden House

Newtonmore Road, Kingussie, PH21 1HE
Tel:01540 661369
Email:ardenhouse@tiscali.co.uk
Web:www.kingussie.co.uk/ardenhouse

Conveniently sited for visiting the beautiful Spey Valley and Cairngorms, Arden House is family run to a high standard. Attractively decorated bedrooms with hospitality trays. Open log fire in comfortable lounge. A personal service and warm welcome assured. Ample parking. Perfect base for touring, golfing, fishing, walking and watersports.

2 Twin	3 En Suite fac	B&B per person	Open Jan-Dec
2 Double	1 Shared fac	from £19.00 Single	BB & Eve.Meal
1 Family		from £19.00 Double	from £29.00
		from £17.00 Room	
		Only	

Scotland's National Booking and Information Line

Tel: 0845 22 55 121
visitscotland.com

VAT is shown at 17.5%: changes in this rate may affect prices.

Key to symbols is on back flap.

Kingussie, Inverness-shire

Map Ref: 4B11

★★★★

GUEST HOUSE

Avondale House

Newtonmore Road, Kingussie, Inverness-shire PH21 1HF
Tel:01540 661731 Fax:01540 662362
Email:avondalehouse@talk21.com
Web:www.avondalehouse.com

A splendid example of an Edwardian home near centre of village, quiet location This family run Guest House is attractively furnished and equipped with all we hope you could need for a comfortable, relaxing stay. Excellent home cooking. A beautiful part of Scotland ideal for outdoor pursuits, ski-ing, cycling, sailing, walking and birdwatching.

2 Twin	All En suite	B&B per person	Open Jan-Dec excl
1 Double		from £24.00 Single	Xmas
		from £24.00 Double	BB & Eve.Meal
			from £35.00

Columba House Hotel & Garden Restaurant

Manse Road, Kingussie, Inverness-shire PH21 1JF
Telephone: 01540 661402 Fax: 01540 661652
W e.mail: reservations@columbahousehotel.com
web: www.columbahousehotel.com

★★★
SMALL HOTEL

Nestling in large grounds. Garden Restaurant, with patio onto landscaped walled garden, ideal for summertime dining, offers superb traditional cuisine. Cosy bar. Open fire in homely lounge. Beautiful en-suite bedrooms, views, romantic four-poster rooms, with double baths. Friendly atmosphere, your comfort and enjoyment is our priority. Ample parking. AA ◆◆◆◆

★★★

SMALL HOTEL

Columba House & Garden Restaurant

Manse Road, Kingussie, PH21 1JF
Tel:01540 661402 Fax:01540 661652
Email:reservations@columbahousehotel.com
Web:www.columbahousehotel.com

Nestling in large grounds. Excellent cuisine in Garden Restaurant in the landscaped, walled garden. Warm, cosy bar, open fire in lounge. Friendly atmosphere. Romantic Four-Poster rooms. Ample parking.

3 Twin	All En Suite	B&B per person	Open Jan-Dec
3 Double		from £35.00 Single	BB & Eve.Meal
2 Family		from £30.00 Double	from £48.00

GLENGARRY
Bed & Breakfast
★★★★

East Terrace, Kingussie, Inverness-shire PH21 1JS
Telephone/Fax: 01540 661386
e.mail: glengarry@scot89.freeserve.co.uk Web: www.scot89.freeserve.co.uk

Traditional Victorian villa situated in its own tranquil grounds with private off-road parking. Glengarry has an enviable reputation for comfort and quality, provides the perfect base for all year round pursuits and is ideally suited to the discerning visitor. A warm welcome is assured.

★★★★

B&B

Glengarry

Janet & Roger Crawford, East Terrace, Kingussie
Inverness-shire, PH21 1JS
Tel/Fax:01540 661386
Email:glengarry@scot89.freeserve.co.uk
Web:www.scot89.freeserve.co.uk

Stone built house c1900 with large garden and summer house, in quiet residential area, only a few minutes walk from centre of Kingussie. No smoking throughout.

2 Single	All En Suite	B&B per person	Open Jan-Dec
1 Twin		from £23.00 Single	BB & Eve.Meal
1 Double		from £23.00 Double	from £38.00

Important: Prices stated are estimates and may be subject to amendments

Kingussie, Inverness-shire   Map Ref: 4B11

Homewood Lodge

Newtonmore Road, Kingussie PH21 1HD   Tel: 01540 661507
e.mail: jennifer@homewood-lodge-kingussie.co.uk
Web: http://www.homewood-lodge-kingussie.co.uk   ★★★★

Homewood Lodge, a beautifully decorated Victorian house set in mature gardens, offers a tranquil base from which to tour in all directions, or enjoy golfing, fishing, bird watching or walking in the surrounding area. Splendid views of the Cairngorms from the dining room where only superb fresh food is served.

★★★★

GUEST HOUSE

Homewood Lodge

Newtonmore Road, Kingussie, Inverness-shire PH21 1HD
Tel:01540 661507
Email:jennifer@homewood-lodge-kingussie.co.uk
Web:www.homewood-lodge-kingussie.co.uk

Detached Victorian stone villa, situated on elevated position at the southern end of the village. Enjoying outstanding vistas towards the River Spey and the Cairngorms. Extensive use of fresh and local produce.

1 Twin	All En Suite	B&B per person	Open Jan-Dec
2 Double		from £15.00 Single	BB & Eve.Meal
1		from £15.00 Double	from £25.00
Dbl/Twn/		from £15.00 Room	
Family		Only	

★★★

SMALL HOTEL

●●

HOME COOKING

The Osprey Hotel

Ruthven Road, Kingussie, Inverness-shire, PH21 1EN
Tel/Fax:01540 661510
Email:aileen@ospreyhotel.co.uk
Web:www.ospreyhotel.co.uk

Personally run hotel in centre of village, imaginative cuisine including vegetarian meals using fresh produce. Taste of Scotland member.

1 Single	All En Suite	B&B per person	Open Jan-Dec
3 Twin		from £25.00 Single	BB & Eve.Meal
4 Double		from £25.00 Double	from £39.00

★★★★

B&B

Rowan House

Homewood, Newtonmore Road, Kingussie
Inverness-shire, PH21 1HD   Tel:01540 662153
Email:info@RowanHouseScotland.com
Web:www.RowanHouseScotland.com

Enjoys outstanding views of the Spey Valley and Cairngorms. Situated in a quiet hillside position at the southern end of Kingussie. On National Cycle Route 7. Accommodation includes suite comprising of double and twin bedrooms, bathroom and lounge with colour TV, video and hi-fi. Ideal for families.

1 Twin	All En Suite	B&B per person	Open Jan-Dec excl
2 Double		from £19.00 Single	Xmas
		from £19.00 Double	

Kinlochewe, Ross-shire   Map Ref: 3G8

★★★

B&B

Cromasaig (Liz Forrest)

Kinlochewe, Wester-Ross, IV22 2PE
Tel:01445 760234
Email:cromasaig@msn.com
Web:www.cromasaig.com

Warm hospitality from climbing hosts in refurbished croft house, with drying room, at foot of Beinn Eighe. Non-smoking throughout. UK (non-passported) dogs welcome indoors. Evening meals available using home grown produce where possible.

1 Twin	3 Pub.Bath/Show	B&B per person	Open Jan-Dec
1 Double		£20.00 Single	BB & Eve.Meal
1 Family		£20.00 Double	£33.00

Kinlochleven, Argyll | Map Ref: 3H12

★★★

B&B

Edencoille
Garbhien Road, Kinlochleven, Argyll, PA40 4SE
Tel/Fax:01855 831358

2 Twin	2 En Suite fac	B&B per person	Open Jan-Dec
1 Double	2 Priv.NOT ensuite	from £36.00 Single	BB & Eve.Meal
1 Family		from £18.00 Double	from £30.00

A warm, friendly welcome and excellent home cooking at our family-run B&B. Perfect base for touring, fishing, skiing, climbing, walking or just relaxing. We are situated opposite the Mamores, famous for their 12 Munroes which are within 5 mins walking distance from Edencoille.

★★★

GUEST HOUSE

Tigh-Na-Cheo Guest House
Garbhein Road, Kinlochleven, PH50 4SE
Tel/Fax:01855 831434
Email:reception@tigh-na-cheo.co.uk
Web:www.tigh-na-cheo.co.uk

2 Twin	All En Suite	B&B per person	Open Jan-Dec excl
2 Double		£25.00-30.00 Single	Xmas/New Year
4 Family		from £23.00 Double	BB & Eve.Meal
			from £35.00

On the edge of the village, with views of the Mamore Hills. Drying facilities available. Hearty cooked breakfast and evening meal provided.

Kyle of Lochalsh, Ross-shire | Map Ref: 3F9

★

B&B

Achomraich
Main Road, Kyle of Lochalsh, IV40 8DA
Tel:01599 534210

1 Twin	1 Priv.NOT ensuite	B&B per person	Open Apr-Oct
2 Double		from £20.00 Single	
		from £17.00 Double	

Warm welcome. Near all amenities. Peaceful. 10 mins walk from railway and bus station.

★★★★

B&B

●●
HOME COOKING

The Old Schoolhouse
Tigh Fasgaidh, Erbusaig, Kyle, Ross-shire IV40 8BB
Tel/Fax:01599 534369
Email:cuminecandj@lineone.net
Web:www.highland.plus.com/schoolhouse

1 Twin	All En Suite	B&B per person	Open Jan-Dec excl
2 Double		from £35.00 Single	Xmas/New Year
		from £25.00 Double	

Spacious family home with very comfortable ensuite accommodation, offering fine dining,using the best of local and Scottish produce.

Scotland's National Booking and Information Line

Tel: 0845 22 55 121
visitscotland.com

Important: Prices stated are estimates and may be subject to amendments

Kyle of Lochalsh, Ross-shire — Map Ref: 3F9

SOLUIS GUEST HOUSE

Braeintra, by Achmore, Stromeferry, Wester Ross IV53 8UP
Tel: 01599 577219 e.mail: marscott@rapidial.co.uk
Web: www.highlandsaccommodation.co.uk

Situated in peaceful and scenic Strath Ascaig amid forestry and a
wide variety of flora and fauna. An ideal centre for exploring
Torridon, Skye, Glenelg and Kintail. Less than 25 minutes drive to
Plockton, Eilean Donan Castle, Stromeferry, Skye Bridge and the
new premises for the Born Free Foundation. Licensed Guest House.

★★

**GUEST
HOUSE**

Soluis Mu Thuath

Braeintra, by Achmore, Lochalsh, Ross-shire
IV53 8UP
Tel/Fax:01599 577219
Email:marscott@rapidial.co.uk

Set amidst open countryside with open views. Excellent centre for North
West of Scotland including Skye, Applecross and Torridon. No smoking.
Evening meal available. Suitable for disabled accommodation.

3 Twin	All En Suite
1 Double	
1 Family	

B&B per person
from £30.00 Single
from £23.00 Double

Open Jan-Dec excl
Xmas/New Year
BB & Eve.Meal
from £35.00

Laide, Ross-shire — Map Ref: 3F6

'CUL NA MARA'

Catalina Slipway, Sand Passage, Laide, Ross-shire IV22 2ND
Tel: 01445 731295   Fax: 01445 731570
e.mail: billhart@dircon.co.uk or billhart@deathsdoor.com
Web: www.culnamara-guesthouse.co.uk

A stay at "Cul Na Mara" (Gaelic – Song of the sea) is an enjoyable experience.
Superior bed and breakfast accommodation. Guest rooms fully ensuite and fitted with
colour television. Private dining room. Scottish high tea – an available option. Fully
laid out garden overlooking the Minch. Private parking. Early booking advisable.

★★★

B&B

Cul Na Mara Guest House

Catalina Slipway, Sand Passage, Laide, Ross-shire IV22 2ND
Tel:01445 731295   Fax:01445 731570
Email:billhart@dircon.co.uk
Web:www.culnamara-guesthouse.co.uk

Modern Highland home in quiet crofting area. Excellent sandy beaches
nearby. Home cooking, with emphasis on fresh produce. Evening high tea
available and evening meals by prior arrangement.

1 Double	All En Suite
1 Family	

B&B per person
from £33.00 Single
from £23.00 Double

Open Jan-Dec excl
Xmas/New Year
BB & Eve.Meal
from £34.00-36.00

Lairg, Sutherland — Map Ref: 4A6

★★★

B&B

Ambleside

Lochside, Lairg, Sutherland, IV27 4EG
Tel:01549 402130

Modern personally run bed and breakfast, comfortable and well
furnished, centrally situated in quiet location with private parking.
Evening meal available on request.

1 Twin	3 En Suite fac
2 Double	

B&B per person
from £18.00 Double

Open Jan-Dec
BB & Eve.Meal
from £26.00

VAT is shown at 17.5%: changes in this rate may affect prices.   **Key to symbols is on back flap.**

Lairg, Sutherland

Map Ref: 4A6

★★★

B&B

Lochview
Lochside, Lairg, Sutherland, IV27 4EH
Tel/Fax:01549 402578
Email:georgemorgan@lochviewlairg.fsnet.co.uk

| 2 Twin | All En Suite |
| 1 Double | |

B&B per person
from £22.00 Single
from £20.00 Double

Open Jan-Dec excl
Xmas/New Year
BB & Eve.Meal
from £30.00

Recently modernised and refurbished house. Located in position on edge of Loch Shin, all amenities close by. Ideal location for touring the Highlands. Boat available for guests for fishing or rowing on Loch Shin. Ideal spot for birdwatching in both Lairg and N.W. Sutherland.

Lochcarron, Ross-shire

Map Ref: 3G9

★★★

B&B

Castle Cottage
Main Street, Lochcarron, Ross-shire, IV54 8YB
Tel:01520 722564

| 1 Twin | 1 En Suite fac |
| 2 Double | 1 Priv.NOT ensuite |

B&B per person
from £25.00 Single
£18.00-23.00 Double

Open Jan-Dec excl
Xmas/New Year

Modernised detached house in village centre with fine views across Loch Carron from all rooms.

Lochinver, Sutherland

Map Ref: 3G5

★★★

GUEST
HOUSE

Ardglas Guest House
Inver, Lochinver, Sutherland, IV27 4LJ
Tel:01571 844257   Fax:01571 844632
Email:ardglas@btinternet.com

1 Single	3 Shared fac
1 Twin	
4 Double	
2 Family	

B&B per person
£17.00-19.00 Single
£17.00-19.00 Double
from £15.00 Room
Only

Open Jan-Dec
BB & Eve.Meal
from £28.00

Set above this popular fishing village with spectacular harbour, sea and mountain views. Homely atmosphere. Private parking. See us on the search engine Google.com

---

★★★★

B&B

Ardmore
80 Torbreck, Lochinver, Sutherland, IV27 4JB
Tel:01571 844310

| 1 Twin | 1 Priv.NOT ensuite |
| 1 Double | |

B&B per person
£20.00-22.00 Double

Open May-Sep

Mrs MacLeod offers warm, comfortable accommodation. Ardmore is an ideal B&B to use as a base for touring the Northern Highlands. Many excellent walks in the area and plenty of wildlife and sandy beaches.

Scotland's National Booking and Information Line

Tel: 0845 22 55 121
visitscotland.com

Important: Prices stated are estimates and may be subject to amendments

DAVAR
LOCHINVER, SUTHERLAND IV27 4LJ
Telephone: 01571 844501 e.mail: jean@davar36.fsnet.co.uk

A friendly welcome awaits you at Davar. In our well
appointed purpose built house, with magnificent
views of the mountains, harbour and bay. It is five
minutes walk into the village.
B&B £20-£23 per person per night.

Davar
Lochinver, Sutherland, IV27 4LJ
Tel:01571 844501
Email:jean@davar36.fsnet.co.uk

Modern family run house overlooking Lochinver Bay, with range of comfortable facilities. Private parking on site.

1 Twin	All En Suite	B&B per person	Open Mar-Nov
1 Double		from £42.00 Double	
1 Family			

Polcraig Guest House
Lochinver, Sutherland, IV27 4LD
Tel/Fax:01571 844429
Email:cathelmac@aol.com

A warm, friendly welcome awaits you here at Polcraig. Ideally situated in a quiet location with views across Lochinver Harbour. A short walk takes you to a choice of places for eating out. Your hosts Jean and Cathel will provide you with a hearty breakfast before you set out for your day. Explore the Highlands, taking in the spectacular views and an abundance of wildlife.

3 Twin	All En Suite	B&B per person	Open Jan-Dec excl
2 Double		from £25.00 Single	Xmas/New Year
		from £22.50 Double	

Tigh-Na-Sith Bed+Breakfast
Cruamer, Lochinver, Sutherland, IV27 4LD
Tel:01571 844740
Email:julie@tigh-na-sith.freeuk.com

Comfortable family run Bed & Breakfast. Panoramic views across Lochinver Harbour from lounge. Close to village centre, for restaurants and shops. Both rooms are ensuite. Sky TV available in the lounge.

1 Twin	All En Suite	B&B per person	Open Apr-Oct
1 Double		from £20.00 Dbl/Twn	

Veyatie
66 Baddidarroch, Lochinver, Sutherland, IV27 4LP
Tel/Fax:01571 844424
Email:veyatie@baddid.freeserve.co.uk
Web:www.veyatie-scotland.co.uk

Spacious modern bungalow, with unique character, in peaceful, secluded location. Facing south, with magnificent views across Lochinver bay to spectacular mountains beyond. Ideally situated for bird watching, walking, fishing, or just relaxing break. Private parking on site.

1 Twin	2 En Suite fac	B&B per person	Open Jan-Dec excl
2 Double		from £25.00 Single	Xmas/New Year
		from £22.00 Double	

VAT is shown at 17.5%: changes in this rate may affect prices. | *Key to symbols is on back flap.*

Loch Ness, Inverness-shire · Map Ref: 4A10

★★★

B&B

Beinn Dhearg
24 Torr Gardens, South Loch Ness, Inverness, IV2 6TS
Tel:01463 751336 Fax:01463 751362
Email:john.morrison24@virgin.net

1 Twin 1 Double 1 Family	All En Suite	B&B per person from £20.00 Double	Open Jan-Dec excl Xmas/New Year

Modern, spacious house, in quiet setting 100yds from Loch Ness,8 miles (13kms) south of Inverness. Wonderful views across the Loch. All ensuite. Private parking. Local Inn serving traditional Scottish Fayre. Nature walks close by. Popular walking and cycling area.

FOYERS BAY HOUSE

Foyers, Loch Ness, Inverness IV2 6YB
Tel: 01456 486624 Fax: 01456 486337
e.mail: carol@foyersbay.co.uk Web: www.foyersbay.co.uk

Splendid Victorian villa overlooking Loch Ness. Lovely grounds adjoining famous falls of Foyers. Conservatory cafe-restaurant with breathtaking views of Loch Ness. Ideal base for touring the many historical and tourist attractions in this beautiful region. Also six self-catering units within grounds.

★★★

**GUEST
HOUSE**

Foyers Bay House
Lower Foyers, Inverness, IV2 6YB
Tel:01456 486624 Fax:01456 486337
Email:carol@foyersbay.co.uk
Web:www.foyersbay.co.uk

2 Twin 3 Double	All En Suite	B&B per person from £29.00 Single from £24.00 Double	Open Jan-Dec BB & Eve.Meal from £32.00

Set in its own 4 acres of wooded pine slopes, rhododendrons and apple orchard, Foyers Bay House offers 5 rooms all with ensuite facilities. Just 500 yards from the famous Falls of Foyers and situated just by Loch Ness, home of the famous monster.

Mallaig, Inverness-shire · Map Ref: 3F11

★★

B&B

Anchorage
Gillies Park, Mallaig, Inverness-shire, PH41 4QS
Tel/Fax:01687 462454
Email:anchoragemallaig@talk21.com Web:www.host.co.uk

1 Twin 1 Double 1 Family	All En Suite	B&B per person from £18.00 Double	Open Jan-Dec excl Xmas/New Year

Family run guest house centrally situated in Mallaig village and only a few minutes walk from ferry terminal and railway station. Two bedrooms with excellent views over harbour and bay. All bedrooms with TV's, tea-trays and ensuite bathrooms. Early breakfasts available for those catching first Skye ferry. Ideal base for walking, visiting the Small Isles and touring.

Scotland's National Booking and Information Line

Tel: 0845 22 55 121
visitscotland.com

Important: Prices stated are estimates and may be subject to amendments

Melvich, Sutherland

Map Ref: 4C3

Tigh-na-Clash Guest House

Mrs Joan Ritchie, Melvich, Sutherland KW14 7YJ

Tel/Fax: 01641 531262
e.mail: joan@tighnaclash.co.uk   Web: www.tighnaclash.co.uk

We offer a high standard of accommodation in peaceful surroundings. Extensive breakfast menu, residents lounge, ample parking, friendly staff. Ideally situated for your tour of this most northerly part of Caithness and Sutherland from John O'Groats to Cape Wrath, RSPB Reserve at Forsinard, Flow Country and Orkney Islands. Wonderful scenery, birdwatching. The Queen Mother's Castle of Mey is now open to the public.

★★★

GUEST
HOUSE

Tigh-Na-Clash

Melvich, Sutherland, KW14 7YJ
Tel/Fax:01641 531262
Email:joan@tighnaclash.co.uk Web:www.tighnaclash.co.uk

Personally run guest house in attractive garden. Seven en-suite rooms, and one with private bathroom. Single rooms available. Choice of eating establishments nearby. Situated on the edge of the village of Melvich. 18 miles from Thurso, and a short inland drive to the Flow Country. Beaches, birdwatching, walking, golf, fishing, all available in the area. The Queen Mother's Castle at Mey & Gardens are now open to the public Tues-Sun. April-October.

2 Single	Some En Suite	B&B per person	Open Apr-Sep
2 Twin	1 Pub.Bath/Show	£22.00-24.00 Single	
4 Double			

Morar, Inverness-shire

Map Ref: 3F11

★★★

B&B

Loch Morar House

Beoraid, Morar, by Mallaig, PH40 4PB
Tel/Fax:01687 462823

2 Twin	All En Suite	B&B per person	Open Apr-Oct
1 Double		from £22.00 Double	

Recently built modern villa in peaceful location near Loch Morar yet only mins from the main A830 Mallaig road. Comfortable, ensuite bedrooms with hospitality trays and TV's. Cosy guests lounge where you can relax with a book from our small library. Extensive breakfast menu - traditional Scottish or continental selection. Home-baked breads etc.

SUNSET GUEST HOUSE

MORAR, MALLAIG, INVERNESS–SHIRE PH40 4PA
TEL: 01687 462259 FAX: 01687 460085
E.MAIL: sunsetgh@aol.com WEB: www.sunsetguesthouse.co.uk

Friendly family run guest house in the peaceful West Highland village of Morar. With excellent views over the famous silver sands and the islands of Eigg and Rhum. Authentic Thai cuisine is our speciality. Cosy TV lounge, ample off-road parking, footpath to the beach etc.

★★

B&B

Sunset Guest House

Morar, Mallaig, Inverness-shire, PH40 4PA
Tel:01687 462259   Fax:01687 460085
Email:sunsetgh@aol.com
Web:www.sunsetguesthouse.co.uk

Small family house in West Highland village, close to Morar sands. Mallaig 3 miles (5kms) with ferries to Skye and Small Isles. Authentic Thai cuisine.

1 Twin	1 En Suite fac	B&B per person	Open Jan-Dec excl
1 Double	1 Priv.NOT ensuite	from £16.00 Single	Xmas/New Year
1 Family		from £13.50 Double	BB & Eve.Meal
			from £20.50

VAT is shown at 17.5%: changes in this rate may affect prices.

Key to symbols is on back flap.

Nairn			Map Ref: 4C8	

HOTEL
★★

Alton Burn Hotel
Alton Burn Road, Nairn, IV12 5ND
Tel:01667 452051 Fax:01667 456697
Email:enquiries@altonburn.co.uk

Family run hotel in extensive grounds: putting green, swimming pool, tennis court, games room, table tennis. Close to beach, overlooking golf course.

6 Single	All En Suite	B&B per person	Open Apr-Nov
14 Twin		from £39.00 Single	BB & Eve.Meal
3 Family		from £37.50 Double	from £47.50
		from £35.00 Room	
		Only	

**SMALL
HOTEL**
★★★

Braeval Hotel
Crescent Road, Nairn, IV12 4NB
Tel:01667 452341
Email:ian@braevalhotel.freeserve.co.uk
Web:www.braeval-hotel.co.uk

A small family run hotel, a Scottish experience with traditional Scottish fayre in a relaxed and friendly atmosphere.

2 Single	All En Suite	B&B per person	Open Jan-Dec excl
2 Twin	1 Priv.NOT ensuite	from £30.00 Single	Xmas/New Year
2 Double		from £30.00 Dbl/Twn	
1 Family		from £25.00 Room	
		Only	

B&B
★★★★

Ceolmara, Mrs I Mackintosh
Links Place, Nairn, IV12 4NH
Tel:01667 452495 Fax:01667 451531
Email:ceolmara15@aol.com Web:www.ceolmara.co.uk
A warm Scottish welcome assured in this seaside cottage situated in the fishertown conservation area with panoramic views over Moray Firth to the Black Isle. A stones throw to the beach and close to Championship Golf Courses. Welcome tray with home baking on arrival. Interesting breakfast menu, vegetarian, vegan and gluten free diets catered for. A member of Scotlands Best B&B's, recommended by Which? Good B&B Guide.

1 Single	All En Suite	B&B per person	Open Jan-Dec excl
1 Double		from £20.00 Single	Xmas/New Year
1 Family		from £20.00 Double	

B&B
★★★

Drumblair B&B
Lochloy Road, Nairn, IV12 5LF
Tel:01667 456692
Email:castlebrinda@hotmail.com

Comfortable modern house with large garden in rural location just 2 miles from Nairn. Access to Culbin Forest, RSPB Culbin Sands Reserve and Nairn East Beach approx 1 mile. Excellent for cycling, walking, birdwatching. Golf nearby. Ideal base for touring Moray coast. Vegetarians very welcome.

1 Single	2 En Suite fac	B&B per person	Open Jan-Dec
1 Twin	1 Priv.NOT ensuite	from £18.00 Single	BB & Eve.Meal
1 Double		from £18.00 Double	from £25.00

B&B
★★★

Durham House
4 Academy Street, Nairn, Inverness-shire, IV12 4RJ
Tel/Fax:01667 452345
Email:durhamhouse@nairn34.freeserve.co.uk
Web:www.durhamhouse-nairn.co.uk

A warm welcome awaits you at Durham House, an elegant 19th century house sitting centrally in Nairn and lying 16 miles east of Inverness on the glorious Moray Firth coast. There are beautiful sandy beaches, two championship golf courses and many places of interest nearby making it an ideal holiday choice for all the family.

1 Twin	2 En Suite fac	B&B per person	Open Jan-Dec
1 Double	1 Pub.Bath/Show	£19.00-23.00 Double	BB & Eve.Meal
1 Family			from £31.00-35.00

Important: Prices stated are estimates and may be subject to amendments

Nairn | Map Ref: 4C8

Glen Lyon Lodge
Waverley Road, Nairn, Nairnshire IV12 4RH
Tel: 01667 452780   e.mail: GLENLYON@bosinternet.com
Web: www.bandbnairn.com

Glen Lyon Lodge is an attractive Victorian Villa set in its own grounds and pleasantly situated in Nairn's West End, 5 minutes walk from town centre and within 10 minutes of harbour, Nairn's three golf courses and all amenities. The Lodge provides Bed & Breakfast accommodation with en-suite facilities in all rooms and private parking. *Credit cards accepted: Visa.*

★★★

GUEST HOUSE

Glen Lyon Lodge
19 Waverley Road, Nairn, Nairnshire, IV12 4RH
Tel:01667 452780
Email:GLENLYON@bosinternet.com
Web:www.bandbnairn.com

Personally run Guest House in a central location with a variety of restaurants nearby. Perfect centre for touring, to the west lies Loch Ness, Fort George and Culloden Battlefield. To the east the Whisky Trail and Monarch country, and castles in every direction.

1 Single	All En Suite	B&B per person
2 Twin		from £20.00 Single
3 Double		from £20.00 Double
		from £20.00 Room
		Only

Open Jan-Dec

★★★★

HOTEL

Golf View Hotel & Leisure Club
The Seafront, Nairn, IV12 4HD
Tel: 01667 458800 Fax: 01667 455267
E-mail: rooms@morton-hotels.com
Web: www.morton-hotels.com

Victorian hotel with modern leisure centre overlooking the sea and the hills of the Black Isle. Championship golf course nearby. Headquarters hotel for 1999 Walker Cup. Local attractions include Brodie Castle, whisky trail, Cairngorms, woollen mills and Loch Ness.

4 Single	All En Suite	B&B per person
25 Twin		from £89.00 Single
15 Double		from £68.00 Dbl/Twn
3 Family		

Open Jan-Dec

★★★★

GUEST HOUSE

Greenlawns
13 Seafield Street, Nairn, Inverness-shire IV12 4HG
Tel/Fax:01667 452738
Email:greenlawns@cali.co.uk
Web:www.greenlawns.uk.com

Comfortable Victorian house with a relaxed atmosphere. Quiet situation near to the town centre and beach.

1 Single	All En Suite	B&B per person
3 Twin		from £25.00 Single
3 Double		from £20.00 Double
		from £20.00 Room
		Only

Open Jan-Dec excl Xmas
BB & Eve.Meal from £33.00

★★★★

HOTEL

Newton Hotel & Highland Conference Centre
Inverness Road, Nairn, IV12 4RX
Tel: 01667 458800 Fax: 01667 455267
E-mail: rooms@morton-hotels.com
Web: www.morton-hotels.com

The Newton Hotel is an elegant Georgian building set in over 20 acres of secluded grounds & overlooks the Nairn Championship Course. Guests are able to use the Leisure facilities at our sister hotel (500 yds), the Golf View. Local attractions include, Cawdor Castle, Malt Whisky Trail, Loch Ness, Culloden Battlefield and 20 golf courses in the area. Golf inclusive packages available. Free car parking. 1 AA rosette for food.

6 Single	All En Suite	B&B per person
31 Twin		from £89.00 Single
18 Double		from £55.00 Dbl/Twn
2 Family		

Open Jan-Dec excl Xmas

Nethy Bridge, Inverness-shire | Map Ref: 4C10

★★★★★

B&B

Aultmore House
Nethy Bridge, Inverness-shire, PH25 3ED
Tel:01479 821473 Fax:01479 821750
Email:taylor@aultmorehouse.co.uk
Web:www.aultmorehouse.co.uk

Impressive Edwardian Manor house enjoying fine views of Cairngorms.
Set in 25 acres of secluded wooded and landscaped grounds. Relaxed
country house atmosphere in heart of Spey Valley.

1 Twin	2 En Suite fac	B&B per person	Open Jan-Dec excl
2 Double	1 Priv.Bath/Show	from £40.00 Single	Xmas/New Year
		from £32.50 Double	

★★★

B&B

Tigh-na-Drochaid
Nethybridge, Inverness-shire, PH25 3DW
Tel:01479 821666
Email:tempest.nethybridge@tinyworld.co.uk
Web:www.nethybridge.com

Phil and Val Tempest would be very pleased to welcome you to their
home in the Highlands. Tigh-na-Drochaid (Gaelic for Bridge House) is
situated, as the name implies, right by the Telford Bridge over the River
Nethy at the heart of the village. The house has a great deal of character,
and dates from the early 1900s.

1 Twin	2 En Suite fac	B&B per person	Open Jan-Dec excl
1 Double	1 Priv.Bath/Show	from £26.00 Single	Xmas
1 Family		from £19.50 Double	

Newtonmore, Inverness-shire | Map Ref: 4B11

★★★

GUEST
HOUSE

Glenquoich House
Glen Road, Newtonmore, Inverness-shire, PH20 IDZ
Tel:01540 673461

Distinctive, pretty Victorian house in quiet village centre. Ideal
Touring/Walking area.

1 Single	1 En Suite fac	B&B per person	Open Jan-Dec
2 Twin	2 Priv.NOT ensuite	from £18.00 Single	
1 Double		from £18.50 Double	
1 Family			

North Kessock, Ross-shire | Map Ref: 4B8

★★★★

B&B

Craigiewood
North Kessock, Inverness, IV1 3XG
Tel/Fax:01463 731628
Email:gavdal@netcomuk.co.uk Web:www.craigiewood.co.uk

Situated in superb countryside, Craigiewood is only 4 miles from
Inverness on the Black Isle . The house is ideally situated for short trips
to Inverness, Loch Ness, and the castles of Brodie and Cawdor. The
famous Moray Firth dolphins are nearby. Craigiewood is an excellent
starting point for journeys to Orkney or the West Coast. Inverewe
Gardens, Loch Maree, Torridon and Skye are an easy day trip away.
Come and spoil yourself!

2 Twin	1 En Suite fac	B&B per person	Open Jan-Dec excl
	1 Priv.Bath/Show	from £25.00 Single	Xmas/New Year
		from £24.00 Double	

Onich, by Fort William, Inverness-shire | Map Ref: 3G12

★★

B&B

Mr T Collins
Tom-na-Creige, Onich, Inverness-shire, PH33 6RY
Tel/Fax:01855 821405
Email:creige@thehighlands.co.uk
Web:www.glencoebedandbreakfast.co.uk

Comfortable modern accommodation with spectacular views over Loch
Linnhe to the Glencoe and Morvern Hills. An ideal centre for hillwalking,
climbing, skiing, canoeing and touring the West Highlands or just
relaxing through the four seasons. Family room available with
outstanding loch views.

1 Twin	All En Suite	B&B per person	Open 27 Dec-1 Nov excl
1 Double		from £20.00 Single	New Year
		from £18.00 Double	
		from £15.00 Room	
		Only	

Important: Prices stated are estimates and may be subject to amendments

Onich, by Fort William, Inverness-shire

Map Ref: 3G12

★★★

B&B

Old Manse

Onich, Inverness-shire, PH33 6RY
Tel:01855 821202   Fax:01855 821312
Email:mary@onich.co.uk   Web:www.onich.co.uk

Early 19c former manse, a Listed Thomas Telford building, set in its own garden in the village of Onich, with loch and mountain views. Pets welcome. Substantial continental breakfast provided. Laundry and drying facilities available. Swimming and leisure facilities free of charge at a nearby hotel. Wide choice of eating places in the area. Twixt Ben Nevis and Glencoe.

1 Double	1 En Suite fac	B&B per person	Open Mar-Oct
1 Family	1 Pub.Bath/Show	from £25.00 Single	
		from £20.00 Double	

Plockton, Ross-shire

Map Ref: 3F9

★★★

B&B

Hill View

2 Firthard Road, Plockton, Ross-shire, IV52 8TQ
Tel/Fax:01599 544226

Semi-detached house, comfortable warm and quiet. Ideal for all ages. Situated near village and loch. Ground floor rooms.

1 Twin	Priv fac	B&B per person	Open Jan-Dec
2 Double	En Suite fac	£16.00-20.00 Double	

SEANN BHRUTHACH

MRS M. MACKENZIE, SEANN BHRUTHACH, DUIRINISH IV40 8BE
TELEPHONE: 01599 544204
E.MAIL: ian-morag@mackenzie29.fsnet.co.uk
SITUATED ON A WORKING CROFT WITH HIGHLAND CATTLE IN A
QUIET ATTRACTIVE CROFTING TOWNSHIP, MID-WAY BETWEEN
KYLE OF LOCHALSH AND THE VILLAGE OF PLOCKTON.
AFFORDING BEAUTIFUL VIEWS OVER THE SOUND OF RAASAY
TO THE ROMANTIC ISLE OF SKYE.

★★★

B&B

Seann Bhruthach

Duirinish, by Plockton, Ross-shire, IV40 8BE
Tel:01599 544204
Email:ian-morag@mackenzie29.fsnet.co.uk

A very warm welcome in our comfortable modern home in picturesque crofting township with outstanding views over the Inner Hebrides. Home cooked evening meal available.

1 Twin	2 En Suite fac	B&B per person	Open Jan-Dec excl
2 Double	1 Pub.Bath/Show	from £20.00 Single	Xmas
		from £20.00 Double	BB & Eve.Meal
			from £32.00

Scotland's National Booking and Information Line

Tel: 0845 22 55 121
visitscotland.com

VAT is shown at 17.5%: changes in this rate may affect prices. | *Key to symbols is on back flap.*

Plockton, Ross-shire   Map Ref: 3F9

JANET JONES, TOMAC'S
FRITHARD ROAD, PLOCKTON, ROSS–SHIRE IV52 8TQ
TEL/FAX: 01599 544321

We are situated at the far end of Plockton, five minutes' walk
from the hotels and shops. Our comfortable family home has
spectacular views of Loch Carron and the Applecross Hills.
Plockton is renowned for its scenery and won the Scottish
Tourism Oscar for *Best Village for Tourism 1994*.

★★★

B&B

Tomac's			
Frithard, Plockton, Ross-shire, IV52 8TQ	1 Twin	1 En Suite fac	B&B per person	Open Jan-Dec excl
Tel/Fax:01599 544321	2 Double	1 Priv.NOT ensuite	£18.00-20.00 Double	Xmas/New Year
		1 Pub.Bath/Show		

A warm welcome in very comfortable family home in quiet location in
village of Plockton. Lovely views towards Applecross and Loch Carron to
rear.

Scourie, Sutherland   Map Ref: 3H4

★★

B&B

An-Sean-Dachaich

55 Scourie, by Lairg, Sutherland, IV27 4TE
Tel:01971 502001
Email:margaret.elder@btinternet.com

1 Twin   All En Suite   B&B per person   Open Apr-Oct
2 Double   £16.00-18.00 Double

Comfortable Bed and Breakfast in former Crofter's house. Views across
Scourie Bay. Private parking. All en-suite rooms. Ideal base for touring
North West Scotland. Within walking distance of hotel and restaurant.
Quiet yet central location within the village.

★★★

B&B

Fasgadh

Scouriemore, By Lairg, Sutherland, IV27 4TG
Tel:01971 502402
Email:sandra@scouriemore.co.uk

1 Twin   Priv.Bath/Show   B&B per person   Open Mar-Oct
1 Double   En Suite   from £17.00-18.00
                                Double

Modern purpose built bungalow, situated above village of Scourie, with
views across village and bay. A short walk to village will take you to the
villlage amenities, Hotel and restaurant, also the beach.

★★★★

B&B

Scourie Lodge

Scourie, Sutherland, IV27 4TE
Tel/Fax:01971 502248

1 Twin   All En Suite   B&B per person   Open Mar-Nov
2 Double   2 with Shower etc   from £35.00 Single BB & Eve.Meal
            1 Shower/Bath   from £25.00 Double from £42.50

Beautifully situated on Scourie Bay on the west coast of Sutherland. Near
its picturesque harbour. Location for visiting the many local beauty spots.
The beautiful gardens can be accessed by guests at their leisure.

Important: Prices stated are estimates and may be subject to amendments

Shieldaig, Ross-shire
Map Ref: 3F8

Mrs M. C. Calcott

TIGH FADA, 117 DOIRE-AONAR, NR SHIELDAIG, BY STRATHCARRON IV54 8XH

Telephone: 01520 755248 Fax: 01520 755248

Quiet accommodation in comfortable modern crofthouse set in isolated
crofting village with access to seashore and woodlands. Situated off
the A896 on Kenmor Road, approximately 2 miles from Shieldaig.
Good centre for walking, nature watching, photography, painting,
home produced wools and knitwear available from croft shop.

★★

B&B

Mrs M Calcott

**Tigh Fada, 117 Doire-Aonar, nr Shieldaig,
by Strathcarron IV54 8XH
Tel/Fax: 01520 7552480**

1 Twin	1 Pub.Bath/Show	B&B per person	open Feb-Oct
1 Family		from £15.50 Single	D,B&B per person
		from £15.50 Dbl/Twn	from £24.00

Quiet accommodation in comfortable modern crofthouse set in isolated
crofting village with access to seashore and woodlands. situated off A896
Kenmore road, approximately 2 miles from Shieldaig. good centre for
walking, photography, painting. home produced wools and knitwear
available from croft shop.

Ardvasar, Sleat, Isle of Skye, Inverness-shire
Map Ref: 3E11

★★★

B&B

Homeleigh

**Ardvasar, Sleat, Isle of Skye, IV45 8RU
Tel:01599 534011 Fax:01599 534001
Email:homeleigh@eyeconvista.co.uk**

2 Twin	All En Suite	B&B per person	Open Jan-Dec
1 Double		from £30.00 Single	
		from £20.00 Double	

Modern, detached house, looking across Sound of Sleat to Mallaig and
Knoydart. Close to Armadale ferry. All rooms en-suite. Home-cooking.
Non-smoking. Downstairs bedroom available.

Borve, by Portree, Isle of Skye, Inverness-shire
Map Ref: 3E8

★★★★

B&B

Moorside

**20 Borve, By Portree, Isle of Skye, IV51 9PE
Tel/Fax:01470 532301**

2 Double	All En Suite	B&B per person	Open Apr-Oct
	1 Priv.NOT ensuite	from £22.00 Double	

Modern house situated on a working croft, within 3 miles of Portree.
Ideally suited for touring the island. A warm welcome awaits you.

Breakish, Isle of Skye, Inverness-shire
Map Ref: 3F10

★★★

B&B

Ashfield

**14 Upper Breakish, Isle of Skye, Inverness-shire
IV42 8PY
Tel:01471 822301**

1 Double	Ensuite Shower	B&B per person	Open Easter-Oct
1 Double	Priv Bath/Show	from £18.00 Single	
		£18.00-20.00 Double	

A warm Highland welcome in our very comfortable bungalow set in
croftland. Open views to Scalpay, Pabbay and the Applecross Mountains
on the Mainland. Gaelic spoken. Four miles from Skye bridge.

VAT is shown at 17.5%: changes in this rate may affect prices.

Key to symbols is on back flap.

Breakish, Isle of Skye, Inverness-shire — Map Ref: 3F10

Nethallan

12 Lower Breakish, Breakish
Isle of Skye, Inverness-shire, IV42 8QA
Tel/Fax:01471 822771
Email:nethallanskye@aol.com
Web:www.nethallan.co.uk

B&B

Warm friendly welcome in spacious traditional Skye house. Set in a quiet waters edge location with stunning views over islands to The Cuillins and Rasaay. Secluded sandy beach nearby. Abundant local wildlife including otters, seals and many birds.

1 Twin	All En Suite	B&B per person	Open Jan-Dec excl
1 Double		£25.00-30.00 Single	Xmas/New Year
1 Family		£20.00-25.00 Double	

Broadford, Isle of Skye, Inverness-shire — Map Ref: 3E10

ASHGROVE

11 Black Park, Broadford, Isle of Skye IV49 9DE
Telephone and Fax: 01471 822327
e.mail: ashgrove@isleofskye.net Web: www.isleofskye.net/ashgrove
Comfortable accommodation in three-bedroomed bungalow. Colour TV lounge, tea-making facilities. Two bedrooms with WHB, shower and toilet ensuite, one bedroom with private bathroom. Seven miles from Skye Bridge. Turn off main road at Lime Park/Black Park junction.

From £18 to £20 per person.   ★★★ B&B

Ashgrove

11 Black Park, Broadford
Isle of Skye, Inverness-shire, IV49 9DE
Tel/Fax:01471 822327
Email:ashgrove@isleofskye.net
Web:www.isleofskye.net/ashgrove

B&B

Modern bungalow with fine views of sea and mountains.

1 Twin	2 En Suite fac	B&B per person	Open Jan-Dec
2 Double		from £18.00 Double	

EARSARY

7-8 HARRAPOOL, BROADFORD, ISLE OF SKYE IV49 9AQ
Telephone: 01471 822697   Fax: 01471 822781
e.mail: earsary@isleofskye.net Web: http://www.isleofskye.net/earsary
Friendly accommodation on working farm with a fold of pedigree highland cattle. Superb panoramic views of Broadford Bay, islands and Red Cuillins. Quietly situated 200 yards from the shore where otters and seals can be found. Close to restaurants and pubs. Perfect location to base yourself for your island holiday.

Earsary

7-8 Harrapool, Broadford
Isle of Skye, Inverness-shire, IV49 9AQ
Tel:01471 822697 Fax:01471 822781
Email:earsary@isleofskye.net
Web:www.isleofskye.net/earsary

B&B

Modern house with high standard of accommodation on working croft with pedigree Highland Cattle. Panoramic views over Broadford Bay. Restaurants & pubs close by. Property on working farm/croft. Gaelic spoken.

1 Twin	All En Suite	B&B per person	Open Jan-Dec excl
1 Double		from £25.00 Single	Xmas/New Year
1 Family		from £18.00 Double	

Important: Prices stated are estimates and may be subject to amendments

Broadford, Isle of Skye, Inverness-shire　　　　　Map Ref: 3E10

B&B ★★★

Caberfeidh
1 Lower Harrapool, Broadford, Isle of Skye
IV49 9AQ
Tel:01471 822664
Email:peggymackenzie@amserve.com

Modern bungalow situated at waters edge. Minutes walk from Broadford.
A warm welcome, very comfortable rooms, both ensuite, and a
substantial home cooked breakfast. Good stopping off point for the Uig
Ferry to Outer Isles.

2 Double	All En Suite	B&B per person	Open Jan-Dec excl
	1 Priv.NOT ensuite	from £18.00 Double	Xmas/New Year
	1 Pub.Bath/Show		

Fairwinds ★★★★ B&B
Elgol Road, Broadford, Isle of Skye, IV49 9AB
Tel/Fax:01471 822270
Email:janet.donaldson@talk21.com
Web:www.isleofskye.net/fairwinds

Peacefully situated bungalow in extensive garden overlooking Broadford
River and the mountains. Bicycles for hire. Ideal base for walking,
touring and birdwatching.

1 Twin	All En Suite	B&B per person	Open Apr-Oct
1 Double		from £24.00 Single	
		£20.00-22.00 Double	

LIME STONE COTTAGE
**KATHIE M McLOUGHLIN, 4 LIME PARK,
BROADFORD, SKYE IV49 9AE
Telephone: 01471 822142**
e.mail: kathielimepark@btinternet.com
Web: www.limestonecottage.co.uk

*Welcome to Lime Stone Cottage. A charming turn of
the century crofters cottage originally built for
workers at the local lime kiln now fully restored
offering highest standards of modern comfort whilst
retaining all its original character. Add to this a truly
romantic atmosphere combined with panoramic
views over Broadford Bay and the mainland beyond.
Experience the real delight of a living fire in the
comfortable quiet surrounding of the sitting/dining
room or take the air in the floral garden and feel the
rolling sea breezes with scent of heather. All this
within easy walking distance of local amenities.*

B&B ★★★

Lime Stone Cottage
4 Lime Park, Broadford, Isle of Skye, IV49 9AE
Tel:01471 822142 Fax:01471 822142 (on demand)
Email:kathielimepark@btinternet.com
Web:www.limestonecottage.co.uk

Over the sea to Skye! & This 'old fashioned' bonny wee cottage offers a
rare blend of Romance, History, Panorama, Comfort & old-time
hospitality. Often quoted as a 'heart stopper'. The Lime Stone Cottage is
so much more than just ordinary.

1 Twin	All En Suite	B&B per person	Open Jan-Dec
1 Double		from £36.00 Single	
1 Family		from £19.00 Double	

VAT is shown at 17.5%: changes in this rate may affect prices.　　　*Key to symbols is on back flap.*

Broadford, Isle of Skye, Inverness-shire Map Ref: 3E10

★★ B&B

Hillcrest
8 Black Park, Broadford
Isle of Skye, Inverness-shire, IV49 9AE
Tel:01471 822375

Family run bed and breakfast with off road parking. Eating places within 0.5 mile (1km) distance. Children welcome. Family room available for up to 4 people. Both rooms are ensuite.

1 Twin   All En Suite   B&B per person   Open Jan-Dec
1 Double   from £18.00 Double
1 Family

★★★★ B&B

Hillview
Black Park, Broadford, Isle of Skye, IV49 9DE
Tel:01471 822083
Email:isabelmacleod@hillview.co.uk
Web:www.hillview.co.uk

Very comfortable modern home in elevated position with views over to Applecross and Torridon Hills. Good location for Cuillin Hills and Skye Touring. There is a double ensuite and a family room that sleeps up to 4.

1 Twin   1 En Suite   B&B per person   Open Jan-Dec excl
1 Double 1 Pub Bath/Show   from £20.00 Double   Xmas/New Year
1 Family 1 Priv.NOT En Suite

Ptarmigan
Broadford, Isle of Skye IV49 9AQ
Telephone: 01471 822744 Fax: 01471 822745
e.mail: info@ptarmigan-cottage.com Web: www.ptarmigan-cottage.com

15 metres from seashore, all bedrooms are on the ground floor and enjoy truly outstanding views over Broadford Bay and beyond. Ideal otter/bird watching – binoculars and tide clock supplied. Superb central location for touring with the spectacular world famous Cuillins nearby and the mountainous mainland within 10 minutes drive.

★★★★ B&B

Ptarmigan, Mrs Doreen Macphie
Broadford, Isle of Skye, IV49 9AQ
Tel:01471 822744 Fax:01471 822745
Email:info@ptarmigan-cottage.com
Web:www.ptarmigan-cottage.com

Attractive, friendly family home on Broadford Bay. Panoramic views across islands to mainland. 15 metres over lawns to seashore. All rooms on ground floor and with views over water.

1 Twin   All En Suite   B&B per person   Open Jan-Dec
2 Double   from £25.00 Double

★★ B&B

Tigh-na-Mara
Lower Harrapool, Broadford, Isle of Skye, IV49 9AQ
Tel:01471 822475 Fax:01471 820032
Email:jackieconder@talk21.com

Family room in 150 year old cottage on the sea shore. 8 miles from Skye Bridge. Own sitting room. French and Italian spoken, children welcome.

1 Family 1 Pub.Bath/Show   B&B per person   Open May-Sep
                             from £20.00 Double

Important: Prices stated are estimates and may be subject to amendments

Broadford, Isle of Skye, Inverness-shire
Map Ref: 3E10

★★★★

B&B

Westside
Elgol Road, Broadford, Isle of Skye, IV49 9AB
Tel:01471 822320

1 Single	All En Suite	B&B per person	Open Feb-Nov
1 Twin		from £22.00 Single	
1 Double		from £22.00 Double	

A warm welcome and good food at this modern bungalow in a quiet lane, with views across to Beinn Na Cailleach. Full central heating. Convenient for all local facilities and touring Skye. Gaelic Spoken.

Dunvegan, Isle of Skye, Inverness-shire
Map Ref: 3D9

★★

B&B

4 Harlosh (Mrs C Allan)
Dunvegan, Isle of Skye, IV55 8ZG
Tel:01470 521248
Email:Wallan8333@aol.com
Web:www.skyehigh.co.uk

1 Double	All En Suite	B&B per person	Open Mar-Oct
1 Family		from £20.00 Single	
		£19.00-22.00 Double	

A warm highland welcome in comfortable modern family home in quiet crofting community. Splendid sea and mountain views. 4 miles from Dunvegan. Families with children most welcome.

★★★

B&B

5 Harlosh
by Dunvegan, Isle of Skye, IV55 8ZG
Tel:01470 521483

1 Twin	2 En Suite shower	B&B per person	Open Mar-Oct
1 Double	1 Pub bath	from £19.00 Single	
		from £19.00 Double	

Very comfortable modern croft in elevated rural location with magnificent views over Loch Bracadale and to Cuillin Hills. Very friendly warm welcome. Good base for touring Skye, hill walking and other outdoor pursuits. Gaelic spoken.

KILMUIR PARK
Dunvegan, Isle of Skye IV55 8GU
Tel/Fax: 01470 521586 e.mail: info@kilmuirpark.co.uk
Web: www.milford.co.uk/go/kilmuir.html
George and Mairi extend a warm welcome to their recently built home. Situated close to Dunvegan Castle and enjoying panoramic views of MacLeods tables. Quality accommodation is complimented by freshly prepared traditional meals. Ideal base for touring Skye.

★★★★

B&B

Kilmuir Park
Dunvegan, Isle of Skye, Inverness-shire, IV55 8GU
Tel/Fax:01470 521586
Email:info@kilmuirpark.co.uk
Web:www.milford.co.uk/go/kilmuir.html

2 Twin	All En Suite	B&B per person	Open Jan-Dec
1 Double		from £27.00 Single	BB & Eve.Meal
		from £27.00 Double	from £45.00

Modern family home with panoramic views to Macleods' Tables. 2 kms from the centre of Dunvegan village also ideal for touring the northern part of the island. Evening meals available by arrangement. Fishing and other field sports can be arranged on request.

VAT is shown at 17.5%: changes in this rate may affect prices.

| Key to symbols is on back flap. |

Dunvegan, Isle of Skye, Inverness-shire | Map Ref: 3D9

GUEST HOUSE

●

HOME COOKING

Roskhill House
Roskhill, by Dunvegan, Isle of Skye, Inverness-shire, IV55 8ZD
Tel:01470 521317 Fax:01470 521761
Email:stay@roskhill.demon.co.uk
Web:www.roskhill.demon.co.uk

This cosy crofthouse is beautifully situated 3 miles south of Dunvegan Castle, ideal for touring this historic & romantic island, walking, climbing, bird watching, etc. Delicious old fashioned home cooking prepared fresh each day and served in the stone walled dining room with log fire & resident's bar. High standards, peaceful surroundings and personal attention assured. Your 'home away from home', stay a while.

1 Single 3 En Suite fac
1 Twin   2 Pub.Bath/Show
3 Double

B&B per person
from £35.00 Single
from £27.00 Double

Open Feb-Nov
BB & Eve.Meal
from £43.00

B&B

Uiginish Farmhouse
Uiginish Farm, Dunvegan, Isle of Skye
Inverness-shire, IV55 8ZR
Tel:01470 521431
Email:heather@uiginish.fsnet.co.uk

Modern farmhouse on working farm. Scenic lochside location looking towards Dunvegan Castle. Quiet rural area only 4 miles from village with all its amenities.

1 Twin All En Suite
2 Double

B&B per person
from £20.00 Single
from £20.00 Double

Open May-Sep

Elgol, Isle of Skye, Inverness-shire | Map Ref: 3E10

ROWAN COTTAGE
9 Glasnakille, by Elgol, Isle of Skye IV49 9BQ
Tel: 01471 866287 Fax: 01471 866287
e.mail: ruth@rowancottage-skye.co.uk
Web: www.rowancottage-skye.co.uk
Situated in a beautiful quiet location with panoramic sea views. Specialising in fresh local seafood dinners by prior arrangement, including a table licence. The perfect base for boat trips to the famous Loch Coruisk in the heart of the Cuillin Mountains. Also open for winter breaks by prior arrangement.

B&B

●●

HOME COOKING

Rowan Cottage
9 Glasnakille, Elgol, Isle of Skye, IV49 9BQ
Tel/Fax:01471 866287
Email:ruth@rowancottage-skye.co.uk
Web:www.rowancottage-skye.co.uk

Traditional croft house with log fire. Magnificent views to Sleat and Rhum. Very cosy, comfortable rooms, warm welcome local seafood dinners - All fresh home cooking available in our licenced dining room.

1 Twin   1 En Suite fac
2 Double 1 Pub.Bath/Show

B&B per person
£20.00-25.00 Double

Open Mar-Oct
BB & Eve.Meal
from £37.00-42.00

Important: Prices stated are estimates and may be subject to amendments

Glenhinnisdale, Isle of Skye, Inverness-shire   Map Ref: 3D8

★★★

B&B

Cnoc Preasach
Glenhinnisdale, by Portree, Isle of Skye, IV51 9UY
Tel: 01470 542406

1 Twin	1 Priv.NOT ensuite	B&B per person	Open Feb-Oct
1 Double	1 Pub.Bath/Show	from £16.50 Double	BB & Eve.Meal
1 Family			from £26.00

Comfortable Farmhouse on working croft in quiet elevated position overlooking Glenhinnisdale. Excellent views down glen. 11 miles north of Portree. 6 miles (9.6Kms) from Uig Ferry. 100 acre croft. Home cooking.

Kyleakin, Isle of Skye, Inverness-shire   Map Ref: 3F10

Blairdhu House
Old Kyle Farm Road, Kyleakin, Isle of Skye IV41 8PR
Tel: 01599 534760 Fax: 01599 534623
e.mail: blairdhu@aol.com Web: www.blairdhuhouse.co.uk

Beautifully situated house with the most spectacular scenery. All rooms ensuite with TV, radio, tea/coffee making facilities, hairdryers. Ideal for bird-watching – binoculars supplied. Cruises available around the sheltered water to see seals and a variety of birds on our cruising boat *The Seacruise*.

★★★★

B&B

Blairdhu House
Old Kyle Farm Road, Kyleakin, Isle of Skye IV41 8PR
Tel: 01599 534760 Fax: 01599 534623
Email: blairdhu@aol.com
Web: www.blairdhuhouse.co.uk

1 Twin	All En Suite	B&B per person	Open Jan-Dec excl
4 Double		from £20.00 Single	Xmas/New Year
1 Family		from £20.00 Double	
		from £20.00 Room	
		Only	

A friendly welcome at this family run B&B, a modern home just over the Skye Bridge. Excellent views and comfortable ensuite rooms. Non smoking house.

VAT is shown at 17.5%: changes in this rate may affect prices. | *Key to symbols is on back flap.* |

Kyleakin, Isle of Skye, Inverness-shire　　　　　Map Ref: 3F10

Morrison B&B
4 Olaf Road, Kyleakin, Isle of Skye, IV41 8PJ
Tel:01599 534483

★★★

B&B

1 Single	1 Priv.NOT ensuite	B&B per person	Open Apr-Oct
2 Double		from £16.00 Single	
		from £16.00 Double	

Very comfortable rooms and a warm welcome in cosy B&B in quiet
residential area of Kyleakin. Convenient for bus route, 2 mins walk to
village pubs and restaurants.

TV ☕ 🍵 ✕ 🍽 ♨

V

Portree, Isle of Skye, Inverness-shire　　　　　Map Ref: 3E9

An-Airidh
6 Fisherfield, Portree, Isle of Skye, IV51 9EU
Tel:01478 612250

★★

GUEST
HOUSE

2 Single	Some En Suite	B&B per person	Open Jan-Dec excl
2 Twin		from £20.00 Single	Xmas/New Year
3 Double		£24.00-26.00 Double	

Modern guest house on edge of Portree overlooking the bay towards Ben
Tianavaig and Raasay. Excellent base for exploring Skye.

TV 🗡 🎮 P ☕ 🍵 ✕ 📶

Ardachaidh
12 Fraser Crescent, Portree
Isle of Skye, Inverness-shire, IV51 9DR
Tel:01478 612529
Email:enquiry@ardachaidh.co.uk
Web:www.ardachaidh.co.uk

★★★

B&B

1 Single	2 Priv.NOT ensuite	B&B per person	Open Jan-Dec
1 Twin	1 Pub.Bath/Show	from £18.00 Single	
1 Double		from £18.00 Double	

Comfortable family home in quiet residential area of Portree. Easy
walking distance to town centre.

TV P ☕ 🍵 ✕ 🍽 📶

🐾 V

Balloch
Viewfield Road, Portree
Isle of Skye, Inverness-shire, IV51 9ES
Tel/Fax:01478 612093

★★★★

B&B

| 1 Twin | All En Suite | B&B per person | Open Easter-Oct |
| 3 Double | | from £23.00 Double | |

Large comfortable villa standing in its own garden. 5 minutes walk to
Portree town centre where there is a good range of restaurants and other
local amenities. Excellent centre for touring Skye. A very warm welcome
awaits you at Balloch.

TV 🎮 P ☕ 🍵 🍽 📶 ♨

🐾 W V

Bed + Breakfast
25 Urquhart Place, Portree
Isle of Skye, Inverness-shire, IV51 9HJ
Tel:01478 612374
Email:elizabethmacdonald@talk21.com

★★★

B&B

1 Single	1 En Suite fac	B&B per person	Open Jan-Dec
1 Twin	1 Priv.NOT ensuite	from £20.00 Single	
1 Double		from £16.00 Double	
1 Family			

Traditional Highland hospitality in friendly family home. 1 mile from
town centre. Gaelic spoken.

TV 🎮 P ☕ 🍵 ✕ 🍽 📶 ♨

C 🐾 W V

Portree, Isle of Skye, Inverness-shire

Map Ref: 3E9

★★★

B&B

Sandra Campbell B&B
9 Stormyhill Road, Portree, Isle of Skye, IV51 9DY
Tel/Fax:01478 613332
Email:sandra_campbell_b_b@yahoo.co.uk

A very warm welcome in comfortable family home. 5 minutes walk from Portree village centre, open all year.

| 3 Double | All En Suite | B&B per person from £25.00 Single from £20.00 Double | Open Jan-Dec |

CNOC IAIN
3 Sluggans, Portree, Isle of Skye IV51 9LY
Tel: 01478 612143 e.mail: cnociain@tinyworld.co.uk
Web: www.cnociain.com
Comfortable modern house with friendly atmosphere offering panoramic views from ensuite accommodation that has TV and hospitality tray in all rooms. Guest lounge available at all times. Ideal location for touring Skye.

★★★★

B&B

Cnoc Iain
3 Sluggans, Portree, Isle of Skye, Inverness-shire IV51 9LY
Tel:01478 612143
Email:cnociain@tinyworld.co.uk
Web:www.cnociain.com

Large modern house in elevated position overlooking Portree and out to Rasaay. Warm friendly welcome and comfortable rooms. An excellent base for touring, very central yet quiet.

| 1 Twin 2 Double | All En Suite | B&B per person from £20.00 Double from £18.00 Room Only | Open Easter-Oct |

★★★

GUEST HOUSE

Corran Guest House
Kensaleyre, Portree, Isle of Skye, Inverness-shire
IV51 9XE
Tel:01470 532311

In a small country village overlooking Loch Snizort, 8 miles (10kms) from Portree and from Uig ferry terminal. Extensive gardens with lovely views.

| 1 Single 1 Double 2 Family | Some En Suite 3 Pub.Bath/Show | B&B per person £22.00-24.00 Single £22.00-24.00 Double | Open Jan-Nov |

★★★

B&B

Feochan
11 Fisherfield, Portree, Isle of Skye, IV51 9EU
Tel/Fax:01478 613508
Email:feochan@lineone.net

Family home with spendid views over Portree, a warm welcome and very comfortable rooms. Ideal base for touring the island and exploring the Cuillins and Trotternish Ridge.

| 1 Twin 2 Double | All En Suite | B&B per person from £18.00 Double | Open Easter-Oct |

VAT is shown at 17.5%: changes in this rate may affect prices.

Key to symbols is on back flap.

G

Portree, Isle of Skye, Inverness-shire | Map Ref: 3E9

★★★

B&B

Grenitote
9 Martin Crescent, Portree
Isle of Skye, Inverness-shire, IV51 9DW
Tel:01478 612808
Email:ea.matheson@amserve.net

A warm welcome and comfortable rooms in our friendly home in quiet residential area 5 minutes walk from Portree village centre. Gaelic spoken.

1 Twin   All En Suite
1 Double

B&B per person
£18.00-22.00 Double

Open Jan-Dec

★★★

GUEST
HOUSE

Rosebank House
Springfield Road, Portree, Isle of Skye, IV51 9LX
Tel:01478 612282

Large modern house in quiet residential area on outskirts of village, very comfortable rooms. 5 minutes walk from village square, shops, restaurants and other local amenities. Hairdressing/Beauty salon attached.

2 Single   4 En Suite
1 Twin   1 Pub Bath/Show
3 Double

B&B per person
from £20.00 Single
from £20.00 Double

Open Apr-Sep

---

by Portree, Isle of Skye, Inverness-shire | Map Ref: 3E9

SHOREFIELD GUEST HOUSE
Edinbane, Isle of Skye IV51 9PW
Tel: 01470 582444 *Fax:* 01470 582414
e.mail: shorefieldhouse@aol.com *Web:* www.shorefield.com
Welcoming family run guest house. Overlooking Loch Greshornish.
Quality en-suite bedrooms. Childrens play area, games and television.
Located between Dunvegan and Portree. Well situated for touring.
Non smoking throughout. Cat 1 Disabled. Special diets catered for.
Excellent breakfasts using fresh local produce. Private parking.
AA ♦♦♦♦ RAC ♦♦♦♦ award winner.

★★★★

GUEST
HOUSE

Shorefield Guest House
Edinbane, by Portree, Isle of Skye, IV51 9PW
Tel:01470 582444 Fax:01470 582414
Email:shorefieldhouse@aol.com
Web:www.shorefield.com

Award winning family run guest house offering quality ensuite accommodation. Disabled facilities category 1. Non-smoking. Excellent breakfasts using local produce. Some of Skye's finest restaurants nearby. Private parking.

1 Single   All En Suite
1 Twin
1 Double
2 Family

B&B per person
from £27.00

Open Jan-Dec excl
Xmas/New Year

Important: Prices stated are estimates and may be subject to amendments

nr Portree, Isle of Skye, Inverness-shire

Map Ref: 3E9

★★★

B&B

Hillcroft Bed + Breakfast
2 Treaslane, by Portree, Isle of Skye, IV51 9NX
Tel:01470 582 304
Email:arthurnorma.woodcock@tesco.net
Web:http://homepages.tesco.net/~arthurnorma.woodcock

Friendly welcome at modernised house on working croft overlooking
Loch Snizort. On A850 9 miles (14 kms) north of Portree.

2 Double   All En Suite

B&B per person
£20.00-25.00 Double

Open Feb-Nov

Sleat, Isle of Skye, Inverness-shire

Map Ref: 3F10

★

B&B

3 Kilmore
Sleat, Isle of Skye, Inverness-shire, IV44 8RG
Tel:01471 844272   Fax:01471 844440
Email:peter.macdonald1@talk21.com

Modern bungalow in elevated position. On working croft with panoramic
views towards Knoydart hills. 2.5 miles (4 kms) from Armadale ferry.

1 Single   1 En Suite fac
1 Twin   1 Priv.NOT ensuite
1 Double

B&B per person
from £20.00 Single
from £18.00 Double
from £14.00 Room
Only

Open Apr-Sep

★★★

B&B

Coillechalltainn
6 Duisdale Beag, Isle Ornsay, Sleat, Isle of Skye
IV43 8QU
Tel:01471 833230
Email:macdonald@coillechalltainn.idps.co.uk

Modern bungalow in elevated position in small country village
overlooking the sea. Gaelic spoken. Non-smoking house.

1 Twin   All En Suite
2 Double

B&B per person
from £19.00 Double

Open Feb-Nov

Scotland's National Booking and Information Line

Tel: 0845 22 55 121
visitscotland.com

VAT is shown at 17.5%: changes in this rate may affect prices.

Key to symbols is on back flap.

Staffin, Isle of Skye, Inverness-shire   Map Ref: 3E8

★★

SMALL
HOTEL

Glenview Hotel
Culnacnoc, Staffin, Isle of Skye, IV51 9JH
Tel:01470 562248 Fax:01470 562211
Email:enquiries@glenview-skye.co.uk
Web:www.glenview-skye.co.uk

Tastefully converted traditional island house, ideally situated for
exploring Northern Skye. Friendly atmosphere, good food. Adequate
parking available. The restaurant specialises in local fish and seafood
and a choice of traditional vegetarian and ethnic delicacies are offered.

1 Twin	4 En Suite fac	B&B per person
3 Double	1 Pub.Bath/Show	from £25.00 Double
1 Family		

Open Mar-Oct
BB & Eve.Meal
from £45.00

Struan, by Dunvegan, Isle of Skye, Inverness-shire   Map Ref: 3D9

★★★

B&B

Glenside
4 Lower Totarder, Struan, Isle of Skye, IV56 8FW
Tel:01470 572253

Traditional Highland hospitality on working 40 acre croft. Centrally
situated for touring all areas of Skye.

1 Twin	1 En Suite fac	B&B per person
1 Double	1 Pub.Bath/Show	from £20.00 Single
		from £18.00 Double

Open Mar-Oct

Uig, Isle of Skye, Inverness-shire   Map Ref: 3D8

★

B&B

Harris Cottage
Uig, Isle of Skye, IV51 9XU
Tel:01470 542268
Email:harriscottage@altavista.net
Web:http://website.lineone.net/~trotternish/harrisc.html

A warm welcome in comfortable home with elevated position enjoys
splendid open views over Uig Bay. 15 mins walk to ferry terminal.

1 Twin	2 Priv.NOT ensuite	B&B per person
1 Double		from £16.00 Double
1 Family		

Open May-Sep
BB & Eve.Meal
from £28.00

★★★

B&B

Mrs M MacLeod
11 Earlish, Uig, Isle of Skye, IV51 9XL
Tel:01470 542319

Crofthouse on a working croft about 2 miles (3kms) from Uig Ferry
Terminal. Complimentary tea and cakes served at 9pm. Emphasis on
friendly welcome and a hearty breakfast. Quiet location.

1 Twin	2 Priv.NOT ensuite	B&B per person
1 Double		from £17.00 Single
1 Family		from £17.00 Double

Open Mar-Nov

Scotland's National Booking and Information Line

Tel: 0845 22 55 121
visitscotland.com

Important: Prices stated are estimates and may be subject to amendments

Spean Bridge, Inverness-shire   Map Ref: 3H12

The Braes Guest House

Spean Bridge PH34 4EU e.mail: enquiry@thebraes.co.uk
Tel: 01397 712437 or 0870 225 7037 Web: www.thebraes.co.uk

This is a family run guest house, situated in its own grounds, overlooking Ben Nevis mountain range on outskirts of Spean Bridge. Ideal base for touring, climbing, ski-ing and fishing. Central heating, tea/coffee facilities, (6 rooms ensuite, 1 private facilities). Comfortable lounge with TV. Home cooking. Parking. **Open all year.**

★★★

GUEST HOUSE

The Braes Guest House

Tirindrish, Spean Bridge, Inverness-shire PH34 4EU
Tel:01397 712437 Fax:01397 712108
Email:enquiry@thebraes.co.uk
Web:www.thebraes.co.uk

Family run guest house in elevated position with outstanding views of Ben Nevis Mountain Range. Set in own grounds with small terraced garden. Relax in our comfortable lounge and enjoy the magnificent view. Friendly welcome, tasty home-cooking, personal attention. Ample parking. Ideal base for touring and walking. Drying facilities available.

1 Single	6 En Suite fac	B&B per person	Open Jan-Dec
1 Twin	1 Pub.Bath/Show	from £20.00 Single	BB & Eve.Meal
5 Double		from £20.00 Double	from £34.00

★★★★

GUEST HOUSE

Distant Hills Guest House

Roy Bridge Road, Spean Bridge, Inverness-shire PH34 4EU
Tel/Fax:01397 712452
Email:enquiry@distanthills.com
Web:www.distanthills.com

Comfortable modern bungalow set in large garden at edge of Spean Bridge. Friendly and personal attention. Excellent views of Aonach Mor, ideally situated for touring, skiing, walking and cycling. Evening meals by prior arrangement. Children and pets welcome.

4 Twin	All En Suite	B&B per person	Open Jan-Dec excl
3 Double		from £30.00 Single	Xmas
		from £20.00 Double	BB & Eve.Meal
			from £34.50

Faegour House ★★★★
B&B

Tirindrish, Spean Bridge PH34 4EU
Tel: 01397 712903 Fax: 01397 712903
E.mail: enquiry@faegour.co.uk Web: www.faegour.co.uk

Faegour House situated in own private grounds with panoramic views of Ben Nevis mountain range, offers a high standard of comfort throughout. A warm welcome awaits you. Spean Bridge village with restaurants, hotels, woollen mill, shop and tourist board ten minutes walk. An ideal touring base. Non smoking. Prices from £20.

★★★★

B&B

Faegour House

Tirindrish, Spean Bridge, Inverness-shire PH34 4EU
Tel/Fax:01397 712903
Email:enquiry@faegour.co.uk
Web:www.faegour.co.uk

Expect to receive a very warm welcome at this modern bungalow in an elevated position, located by the village of Spean Bridge, it has an open outlook with mountain views. Spacious, and comfortable with ample private parking.

2 Double	All En Suite	B&B per person	Open Jan-Dec
		from £20.00 Double	

VAT is shown at 17.5%: changes in this rate may affect prices.

| Key to symbols is on back flap. |

Spean Bridge, Inverness-shire | Map Ref: 3H12

★★★

B&B

Highbridge
Spean Bridge, Inverness-shire, PH34 4EX
Tel:01397 712493
Email:smh43@hotmail.com

A comfortable family home in a delightful rural setting. Excellent views of Ben Nevis and Aonach Mor. Fort William 9 Miles (14kms), Spean Bridge 1.5 miles (2kms).

1 Double	En Suite	B&B per person	Open Apr-Sep
1 Twin	En Suite show.	from £15.00 Double	
	1 Pub bath/show		

Inverour Guest House
Roybridge Road, Spean Bridge, Inverness-shire PH34 4EU
Tel: 01397 712218   Fax: 01397 712218
e.mail: janelegge2@tiscali.co.uk
Web: www.fort-william.net/inverour

Charming welcoming Victorian guest house offering comfortable bedrooms, hearty breakfasts and friendly courteous service. Cosy lounge with log fire and conservatory. Ideally situated in the village and close to local amenities and restaurants. Perfect base for exploring the West Highlands. Nevis ski resort 4 miles. Parking. Laundry and drying facilities.

★★★

GUEST HOUSE

Inverour Guest House
Roy Bridge Road, Spean Bridge, Inverness-shire PH34 4EU
Tel/Fax:01397 712218
Email:janelegge2@tiscali.co.uk
Web:www.fort-william.net/inverour

Charming welcoming Victorian Guest House offering comfortable bedrooms, hearty breakfasts and friendly courteous service. Cosy lounge with log fire and conservatory. Ideallly situated in the village and close to local amenities and restaurants. Ideal base for exploring the West Highlands. Nevis Ski Resort 4 miles. Parking, laundry and drying facilities. Evening meals by prior arrangement.

2 Single	Some En Suite	B&B per person	Open Jan-Dec
3 Twin	1 Priv.NOT ensuite	from £20.00 Single	
3 Double		from £22.00 Double	

★★★★

B&B

Riverside House
Invergloy, by Spean Bridge, Inverness-shire PH34 4DY
Tel:01397 712684
Email:enquiries@riversidelodge.org.uk
Web:www.riversidelodge.org.uk

Comfortable Bed and Breakfast situated in a superb location. The house and extensive gardens front onto Loch Lochy where a gentle walk can be taken along the shores, or a longer walk through the grounds taking in the gorge walk. Or quite simply relax in the lounge which commands views of the gardens, the Loch and the hills beyond. An amazing collection of rhododendrons can be seen in the spring although anytime of the year the gardens can be enjoyed.

1 Family	All En Suite	B&B per person	Open Jan-Dec excl
		from £25.00 Single	Xmas/New Year
		from £25.00 Double	

★★

B&B

Tirindrish House
Spean Bridge, Inverness-shire, PH34 4EU
Tel:01397 712398   Fax:01397 712595
Email:wpeterwilson@aol.com
Web:www.tirindrish.com

Tirindrish House is a lovely historic Highland house dating from Jacobite times. Set in 15 acre grounds with outstanding views of Nevis Range mountains. It is an ideal base for exploring the Highlands and Islands. Warm welcome assured in this comfortable family home. Pets welcome. Tennis available. Evening meal by arrangement.

1 Twin	1 En Suite fac	B&B per person	Open Jan-Oct excl
1 Double	2 Pub.Bath/Show	£17.00-28.00 Single	Xmas
1 Family		£17.00-19.00 Double	BB & Eve.Meal
			from £29.00-31.00

Important: Prices stated are estimates and may be subject to amendments

Strathpeffer, Ross-shire | Map Ref: 4A8

★★★

SMALL HOTEL

Brunstane Lodge Hotel
Golf Road, Strathpeffer, Ross-shire, IV14 9AT
Tel/Fax:01997 421261
Email:chris@guichot.freeserve.co.uk
Web:www.brunstanelodge.freeserve.co.uk

Family run hotel set in its own mature garden in residential area and close to golf course. All rooms with private facilities. Conveniently situated for touring Northern Highlands. Fresh local produce prepared and served by French chef/manager Chris Guichot and his wife Morag.

1 Single	6 En Suite fac	B&B per person	Open Jan-Dec
1 Twin	1 Pub.Bathroom	from £32.00 Single	
2 Double		from £30.00 Double	
2 Family		from £25.00 Room Only	

★★★★

B&B

Craigvar
The Square, Strathpeffer, Ross-shire, IV14 9DL
Tel/Fax:01997 421622
Email:craigvar@talk21.com
Web:www.craigvar.com

Elegant residence in unique Highland village. Splendid breakfast menu, personal touches, and a wonderful Highland welcome.

1 Single	All En Suite	B&B per person	Open Jan-Dec excl
1 Twin		£30.00-35.00 Single	Xmas/New Year
1 Double		£22.00-30.00 Double	

THE GARDEN HOUSE GUEST HOUSE

STRATHPEFFER, ROSS-SHIRE IV14 9BJ
Tel/Fax: 01997 421242
e.mail: garden.house@virgin.net
Web: freespace.virgin.net/garden.house

Set in the Victorian spa village of Strathpeffer it provides an ideal central touring base for Ross and Cromarty and other parts of the Northern Highlands. The guest house is located on the southwest side of the village surrounded by woodland and fields. The house is set well back from the main road through the village, about 250 metres from the village square. A lounge is available for guests at all times. Dinner is served each evening for guests wishing to sample home cooking. A table licence permits the sale of wine with meals.
NON-SMOKING ESTABLISHMENT

★★★

GUEST HOUSE

Garden House Guest House
Garden House Brae, Strathpeffer, IV14 9BJ
Tel/Fax:01997 421242
Email:garden.house@virgin.net

Friendly welcome at family run guest house in Spa village. Good walking country and touring base. 21 miles (32kms) from Inverness. Open March - October. Telephone/Fax bookings all year. Visa and Mastercard accepted.

2 Twin	All En Suite	B&B per person	Open Mar-Oct
2 Double		from £25.00 Single	BB & Eve.Meal
1 Family		from £20.00 Double	from £30.00

VAT is shown at 17.5%: changes in this rate may affect prices. | Key to symbols is on back flap.

Strathpeffer, Ross-shire — Map Ref: 4A8

SCORAIG

8 Kinnettas Square, Strathpeffer, Ross-shire IV14 9BD
Telephone: 01997 421847
e.mail: macdonald@kinnettas.freeserve.co.uk

Peaceful location in Victorian village. Ideal base for touring Highlands.
Ensuite facilities available. Guests' lounge with open fire. Tea/coffee
making facilities and TV in bedrooms. Reduced rates for longer stay.
B&B £15-£17 per person per night.

★★★

B&B

Scoraig
8 Kinnettas Square, Strathpeffer, Ross-shire
IV14 9BD
Tel:01997 421847
Email:macdonald@kinnettas.freeserve.co.uk

Comfortable, personally run B & B, situated in quiet residential area
close to the centre of this Victorian spa village. Private parking. Ideal
base for day trips to Skye, the far North and West Highlands. Walkers
and cyclists welcome.

1 Twin   1 En Suite fac
1 Double 2 Priv.NOT ensuite
1 Family

B&B per person
from £15.00 Single
from £15.00 Double

Open Jan-Dec

Strathy Point, Sutherland — Map Ref: 4B3

★★★

B&B

Sharvedda
Strathy Point, by Thurso, Sutherland, KW14 7RY
Tel:01641 541311
Email:patsy@sharvedda.co.uk
Web:www.sharvedda.co.uk

Modern family home with views to sea and open croft land. Evening
meals available. Home baking. Lots of advice available on day trips and
tours, both in the area and further afield, including Orkney. Wildlife,
birdwatching, hillwalking and sandy beaches.

2 Twin   2 En Suite fac
1 Double 1 Pub.Bath/Show

B&B per person
from £30.00 Single
£22.00-24.00 Double

Open Jan-Dec excl
Xmas/New Year
BB & Eve.Meal
from £37.00-39.00

Scotland's National Booking and Information Line

Tel: 0845 22 55 121
visitscotland.com

Important: Prices stated are estimates and may be subject to amendments

Strontian, Argyll   Map Ref: 1E1

★★

B&B

Craig-Na-Shee
Anaheilt, Strontian, Argyll, PH36 4JA
Tel:01967 402051
Email:jacamelli@aol.com

Modern bungalow in peaceful glen, about 1 mile from the village. Open views to the surrounding hills. Full Scottish breakfast and vegetarian alternative. Ironing/drying facilities. Home baking and packed lunches. Guests lounge with colour TV. Pets welcome. Reduced rates for stays of (a) more than 3 days and (b) a week.

1 Twin	All En Suite	B&B per person	Open Easter-Oct
1 Double		from £17.50 Single	
		from £17.50 Double	

★★★

B&B

Struan
19 Anaheilt, Strontian, Acharacle, Argyll
PH36 4JA
Tel:01967 402057

A warm comfortable Highland welcome awaits you at 'Struan'. The B & B enjoys magnificent views of Ariundle Glen and Sgurr Dhomhnuill. Ariundle Nature Trail is within easy walking distance as is the compact village of Strontian set on the beautiful banks of Loch Sunart. Ideal base for walking, fishing and exploring the beautiful Ardnamurchan Peninsula.

1 Single	All En Suite fac	B&B per person	Open Apr-Oct
1 Twin		£20.00-22.00 Single	
1 Double		£20.00-22.00 Double	

Tain, Ross-shire   Map Ref: 4B7

CARRINGTONS B&B

★★★

Carringtons, Morangie Road, Tain IV19 1PY
Telephone/Fax: 01862 892635
e.mail: molliel@btinternet.com Web: www.stelogic.com/carringtons

Victorian house facing sea and mountains. Comfortable atmosphere. Home baking. Good spot for touring North, West Islands. Good golf courses within easy reach. Two minutes from town centre. A genuine welcome home from home.

★★★

B&B

Carringtons
Morangie Road, Tain, Ross-shire, IV19 1PY
Tel/Fax:01862 892635
Email:mollie1@btinternet.com
Web:www.stelogic.com/carringtons

Detached Victorian family home on the outskirts of Tain overlooking the sea. Close to town centre and golf course. Excellent base for exploring - John O'Groats, Ullapool and Inverness all within easy reach. Good stopover point enroute to Orkney, being just off the A9.

1 Double	2 En Suite fac	B&B per person	Open Jan-Dec excl
2 Family	1 Pub.Bath/Show	£18.00-20.00 Single	Xmas/New Year
		£16.00-18.00 Double	

HEATHERDALE BED & BREAKFAST
2 Well Street, Tain, Ross-shire IV19 1HJ
Tel: 01862 894340
e.mail: heatherdale74@zoom.co.uk Web: www.heatherdale.info
Heatherdale Bed & Breakfast is a comfortable modern house situated close
to the centre of historic Tain. Base yourself here while you explore the
towns and villages of Easter Ross and East Sutherland, or visit the far
North and West Coast. Fishing, shooting and several golf courses are in the
area.

★★★

B&B

Mrs Alice Fraser
Heatherdale, 2 Well Street, Tain, Ross-shire IV19 1HJ
Tel:01862 894340
Email:heatherdale74@zoom.co.uk
Web:www.heatherdale.info

Comfortable modern house situated close to the centre of historic Tain.
Two rooms ensuite and one with private facilities. Off-street parking.
Base yourself here whilst you explore the towns and villages of Easter
Ross and East Sutherland, or visit the far North and West Coast.

1 Twin	2 En Suite fac
1 Double	1 Pub.Bath/Show
1 Family	

B&B per person
from £25.00 Single
from £18.00 Double
from £15.00 Room
Only

Open Jan-Dec excl
Xmas/New Year

★★★★

GUEST HOUSE

Golf View House
13 Knockbreck Road, Tain, Ross-shire, IV19 1BN
Tel:01862 892856 Fax:01862 892172
Email:golfview@btinternet.com
Web:www.golf-view.co.uk

Secluded Victorian house with panoramic views over golf course and
across the Dornoch Firth. Centrally situated in Scotland's oldest Royal
Burgh.

3 Twin	3 En Suite fac
1 Double	2 Priv.NOT ensuite
1 Family	

B&B per person
from £25.00 Single
from £25.00 Double

Open Feb-Nov

★★★

B&B

Northfield Bed + Breakfast
23 Moss Road, Tain, Ross-shire, IV19 1HH
Tel:01862 894087
Email:may-mclean@northfield23.fsnet.co.uk

Comfortable family-run home in quiet location. Log burning stove in
lounge and a warm welcome assured. Tea, coffee and home baking on
arrival. Golfing can be arranged locally. A wide choice of day trips
available, perhaps to the far north or over to the rugged west coast.One
twin ensuite, one double ensuite, one single private facilities.

1 Single	Private fac
1 Double	Ensuite
1 Twin	Ensuite

B&B per person
from £18.00-20.00

Open Mar-Oct

Scotland's National Booking and Information Line

Tel: 0845 22 55 121
visitscotland.com

Important: Prices stated are estimates and may be subject to amendments

Talmine, Sutherland

Map Ref: 4A3

CLOISTERS

"Church Holme", Talmine (near Tongue), Sutherland IV27 4YP
Tel/Fax: 01847 601286 e.mail: reception@cloistertal.demon.co.uk
Web: www.cloistertal.demon.co.uk

Built in traditional style overlooking the beautiful Kyle of Tongue, "Cloisters" commands stunning sea views over inshore islands to the Orkneys beyond. Off the main tourist route it is an ideal base for exploration of Scotland's rugged north coast, mountains, rivers and lochs where wildlife abounds. *A photographers paradise.*

★★★★

B&B

Cloisters

Church Holme, Talmine, nr Tongue, Sutherland IV27 4YP
Tel/Fax:01847 601286
Email:reception@cloistertal.demon.co.uk
Web:www.cloistertal.demon.co.uk

Located four miles north of Tongue off the A838, Cloisters, built in traditional style alongside our home, a converted 19th century church, offers superb B&B accommodation with stunning sea views. Enjoy birdwatching, fishing, climb majestic Ben Loyal or Ben Hope. Pack lunches are available and an excellent licensed restaurant is within easy walking distance. Why not escape to the peace and tranquility of Scotland's outback.

3 Twin	All En Suite	B&B per person from £25.00 Single from £20.00 Double	Open Jan-Dec

---

Thurso, Caithness

Map Ref: 4D3

★★★★

B&B

Annandale (Mrs D Thomson)

2 Rendel Govan Road, Thurso, Caithness, KW14 7EP
Tel:01847 893942
Email:thomson@annandale2.freeserve.co.uk

Comfortable B & B situated in quiet residential area. Ideal base for touring north coast and convenient for Orkney ferry.

2 Twin 1 Double	2 Priv.NOT ensuite	B&B per person £18.50-19.00 Double	Open Jan-Dec excl Xmas/New Year

---

★★★★

B&B

Mrs Catherine Murray

1 Granville Crescent, Thurso, Caithness, KW14 7NP
Tel/Fax:01847 892993

Quietly situated, yet within easy reach of station and all facilities. All ground floor rooms, one ensuite, one with private bathroom. 5 minutes drive to Scrabster for Orkney Ferry.

2 Twin	1 En Suite fac 1 Priv.Bath/Show	B&B per person from £20.00 Single from £18.00 Double	Open Jan-Dec

---

Thurso, Caithness | Map Ref: 4D3

THE SHEILING GUEST HOUSE
Melvich, Sutherland, By Thurso KW14 7YJ
Tel/Fax: 01641 531256
e.mail: thesheiling@btinternet.com
Web: www.b-and-b-scotland.co.uk/thesheiling.htm
Spectacular views! Fantastic breakfast in splendid dining room overlooking Melvich Bay. Guests return annually to very high standards in comfort, food and hospitality. Walking, golfing, fishing. Short drive to RSPB Forsinard and Orkney Ferry. Eating out establishments nearby. AA selected ◆◆◆◆◆. Award winner *Which?* Best B&B recommended by many guides.
Contact Joan Campbell. From £26 pppn B&B.

★★★★

GUEST HOUSE

The Sheiling Guest House
Melvich, Thurso, KW14 7YJ
Tel/Fax:01641 531256
Email:thesheiling@btinternet.com
Web:www.b-and-b-scotland.co.uk/thesheiling.htm

Peaceful and spacious accommodation in the village of Melvich, with spectacular views over the bay. Two guests' lounges. Extensive breakfast selection. Genuine Highland hospitality. 17 miles to Orkney ferry, 16 miles to Forsinard RSPB reserve.

1 Twin   All En Suite   B&B per person   Open Apr-Oct
2 Double   from £26.00 Double

★★★

B&B

Varrich
Halkirk, Caithness, KW12 6UU
Tel:01847 831481

Spacious modern house situated 6 miles south of Thurso, and 2 miles from the village of Halkirk. Excellent base for exploring the far north coast and the flow country. Walking, fishing, birdwatching all available in the area. Good stopover point for the Orkney Ferry.

1 Double   All En Suite   B&B per person   Open Apr-Oct
1 Family   from £20.00 Single
                           from £20.00 Double

by Thurso, Caithness | Map Ref: 4D3

★★

B&B

Dunnet Head B&B
Brough Village, Dunnet Head, by Thurso, KW14 8YE
Tel:01847 851774
Email:briansparks@dunnethead.co.uk
Web:www.dunnethead.co.uk

Bed & Breakfast at the most Northerly point of mainland Britain. Evening meals available by arrangement. Superb views of the Pentland Firth and seals in Brough Bay. Cliff top walks, 3 miles to Dunnet Head lighthouse.

1 Single   2 En Suite fac   B&B per person   Open Apr-Sep
1 Double   from £21.50 Single   BB & Eve.Meal
1 Family   from £19.50 Double   from £30.00

Scotland's National Booking and Information Line

Tel: 0845 22 55 121
visitscotland.com

Important: Prices stated are estimates and may be subject to amendments

Tongue, Sutherland — Map Ref: 4A3

Mrs MacIntosh
77 Dalcharn, Tongue, Lairg, Sutherland, IV27 4XU
Tel:01847 611251

★★ B&B

1 Double	1 Pub Show	B&B per person	Open Jan-Dec excl
1 Family		from £15.00 Single	Xmas/New Year
		from £13.00 Double	BB & Eve.Meal
			from £20.00

Modernised croft house, situated in peaceful rural location. Idyllic sandy beaches within walking distance. Gaelic spoken. Hairdryer and iron supplied. Cheaper rates applicable to children up to 12 years.

Rhian Guest House
Tongue, Sutherland, IV27 4XJ
Tel/Fax:01847 611257
Email:jenny.anderson@tesco.net
Web:www.scotland-index.co.uk/sutherland/tongue/rhian/guest_house.htm

★★★ B&B

1 Twin	4 En Suite fac	B&B per person	Open Jan-Dec
2 Double	1 Priv.Bath	from £35.00 Single	BB & Eve.Meal
2 Family		from £23.00 Double	from £39.00

Charming modernised croft cottage, 0.5 miles (1km) outside village. Dramatic views of Ben Loyal. Ideal base for fishing, bird watching, walking and touring. Annex accommodation is available.

Ullapool, Ross-shire — Map Ref: 3G6

3 Castle Terrace - Mrs P Browne
3 Castle Terrace, Ullapool, Wester Ross, IV26 2XD
Tel:01854 612409

★★★ B&B

1 Single	1 En Suite fac	B&B per person	Open Apr-Oct
1 Twin	1 Priv.NOT ensuite	£18.00-20.00 Single	
1 Double		£17.00-20.00 Double	

Bed and Breakfast in family home, with ensuite available. Quiet residential location within walking distance of town amenities. House has views to Summer Isles. Vegetarian breakfast a speciality.

★★★ B&B

ARDLAIR

MOREFIELD BRAE, ULLAPOOL IV26 2TH
Telephone/Fax: 01854 612087
e.mail: ann@1broomcottage.freeserve.co.uk
Ardlair is situated on an elevated site overlooking Loch Broom and Ullapool. Ideal for walking, climbing, sailing, touring, bird-watching. New 9-hole golf course three minutes drive. Ferry terminal to Western Isles. One hour to the sub-tropical gardens at Inverewe. Ample parking. Follow the A835 for approx 1½ miles North of Ullapool. Third house on right.

Ardlair
Morefield Brae, Ullapool, Ross-shire, IV26 2TH
Tel/Fax:01854 612087
Email:ann@1broomcottage.freeserve.co.uk

★★★ B&B

2 Double	2 En Suite fac	B&B per person	Open Easter-Oct
2 Family	1 Priv.NOT ensuite	from £18.00 Double	
	1 Pub.Bath/Show		

Modern house in elevated position, with large garden giving excellent views over Loch Broom. Under 2 miles (3kms) north of Ullapool. Leisure centre and golf course close by.

VAT is shown at 17.5%: changes in this rate may affect prices.

Key to symbols is on back flap.

Ullapool, Ross-shire   Map Ref: 3G6

Ardvreck Guest House
Morefield Brae, Ullapool IV26 2TH
Tel: 01854 612028   *e.mail:* Ardvreck@btinternet.com
Fax: 01854 613000   *Web:* www.SmoothHound.co.uk/hotels/ardvreck.html

Spacious and well-appointed accommodation. All rooms ensuite with television and tea/coffee facilities, rural setting with spectacular views of sea, mountains, and Ullapool. Durness on the North Coast (75 miles) can be reached in a day as can the famous Inverewe Gardens (55 miles south).
B&B from £23–£30 *Contact Mrs Stockall*   ★★★★ GUEST HOUSE

★★★★

GUEST HOUSE

Ardvreck House
Morefield Brae, Ullapool, IV26 2TH
Tel:01854 612028 Fax:01854 613000
Email:ardvreck@btinternet.com
Web:www.smoothhound.co.uk/hotels/ardvreck.html

Guest house set amidst some of the best hillwalking country and breathtaking scenery in Scotland. Elevated country position overlooking Ullapool and Lochbroom. Spacious, well appointed rooms most with spectacular sea view, all with ensuite shower room, T.V and tea/coffee facility. Residents lounge available at all times. Local facilities include a leisure centre, swimming pool, sauna, golf course, fishing and museum.

2 Single	All En Suite	B&B per person	Open Feb-Oct
2 Twin		£23.00-30.00 Single	
4 Double		£23.00-30.00 Double	
2 Family		£20.00-25.00 Room	
		Only	

★★★★

B&B

Braemore Square Bed+Breakfast
Braemore Square, Loch Broom, Wester Ross, IV23 2RX
Tel/Fax:01854 655357
Email:eddiehughes@supanet.com
Web:www.braemoresquare.com

Braemore Square is set amongst 46 acres of croft and woodland beside the road to Ullapool, just a short walk from the famous Corrieshalloch Gorge and with fishing rights on the River Broom. Your experienced hosts Ed and Wendy Hughes guarantee a warm and friendly welcome.

3 Double	2 En Suite	B&B per person	Open Jan-Dec
	1 Pub.Bath/Show	£16.00-26.00 Single	BB & Eve.Meal
		£16.00-26.00 Double	from £28.00-38.00

★★★

B&B

Broombank B&B
4 Castle Terrace, Ullapool, Ross-shire, IV26 2XD
Tel:01854 612247
Email:shirley.couper@tesco.net
Web:www.broombank.fsnet.co.uk

A warm welcome awaits in our modern comfortable bungalow with open views to hills and down the Loch to the Summer Isles. Quiet area but only 5 minutes walk to village centre.

1 Twin	All En Suite	B&B per person	Open Jan-Dec
1 Double		from £20.00 Double	

★★★

B&B

Clisham
Rhue, Ullapool, Rosshire, IV26 2TJ
Tel:01854 612498

Small working croft peacefully situated in elevated position, giving superb views over Loch Broom. 3 miles (5kms) north of Ullapool.

2 Family	1 Priv.NOT ensuite	B&B per person	Open May-Sep
		from £18.00 Double	

Important: Prices stated are estimates and may be subject to amendments

Ullapool, Ross-shire | Map Ref: 3G6

★★★
B&B

Creagan House
18 Pulteney Street, Ullapool, Ross-shire, IV26 2UP
Tel:01854 612397   Fax:01854 613396
Email:kmullapool@aol.com
Web:www.ullapool.co.uk/creaganhouse

Traditional stone built cottage dating back to 1840. Situated in centre of village, close to all amenities, leisure centre and golf course. Ideal base for hillwalking, cycling and touring the west coast. Travel cots available. Pets by arrangement.

2 Twin	2 En Suite fac	B&B per person	Open Jan-Dec
2 Double	1 Priv.NOT ensuite	from £18.00 Single	
1 Family		£16.00-22.00 Double	

DROMNAN GUEST HOUSE
Garve Road, Ullapool IV26 2SX
Telephone: 01854 612333   Fax: 01854 613364
e-mail: dromnan@msn.com   Web: www.dromnan.co.uk

This modern family run guest house is ideally situated on the outskirts of Ullapool. All our rooms are furnished to a high standard with private facilities, colour TVs, hairdryers and courtesy trays. Our open-plan lounge and dining room have beautiful views overlooking Loch Broom. Easy access to Summer Isles and Outer Hebrides.

★★★★
GUEST HOUSE

Dromnan Guest House
Garve Road, Ullapool, Ross-shire, IV26 2SX
Tel:01854 612333   Fax:01854 613364
Email:dromnan@msn.com
Web:www.dromnan.co.uk

Family run guest house on outskirts of the west coast fishing village of Ullapool, overlooking Loch Broom. 5 minutes from ferry to the Outer Isles.

2 Twin	All En Suite	B&B per person	Open Jan-Dec excl
3 Double		from £24.00 Double	Xmas/New Year
2 Family			

★★★
B&B

Hillview
1 Vyner Place, Ullapool, Ross-shire, IV26 2XR
Tel:01854 612700

A warm welcome awaits you at Hillview. Ideally situated for the golf course, hill walks and touring the Highlands.

1 Single	1 Priv.NOT ensuite	B&B per person	Open Mar-Oct
1 Double		from £16.00 Single	
		from £16.00 Double	

★★★★
B&B

Mrs J Macrae
3 Vyner Place, Ullapool, Ross-shire, IV26 2XR
Tel/Fax:01854 612023

Comfortable and modern accommodation in residential area of Ullapool. Close to golf course and leisure centre. Ideal base for touring Western Highlands.

2 Family	1 En Suite fac	B&B per person	Open Jan-Dec excl
	1 Priv.Bath/Show	from £20.00 Single	Xmas
		£18.00-20.00 Double	
		from £15.00 Room Only	

VAT is shown at 17.5%: changes in this rate may affect prices.   *Key to symbols is on back flap.*

| Ullapool, Ross-shire | | Map Ref: 3G6 | |

Northbank
11 Moss Road, Ullapool, Ross-shire, IV26 2TF
Tel:01854 612093

| 1 Twin | 1 Pub Bath/Show | B&B per person | Open Apr-Oct |
| 1 Double | | from £18.00 Double | |

B&B

Comfortable family home near centre of Ullapool set in quiet residential area. Ferry terminal just a few minutes. Close to North West Highlands Tourist Route. Vegetarian breakfast available.

Oakworth
Riverside Terrace, Ullapool, Ross-shire, IV26 2TE
Tel:01854 612290
Email:oakworth@ecosse.net

| 3 Double | All En Suite | B&B per person | Open Jan-Dec excl |
| | | from £18.00 Double | Xmas/New Year |

B&B

Modern bungalow set in quiet residential area of this Highland town. Fine views. All rooms ensuite. Pets welcome by arrangement. New conservatory added for breakfast room.

Point Cottage Guest House
22 West Shore Street, Ullapool, Ross-shire IV26 2UR
Tel:01854 612494
Email:stay@pointcottage.co.uk
Web:www.pointcottage.co.uk

1 Twin	All En Suite	B&B per person	Open Feb-Nov
2 Double		from £25.00 Single	
		from £22.00 Double	

GUEST
HOUSE

Tastefully converted 18c fisherman's cottage where a warm welcome and a high level of local knowledge are assured. Marvellous lochside views to mountains beyond. Very quiet location but only 2 minutes walk to village centre. Vegetarian cooked breakfast available.

The Sheiling
GARVE ROAD
ULLAPOOL IV26 2SX
Tel/Fax: 01854 612947
Web: www.thesheilingullapool.co.uk

A warm welcome is assured at the MacKenzies comfortable house which stands in its own one acre landscaped garden beside the picturesque shore of Loch Broom. Facilities include guests laundry, sauna, drying room and a rod room to complement the 40sq. miles of trout loch fishing exclusive to guests.

Sheiling Guest House
Garve Road, Ullapool, Ross-shire, IV26 2SX
Tel:01854 612947
Web:www.thesheilingullapool.co.uk

| 2 Twin | All En Suite | B&B per person | Open Jan-Dec excl |
| 4 Double | | from £25.00 Double | Xmas/New Year |

GUEST
HOUSE

Modern house with large loch facing garden in peaceful location on shore of Loch Broom. 1/2 mile from the village. Free trout fishing on many local lochs, partly exclusive. Use of local produce features highly with homemade sausages and local smoked fish. Sauna in grounds for use of guests.

Important: Prices stated are estimates and may be subject to amendments

Ullapool, Ross-shire | Map Ref: 3G6

"TORRAN"

LOGGIE, LOCH BROOM, ULLAPOOL, ROSS-SHIRE IV23 2SG
TEL: 01854 655227 FAX: 01854 655344 MOBILE: 07753 854 281
E.MAIL: macktorran@ecosse.net WEB: www.torranloggie.co.uk
A warm welcome awaits you at our family croft house peacefully situated
overlooking the beautiful Loch Broom. Salmon farm and historic sites close by.
This area is renowned for its beauty and you won't be disappointed. Very central
for walking, several Munro's within sight and easy reach. Come have a relaxing
holiday at 'Torran'. Double room ensuite & twin room with private bathroom.
Prices from £20.00.

★★★

B&B

Torran

Loggie, Lochbroom, Ullapool, Ross-shire, IV23 2SG
Tel:01854 655227 Fax:01854 655344
Email:macktorran@ecosse.net
Web:www.torranloggie.co.uk

Family home on working croft in peaceful setting overlooking the
beautiful Loch Broom. Enjoy a Scottish breakfast using our own free
range eggs. Iron age brochs & salmon farm close by. A relaxing and
peaceful holiday location.

| 1 Twin | Priv bathroom | B&B per person | Open Jan-Dec excl |
| 1 Double | En Suite | from £20.00 Dbl/Twn | Xmas/New Year |

🅿 ☕ 📶 ✗ 🛏 🎗 🌣

Ⓥ ♿

Wick, Caithness | Map Ref: 4E3

★★★★

B&B

The Clachan

13 Randolph Place, South Road, Wick, Caithness Tel:01955
605384
Email:enquiry@theclachan.co.uk
Web:www.theclachan.co.uk

Family run detached house dating back to 1938. Purpose built
accommodation to the back of the house, with all rooms ensuite,
ensuring a peaceful and relaxing stay. A wide variety of interests with
John O' Groats on the doorstep, where there are daily trips to Orkney in
the summer. Wick has many sites of historical interest. Meals available
within walking distance. Totally non-smoking house.

| 1 Twin | All En Suite | B&B per person | Open Jan-Dec excl |
| 2 Double | | £20.00-22.00 Double | Xmas/New Year |

📺 🖥 🅿 ☕ 📶 ✗

Ⓦ ♿

Scotland's National Booking and Information Line

Tel: 0845 22 55 121
visitscotland.com

Key to symbols is on back flap.

Welcome to Scotland

The Outer Islands: Western Isles, Orkney, Shetland

The Outer Isles are for visitors seeking adventure, a sense of being outside Britain – yet still a part of it – and seeing a different culture. All three island groupings – the Western Isles, Orkney and Shetland – contrast with each other. Orkney and Shetland share a Norse heritage, while the Western Isles are the stronghold of the Gael. Excellent ferry and air links mean getting to any of these groups of islands is straight forward.

Stornoway, Isle of Lewis

The Western Isles offer some of Scotland's finest seascapes and beaches, as well as the springtime flowers of the machair – the shell-sand coastal pasture. Ancient monuments such as the spectacular Callanais Standing Stones are a reminder of the heritage of prehistory on the islands. The preserved Black House at Arnol is a reminder of the more recent life of the crofters on these islands, and is one of many heritage museums on the islands.

Orkney's green islands, like the Western Isles, have a strong sense of continuity stretching back to ancient times. The past is all around at places like Skara Brae, a magnificently preserved Stone Age village, and Maes Howe, a unique burial chamber already more than a millennium old when pillaged by Vikings.

Kirkwall is the setting for St Magnus Cathedral, the most magnificent Norman work in Scotland. Another theme to explore is the seagoing tradition, including the recent history of Scapa Flow as a naval anchorage, portrayed at the fascinating museum at Lyness on Hoy. Orkney's wildlife includes spectacular seabird colonies along its dramatic coastline.

The Outer Islands: Western Isles, Orkney, Shetland

Esha Ness, Shetland

The Outer Islands: Western Isles, Orkney, Shetland

Harbour at Kirkwall, Orkney

Shetland has the strongest sense of somewhere different. Here the Scandinavian influence is apparent – in dialect, music, even architecture and traditions. The sea pervades the way of life, with nowhere more than three miles from salt water.

Like Orkney, there is an abundance of wildlife – seals, otters and seabirds – from Sumburgh Head in the south of the islands past the national nature reserve at Hermaness on Unst to Muckle Flugga at the most northerly point of Britain.

Shetland is for adventurers, with long summer daylight hours in 'the land of the simmer dim' leaving even more time to enjoy the unique island ambience.

Events
The Outer Islands: Western Isles, Orkney, Shetland

1 JANUARY & 25 DECEMBER
The Ba', Orkney
Historical game of street
football with around 400
players.
Tel: 01856 873166
www.visitorkney.com

28 JANUARY
Up Helly Aa
Annual Viking Fire Festival
Tel: 01595 693434
www.visitshetland.com

MAY – SEPTEMBER
Simmer'n Sessions, Various venues
Award-winning traditional
music sessions.
Tel: 01595 693434
www.visitshetland.com

22-25 MAY
Orkney Folk Festival
Tel: 01856 851331
www.orkneyfolkfestival.com

24-30 MAY
Wake Up To Birds Week
Royal Society for the
Protection of Birds. Wide
range of events and activities
at the 60 RSPB reserves across
Scotland. Free entry to all
reserves on one day during
this week.
Tel: 0131 311 6500
www.rspb.org.uk/scotland

26-29 JUNE*
Shetland Race, Lerwick
400 mile yacht race from
Bergen to Lerwick.
Tel: 01595 744839

MID JULY
Ceolas Music Summer School, South Uist
Expert tuition in piping,
fiddling, singing, scotch reels,
step dancing and the Gaelic
language.
Tel: 01870 620333
www.ceolas.co.uk

16-19 JULY*
Hebridean Celtic Festival, Stornoway
Festival of Celtic music and
related arts.
Tel: 07001 878787
www.hebceltfest.com

23-26 JULY*
Inter-club Sailing Regatta, Lerwick
Tel: 01957 711417
www.ceolas.co.uk

EARLY AUGUST
Hebridean Maritime Festival, Stornoway
Boat and sailing festival.
Tel: 01851 703562
www.sailhebrides.com

19-21 SEPTEMBER*
Orkney Food Festival
A week of delicious
opportunities to sample the
finest local produce and
cuisine.
Tel: 01856 872856
www.visitorkney.com

* denotes provisional date. Events can be subject to change, please check before travelling.

For up to date events, log on to:
visitscotland.com

Area Tourist Boards
The Outer Islands: Western Isles, Orkney, Shetland

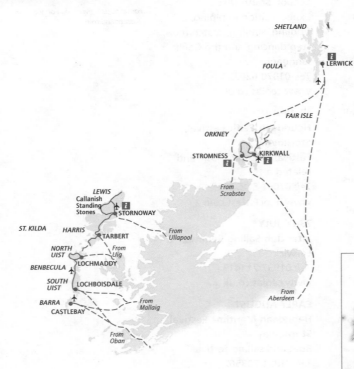

Western Isles Tourist Board
26 Cromwell Street
Stornoway
Isle of Lewis
HS1 2DD

Tel: 01851 703088
Fax: 01851 705244
E-mail: stornowaytic@
visitthehebrides.co.uk
www.witb.co.uk

Orkney Tourist Board
6 Broad Street
Kirkwall
Orkney
KW15 1NX

Tel: 01856 872856
Fax: 01856 875056
E-mail: info@otb.ossian.net
www.visitorkney.com

Shetland Islands Tourism
Market Cross
Lerwick
Shetland
ZE1 0LU

Tel: 01595 693434
Fax: 01595 695807
E-mail: shetland.tourism@
zetnet.co.uk
www.visitshetland.com

Tourist Information Centres
The Outer Islands: Western Isles, Orkney, Shetland

Western Isles Tourist Board

Castlebay
Main Street
Isle of Barra
Tel: (01871) 810336
Easter-Oct

Lochboisdale
Pier Road
Isle of South Uist
Tel: (01878) 700286
Easter-Oct

Lochmaddy
Isle of North Uist
Tel: (01876) 500321
Easter-Oct

Stornoway
26 Cromwell Street
Isle of Lewis
Tel: (01851) 703088
Jan-Dec

Tarbert
Pier Road
Isle of Harris
Tel: (01859) 502011
Easter-Oct

Orkney Tourist Board

Kirkwall
6 Broad Street
Orkney
Tel: (01856) 872856
Jan-Dec

Stromness
Ferry Terminal Building
The Pier Head
Orkney
Tel: (01856) 850716
Jan-Dec

Shetland Tourist Board

Lerwick
The Market Cross
Shetland
Tel: (01595) 693434
Jan-Dec

Scotland's National Booking and Information Line
0845 22 55 121

Castlebay, Isle of Barra, Western Isles — Map Ref: 3A11

★★

B&B

Heishival Bed + Breakfast
47 Glen, Castlebay, Isle of Barra, HS9 5UQ
Tel:01871 810438
Email:calum&flora@aol.com

2 Single	1 Priv.NOT ensuite	B&B per person
1 Double		from £21.00 Single
		from £21.00 Double
		from £15.00 Room
		Only

Open Jan-Dec

Modern bungalow set in the Glen Road about a 10 minute walk from the ferry terminal. Rural views over the surrounding croftland to the bay. Close to local hotels and shops. Near to the Heritage Centre and an ideal base for exploring Barra and the Isles.

Scaristavore, Isle of Harris, Western Isles — Map Ref: 3C6

SANDVIEW HOUSE
6 SCARISTAVORE, HARRIS, ISLE OF HARRIS HS3 3HX
TEL: 01859 550212   FAX: 01859 550212
Friendly comfortable Bed and Breakfast superbly situated overlooking one of the most beautiful beaches in Harris. Adjacent to the local golf course. Five miles from the Leverbursh ferry to North Uist. All rooms with private facilities and tea making facilities, and have stunning sea and sand views.
House open all day.

★★★

B&B

Sandview House
6 Scaristavore, Isle of Harris, Western Isles
HS3 3HX
Tel/Fax:01859 550212

1 Twin	2 En Suite fac	B&B per person	Open Jan-Dec excl
1 Double	1 Pub.Bath/Show	from £25.00 Single	Xmas/New Year
1 Family		from £20.00 Double	BB & Eve.Meal
		from £15.00 Room	from £35.00-40.00
		Only	

Friendly, comfortable bed & breakfast superbly situated overlooking one of the most beautiful beaches in Harris. Adjacent to the local golf course. 5 miles from the Leverburgh Ferry to North Uist. Evening meals; rooms with private facilities.

Seilebost, Isle of Harris, Western Isles — Map Ref: 3C6

★★★

B&B

Beul-na-Mara B&B
12 Seilebost, Isle of Harris, Western Isles
HS3 3HP
Tel:01859 550205
Email:morrisonc1@talk21.com

1 Twin	2 En Suite fac	B&B per night	Open Apr-Oct
2 Double	1 Priv.NOT ensuite	from £23.00 Single	BB & Eve.Meal
	1 Pub.Bath/Show	from £46.00 Double	from £37.50
		from £18.00 Room	
		Only	

Comfortable bed and breakfast accommodation within attractively maintained garden with excellent sea and beach views. The golden sands of this area are well renowned for peace and beauty.

Tarbert, Isle of Harris, Western Isles — Map Ref: 3C6

★★★★

B&B

Avalon
12 West Side, Tarbert, Isle of Harris, HS3 3BG
Tel:01859 502334 Fax:01859 502570
Email:info@avalonguesthouse.co.uk

2 Twin	Some En Suite	B&B per person	Open Jan-Dec excl
1 Double	1 Pub.Bath/Show	from £20.00 Double	Xmas/New Year
			BB & Eve.Meal
			from £30.00

New house on working croft with magnificent view over West Loch Tarbert. Ideal for hill walking, fishing and bird watching. 0.5 mile to ferry terminal.

Important: Prices stated are estimates and may be subject to amendments

Tarbert, Isle of Harris, Western Isles — Map Ref: 3C6

★★★★ B&B

Hill Crest
Tarbert Leachkin, Isle of Harris, HS3 3AH
Tel:01859 502119

2 Twin	All En Suite	B&B per person	Open Jan-Dec excl
2 Double		from £20.00 Double	Xmas/New Year
1 Family			BB & Eve.Meal
			from £33.00

Modern croft in an elevated position overlooking West Loch Tarbert with fine views of mountains and islands. This is an excellent base for exploring all of Harris and Lewis. Miles of unspoilt beaches and an abundance of wildlife, with a variety of plantlife practically on our doorstep. Wonderful walking, country fishing trips and scenic cruises available. 1 mile from ferry terminal.

Aignish, Point, Isle of Lewis, Western Isles — Map Ref: 3E4

★★★ B&B

Sarah MacDonald
Ceol-Na-Mara, 1a Aignish, Isle of Lewis, HS2 0PB
Tel/Fax:01851 870339
Email:sarah@lesmacdonald.freeserve.co.uk
Web:www.lesmacdonald.freeserve.co.uk

1 Twin	1 Priv.NOT ensuite	B&B per person	Open Jan-Dec
1 Double	1 Pub.Bath/Show	from £20.00 Single	BB & Eve.Meal
1 Family		from £18.00 Double	from £30.00

Comfortable modern home in pleasant rural area near Stornoway, on the Eye Peninsula. Friendly and welcoming. Home cooking. Evening meals by arrangement. Ample off street parking.

Back, Isle of Lewis, Western Isles — Map Ref: 3E4

★★★★ B&B

Seaside Villa
Back, Isle of Lewis, HS2 0LQ
Tel/Fax:01851 820208
Email:seasidevilla@talk21.com

1 Twin	All En Suite	B&B per person	Open Jan-Dec
2 Double		from £30.00 Single	BB & Eve.Meal
		from £22.00 Double	from £37.00
		from £15.00 Room	
		Only	

Beautiful views overlooking picturesque bay with miles of unspoilt sandy beaches and Sutherland Hills in the distance. Home cooking and baking using all local fayre - vegetarians welcome. Special highland hospitality. 15 minutes drive from Stornoway.

Callanish, Isle of Lewis, Western Isles — Map Ref: 3D4

ESHCOL GUEST HOUSE
21 Breasclete, Callanish, Isle of Lewis, Scotland HS2 9ED
Tel/Fax: 01851 621357
e.mail: neil@eshcol.com Web: www.eshcol.com
Well established guest house centrally situated for touring Lewis and Harris. Only two miles from the famous standing stones at Callanish. Your hosts, Neil and Isobel Macarthur run Eshcol with an emphasis on quality and attention to detail. Their menu's are created around the wonderful local produce available.

★★★★ GUEST HOUSE

Eshcol Guest House
21 Breasclete, Callanish, Lewis, Outer Hebrides HS2 9ED
Tel/Fax:01851 621357
Email:neil@eshcol.com
Web:www.eshcol.com

2 Twin	2 En Suite fac	B&B per person	Open Jan-Dec excl
1 Double	1 Pub.Bath/Show	from £27.00 Single	Xmas/New Year
		from £27.00 Double	BB & Eve.Meal
			from £45.00

Modern detached house quietly situated in the crofting village of Breasclete, with an open outlook over Loch Roag towards the Uig hills. Good base to explore Lewis, or just to relax. Only 2 miles to the Callanish standing stones. All bedrooms non-smoking. Local produce used where possible in our highly recommended evening meals. B.Y.O.B.

VAT is shown at 17.5%: changes in this rate may affect prices.

Key to symbols is on back flap.

Callanish, Isle of Lewis, Western Isles — Map Ref: 3D4

★★★

B&B

Mrs C Morrison
27 Callanish, Isle of Lewis, HS2 9DY
Tel:01851 621392

1 Twin	1 En Suite fac	B&B per person	Open Mar-Sep
1 Double	1 Priv.NOT ensuite	£20.00-22.00 Double	
	1 Pub.Bath/Show		

Comfortable accommodation, with attractive garden, set on working croft; overlooking Loch Roag to the mountains beyond. Closest bed and breakfast to the famous standing stones, some 150 yds away, with their nearby interpretation and visitor centre.

Lochs, Isle of Lewis, Western Isles — Map Ref: 3D5

★★

B&B

Gledfield
5 Balallan, Lochs, Isle of Lewis, HS2 9PN
Tel:01851 830233
Email:mgledfield@hotmail.com

1 Family	All En Suite	B&B per person	Open Apr-Oct
		from £20.00 Single	BB & Eve.Meal
		from £40.00 Double	from £32.00
		from £15.00 Room Only	

Family run B&B in modern croft house on working croft. Balallan is an excellent centre for touring both Lewis and Harris. Children and pets wecome by prior arrangement. Traditional home cooking using local produce. Evening meal by prior arrangement.

nr Stornoway, Isle of Lewis, Western Isles — Map Ref: 3D4

★★★

B&B

Caladh
44 Gress, Isle of Lewis, Western Isles, HS2 0NB
Tel:01851 820743
Email:EVE@Caladh.fsbusiness.co.uk

2 Twin	All En Suite	B&B per person	Open Jan-Dec
		from £19.00 Single	BB & Eve.Meal
		from £18.00 Double	from £30.00
		from £12.00 Room Only	

Modernised croft house situated in quiet crofting village, 9 miles north of Stornoway. Open outlook over Gress river and saltings, and to the nearby sandy beach. Good area for birdwatching trips. Resident talkative parrot provides free in-house entertainment. Room only rates available on request. Home cooked evening meals by special arrangement.

Berneray, Isle of North Uist, Western Isles — Map Ref: 3B7

★★★

B&B

Burnside Croft
Berneray, North Uist, Western Isles, HS6 5BJ
Tel:01876 540235
Email:splashmackillop@burnsidecroft.fsnet.co.uk
Web:www.burnsidecroft.com

1 Twin	2 En Suite fac	B&B per person	Open Feb-Nov
1 Double	1 Priv.Bath/Show	from £22.00 Single	BB & Eve.Meal
1 Family		from £22.00 Double	from £46.00
		from £20.00 Room Only	

A fine example of traditional Highland hospitality. You quickly become one of the family enjoying Gloria's good food and Don Alick's wide ranging conversation.

Birsay, Orkney — Map Ref: 5B11

★★★

B&B

Primrose Cottage
Birsay, Orkney, KW17 2NB
Tel/Fax:01856 721384
Email:i.clouston@talk21.com

1 Single	2 En Suite fac	B&B per person	Open Jan-Dec excl
1 Twin	1 Priv.NOT ensuite	from £14.00 Single	Xmas
1 Double		from £18.00 Double	BB & Eve.Meal
			from £25.00

In quiet location overlooking Marwick Bay, close to RSPB reserves. Ideal for bird watching, trout fishing and quiet cliff top walks. Local produce used whenever possible, fresh fish and shellfish. Reduced rates for longer stays.

Important: Prices stated are estimates and may be subject to amendments

Evie, Orkney

SMALL HOTEL

•

HOME COOKING

Woodwick House
Evie, Orkney, KW17 2PQ
Tel:01856 751330 Fax:01856 751383
Email:mail@woodwickhouse.co.uk
Web:www.woodwickhouse.co.uk

A warm and welcoming country house, in romantic setting of 12 acre bluebell woodlands, leading down to secluded bay. Views out towards the islands. An informal, peaceful and relaxing environment, yet only 20 minutes from Kirkwall and Stromness. Close to ancient sites and bird reserves. Taste of Scotland member - meals prepared using Orkney organic produce whenever available and seafood.

Map Ref: 5B11

1 Single   4 En Suite fac
3 Twin   1 Pub.Bath/Show
4 Double
2 Family

B&B per person
from £32.00 Single
from £28.00 Double

Open Jan-Dec
BB & Eve.Meal
from £52.00

Harray, Orkney

B&B

Rickla
Harray, Orkney, KW17 2JT
Tel:01856 761575 Fax:01856 761575
Email:jacky@rickla.com Web:www.rickla.com

Luxury en-suite accommodation in the Neolithic Heartland of Orkney. Guest suites have individual private lounges with panoramic views over lochs, hills and the World Heritage Site. Non-smoking, supremely quiet, far from the madding crowd yet centrally situated and close to restaurants. Discrete hospitality, private dining tables, bedrooms with no shared walls - the ideal touring base.

Map Ref: 5B11

1 Twin   All En Suite
2 Double

B&B per person
from £50.00 Single
£30.00-35.00 Double

Open Feb-Oct

Kirkwall, Orkney   Map Ref: 5B12

GUEST HOUSE

Sanderlay Guest House
2 Viewfield Drive, Kirkwall, Orkney, KW15 1RB
Tel:01856 875587 Fax:01856 876350
Email:enquiries@sanderlay.co.uk
Web:www.sanderlay.co.uk

Comfortable modern house in quiet residential area on outskirts of town. Some ensuite and 3 self-contained family units. Private parking available. Credit cards accepted. Ideal base for exploring the Orkney mainland or for visiting the North Isles.

1 Single   4 En Suite fac
1 Twin   1 Priv.NOT ensuite
2 Double
2 Family

B&B per person
£18.00-24.00 Single
£14.00-22.00 Double
£11.00-21.00 Room Only

Open Jan-Dec

B&B

Shearwood
Muddisdale Road, off Pickaquoy Road, Kirkwall
Orkney, KW15 1RR
Tel:01856 873494

Bungalow situated in quiet residential area, 10 minutes walk from the town centre with own enclosed garden. New leisure centre nearby. Pick up with luggage from tourist board - available.

1 Twin   Some En Suite
1 Double 1 Priv.NOT ensuite

B&B per person
from £17.00 Single
£16.00-20.00 Double

Open Jan-Dec excl Xmas/New Year

Scotland's National Booking and Information Line

Tel: 0845 22 55 121
visitscotland.com

VAT is shown at 17.5%: changes in this rate may affect prices.   Key to symbols is on back flap.

Orphir, Orkney

Map Ref: 5B11

SCORRALEE
Scorradale Road, Orphir, Orkney KW17 2RF
Tel/Fax: 01856 811268 e.mail: ebclouston@aol.com
Web: www.s-h-systems.co.uk/hotels/scorrale.html

An Orcadian family home within a peaceful quiet area near to Scapa Flow, famous
in wartime now famous for diving on the wrecks, nine miles from
Kirkwall and Stromness, our main towns. Lots of birdwatching and nice walks,
plenty parking, small ferries services to outer islands.
Just 200 yards from Scarrabrae Inn. All bedrooms ensuite.

★★★

B&B

Scorralee
Orphir, Orkney, KW17 2RF
Tel/Fax:01856 811268
Email:ebclouston@aol.com
Web:www.s-h-systems.co.uk/hotels/scorrale.html

A warm welcome assured at this warm, comfortable, modern house on
elevated site, looking out over Scapa Flow. Equal distance from Kirkwall
and Stromness. Evening meals by arrangement.

1 Twin   All En Suite
2 Double

B&B per person
from £25.00 Single
from £20.00 Double

Open Jan-Dec

Rendall, Orkney

Map Ref: 5B11

★★★

B&B

Ida Sinclair
Riff, Rendall, Orkney, KW17 2PB
Tel/Fax:01856 761541
Email:ida.sinclair@btopenworld.com
Web:www.orkney.co.uk/riff

Riff Farm is situated 4 miles from Rousay Ferry close to the shore of
Puldrite Bay with expansive views across to the Northern Isles. A warm
Orcadian welcome assured.

1 Twin   All En Suite
2 Double

B&B per person
from £18.00 Single
from £16.00 Double

Open Jan-Dec

Stromness, Orkney

Map Ref: 5B12

★★

B&B

Mrs A Brow
Burnmouth, Cairston Road, Stromness, Orkney
KW16 3JS
Tel:01856 850186

Overlooking Stromness harbour and Scapa Flow. Comfortable
accommodation comprising 2 rooms both with showers and washbasins.
Skara Brae, Maes Howe, Standing Stones all nearby. Ideal as a base to
tour mainland Orkney and outer islands.

1 Single   All En Suite
1 Double

B&B per person
£18.00-20.00 Single
£18.00-20.00 Double

Open Jan-Dec excl
Xmas/New Year

★★★★

B&B

Ferry Bank
2 North End Road, Stromness, Orkney, KW16 3AG
Tel:01856 851250

Ferrybank is ideally located for accessing all of Stromness's facilities or
for exploring further a field. Extensive garden with many flowers: take a
few minutes to watch the world go by while you're here.

1 Double   All En Suite
1 Family

B&B per person
from £21.00 Double

Open Jan-Dec excl
Xmas/New Year

Important: Prices stated are estimates and may be subject to amendments

Stromness, Orkney

Map Ref: 5B12

★★★

B&B

Mrs M Tulloch
Olnadale, Innertown, Stromness, Orkney, KW16 3JW
Tel/Fax:01856 850418

1 Twin	1 En Suite fac	B&B per person	Open Apr-Sep
2 Double	1 Priv.NOT ensuite	from £20.00 Single	
		£18.00-20.00 Double	

Modern house with panoramic views of Hoy Sound. Quiet location on the edge of town, but only a short walk down to the main street. This fascinating and charming town, with its sea-faring associations, is best explored on foot - do allow time for this. Many of Orkney's historic sites are just a short drive away.

Lerwick, Shetland

Map Ref: 5G6

★★★

**GUEST
HOUSE**

Bonavista Guest House
26 Church Road, Lerwick, Shetland, ZE1 0AE
Tel:01595 692269

4 Twin	5 En Suite fac	B&B per person	Open Jan-Dec
3 Double	1 Priv.NOT ensuite	from £20.00 Single	BB & Eve.Meal
1 Family	1 Pub.Bath/Show	from £18.00 Double	from £25.00
		from £16.00 Room Only	

Former Laird's Town House, now a 'B' Listed building, close to the hub of the town. A short walk from the Knab, the public golf course. The main ferry terminal is close by and aslo ferries available to Bressay and Out Skerries.

North Mainland, Shetland

Map Ref: 5F3

★★★★

B&B

Westayre Bed & Breakfast
Muckle Roe, Brae, Shetland, ZE2 9QW
Tel:01806 522368
Email:westayre@ukonline.co.uk
Web:www.westayre.shetland.co.uk

1 Single	2 En Suite fac	B&B per person	Open Mar-Dec excl
1 Twin	1 Priv.NOT ensuite	from £20.00 Single	Xmas/New Year
1 Double		from £22.00 Double	BB & Eve.Meal from £34.00

A warm welcome awaits you at our 110 acre working croft on the picturesque island of Muckle Roe where we have been breeding sheep, pet lambs and ducks. Joined to the mainland by a small bridge and an ideal place for children. High standards of home cooking and baking. In the evening sit by the open peat fire and enjoy the view over Swarbacks Minn. Spectacular cliff scenery and clean, safe sandy beaches. Bird watching. Central for touring.

Trondra, by Scalloway, Shetland

Map Ref: 5F6

★★★★

B&B

Bed + Breakfast
South Burland, Trondra, Shetland, ZE1 0XL
Tel:01595 880961   Fax:01595 880962

1 Twin	All En Suite	B&B per person	Open Feb-Dec excl
1 Double		£24.00-28.00 Double	Xmas/New Year
1 Family		from £20.00 Room Only	

Scandinavian-style house with spacious rooms all with luxury ensuite facilities. Excellent views overlooking the Island of Foula and entrance to Scalloway Harbour. 8 miles to Lerwick 3 miles to Scalloway. Road bridge connection to Trondra. Pay for 5 nights and get 6th night free.

Scotland's National Booking and Information Line

Tel: 0845 22 55 121
visitscotland.com

VAT is shown at 17.5%: changes in this rate may affect prices. | *Key to symbols is on back flap.*

Facilities

For visitors with disabilities

VisitScotland, in conjunction with the English Tourism Council and Wales Tourist Board operates a national accessible scheme that identifies, acknowledges and promotes those accommodation establishments that meet the needs of visitors with disabilities.

The three categories of accessibility, drawn up in close consultation with specialist organisations concerned with the needs of people with disabilities are:

Category 1

Unassisted wheelchair access for residents

Category 2

Assisted wheelchair access for residents

Category 3

Access for residents with mobility difficulties

Category 1

Achilty Hotel
Achilty, Contin, by Strathpeffer
Ross-shire, IV14 9EE
Tel: 01997 421355

Airlie House
Main Street, Strathyre
Stirlingshire, FK18 8NA
Tel: 01877 384622

Ard Mhor
Pier Road, Salen
Isle of Mull, PA72 6JL
Tel: 01680 300255

Ardgarth Guest House
1 St Mary's Place, Portobello
Edinburgh, EH15 2QF
Tel: 0131 669 3021

Atholl Villa
29 Atholl Road, Pitlochry
Perthshire, PH16 5BX
Tel: 01796 473820

Balcary Bay Hotel
Auchencairn, By Castle Douglas
Kirkcudbrightshire, DG7 1QZ
Tel: 01556 640217

Battledown Bed & Breakfast
Off Station Road, Forgandenny
Perthshire, PH2 9EL
Tel: 01738 812471

Beardmore Hotel
Beardmore Street, Clydebank
Greater Glasgow, G81 4SA
Tel: 0141 951 6000

Brae Lodge Guest House
30 Liberton Brae, Edinburgh
Lothian, EH16 6AF
Tel: 0131 672 2876

Burrastow House Hotel & Restaurant
Walls, Shetland, ZE2 9PD
Tel: 01595 809307

Cameron House
Loch Lomond, Alexandria
Dunbartonshire, G83 8QZ
Tel: 01389 755565

Carlogie House Hotel
Carlogie Road, Carnoustie
Angus, DD7 6LD
Tel: 01241 853185

Carlton George Hotel
44 West George Street
Glasgow, G2 1DH
Tel: 0141 353 6373

Ceilidh B&B
34 Clifton Road, Lossiemouth
Moray, IV31 6DP
Tel: 01343 815848

Claymore House Hotel
45 Seabank Road, Nairn
Inverness-shire, IV12 4EY
Tel: 01667 453731

Coille-Mhor House
20 Houston Mains Holdings
Uphall, West Lothian, EH52 6PA
Tel: 01506 854044

Copthorne Hotel
122 Huntly Street
Aberdeen, AB10 1SU
Tel: 01224 630404

Covenanters' Inn,
High Street, Auldearn
Nairn, IV12 5TG
Tel: 01667 452456

Craigievar
112 Glasgow Road, Edinburgh
Midlothian, EH12 8LP
Tel: 0131 539248

Crossroads
Stoneybridge, South Uist
Western Isles, HS8 5SD
Tel: 01870 620321

The Crown Hotel
8 Bruce Street, Lochmaben
Dumfriesshire, DG11 1PD
Tel: 01387 811750

Cruachan Guest House
Dalmally
Argyll, PA33 1AA
Tel: 01838 200496

Facilities

For visitors with disabilities

Cuil-Na-Sithe
Lochyside, Fort William
Inverness-shire, PH33 7NX
Tel: 01397 702 267

Days Inn, Welcome Break
M74/A7, Abington
Lanarkshire ML12 6RG
Tel: 01864 502782

Days Inn
80 Ballater Street
Glasgow, G5 0TW
Tel: 0141 4294233

Dhailling Lodge
155 Alexandra Parade
Dunoon, Argyll, PA23 8AW
Tel: 01369 701253

Dolly's B & B
33 Aignish, Point
Lewis, Western Isles, HS2 0PB
Tel: 01851 870755

Drumoig Hotel Golf Resort
Drumoig, Leuchars
by St Andrews, Fife, KY16 0BE
Tel: 01382 541800

Dryburgh Abbey Hotel
St Boswells
Roxburghshire, TD6 0RQ
Tel: 01835 822261

Dunvalanree
Portrigh Bay, Carradale
Argyll, PA28 6SE
Tel: 01583 431226

Edinburgh City Travel Inn Metro
1 Morrison Link
Edinburgh, EH3 8DN
Tel: 0131 656 4345

Empire Travel Lodge
Union Street, Lochgilphead
Argyll, PA31 8JS
Tel: 01546 602381

Express By Holiday Inn
Strathclyde Park M74 Jct 5
Motherwell, Lanarkshire ML1 3RB
Tel: 01698 858585

Express by Holiday Inn
Cartsburn
Greenock, PA15 4R
Tel: 01475 786666

Express by Holiday Inn
Springkerse Business Park
Stirling, Stirlingshire, FK7 7XH
Tel: 01786 449922

The Fishermans Tavern Hotel
10-16 Fort Street, Broughty Ferry
Dundee, Angus, DD5 2AD
Tel: 01382 775941

Gattaway Farm
Abernethy
Perthshire, PH2 9LQ
Tel: 01738 850746

Glasgow Hilton
1 William Street,
Glasgow, G3 8HT
Tel: 0141 204 5555

Glasgow Marriott
500 Argyle Street
Glasgow, G3 8RR
Tel: 0141 221 9202

Glasgow North Premier Lodge
Milngavie Road
Glasgow, G61 3TA
Tel: 0870 700 1400

The Gleneagles Hotel
Auchterarder
Perthshire, PH3 1NF
Tel: 01764 662231

The Glenholm Centre
Broughton, by Biggar
Lanarkshire, ML12 6JF
Tel: 01899 830408

Greenacre
Aberfeldy Road, by Killin
Perthshire, FK21 8TY
Tel: 01567 820466

Highland Cottage
Breadalbane Street, Tobermory
Isle of Mull, PA75 6PD
Tel: 01688 302030

Holiday Inn
161 West Nile Street
Glasgow, G1 2RL
Tel: 0141 332 0110

Holiday Inn Glasgow City West
Bothwell Street
Glasgow, G2 7EN
Tel: 0870 400 9032

Hunters Lodge Hotel
Annan Road, Gretna
Dumfriesshire, DG16 5DL
Tel: 01461 338214

Inchyra Grange Hotel
Grange Road, Polmont
Stirlingshire, FK2 0YB
Tel: 01324 711911

The Invercauld Arms Hotel
Invercauld Road, Braemar
Aberdeenshire, AB35 5YR
Tel: 01369 720027

Inverness Marriott
Culcabock Road, Inverness
Inverness-shire, IV2 3LP
Tel: 01463 237166

Invernettie Guest House
South Road, Peterhead
Aberdeenshire, AB42 0YX
Tel: 01779 473530

Isle of Skye Hotel
Queensbridge, 18 Dundee Road
Perth, Tayside, PH2 7AB
Tel: 01738 624471

**Isles of Glencoe Hotel
& Leisure Centre**
Ballachulish, Argyll, PA39 4HL
Tel: 01855 821582

James Watt College
Waterfront Campus
Customhouse Way, Greenock
Renfrewshire, PA15 1EN
Tel: 01475 731360

Jurys Edinburgh Inn
43 Jeffrey Street
Edinburgh, Lothian, EH1 1DH
Tel: 0131 200 3300

Facilities

For visitors with disabilities

Kings Hall
University of Aberdeen
Aberdeen, AB24 3FX
Tel: 01224 272662

Lav'rockha Guest House
Inganess Road, Kirkwall
Orkney, KW15 1SP
Tel: 01856 876103

Loch Torridon Hotel
Torridon, Achnasheen
Ross-shire, IV22 2EY
Tel: 01445 791242

The Lodge at Daviot Mains
Daviot, Inverness-shire, IV2 5ER
Tel: 01463 772215

Marcliffe at Pitfodels
North Deeside Road
Pitfodels, Aberdeen, AB15 9YA
Tel: 01224 861000

Melville Guest House
2 Duddingston Crescent
Edinburgh, Lothian, EH15 3AS
Tel: 0131 6697856

Motherwell College Stewart Hall
Dalzell Drive, Motherwell
Lanarkshire, ML1 2DD
Tel: 01698 261890

Northbay House
Balnabodach, Castlebay
Isle of Barra, Outer Hebrides
HS9 5UT
Tel: 01871 890 255

Novotel Glasgow
181 Pitt Street
Glasgow, G2 4DT
Tel: 07799 478179

The Old House
4 Lewis Street, Stornoway
Isle of Lewis, HS1 2QH
Tel: 01851 704495

Old Pines Restaurant with Rooms
By Spean Bridge
Inverness-shire, PH34 4EG
Tel: 01397 712324

The Old Station
Stravithie Bridge, St Andrews
Fife, KY16 8LR
Tel: 01334 880505

Panmure Hotel
Tay Street, Monifieth
Angus, DD5 4AX
Tel: 01382 532911

Patio Hotel Aberdeen
Beach Boulevard, Aberdeen
Aberdeenshire, AB24 5EF
Tel: 01224 633339

Ramada Jarvis Livingston
Almondview, Livingston
West Lothian, EH54 6QB
Tel: 01506 431222

Rosslea Hall Hotel
Ferry Road, Rhu
Dunbartonshire, G84 8NF
Tel: 01436 439955

Rowantree Guest House
38 Main Street, Glenluce
Newton Stewart,
Wigtownshire, DG8 OPS
Tel: 01581 300244

Ryrie
24 Lindsay Drive, Wick
Caithness, KW1 4PG
Tel: 01955 603001

**Sheraton Grand Hotel
& Spa Edinburgh**
1 Festival Square
Edinburgh, EH3 9SR
Tel: 0131 229 9131

Shetland Hotel
Holmsgarth Road, Lerwick
Shetland, ZE1 OPW
Tel: 01595 695515

Shorefield
Edinbane
Isle of Skye, IV51 9PW
Tel: 01470 582444

Silverwells Guest House
28 Ness Bank
Inverness, IV2 4SF
Tel: 01463 232113

Simpsons Hotel
79 Lauriston Place
Edinburgh, EH3 9HZ
Tel: 0131 622 7979

Speedbird Inn
Argyll Road, Dyce, Aberdeen
Aberdeenshire, AB21 0AF
Tel: 01224 772884

Stirling Management Centre
University of Stirling
Stirling, FK9 4LA
Tel: 01786 451666

Strathpeffer Hotel
Strathpeffer,
Ross-shire, IV14 9DF
Tel: 01997 421200

Strathwhillan House
Brodick
Isle of Arran, KA27 8BQ
Tel: 01770 302331

Stronsay Hotel
Stronsay
Orkney, KW17 2AR
Tel: 01857 616213

Thistle Aberdeen Airport Hotel
Argyll Road, Aberdeen
Aberdeenshire, AB21 0AF
Tel: 0141 332 3311

Thistle Aberdeen Altens
Souterhead Road, Altens
Aberdeen, Aberdeenshire
AB12 3LF
Tel: 0141 332 3311

Thistle Edinburgh
107 Leith Street
Edinburgh, EH1 3SW
Tel: 0141 3323311

Thistle Irvine
46 Annick Road, Irvine
Ayrshire, KA11 4LD
Tel: 0141 332 3311

Thorndale
Manse Road, Stonehouse
Lanarkshire, ML9 3NX
Tel: 01698 791133

Facilities
For visitors with disabilities

Tigh-Na-Cheo
Garbhein Road, Kinlochleven
Argyll, PA40 4SE
Tel: 01855 831434

Traquair Arms Hotel
Traquair Road, Innerleithen
Peeblesshire, EH44 6PD
Tel: 01896 830229

The Trefoil Centre
Gogarbank
Edinburgh, EH12 9DA
Tel: 0131 339 3148

Viewfield House Hotel
Portree
Isle of Skye, IV51 9EU
Tel: 01478 612217

Welcome Lodge
Welcome Break Service Area M74
Gretna Green, Dumfriesshire
DG16 5HQ
Tel: 01461 337566

West Park Villas
West Park Road
Dundee, Angus, DD2 1NN
Tel: 01382 344039

The Westin Turnberry Resort
Turnberry
Ayrshire, KA26 9LT
Tel: 01655 331000

Westwood House
Houndwood, By St Abbs
Berwickshire, TD14 5TP
Tel: 01361 850232

Windsor Hotel
18 Albert Street, Nairn
Inverness-shire, IV12 4HP
Tel: 01667 453108

Woodland House
Torlundy, Fort William
Inverness-shire, PH33 6SN
Tel: 01397 701698

Category 2

**Aberdeen City Centre
Premier Lodge**
Invelair House, West North Street
Aberdeen, Aberdeenshire, AB24 5AR
Tel: 0870 700 1304

Aberdeen Marriott Hotel
Riverview Drive, Farburn
Dyce, Aberdeenshire AB21 7AZ,
Tel: 01224 770011

**Aberdeen South West
Premier Lodge**
Straik Road, Westhill,
Aberdeenshire, AB32 6JN
Tel: 0870 700 1303

Aberdeen West Premier Lodge
North Anderson Drive, Aberdeen
Aberdeenshire, AB15 6DW
Tel: 0870 700 1300

Arden House
Newtonmore Road, Kingussie
Inverness-shire, PH21 1HE
Tel: 01540 661369

Auchendinny Guest House
Treaslane, Portree, Isle of Skye
Inverness-shire, IV51 9NX
Tel: 01470 532470

Auchenskeoch Lodge
By Dalbeattie
Kirkcudbrightshire, DG5 4PG
Tel: 01387 780277

Auchrannie Country House Hotel
Brodick
Isle of Arran, KA27 8BZ
Tel: 01770 302234

Balbirnie House Hotel
Balbirnie Park, Markinch
by Glenrothes, Fife, KY7 6NE
Tel: 01592 610066

The Ballachulish Hotel
Ballachulish
Argyll, PA39 4JY
Tel: 01855 811606

The Baltasound Hotel
Baltasound, Unst,
Shetland, ZE2 9DS
Tel: 01957 711334

Barony Hotel
Birsay
Orkney, KW17 2LS
Tel: 01856 721327

Bewleys Hotel Glasgow
110 Bath Street,
Glasgow, G2 2EN
Tel: 0141 3530800

Burnside Apartments
19 West Moulin Road, Pitlochry
Perthshire, PH16 5EA
Tel: 01796 472203

Caledonian Hilton Hotel
Princes Street
Edinburgh, EH1 2AB
Tel: 0131 222 8888

Clan MacDuff Hotel
Achintore Road, Fort William
Inverness-shire, PH33 6RW
Tel: 01397 702341

Cloisters
Church Holme, Talmine
Sutherland, IV27 4YP
Tel: 01847 601286

Comely Bank
32 Burrell Street, Crieff
Perthshire, PH7 4DT
Tel: 01764 653409

Crombie Johnston Hall
University of Aberdeen
Aberdeen, AB24 3TS
Tel: 01224 272662

Cuil-an-Darraich
Logierait, Perth
Perthshire, PH9 0LH
Tel: 01796 482750

Dall Lodge Country House Hotel
Main Street, Killin
Perthshire, FK21 8TN
Tel: 01567 820217

Dovecote Beefeater
4 South Muirhead Road,
Cumbernauld, Glasgow, G67 1AX
Tel: 01236 725339

Facilities

For visitors with disabilities

Dryfesdale Hotel
Dryfebridge, Lockerbie
Dumfriesshire, DG11 2SF
Tel: 01576 202427

Dundee East Premier Lodge
115-117 Lawers Drive
Panmurefield Village
Broughty Ferry, Dundee, DD5 3TS
Tel: 0870 700 1360

Dundee North Premier Lodge
Camperdown Leisure Park
Dayton Drive, Kingsway
Dundee, DD2 3SQ
Tel: 0870 700 1362

Dyce Skean Dhu Hotel
Farburn Terrace, Dyce
Aberdeenshire, AB21 7DW
Tel: 0141 332 3311

East Kilbride Premier Lodge
Eaglesham Road, East Kilbride
Glasgow, G75 8LW
Tel: 0870 700 1398

Edinburgh East Premier Lodge
City Bypass, Newcraighall
Edinburgh, EH2 8SG
Tel: 0870 700 1372

Edinburgh Marriott
111 Glasgow Road
Edinburgh, EH12 8NF
Tel: 0131 334 9191

Express by Holiday Inn
200 Dunkeld Road, Inveralmond
Perth, Perthshire, PH1 3AQ
Tel: 01738 636666

Falkirk Premier Lodge
Glenbervie Business Park
Bellsdyke Rd, Larbert, Falkirk
Stirlingshire, FK5 4EG
Tel: 0870 700 1386

Garvock House Hotel
St John's Drive, Transy
Dunfermline, Fife, KY12 7TU
Tel: 01383 621067

Glasgow Moat House
Congress Road
Glasgow, G3 8QT
Tel: 0141 306 9988

Glenaveron
Golf Road, Brora
Sutherland, KW9 6QS
Tel: 01408 621 601

The Glentress Hotel
Kirnlan, Peebles,
Peebles-shire, EH45 8NB
Tel: 01721 720100

The Gretna Chase Hotel
Sark Bridge, Gretna,
Dumfriesshire, DG16 5JB
Tel: 01461 337517

Hetland Hall Hotel
Carrutherstown,
Dumfriesshire, DG1 4JX,
Tel: 01387 840201

Hilcroft Hotel
East Main Street, Whitburn
West Lothian, EH47 0JU
Tel: 01501 740818

Hilton Edinburgh Airport
Edinburgh International Airport
Edinburgh, EH28 8LL
Tel: 0131 519 4400

Hilton Edinburgh Grosvenor
7-21 Grosvenor Street
Edinburgh, EH12 5EF
Tel: 0131-226-6001

Holiday Inn Edinburgh
Corstorphine Road
Edinburgh, EH12 6UA
Tel: 0870 400 9026

Holiday Inn Edinburgh-North
107 Queensferry Road
Edinburgh, EH4 3HL
Tel: 0131-332-2442

Huntingtower Hotel
Crieff Road, Perth
Perthshire, PH1 3JT
Tel: 01738 583771

Ibis Hotel Glasgow
220 West Regent Street
Glasgow, G2 4DQ
Tel: 0141 225 6000

The Inn at Roy Bridge
Roy Bridge
Inverness-shire, PH31 4AG
Tel: 01397 712253

Ivory House
14 Vogrie Road, Gorebridge
Midlothian, EH23 4HH
Tel: 01875 820755

Keavil House Hotel
Crossford, Dunfermline
Fife, KY12 8QW
Tel: 01383 736258

Kinloch House Hotel
By Blairgowrie, Perthshire
PH10 6SG
Tel: 01250 884237

Kynachan Loch Tummel Hotel
Tummel Bridge
Perthshire, PH16 5SB
Tel: 01389 713713

Loch Fyne Hotel
Newtown, Inveraray
Argyll, PA32 8XT
Tel: 0131 554 7173

The Lodge on the Loch
Creag Dhu, Onich,
by Fort William
Inverness-shire, PH33 6RY
Tel: 01855 821237

The Log Cabin Hotel
Glen Derby, Kirkmichael
Blairgowrie
Perthshire, PH10 7NB
Tel: 01250 881288

The Mill
Grahamshill, Kirkpatrick Fleming
by Lockerbie
Dumfriesshire, DG11 3BQ
Tel: 01461 800344

**Milton Hotel &
Leisure Club Glasgow**
27 Washington Street,
Glasgow, G3 6AZ
Tel: 01786 468714

Minard Castle
Minard
Argyll, PA32 8YB
Tel: 01546 886272

Facilities

For visitors with disabilities

Moorings Hotel
114 Hamilton Road, Motherwell
Lanarkshire, ML1 3DG
Tel: 01698 258131

Morangie House Hotel
Morangie Road, Tain
Ross-shire, IV19 1PY
Tel: 01862 892281

Muckrach Lodge Hotel
Dulnain Bridge,
Grantown-on-spey, Moray
PH26 3LY
Tel: 01479 851257,

Murraypark Hotel
Connaught Terrace, Crieff
Perthshire, PH7 3DJ
Tel: 01764 653731

Nethybridge Hotel
Nethybridge
Inverness-shire, PH25 3DP
Tel: 01479 821203

New Lanark Mill Hotel
New Lanark
Lanarkshire, ML11 9DB
Tel: 01555 667200

New Weigh Inn Hotel
Burnside, Thurso
Caithness, KW14 7UG
Tel: 01847 893 722

Observatory Guest House
North Ronaldsay
Orkney, KW17 2BE
Tel: 011857 633200

Orasay Inn
Lochcarnan, South Uist
Outer Hebrides, HS8 5PD
Tel: 01870 610 298

Patio Hotel
1 South Avenue
Clydebank Business Park
Clydebank, Glasgow
Dunbartonshire, G81 2RW
Tel: 0141 951 1133

Plockton Hotel
Harbour Street, Plockton
Ross-shire, IV52 8TN
Tel: 01599 544274

Quality Hotel Central
Gordon Street
Glasgow, G1 3SF
Tel: 0141 221 9680

Queen Margaret College
36 Clerwood Terrace
Edinburgh, EH12 8TS
Tel: 0131 317 3314/3310

Ramada Jarvis Inverness
Church Street, Invernes,
Inverness-shire, IV1 1DX
Tel: 01463 235181

Roineabhal Country House
Kilchrenan, by Taynuilt
Argyll, PA35 1HD
Tel: 01866 833207

Stromabank
Hoy, Orkney, KW16 3PA
Tel: 01856 701494

**Sweethope Beefeater
& Travel Inn**
Carberry Road, Musselburgh
East Lothian, EH21 8PT
Tel: 0131 665 3005

The Underwater Centre
Fort William
Inverness-shire, PH33 6LZ
Tel: 01397 703786

Whitchester Guest House
Hawick, Roxburghshire, TD9 7LN
Tel: 01450 377477

Category 3

Aaron Glen Guest House
7 Nivensknowe Road
Loanhead
Midlothian, EH20 9AU
Tel: 0131 440 1293

Abbey Lodge Hotel
137 Drum Street, Gilmerton
Edinburgh, EH17 8RJ
Tel: 0131 664 9548

Aberdour Hotel
38 High Street, Aberdour
Fife, KY3 0SW
Tel: 01383 860325

Aberfeldy Lodge
11 Southside Road, Inverness
Inverness-shire, IV2 3BG
Tel: 01463 231120/234741

Achray House Hotel
St Fillans, Crieff
Perthshire, PH6 2NF
Tel: 01764 685 231

Alcorn Guest House
5 Hyndford Street, Dundee
Angus, DD2 3DY
Tel: 01382 668433

Anchorage Guest House
31 Balloch Road, Balloch
Dunbartonshire, G83 8SS
Tel: 01389 753336

Ardbeg Cottage
19 Castle Street, Lochmaben
Dumfries-shire, DG11 1NY
Tel: 01387 811855

Ardgowan Town House Hotel
94 Renfrew Road, Paisley
Renfrewshire, PA3 4BJ
Tel: 0141 889 4763

Arnabhal
5 Gerraidh Bhailteas
Bornish South Uist
Western Isles, HS8 5RY
Tel: 01878 710371

Avalon
12 West Side, Tarbert
Harris, Western Isles, HS3 3BG
Tel: 01859 502334

Avalon Guest House
79 Glenurquhart Road
Inverness, Inverness-shire, IV3 5PB
Tel: 01463 239075

Balavil Sport Hotel
Main Street, Newtonmore
Inverness-shire, PH20 1DL
Tel: 01540 673220

Ballathie House Hotel
Kinclaven, by Stanley
Perthshire, PH1 4QN
Tel: 01250 883268

Facilities

For visitors with disabilities

Barn Lodge
Croftside, Pirnhall, Stirling
Stirlingshire, FK7 8EX
Tel: 01786 813591

Baxters Country Inn
Darvel Road, Strathaven
Lanarkshire, ML10 6QR
Tel: 01357 440341

Bellevue B & B
Port Road
Dalbeattie, DG5 4AZ
Tel: 01556 611833

Belvedere Guest House
Alma Road, Brodick
Isle of Arran, KA27 8AZ
Tel: 01770 302397

Best Western Links Hotel
Mid Links, Montrose
Angus, DD10 8RL
Tel: 01674 671000

Birchbank Activity Lodge
Knockan, Elphin, by Lairg
Sutherland, IV27 4HH
Tel: 01854 666203 / 666215

Birchgrove
Lochdon
Isle of Mull, PA64 4AN
Tel: 01680 812364

Black Bull Hotel
Churchgate, Moffat
Dumfriesshire, DG10 9EG
Tel: 01683 220206

Blarglas
Luss
Dumbartonshire, G83 8RG
Tel: 01389 850278

Braefield Guest House
Braefield Road, Portpatrick
Wigtownshire, DG9 8TA
Tel: 01776 810255

Britannia Hotel
Malcolm Road, Aberdeen
Grampian, AB21 9LN
Tel: 01224 409988

The Bungalow
81 High Street, Buckie
Banffshire, AB56 1BB
Tel: 01542 832367

Cambria Guest House
141 Bannockburn Road
Stirling FK7 0EP
Tel: 01786 814603

Canon Court
20 Canonmills, Edinburgh
Mid Lothian, EH3 5LH
Tel: 0131 474 7000

Carberry Conference Centre
Carberry Tower, Musselburgh
East Lothian, EH21 8PY
Tel: 0131 665 3135

Cherrybank Inn
210 Glasgow Road
Perth, PH2 0NA
Tel: 01738 624349

Chesterton House
Formaston Park, Aboyne
Aberdeenshire, AB34 5HF
Tel: 013398 86740

Clarke Cottage Guest House
139 Halbeath Road, Dunfermline
Fife, KY11 4LA
Tel: 01383 735935

Clonyard House Hotel
Colvend, Dalbeattie
Kircudbrightshire, DG5 4QW
Tel: 01556 630372

Cormiston Cottage
Cormiston Road, Biggar
Lanarkshire, ML12 6NS
Tel: 01899 220200

Corsewall Lighthouse Hotel
Kirkcolm, by Stranraer
Wigtownshire, DG9 0QG
Tel: 01776 853220

Coul House Hotel
Contin, by Strathpeffer
Ross-shire, IV14 9ES
Tel: 01997 421487

Craig Nevis West
Belford Road, Fort William
Inverness-shire, PH33 6BU
Tel: 01397 702023

Craigatin House
165 Atholl Road, Pitlochry
Perthshire, PH16 5QL
Tel: 01796 472478

Craiglynne Hotel
Woodlands Terrace
Grantown-on-Spey
Morayshire, PH26 3JX
Tel: 0131 554 7173

Craignethan House
Jedburgh Road, Kelso
Roxburghshire, TD5 8AZ
Tel: 01573 224818

Craigvrack Hotel
38 West Moulin Road, Pitlochry
Perthshire, PH16 5EQ
Tel: 01796 472399

Crannog
New Liston Road, Kirkliston
West Lothian, EH29 9EA
Tel: 0131 333 4621

Crieff Hydro Hotel
Crieff
Perthshire, PH7 3LQ
Tel: 01764 655555

Croit Anna Hotel
Achintore Road, Fort William
Inverness-shire, PH33 6RR
Tel: 01397 702268

Cromasaig
Torridon Road, Kinlochewe
Ross-shire, IV22 2PE
Tel: 01445 760234

Cross Keys Hotel
36-37 The Square, Kelso
Roxburghshire, TD5 7HL
Tel: 01573 223303

Culcreuch Castle
Culcreuch Castle Country Park
Fintry, Stirlingshire, G63 0LW
Tel: 01360 860555

Facilities

For visitors with disabilities

Dalerb
Craignavie Road, Killin
Perthshire, FK21 8SH
Tel: 01567 820961

Darroch Learg Hotel
Braemar Road, Ballater
Aberdeenshire, AB35 5UX
Tel: 013397 55443

Distant Hills Guest House
Roybridge Road, Spean Bridge
Inverness-shire, PH34 4DU
Tel: 01397 712452

Dreamweavers
Mucomir, By Spean Bridge
Inverness-shire, PH34 4EQ
Tel: 01397 712 548

Dromnan Guest House
Garve Road, Ullapool
Ross-shire, IV26 2SX
Tel: 01854 612333

Druimard Country House
Dervaig, Tobermory
Isle of Mull, PA75 6QW
Tel: 01688 400345

Drumfork Farm
Helensburgh
Dunbartonshire, G84 7JY
Tel: 01436 672329

Drumossie Park Cottage
Drumossie Brae, Inverness
Inverness-shire, IV2 5BB
Tel: 01463 224127

Dunallan House
Woodside Avenue
Grantown-on-Spey
Moray, PH26 3JN
Tel: 01479 872140

Dunedin
42 Strath, Gairloch
Ross-shire, IV21 2DB
Tel: 01445 712050

Dunlaverock
Coldingham Bay
Berwickshire, TD14 5PA
Tel: 01890 771450

East Haugh House Country Hotel and Restaurant
East Haugh, by Pitlochry
Perthshire, PH16 5JS
Tel: 01796 47 3121

Eddrachilles Hotel
Badcall Bay, Scourie
Sutherland, IV27 4TH
Tel: 01971 502080

Edenmouth Farm
Kelso, Roxburghshire, TD5 7QB
Tel: 01890 830391

Edinburgh Premier Lodge
94-96 Grassmarket
Edinburgh, Lothian, EH1 2JR
Tel: 0870 700 1370

Enterkine House
Annbank, by Ayr
Ayrshire, KA6 5AL
Tel: 01292 521608

Erskine Bridge Hotel
Erskine
Renfrewshire, PA8 6AN

Ettrickvale
33 Abbotsford Road, Galashiels
Selkirkshire, TD1 3HW
Tel: 01896 755224

Express by Holiday Inn
Stoneyfield
Inverness, IV2 7PA
Tel: 01463 732700

Fairfield House Hotel
12 Fairfield Road, Ayr
Ayrshire, KA7 2AR
Tel: 01292 267461

Falls of Lora Hotel
Connel Ferry, by Oban
Argyll, PA37 1PB
Tel: 01631 710483

Fendoch Guest House
Sma' Glen, Crieff
Perthshire, PH7 3LW
Tel: 01764 653446

Fenwick Hotel
Fenwick, by Kilmarnock
Ayrshire, KA3 6AU
Tel: 01560 600 478

The Fernhill Hotel
Heugh Road, Portpatrick
Wigtownshire, DG9 8TD
Tel: 01776 810220

Finlay Ross (Iona) Ltd
Martyr's Bay, Isle of Iona
Argyll, PA76 6SP
Tel: 01505 324461

Fishers Hotel
75-79 Atholl Road, Pitlochry,
Perthshire, PH16 5BN
Tel: 0131 554 7173

Forss House Hotel
Forss, by Thurso
Caithness, KW14 7XY
Tel: 01847 861201

Freedom Inn
Aviemore Centre, Aviemore
Inverness-shire, PH22 1PF
Tel: 01479 810781

The Gables Hotel
1 Annan Road, Gretna
Dumfriesshire, DG16 5DQ
Tel: 01461 338300

Gairloch View
3 Digg, Staffin
Isle of Skye, IV51 9LA
Tel: 01470 562718

Galley of Lorne Inn
Ardfern, by Lochgilphead
Argyll, PA31 8QN
Tel: 01852 500284

Glen Mhor Hotel
9-12 Ness Bank, Inverness
Inverness-shire, IV2 4SG
Tel: 01463 234308

Glen Orchy Guest House
20 Knab Road, Lerwick
Shetland, ZE1 0AX
Tel: 01595 692031

Glenmarkie Guest House
Glenisla, by Blairgowrie
Perthshire, PH11 8QB
Tel: 01575 582295

Facilities

For visitors with disabilities

Glenorchy Lodge Hotel
Dalmally, Argyll, PA33 1AA
Tel: 018382 00312

Goldenstones Hotel
Queens Road, Dunbar
East Lothian, EH42 1LG
Tel: 01368 862356

Green Park Hotel
Clunie Bridge Road, Pitlochry
Perthshire, PH16 5JY
Tel: 01796 473248

Greenlawns
13 Seafield Street, Nairn
Inverness-shire, IV12 4HG
Tel: 01667 452738

Hazeldean Guest House
4 Moffat Road
Dumfries, DG1 1NJ
Tel: 01387 266178

The Heathers
Invergloy Halt, Spean Bridge
Inverness-shire, PH34 4DY
Tel: 01397 712077

Heathpete
24 Balloch Road, Balloch
Dunbartonshire, G83 8LE
Tel: 01389 752195

Hideaway
Craigdarroch Drive, Contin
Ross-shire, IV14 9EL
Tel: 01997 421127

Hilton Dundee
Earl Grey Place, Dundee
Angus , DD1 4DE
Tel: 01382 229271

Hilton East Kilbride
Stewartfield Way, East Kilbride
Lanarkshire, G74 5LA
Tel: 01355 236300

Hilton Strathclyde
Pheonix Crescent, Bellshill
North Lanarkshire, ML4 3JQ
Tel: 01698 395500

Holland House
Pollock Halls
18 Holyrood Park Road
Edinburgh, EH16 5AY
Tel: 0131 651 2191

Holly Tree Hotel
Kentallen, Appin
Argyll, PA38 4BY
Tel: 01631 740292

Holmrigg
Wester Essendy, Blairgowrie
Perthshire, PH10 6RD
Tel: 01250 884309

Holyrood Aparthotel
1 Nether Bakehouse, Holyrood
Edinburgh, EH8 8PE
Tel: 0131 524 3200

Honeysuckle Cottage
1 Victoria Place, Falkland
Fife, KY15 7AU
Tel: 01337 858600

Horizon Hotel
Esplanade, Ayr
Ayrshire, KA7 1DT
Tel: 01292 264384

Hotel Ceilidh-Donia
14-16 Marchhall Crescent,
Edinburgh, EH16 5HL
Tel: 0131 667 2743

The Inn at Ardgour
Ardgour, by Fort William
Inverness-shire, PH33 7AA
Tel: 01855 841225

International Guest House
37 Mayfield Gardens
Edinburgh, EH9 2BX
Tel: 0131 667 2511

Kalmar
Balmaclellan,
Kirkcudbrightshire, DG7 3QF
Tel: 01644 420685

Kelly's Guest House
3 Hillhouse Road
Edinburgh, Lothian, EH4 3QP
Tel: 0131 332 3894

Kilspindie House Hotel
High Street, Aberlady
Longniddry, EH32 0RE
Tel: 01875 870 682

The Kimberley Hotel
Dalriach Road, Oban
Argyll, PA34 5EQ
Tel: 01631 571115

Kingspark Llama Farm
Berriedale
Caithness, KW7 6HA
Tel: 01593 751202

Kinkell House Hotel
Easter Kinkell, by Conon Bridge
Ross-shire, IV7 8HY
Tel: 01349 861270

Kinross House Guest House
Woodside Avenue
Grantown-on-Spey,
Moray, PH26 3JR
Tel: 01479 872042,

Kirklands Hotel
Ruthwell
Dumfriesshire, DG1 4NP
Tel: 01387 870284

Kirkton Inn
1 Main Street, Dalrymple
Ayrshire, KA6 6DF
Tel: 01292 560241

The Knowe
5 Ancaster Road, Callander
Perthshire, FK17 8EL
Tel: 01877 330076

The Knowes
32 Riddrie Knowes, Glasgow
Strathclyde, G33 2QH
Tel: 0141 770 5213

The Laurels
320 Gilmerton Road, Edinburgh
Midlothian, EH17 7PR
Tel: 0131 666 2229

Lilybank
Shore Road, Lamlash
Isle of Arran, KA27 8LS
Tel: 01770 600230

Facilities

For visitors with disabilities

Lindsay Guest House
108 Polwarth Terrace, Edinburgh
Midlothian, EH11 1NN
Tel: 0131 337 1580

Loch Maree Hotel
Talladale, Loch Maree
by Achnasheen
Ross-shire, IV22 2HN
Tel: 01445 760288

Loch Tummel Inn
Strathtummel, Pitlochry
Perthshire, PH16 5RP
Tel: 01882 634272

Lochan Cottage Guest House
Lochyside, Fort William
Inverness-shire, PH33 7NX
Tel: 01397 702695

Lochside Guest House
Blackwaterfoot
Isle of Arran, KA27 8EY
Tel: 01770 860276

Lomond Country Inn
Main Street, Kinnesswood
Kinross, KY13 9HN
Tel: 01592 840253

Lower Plaidy
Turriff,
Aberdeenshire, AB53 7RJ
Tel: 01888 551679

Lyndale
Station Road, Beauly
Inverness-shire, IV4 7EH
Tel: 01463 783672

Lynedoch
7 Mayne Avenue, Bridge of Allan
Stirlingshire, FK9 4QU
Tel: 01786 832178

Mardon
37 Kenneth Street
Inverness, IV3 5DH
Tel: 01463 231005

Masson House
18 Holyrood Park Road
Edinburgh EH16 5AY
Tel: 0131 667 0662

Meadows Festival Rooms
7 Hope Park Terrace, Edinburgh
Midlothian, EH8 9LZ
Tel: 0790 034 8977

Milton Inn
Dumbarton Road, Milton
Dunbartonshire, G82 2DT
Tel: 01389 761318

Moir Lodge
28 Linkfield Road, Musselburgh
East Lothian, EH21 7LL
Tel: 0131 653 2827

Moraydale
276 High Street, Elgin
Morayshire, IV30 1AG
Tel: 01343 546381

Moyness House
6 Bruce Gardens
Inverness, IV3 5EN
Tel: 01463 233836

Napier
60 Seabank Road
Nairn, IV12 4HA
Tel: 01667 453330

Netherfield
Lochanhead, Dumfries
Dumfries & Galloway, DG2 8JE
Tel: 01387 730217

Newbyres Cottage
8 Hunterfield Road, Gorebridge
Midlothian, EH23 4TR
Tel: 01875 821268

Northern Hotel
1 Great Northern Road
Aberdeen, AB24 3PS
Tel: 01224 483342

Piersland House Hotel
15 Craigend Road, Troon
Ayrshire, KA10 6HD
Tel: 01292 31474

Pitbauchlie House Hotel
Aberdour Road, Dunfermline
Fife, KY11 4PB
Tel: 01383 722282

Portpatrick Hotel
Heugh Road, Portpatrick
Wigtownshire, DG9 8TQ
Tel: 01369 702227

The Priory
Bracklinn Road, Callander
Perthshire, FK17 8EH
Tel: 01877 330001

Priory Lodge
8 The Loan, South Queensferry
West Lothian, EH30 9NS
Tel: 0131 331 4345

Quality Hotel Station Perth
Leonard Street, Perth
Perthshire, PH2 8HE
Tel: 0181 233 201

RSR Braeholm
31 East Montrose Street
Helensburgh
Argyll & Bute, G84 7HR
Tel: 01436 671880

Red House Hotel
Station Road, Coupar Angus,
Perthshire, PH13 9AL
Tel: 01828 628500

The Reiver's Rest
81 High Street, Langholm
Dumfriesshire, DG13 0DJ
Tel: 01387 381343

Richmond Park Hotel
26 Linlithgow Road, Bo'ness
West Lothian, EH51 0DN
Tel: 01506 823213

Rob Roy Motel
Aberfoyle,
Stirlingshire, FK8 3UX
Tel: 01877 382245

Rockmount Cottage
Dura Den Road, Pitscottie
Cupar, KY15 5TG
Tel: 01334 828 164

Roman Camp Hotel
Main Street, Callander
Perthshire, FK17 8BG
Tel: 01877 330003

Facilities

For visitors with disabilities

Royal Garden Apartments
York Buildings, Queen Street
Edinburgh, EH2 1HY
Tel: 0131 220 1613

Rufflets Country House Hotel
Strathkinness Low Road
St Andrews, Fife, KY16 9TX
Tel: 01334 472594

Scotties B&B
213 Nicol Street, Kirkcaldy
Fife, KY1 1PF
Tel: 01592 268596

Shawlands Hotel
Ayr Road, Canderside Toll
by Larkhall
Lanarkshire, ML9 2TZ
Tel: 01698 791111

Soluis Mu Thuath
Braeintra, by Achmore
Lochalsh, IV53 8UP
Tel: 01599 577219

Spinnaker Hotel
121 Albert Road, Gourock
Renfrewshire, PA19 1BU
Tel: 01475 633107

Springvale Hotel
18 Lethame Road, Strathaven
Lanarkshire, ML10 6AD
Tel: 01357 521131

Strathburn Hotel
Burghmuir Drive, Inverurie
Aberdeenshire, AB51 4GY
Tel: 01467 624422

Sunbank House Hotel
50 Dundee Road, Perth
Perthshire, PH2 7BA
Tel: 01738 624882

Swallow Hotel
Kingsway West, Invergowrie
Dundee, Angus, DD2 5JT
Tel: 01382 641122

Tobermory Hotel
53 Main Street, Tobermory
Isle of Mull, PA75 6NT
Tel: 01688 302091

Tontine Hotel
6 Ardgowan Square, Greenock
Renfrewshire, PA16 8NG
Tel: 01475 723316

Torbay Lodge
31 Lovers Walk
Dumfries,DG1 1LR
Tel: 01387 253922

Travelodge Glasgow Central
5 Hill Street, Glasgow, G3 6RP
Tel: 01468 342082

Tuchethill House
Dollerie, Crieff
Perthshire, PH7 3NX
Tel: 01764 653188

Vestlaybanks
Burray
Orkney, KW17 2SX
Tel: 01856 731305

Virdafjell
Shurton Brae, Gulberwick
Shetland, ZE2 9TX
Tel: 01595 694336

Wallamhill House
Kirkton, by Dumfries
Dumfriesshire, DG1 1SL
Tel: 01387 248249

Waverley
35 Strathspey Avenue
Aviemore, Inverness-shire
PH22 1SN
Tel: 01479 811226

Western Guest House
92 Corstorphine Road
Edinburgh, EH12 6JG
Tel: 0131 5387490

Whinrig
12 Burgh Road, Lerwick
Shetland, ZE1 0LB
Tel: 01595 693554

White House
Drumndrochit
Inverness-shire, IV63 6TU
Tel: 01456 450 337

Index
By location

Area Codes

A South of Scotland: 2
Ayrshire and Arran,
Dumfries and Galloway,
Scottish Borders

B Edinburgh and Lothians   43

C Greater Glasgow   91
and Clyde Valley

D West Highlands & Islands,   107
Loch Lomond, Stirling
and Trossachs

E Perthshire, Angus and   151
Dundee and the Kingdom
of Fife

F Aberdeen and Grampian   209
Highlands – Scotland's Castle and
Whisky Country

G The Highlands and Skye   237

H Outer Islands: 336
Western Isles,
Orkney, Shetland

Location	Area code	Page no.	Location	Area code	Page no.
Aberdeen	F	215	Ardchattan	D	114
Aberfeldy	E	157	Ardgay	G	243
Aberfoyle	D	113	Ardnamurchan	G	243
Abernethy	E	158	Ardvasar, Sleat, Isle of Skye	G	311
Aboyne	F	218	Arisaig	G	244
Aignish, Point, Isle of Lewis	H	343	Arrochar	D	114
Airdrie	C	97	Ascog, Isle of Bute	D	118
Alford	F	218	Auchencairn, by Castle Douglas	A	10
Alexandria	D	113	Auchterarder	E	160
Alness	G	243	Auchtermuchty	E	161
Anstruther	E	158	Aultbea	G	244
Appin	D	113	Aviemore	G	244
Arbroath	E	160	Ayr	A	10

Index
By location

Location	Area code	Page no.	Location	Area code	Page no.
Back, Isle of Lewis	H	343	Brackla, Loch Ness-side	G	251
Ballachulish	G	248	Braemar	F	222
Ballantrae	A	12	Breakish, Isle of Skye	G	311
Ballater	F	218	Brechin	E	164
Ballingry	E	161	Bridge of Allan	D	117
Balloch	D	115	Brig O'Turk	D	118
Ballygrant, Isle of Islay	D	132	Broadford, Isle of Skye	G	312
Balmaha	D	117	Brodick, Isle of Arran	A	8
Balquhidder	D	117	Brora	G	251
Banchory	F	219	Broughton, by Biggar	A	13
Banff	F	221	Broughty Ferry	E	164
Beauly	G	249	Broxburn	B	49
Beith	A	12	Buckie	F	223
Berneray, Isle of North Uist	H	344	Bunessan, Isle of Mull	D	134
Biggar	C	97	Burntisland	E	165
Birnam	E	161	Cairndow	D	118
Birsay, Orkney	H	344	Callander	D	118
Blackburn	B	49	Callanish, Isle of Lewis	H	343
Blackwaterfoot, Isle of Arran	A	8	Carnoustie	E	165
Blair Atholl	E	162	Carradale	D	122
Blairgowrie	E	162	Carrbridge	G	253
Blairlogie, by Stirling	D	117	Carron Bridge	D	124
Boat of Garten	G	250	Castlebay, Isle of Harris	H	342
Borve, by Portree, Isle of Skye	G	311	Castle Douglas	A	13

Index
By location

Location	Area code	Page no.	Location	Area code	Page no.
Cawdor	G	253	Doune	D	126
Ceres	E	166	Drumnadrochit	G	259
Cockburnspath	A	15	Drymen	D	127
Comrie	E	166	Dufftown	F	223
Connel	D	122	Dumfries	A	16
Contin	G	254	Dunbar	B	50
Corpach, by Fort William	G	254	Dunbeath	G	261
Corrie, Isle of Arran	A	9	Dunblane	D	127
Craignure, Isle of Mull	D	134	Dundee	E	170
Crail	E	166	Dundonnell	G	261
Craobh Haven, by Lochgilphead	D	124	Dunfermline	E	172
Crawford	C	98	Dunkeld	E	173
Crieff	E	167	Dunoon	D	128
Cromarty	G	255	Dunshalt	E	174
Cullen	F	223	Dunure, by Ayr	A	17
Culloden Moor	G	256	Dunvegan, Isle of Skye	G	315
Culross	E	170	Durness	G	262
Dalcross, by Inverness	G	256	Eaglesham, by Glasgow	C	98
Dalgety Bay	E	170	East Calder	B	50
Dalmally	D	125	East Linton	B	52
Dervaig, Isle of Mull	D	134	Ecclefechan	A	18
Dingwall	G	256	Edinburgh	B	52
Dornie, by Kyle of Lochalsh	G	257	near Edinburgh	B	82
Dornoch	G	258	Edzell	E	174

Index

By location

Location	Area code	Page no.	Location	Area code	Page no.
Elgin	F	224	Glenhinnisdale, Isle of Skye	G	317
Elgol, Isle of Skye	G	316	Glenkindie	F	229
Eskbank	B	83	Glenlivet	F	230
Evie, Orkney	H	345	Gorebridge	B	83
Fairlie	A	18	Grantown-on-Spey	G	280
Falkirk	D	129	Greenock	C	104
Findhorn	F	226	Gretna	A	20
Fionnphort, Isle of Mull	D	136	Gullane	B	85
Forfar	E	175	Haddington	B	85
Forgandenny	E	177	Hamilton	C	104
Forres	F	227	Harray, Orkney	H	345
Fortingall	E	177	Hawick	A	20
Fort Augustus	G	263	Helensburgh	D	130
Fort William	G	264	Helmsdale	G	284
Fyvie	F	228	Huntly	F	230
Gairloch	G	277	Innerleithen	A	21
Galashiels	A	18	Invergarry	G	284
Gardenstown	F	229	Invergordon	G	285
Garve	G	279	Inverkeithing	E	178
Girvan	A	18	Invermoriston	G	285
Glamis	E	178	Inverness	G	285
Glasgow	C	98	Inversnaid	D	131
by Glasgow	C	104	Inverurie	F	231
Glencoe	G	279	Iona, Isle of	D	131

Index

By location

Location	Area code	Page no.	Location	Area code	Page no.
Irvine	A	21	Lagavulin, by Port Ellen, Isle of Islay	D	132
Jedburgh	A	21	Laide	G	301
John O'Groats	G	295	Lairg	G	301
Keith	F	231	Lanark	C	104
Kelso	A	24	Largs	A	27
Killin	D	132	Lasswade	B	86
Kilmarnock	A	25	Lauder	A	28
Kilwinning	A	26	Lerwick, Shetland	H	347
Kincraig, by Kingussie	G	296	Lesmahagow	C	105
Kingsbarns, by St Andrews	E	178	Letham, by Forfar	E	183
Kingussie	G	297	Leven	E	183
Kinloch Rannoch	E	179	Limekilns	E	183
Kinlochewe	G	299	Linlithgow	B	87
Kinlochleven	G	300	Lochcarron	G	302
Kinlochspelvie, Isle of Mull	D	137	Lochearnhead	D	133
Kinross	E	179	Lochgilphead	D	133
Kippford, by Dalbeattie	A	26	Lochgoilhead	D	133
Kirkcaldy	E	180	Lochinver	G	302
Kirkcudbright	A	26	Lochmaben	A	29
Kirkmichael	E	181	Loch Ness (South)	G	304
Kirkwall, Orkney	H	345	Lochs, Isle of Lewis	H	344
Kirriemuir	E	182	Lochwinnoch	C	105
Kyleakin, Isle of Skye	G	317	Lockerbie	A	29
Kyle of Lochalsh	G	300	Lossiemouth	F	232

Index

By location

Location	Area code	Page no.	Location	Area code	Page no.
Lundin Links	E	184	Oldmeldrum	F	232
Luss	D	134	Onich, by Fort William	G	308
Mallaig	G	304	Orphir, Orkney	H	346
Markinch	E	184	Paisley	C	106
Mauchline	A	30	Peebles	A	35
Melrose	A	30	Penicuik	B	89
Melvich	G	305	Perth	E	187
Methlick	F	232	Peterhead	F	233
Millport, Isle of Cumbrae	A	15	Pitlochry	E	191
Milnathort, by Kinross	E	184	Plockton	G	309
Moffat	A	31	Port Charlotte, Isle of Islay	D	132
Montrose	E	184	Port of Menteith	D	145
Morar	G	305	Port Seton	B	89
Motherwell	C	106	Portree, Isle of Skye	G	318
Muckle Roe	H	369	Portsoy	F	233
Musselburgh	B	88	Prestwick	A	37
Nairn	G	306	Rendall, Orkney	H	346
Nethy Bridge	G	308	Rothesay, Isle of Bute	D	118
Newton Stewart	A	33	St Abbs	A	38
Newtonmore	G	308	St Andrews	E	200
North Kessock	G	308	St Boswells	A	38
North Mainland, Shetland	H	347	Salen, Aros, Isle of Mull	D	137
North Queensferry	E	186	Scaristavore, Isle of Harris	H	342
Oban	D	137	Scone, by Perth	E	207

Index
By location

Location	Area code	Page no.	Location	Area code	Page no.
Scourie	G	310	Tarbert, Loch Fyne	D	148
Seilebost, Isle of Harris	H	342	Tarbet, by Arrochar	D	149
Selkirk	A	38	Tarbert, Isle of Harris	H	342
Shieldaig	G	311	Tayport	E	208
Sleat, Isle of Skye	G	321	Thornhill	A	41
South Queensferry	B	90	Thurso	G	329
Sorbie	A	39	Tillicoultry	D	150
Spean Bridge	G	323	Tobermory, Isle of Mull	D	137
Staffin, Isle of Skye	G	322	Tomintoul	F	235
Stirling	D	145	Tongue	G	331
Stonehaven	F	234	Trondra, by Scalloway, Shetland	H	347
Stornoway, Isle of Lewis	H	344	Troon	A	41
Stranraer	A	39	Turriff	F	236
Strathaven	C	106	Twynholm	A	41
Strathdon	F	235	Uig, Isle of Skye	G	322
Strathkinness, by St Andrews	E	208	Ullapool	G	331
Strathpeffer	G	325	West Linton	A	41
Strathy Point	G	326	Whithorn	A	42
Strathyre	D	148	Wick	G	335
Stromness, Orkney	H	346	Winchburgh	B	90
Strontian	G	327	Yetholm, by Kelso	A	42
Struan, by Dunvegan, Isle of Skye	G	322			
Tain	G	327			
Talmine	G	329			